Instructor's Solutions Guide and Test Item File for

Elementary Linear Algebra

Fifth Edition

Larson/Edwards

Bruce H. Edwards
University of Florida

BROOKS/COLE
CENGAGE Learning

Australia • Brazil • Japan • Korea • Mexico • Singapore • Spain • United Kingdom • United States

BROOKS/COLE
CENGAGE Learning

ISBN-13: 978-0-618-33569-5
ISBN-10: 0-618-33569-2

Brooks/Cole
10 Davis Drive
Belmont, CA 94002-3098
USA

Cengage Learning is a leading provider of customized learning solutions with office locations around the globe, including Singapore, the United Kingdom, Australia, Mexico, Brazil, and Japan. Locate your local office at: **www.cengage.com/international**

Cengage Learning products are represented in Canada by Nelson Education, Ltd.

To learn more about Brooks/Cole, visit **www.cengage.com/brookscole**

Purchase any of our products at your local college store or at our preferred online store **www.ichapters.com**

For product information and technology assistance, contact us at
**Cengage Learning Customer & Sales Support,
1-800-354-9706**

For permission to use material from this text or product, submit all requests online at www.cengage.com/permissions
Further permissions questions can be emailed to
permissionrequest@cengage.com

READ IMPORTANT LICENSE INFORMATION

Printed in the United States of America

3 4 5 6 7   13 12 11 10 09

ED133

Preface

This guide is a supplement to *Elementary Linear Algebra*, Fifth Edition, by Ron Larson, Bruce H. Edwards, and David C. Falvo. Part I contains solutions to all even-numbered text section and review exercises, as well as solutions to Chapter Projects. Part II is a test item file that is keyed to the text by section.

For most students, this is the first mathematics course in which they are exposed to theoretical abstract concepts and proofs. Even students who did well in computational calculus courses often find this course challenging. A primary objective of the course is to teach students the basic skills of logical mathematical reasoning, but for many students, developing the ability to write proofs is the most difficult part of the course. It is no less important, however, than learning how to calculate a discriminant or find an eigenvalue. For this reason, proof-oriented problems are included in this revised edition of the test item file.

Each question in the test item file is followed by a three-item code. The first item of the code indicates the level of difficulty of the question: 1, routine (solution requires only one or two steps); 2, more difficult but still routine (computational or easy, True or False); 3, challenging; 4, difficult (recommended to be used for extra credit). Most of the questions that require a proof or a (counter) example are coded 3. Selected computational problems are also coded 3. The second item of the code indicates the type of question: multiple-choice (M) or open-ended (O). The last item in the code is the answer. Questions that require proof are coded 3—O—Proof. For these, either a key idea or a sketch of a proof is provided as an answer.

Contents

Part I

Part II

Part I
Instructor's Solutions Guide

CHAPTER 1
Systems of Linear Equations

Section 1.1   Introduction to Systems of Linear Equations

2. Since the term xy cannot be rewritten as $ax + by$ for any real numbers a and b, the equation cannot be written in the form $a_1x + a_2y = b$. So this equation is *not* linear in variables x and y.

4. Since the terms x^2 and y^2 cannot be rewritten as $ax + by$ for any real numbers a and b, the equation cannot be written in the form $a_1x + a_2y = b$. So this equation is *not* linear in variables x and y.

6. Since the equation is in the form $a_1x + a_2y = b$, it *is* linear in the variables x and y.

8. Choosing y as the free variable, we let $y = t$ and obtain

$$3x - \tfrac{1}{2}t = 9$$
$$3x = 9 + \tfrac{1}{2}t$$
$$x = 3 + \tfrac{1}{6}t$$

Thus, we can describe the solution set as $x = 3 + \tfrac{1}{6}t$ and $y = t$, where t is any real number.

10. Choosing x_2 and x_3 as free variables, we let $x_3 = t$ and $x_2 = s$ and obtain

$$13x_1 - 26s + 39t = 13.$$

Dividing this equation by 13 we obtain

$$x_1 - 2s + 3t = 1$$

or

$$x_1 = 1 + 2s - 3t.$$

Thus, we can describe the solution set as $x_1 = 1 + 2s - 3t$, $x_2 = s$, and $x_3 = t$, where t and s are any real numbers.

12. From Equation 2 we have $x_2 = 3$. Substituting this value into Equation 1 produces $2x_1 - 12 = 6$ or $x_1 = 9$. Thus, the system has exactly one solution: $x_1 = 9$ and $x_2 = 3$.

14. From Equation 3 we conclude that $z = 2$. Substituting this value into Equation 2 produces $2y + 2 = 6$ or $y = 2$. Finally, substituting $y = 2$ and $z = 2$ into Equation 1, we obtain $x - 2 = 4$ or $x = 6$. Thus, the system has exactly one solution: $x = 6$, $y = 2$ and $z = 2$.

16. From the second equation we have $x_2 = 0$. Substituting this value into Equation 1 produces $x_1 + x_3 = 0$. Choosing x_3 as the free variable, we have $x_3 = t$ and obtain $x_1 + t = 0$ or $x_1 = -t$. Thus, we can describe the solution set as $x_1 = -t$, $x_2 = 0$, and $x_3 = t$.

18.

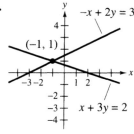

$$x + 3y = 2$$
$$-x + 2y = 3$$

Adding the first equation to the second equation produces a new second equation, $5y = 5$, or $y = 1$.

Hence, $x = 2 - 3y = 2 - 3(1)$, and the solution is $x = -1$, $y = 1$. This is the point where the two lines intersect.

20.

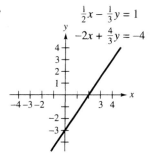

The two lines coincide.

Multiplying the first equation by 2 produces a new first equation.

$$x - \tfrac{2}{3}y = 2$$
$$-2x + \tfrac{4}{3}y = -4$$

Adding 2 times the first equation to the second equation produces a new second equation.

$$x - \tfrac{2}{3}y = 2$$
$$0 = 0$$

Choosing $y = t$ as the free variable, we obtain $x = \tfrac{2}{3}t + 2$. Thus, we can describe the solution set as $x = \tfrac{2}{3}t + 2$ and $y = t$, where t is any real number.

22. (a)

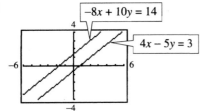

(b) This system is inconsistent, because we see two parallel lines on the graph of the system.

(c) Since the system is inconsistent, we cannot approximate the solution.

(d) Adding -2 times the first equation to the second we obtain $0 = 8$, which is an absurdity. We conclude that this system has no solutions.

(e) We obtained the same answer both geometrically and algebraically.

24. (a)

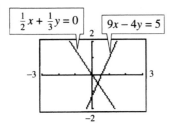

(b) Two lines corresponding to two equations intersect at a point, so we conclude that this system has a unique solution.

(c) $x \approx \frac{1}{3}$, $y \approx -\frac{1}{2}$

(d) Adding -18 times the second equation to the first equation we obtain $-10y = 5$ or $y = -\frac{1}{2}$. Substituting $y = -\frac{1}{2}$ into the first equation we obtain $9x = 3$ or $x = \frac{1}{3}$. We conclude that the solution is $x = \frac{1}{3}$ and $y = -\frac{1}{2}$.

(e) We obtain the same answer both geometrically and algebraically.

26. (a)

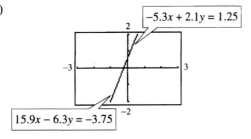

(b) Because each equation has the same line as a graph, we conclude that there are infinitely many solutions.

(c) All solutions of this system lie on the line $y = \frac{53}{21}x + \frac{25}{42}$. So if we let $x = t$, then solution set is $x = t$, $y = \frac{53}{21}t + \frac{25}{42}$ for any real number t.

(d) Adding (3) times the first equation to the second equation we obtain

$$-5.3x + 2.1y = 1.25$$
$$0 = 0$$

Choosing $x = t$ as the free variable, we obtain $2.1y = 5.3t + 1.25$ or $21y = 53t + 12.5$ or $y = \frac{53}{21}t + \frac{25}{42}$. Thus, we can describe the solution set as $x = t$, $y = \frac{53}{21}t + \frac{25}{42}$ for any real number t.

(e) We obtained the same answer both geometrically and algebraically.

28. Adding -2 times the first equation to the second equation produces a new second equation.

$$3x + 2y = 2$$
$$0 = 10$$

Since the second equation is an absurdity, we conclude that the original system of equations has no solution.

30. Adding -6 times the first equation to the second equation produces a new second equation.

$$x_1 - 2x_2 = 0$$
$$14x_2 = 0$$

Now, using back-substitution, we conclude that the system has exactly one solution: $x_1 = 0$ and $x_2 = 0$.

32. Multiplying the first equation by $\frac{3}{2}$ produces a new first equation.

$$x_1 + \tfrac{1}{4}x_2 = 0$$
$$4x_1 + x_2 = 0$$

Adding -4 times the first equation to the second equation produces a new second equation.

$$x_1 + \tfrac{1}{4}x_2 = 0$$
$$0 = 0$$

Choosing $x_2 = t$ as the free variable, we obtain $x_1 = -\tfrac{1}{4}t$. Thus, we can describe the solution set $x_1 = -\tfrac{1}{4}t$ and $x_2 = t$, where t is any real number.

34. To begin, we change the form of the first equation.

$$\frac{x_1}{4} + \frac{x_2}{3} = \frac{7}{12}$$
$$2x_1 - x_2 = 12$$

Multiplying the first equation by 4 yields a new first equation.

$$x_1 + \frac{4}{3}x_2 = \frac{7}{3}$$
$$2x_1 - x_2 = 12$$

Adding -2 times the first equation to the second equation produces a new second equation,

$$x_1 + \frac{4}{3}x_2 = \frac{7}{3}$$
$$-\frac{11}{3}x_2 = \frac{22}{3}$$

—CONTINUED—

34. **—CONTINUED—**

Multiplying the second equation by $-\frac{3}{11}$ yields a new second equation.

$$x_1 + \frac{4}{3}x_2 = \frac{7}{3}$$
$$x_2 = -2$$

Now, using back-substitution, we conclude that the system has exactly one solution: $x_1 = 5$ and $x_2 = -2$.

36. Multiplying the first equation by 20 and the second equation by 100 produces a new system.

$$x_1 - 0.6x_2 = 4.2$$
$$7x_1 + 2x_2 = 17$$

Adding -7 times the first equation to the second equation produces a new second equation.

$$x_1 - 0.6x_2 = 4.2$$
$$6.2x_2 = -12.4$$

Now, using back-substitution, we conclude that the system has exactly one solution: $x_1 = 3$ and $x_2 = -2$.

38. Adding the first equation to the second equation yields a new second equation.

$$x + y + z = 2$$
$$4y + 3z = 10$$
$$4x + y = 4$$

Adding -4 times the first equation to the third equation yields a new third equation.

$$x + y + z = 2$$
$$4y + 3z = 10$$
$$-3y - 4z = -4$$

Dividing the second equation by 4 yields a new second equation.

$$x + y + z = 2$$
$$y + \frac{3}{4}z = \frac{5}{2}$$
$$-3y - 4z = -4$$

Adding 3 times the second equation to the third equation yields a new third equation.

$$x + y + z = 2$$
$$y + \frac{3}{4}z = \frac{5}{2}$$
$$-\frac{7}{4}z = \frac{7}{2}$$

Multiplying the third equation by $-\frac{4}{7}$ yields a new third equation.

$$x + y + z = 2$$
$$y + \frac{3}{4}z = \frac{5}{2}$$
$$z = -2$$

Now, using back-substitution we conclude that the system has exactly one solution: $x = 0$, $y = 4$, and $z = -2$.

40. Interchanging the first and third equations yields a new system.

$$x_1 - 11x_2 + 4x_3 = 3$$
$$2x_1 + 4x_2 - x_3 = 7$$
$$5x_1 - 3x_2 + 2x_3 = 3$$

Adding -2 times the first equation to the second equation yields a new second equation.

$$x_1 - 11x_2 + 4x_3 = 3$$
$$26x_2 - 9x_3 = 1$$
$$5x_1 - 3x_2 + 2x_3 = 3$$

Adding -5 times the first equation to the third equation yields a new third equation.

$$x_1 - 11x_2 + 4x_3 = 3$$
$$26x_2 - 9x_3 = 1$$
$$52x_2 - 18x_3 = -12$$

At this point we realize that Equations 2 and 3 cannot both be satisfied. Thus, the original system of equations has no solution.

42. Adding (-4) times first equation to the second equation and adding (-2) times first equation to the third equation produces new second and third equations. This yields a new system.

$$x_1 + 4x_3 = 13$$
$$-2x_2 - 15x_3 = -45$$
$$-2x_2 - 15x_3 = -45.$$

The third equation can be disregarded since it is the same as the second one. Choosing x_3 as a free variable and letting $x_3 = t$, we find that the solution is

$$x_1 = 13 - 4t,$$
$$x_2 = \frac{45}{2} - \frac{15}{2}t,$$
$$x_3 = t,$$

where t is any real number.

44. Adding -3 times the first equation to the second equation produces a new second equation.

$$x_1 - 2x_2 + 5x_3 = 2$$
$$8x_2 - 16x_3 = -8$$

Dividing the second equation by 8 yields

$$x_1 - 2x_2 + 5x_3 = 2$$
$$x_2 - 2x_3 = -1.$$

Adding 2 times the second equation to the first equation yields

$$x_1 + x_3 = 0$$
$$x_2 - 2x_3 = -1.$$

Letting $x_3 = t$ be the free variable, we have the solution $x_1 = -t$, $x_2 = 2t - 1$, and $x_3 = t$, where t is any real number.

46. Adding -2 times the first equation to the fourth equation, yields

$$\begin{aligned} x_1 \qquad\qquad + 3x_4 &= 4 \\ 2x_2 - x_3 - x_4 &= 0 \\ 3x_2 \qquad - 2x_4 &= 1 \\ -x_2 + 4x_3 - 6x_4 &= -3. \end{aligned}$$

Multiplying the fourth equation by -1, and interchanging it with the second equation, yields

$$\begin{aligned} x_1 \qquad\qquad + 3x_4 &= 4 \\ x_2 - 4x_3 + 6x_4 &= 3 \\ 3x_2 \qquad - 2x_4 &= 1 \\ 2x_2 - x_3 - x_4 &= 0. \end{aligned}$$

Adding -3 times the second equation to the third, and -2 times the second equation to the fourth, produces

$$\begin{aligned} x_1 \qquad\qquad + 3x_4 &= 4 \\ x_2 - 4x_3 + 6x_4 &= 3 \\ 12x_3 - 20x_4 &= -8 \\ 7x_3 - 13x_4 &= -6. \end{aligned}$$

Dividing the third equation by 12 yields

$$\begin{aligned} x_1 \qquad\qquad + 3x_4 &= 4 \\ x_2 - 4x_3 + 6x_4 &= 3 \\ x_3 - \tfrac{5}{3}x_4 &= -\tfrac{2}{3} \\ 7x_3 - 13x_4 &= -6. \end{aligned}$$

Adding -7 times the third equation to the fourth yields

$$\begin{aligned} x_1 \qquad\qquad + 3x_4 &= 4 \\ x_2 - 4x_3 + 6x_4 &= 3 \\ x_3 - \tfrac{5}{3}x_4 &= -\tfrac{2}{3} \\ \tfrac{4}{3}x_4 &= \tfrac{4}{3}. \end{aligned}$$

Using back-substitution, we conclude that the original system has exactly one solution: $x_1 = 1, x_2 = 1, x_3 = 1$ and $x_4 = 1$.

48. Using a computer or graphing calculator, you obtain $x = 10, y = -20$, $z = 40 \ (w = -12)$.

50. Using a computer or graphing calculator, you obtain $x = 0.8, y = 1.2, z = -2.4$.

52. Using a computer or graphing calculator, you obtain $x_1 = 0.6, x_2 = -0.5$, $x_3 = 0.8$.

54. Using a computer or graphing calculator, you obtain $x = 6.8813, y = 163.3111$, $z = 210.2915, w = 59.2913$ (answers may vary slightly).

56 $x = y = z = 0$ is clearly a solution.

Dividing the first equation by 2 produces

$$
\begin{aligned}
x + \tfrac{3}{2}y \qquad\;\; &= 0 \\
4x + 3y - z &= 0 \\
8x + 3y + 3z &= 0.
\end{aligned}
$$

Adding -4 times the first equation to the second equation, and -8 times the first equation to the third, yields

$$
\begin{aligned}
x + \tfrac{3}{2}y \qquad\;\; &= 0 \\
-3y - z &= 0 \\
-9y + 3z &= 0.
\end{aligned}
$$

Adding -3 times the second equation to the third equation yields

$$
\begin{aligned}
x + \tfrac{3}{2}y \qquad\;\; &= 0 \\
-3y - z &= 0 \\
6z &= 0.
\end{aligned}
$$

Using back-substitution we conclude there is exactly one solution: $x = y = z = 0$.

58. $x = y = z = 0$ is clearly a solution.

Dividing the first equation by 12 yields

$$
\begin{aligned}
x + \tfrac{5}{12}y + \tfrac{1}{12}z &= 0 \\
12x + 4y - z &= 0.
\end{aligned}
$$

Adding -12 times equation one to the second yields

$$
\begin{aligned}
x + \tfrac{5}{12}y + \tfrac{1}{12}z &= 0 \\
-y - 2z &= 0.
\end{aligned}
$$

Letting $z = t$ be the free variable, back-substitution yields the solution: $x = \tfrac{3}{4}t$, $y = -2t$, $z = t$, where t is any real number.

60. (a) *False.* Any system of linear equation is either consistent which means it has a unique solution, or infinitely many solutions; or inconsistent, *i.e.,* it has no solutions. This result is stated on page 6 of the text, and will be proved later in Theorem 2.5.

(b) *True.* See definition on page 7 of the text.

(c) *False.* Consider the following system of three linear equations in two unknowns.

$$
\begin{aligned}
2x + y &= -3 \\
-6x - 3y &= 9 \\
x \qquad\; &= 1.
\end{aligned}
$$

The solution to this system is $x = 1, y = -5$.

62. Since $x_1 = t$ and $x_2 = s$, you can write $x_3 = 3 + s - t = 3 + x_2 - x_1$. One system could be

$$x_1 - x_2 + x_3 = 3$$
$$-x_1 + x_2 - x_3 = -3$$

Letting $x_3 = t$ and $x_2 = s$, you obtain $x_1 = 3 + x_2 - x_3 = 3 + s - t$.

64. Letting $X = \dfrac{1}{x}$, $Y = \dfrac{1}{y}$, and $Z = \dfrac{1}{z}$, we have

$$2X + Y - 3Z = 4$$
$$4X + 2Z = 10$$
$$-2X + 3Y - 13Z = -8.$$

We reduce this system to row-echelon form.

$$X + \tfrac{1}{2}Y - \tfrac{3}{2}Z = 2$$
$$-2Y + 8Z = 2$$
$$4Y - 16Z = -4$$

$$X + \tfrac{1}{2}Y - \tfrac{3}{2}Z = 2$$
$$Y - 4Z = -1$$

Letting $t = Z$ be the free variable, we have $Z = t$, $Y = 4t - 1$ and $X = \dfrac{(-t + 5)}{2}$.

Hence, the solution to the original problem is

$$x = \frac{2}{5 - t}, \, y = \frac{1}{4t - 1}, \, z = \frac{1}{t}, \text{ where } t \neq 5, \tfrac{1}{4}, 0.$$

66. Multiplying the first equation by $\sin \theta$ and the second by $\cos \theta$ produces

$$(\sin \theta \cos \theta)x + (\sin^2 \theta)y = \sin \theta$$
$$-(\sin \theta \cos \theta)x + (\cos^2 \theta)y = \cos \theta$$

Adding these two equations yields

$$(\sin^2 \theta + \cos^2 \theta)y = \sin \theta + \cos \theta$$
$$y = \sin \theta + \cos \theta.$$

Hence,

$$(\cos \theta)x + (\sin \theta)y = (\cos \theta)x + \sin \theta(\sin \theta + \cos \theta) = 1 \text{ and }$$
$$x = \frac{(1 - \sin^2 \theta - \sin \theta \cos \theta)}{\cos \theta} = \frac{(\cos^2 \theta - \sin \theta \cos \theta)}{\cos \theta} = \cos \theta - \sin \theta.$$

Finally, the solution is $x = \cos \theta - \sin \theta$ and $y = \cos \theta + \sin \theta$.

68. Interchanging the two equations and row reducing, we obtain

$$x - \tfrac{3}{2}y = -6$$
$$kx + y = 4$$

$$x - \tfrac{3}{2}y = -6$$
$$\left(\tfrac{3}{2}k + 1\right)y = 4 + 6k$$

Hence, if $k = -\tfrac{2}{3}$, there will be an infinite number of solutions.

70. Reducing the system,

$$x + ky \qquad = 2$$
$$(1 - k^2)y = 4 - 2k$$

If $k = \pm 1$, there will be no solution.

72. Interchanging the first two equations and row reducing

$$x + \quad y + \quad z = \quad 0$$
$$ky + 2kz = 4k$$
$$-3y - \quad z = \quad 1.$$

If $k = 0$, then there is an infinite number of solutions. Otherwise, we have

$$x + y + \quad z = \quad 0$$
$$y + 2z = \quad 4$$
$$5z = 13.$$

Since this system has exactly one solution, the answer is all $k \neq 0$.

74. Reducing the system to row-echelon form, we have

$$x + \qquad 5y + \qquad\qquad z = 0$$
$$y - \qquad\qquad 2z = 0$$
$$(a - 10)y + \qquad (b - 2)z = c$$
$$x + \qquad 5y + \qquad\qquad z = 0$$
$$y - \qquad\qquad 2z = 0$$
$$(2a + b - 22)z = c.$$

Hence, we see that

(a) If $2a + b - 22 \neq 0$, then there is exactly one solution.

(b) If $2a + b - 22 = 0$ and $c = 0$, then there is an infinite number of solutions.

(c) If $2a + b - 22 = 0$ and $c \neq 0$, there is no solution.

76. If $c_1 = c_2 = c_3 = 0$, then the system is consistent since $x = y = 0$ is a solution.

78. Multiplying the first equation by c, and the second by a, produces

$$acx + bcy = ec$$
$$acx + day = af.$$

Subtracting the second equation from the first yields

$$acx + bcy = ec$$
$$(ad - bc)y = af - ec.$$

Hence, there is a unique solution if $ad - bc \neq 0$.

80.

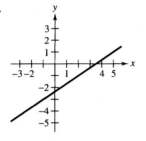

The two lines coincide.

$$2x - 3y = 7$$
$$0 = 0$$

Letting $y = t$, $x = \dfrac{7 + 3t}{2}$.

The graph does not change.

Section 1.2   Gaussian Elimination and Gauss-Jordan Elimination

2. Since the matrix has 2 rows and 4 columns, it has size 2×4.

4. Since matrix has 1 row and 1 column, it has size 1×1.

6. Since matrix has 4 rows and 1 column, it has size 4×1.

8. Since the leading 1 in the first row is not farther to the left than the leading 1 in the second row, the matrix is not in row-echelon form.

10. The matrix satisfies all three conditions in the definition of row-echelon form. However, since the third column does not have zeros above the leading 1 in the third row, the matrix is not in reduced row-echelon form.

12. The matrix satisfies all three conditions in the definition of row-echelon form. Moreover, since each column that has a leading 1 (columns one and four) has zeros elsewhere, the matrix is in reduced row-echelon form.

14. Since the matrix is in reduced row-echelon form, we can simply convert back to a system of linear equations

$$x_1 = 2$$
$$x_2 = 3.$$

16. Since the matrix is in row-echelon form, we convert back to a system of linear equations

$$x_1 + 2x_2 + x_3 = 0$$
$$x_3 = -1.$$

Using back-substitution, we have $x_3 = -1$. Letting $x_2 = t$ be the free variable, we have the solution $x_1 = 1 - 2t$, $x_2 = t$ and $x_3 = -1$.

18. Since the fourth row of this matrix corresponds to the linear equation $0 = 2$, we see that there is no solution to the linear system.

20. The augmented matrix for this system is

$$\begin{bmatrix} 2 & 6 & 16 \\ -2 & -6 & -16 \end{bmatrix}$$

We then use Gauss-Jordan elimination as follows.

$$\begin{bmatrix} 2 & 6 & 16 \\ -2 & -6 & -16 \end{bmatrix} \Rightarrow \begin{bmatrix} 1 & 3 & 8 \\ -2 & -6 & -16 \end{bmatrix} \Rightarrow \begin{bmatrix} 1 & 3 & 8 \\ 0 & 0 & 0 \end{bmatrix}$$

Converting back to system of linear equations, we have

$$x + 3y = 8.$$

Choosing $y = t$ as the free variable, we find that the solution is $x = 8 - 3t$ and $y = t$, where t is any real number.

22. The augmented matrix for this system is

$$\begin{bmatrix} 2 & -1 & -0.1 \\ 3 & 2 & 1.6 \end{bmatrix}.$$

Gaussian elimination produces the following.

$$\begin{bmatrix} 2 & -1 & -0.1 \\ 3 & 2 & 1.6 \end{bmatrix} \Rightarrow \begin{bmatrix} 1 & -\frac{1}{2} & -\frac{1}{20} \\ 3 & 2 & \frac{8}{5} \end{bmatrix}$$

$$\Rightarrow \begin{bmatrix} 1 & -\frac{1}{2} & -\frac{1}{20} \\ 0 & \frac{7}{2} & \frac{7}{4} \end{bmatrix} \Rightarrow \begin{bmatrix} 1 & -\frac{1}{2} & -\frac{1}{20} \\ 0 & 1 & \frac{1}{2} \end{bmatrix} \Rightarrow \begin{bmatrix} 1 & 0 & \frac{1}{5} \\ 0 & 1 & \frac{1}{2} \end{bmatrix}$$

Converting back to a system of equations, we see that the solution is: $x = \frac{1}{5}$ and $y = \frac{1}{2}$.

24. The augmented matrix for this system is

$$\begin{bmatrix} 1 & 2 & 0 \\ 1 & 1 & 6 \\ 3 & -2 & 8 \end{bmatrix}.$$

Gaussian elimination produces the following.

$$\begin{bmatrix} 1 & 2 & 0 \\ 1 & 1 & 6 \\ 3 & -2 & 8 \end{bmatrix} \Rightarrow \begin{bmatrix} 1 & 2 & 0 \\ 0 & -1 & 6 \\ 0 & -8 & 8 \end{bmatrix}$$

$$\Rightarrow \begin{bmatrix} 1 & 2 & 0 \\ 0 & 1 & -6 \\ 0 & -8 & 8 \end{bmatrix} \Rightarrow \begin{bmatrix} 1 & 2 & 0 \\ 0 & 1 & -6 \\ 0 & 0 & -40 \end{bmatrix}$$

Since the third row corresponds to the equation $0 = -40$, we conclude that the system has no solution.

26. The augmented matrix for this system is

$$\begin{bmatrix} 2 & -1 & 3 & 24 \\ 0 & 2 & -1 & 14 \\ 7 & -5 & 0 & 6 \end{bmatrix}.$$

Gaussian elimination produces the following.

$$\begin{bmatrix} 2 & -1 & 3 & 24 \\ 0 & 2 & -1 & 14 \\ 7 & -5 & 0 & 6 \end{bmatrix} \Rightarrow \begin{bmatrix} 1 & -\frac{1}{2} & \frac{3}{2} & 12 \\ 0 & 2 & -1 & 14 \\ 7 & -5 & 0 & 6 \end{bmatrix}$$

$$\Rightarrow \begin{bmatrix} 1 & -\frac{1}{2} & \frac{3}{2} & 12 \\ 0 & 2 & -1 & 14 \\ 0 & -\frac{3}{2} & -\frac{21}{2} & -78 \end{bmatrix}$$

$$\Rightarrow \begin{bmatrix} 1 & -\frac{1}{2} & \frac{3}{2} & 12 \\ 0 & 1 & -\frac{1}{2} & 7 \\ 0 & 0 & -\frac{45}{4} & -\frac{135}{2} \end{bmatrix}$$

Back-substitution now yields

$$x_3 = 6$$
$$x_2 = 7 + \tfrac{1}{2}x_3 = 7 + \tfrac{1}{2}(6) = 10$$
$$x_1 = 12 - \tfrac{3}{2}x_3 + \tfrac{1}{2}x_2 = 12 - \tfrac{3}{2}(6) + \tfrac{1}{2}(10) = 8.$$

Hence, the solution is $x_1 = 8$, $x_2 = 10$ and $x_3 = 6$.

28. The augmented matrix for this system is

$$\begin{bmatrix} 2 & 0 & 3 & 3 \\ 4 & -3 & 7 & 5 \\ 8 & -9 & 15 & 10 \end{bmatrix}.$$

Gaussian elimination produces the following.

$$\begin{bmatrix} 2 & 0 & 3 & 3 \\ 4 & -3 & 7 & 5 \\ 8 & -9 & 15 & 10 \end{bmatrix} \Rightarrow \begin{bmatrix} 1 & 0 & \frac{3}{2} & \frac{3}{2} \\ 4 & -3 & 7 & 5 \\ 8 & -9 & 15 & 10 \end{bmatrix}$$

$$\Rightarrow \begin{bmatrix} 1 & 0 & \frac{3}{2} & \frac{3}{2} \\ 0 & -3 & 1 & -1 \\ 0 & -9 & 3 & -2 \end{bmatrix}$$

$$\Rightarrow \begin{bmatrix} 1 & 0 & \frac{3}{2} & \frac{3}{2} \\ 0 & 1 & -\frac{1}{3} & \frac{1}{3} \\ 0 & 0 & 0 & 1 \end{bmatrix}$$

Since the third row corresponds to the equation $0 = 1$, we see that there is no solution to the original system.

30. The augmented matrix for this system is

$$\begin{bmatrix} 1 & 2 & 1 & 8 \\ -3 & -6 & -3 & -21 \end{bmatrix}.$$

Gaussian elimination produced the following matrix

$$\begin{bmatrix} 1 & 2 & 1 & 8 \\ 0 & 0 & 0 & 3 \end{bmatrix}$$

Since the second row corresponds to the equation $0 = 3$, we see that there is no solution to the original system.

32. The augmented matrix for this system is

$$\begin{bmatrix} 2 & 1 & -1 & 2 & -6 \\ 3 & 4 & 0 & 1 & 1 \\ 1 & 5 & 2 & 6 & -3 \\ 5 & 2 & -1 & -1 & 3 \end{bmatrix}$$

Gaussian elimination produces the following.

$$\begin{bmatrix} 1 & 5 & 2 & 6 & -3 \\ 3 & 4 & 0 & 1 & 1 \\ 2 & 1 & -1 & 2 & -6 \\ 5 & 2 & -1 & -1 & 3 \end{bmatrix} \Rightarrow \begin{bmatrix} 1 & 5 & 2 & 6 & -3 \\ 0 & -11 & -6 & -17 & 10 \\ 0 & -9 & -5 & -10 & 0 \\ 0 & -23 & -11 & -31 & 18 \end{bmatrix}$$

$$\Rightarrow \begin{bmatrix} 1 & 5 & 2 & 6 & -3 \\ 0 & 1 & \frac{6}{11} & \frac{17}{11} & -\frac{10}{11} \\ 0 & -9 & -5 & -10 & 0 \\ 0 & -23 & -11 & -31 & 18 \end{bmatrix}$$

$$\Rightarrow \begin{bmatrix} 1 & 5 & 2 & 6 & -3 \\ 0 & 1 & \frac{6}{11} & \frac{17}{11} & -\frac{10}{11} \\ 0 & 0 & -\frac{1}{11} & \frac{43}{11} & -\frac{90}{11} \\ 0 & 0 & \frac{17}{11} & \frac{50}{11} & -\frac{32}{11} \end{bmatrix}$$

$$\Rightarrow \begin{bmatrix} 1 & 5 & 2 & 6 & -3 \\ 0 & 1 & \frac{6}{11} & \frac{17}{11} & -\frac{10}{11} \\ 0 & 0 & 1 & -43 & 90 \\ 0 & 0 & \frac{17}{11} & \frac{50}{11} & -\frac{32}{4} \end{bmatrix}$$

$$\Rightarrow \begin{bmatrix} 1 & 5 & 2 & 6 & -3 \\ 0 & 1 & \frac{6}{11} & \frac{17}{11} & -\frac{10}{11} \\ 0 & 0 & 1 & -43 & 90 \\ 0 & 0 & 0 & \frac{781}{11} & -\frac{1562}{11} \end{bmatrix}$$

—CONTINUED—

32. **—CONTINUED—**

$$\Rightarrow \begin{bmatrix} 1 & 5 & 2 & 6 & -3 \\ 0 & 1 & \frac{6}{11} & \frac{17}{11} & -\frac{10}{11} \\ 0 & 0 & 1 & -43 & 90 \\ 0 & 0 & 0 & 1 & -2 \end{bmatrix}$$

Back-substitution now yields

$$
\begin{aligned}
w &= & & & -2 \\
z &= 90 & + 43w &= 90 & + 43(-2) &= 4 \\
y &= -\tfrac{10}{11} & - \tfrac{6}{11}(z) - \tfrac{17}{11}(w) &= -\tfrac{10}{11} & - \tfrac{6}{11}(4) - \tfrac{17}{11}(-2) &= 0 \\
x &= -3 - 5y - 2z - 6w &= -3 - 5(0) - 2(4) - 6(-2) &= 1.
\end{aligned}
$$

Hence, the solution is: $x = 1$, $y = 0$, $z = 4$ and $w = -2$.

34. Using a computer or graphing calculator, you obtain

$$x = 14.3629$$
$$y = 32.7569$$
$$z = 28.6356.$$

36. Using a computer or graphing calculator, you obtain

$$x_1 = 2$$
$$x_2 = -1$$
$$x_3 = 3$$
$$x_4 = 4$$
$$x_5 = 1.$$

38. Using a computer or graphing calculator, you obtain

$$x_1 = 1$$
$$x_2 = -1$$
$$x_3 = 2$$
$$x_4 = 0$$
$$x_5 = -2$$
$$x_6 = 1.$$

40. The corresponding equations are

$$x_1 = 0$$
$$x_2 + x_3 = 0$$

Hence, $x_4 = t$ is free, $x_3 = s$ is free, $x_2 = -s$ and $x_1 = 0$.

42. The corresponding equations $0 = 0$ have 3 free variables. Hence, $x_1 = t$, $x_2 = s$, $x_3 = r$, where t, s, r can be any real numbers.

44. (a) If A is the *augmented* matrix of a system of linear equations, then number of equations in this system is three (because it is equal to the number of rows of the augmented matrix). Number of variables is two since it is equal to number of columns of the augmented matrix minus one.

(b) Using Gaussian elimination of the augmented matrix of a system, we have the following.

$$\begin{bmatrix} 2 & -1 & 3 \\ -4 & 2 & k \\ 4 & -2 & 6 \end{bmatrix}$$

$$\begin{bmatrix} 2 & -1 & 3 \\ 0 & 0 & k+6 \\ 0 & 0 & 0 \end{bmatrix}$$

This system is consistent if and only if $k + 6 = 0$, so $k = -6$.

(c) If A is the *coefficient* matrix of a system of linear equations, then number of equations is three, because it is equal the number of rows of the coefficient matrix. The number of variables is also three, because it is equal to the number of columns of the coefficient matrix.

(d) Using Gaussian elimination on A we obtain the following coefficient matrix of an equivalent system.

$$\begin{bmatrix} 1 & -\frac{1}{2} & \frac{3}{2} \\ 0 & 0 & k+6 \\ 0 & 0 & 0 \end{bmatrix}$$

Because the homogeneous system is always consistent the homogeneous system with the coefficient matrix A is consistent for any value of k.

46. Using Gaussian elimination on the augmented matrix, we have the following.

$$\begin{bmatrix} 1 & 1 & 0 & 0 \\ 0 & 1 & 1 & 0 \\ 1 & 0 & 1 & 0 \\ a & b & c & 0 \end{bmatrix} \Rightarrow \begin{bmatrix} 1 & 1 & 0 & 0 \\ 0 & 1 & 1 & 0 \\ 0 & -1 & 1 & 0 \\ 0 & (b-a) & c & 0 \end{bmatrix}$$

$$\Rightarrow \begin{bmatrix} 1 & 1 & 0 & 0 \\ 0 & 1 & 1 & 0 \\ 0 & 0 & 2 & 0 \\ 0 & 0 & (a-b+c) & 0 \end{bmatrix}$$

$$\Rightarrow \begin{bmatrix} 1 & 1 & 0 & 0 \\ 0 & 1 & 1 & 0 \\ 0 & 0 & 1 & 0 \\ 0 & 0 & 0 & 0 \end{bmatrix}$$

From this row-reduced matrix we see that the original system always has a unique solution.

48. Since the system composed of equations 1 and 2 is consistent, but has a free variable, this system must have an infinite number of solutions.

50. We use Gauss-Jordan elimination as follows.

$$
\begin{bmatrix} 1 & 2 & 3 \\ 4 & 5 & 6 \\ 7 & 8 & 9 \end{bmatrix}
\Rightarrow
\begin{bmatrix} 1 & 2 & 3 \\ 0 & -3 & -6 \\ 0 & -6 & -12 \end{bmatrix}
\Rightarrow
\begin{bmatrix} 1 & 2 & 3 \\ 0 & 1 & 2 \\ 0 & 0 & 0 \end{bmatrix}
\Rightarrow
\begin{bmatrix} 1 & 0 & -1 \\ 0 & 1 & 2 \\ 0 & 0 & 0 \end{bmatrix}
$$

52. We begin by finding all possible first rows

$$[0 \ \ 0 \ \ 0], [0 \ \ 0 \ \ 1], [0 \ \ 1 \ \ 0], [0 \ \ 1 \ \ a], [1 \ \ 0 \ \ 0], [1 \ \ 0 \ \ a], [1 \ \ a \ \ b], [1 \ \ a \ \ 0],$$

where a and b are nonzero real numbers.

For each of these we examine the possible remaining rows.

$$
\begin{bmatrix} 0 & 0 & 0 \\ 0 & 0 & 0 \\ 0 & 0 & 0 \end{bmatrix}
\begin{bmatrix} 0 & 0 & 1 \\ 0 & 0 & 0 \\ 0 & 0 & 0 \end{bmatrix},
\begin{bmatrix} 0 & 1 & 0 \\ 0 & 0 & 0 \\ 0 & 0 & 0 \end{bmatrix}
\begin{bmatrix} 0 & 1 & 0 \\ 0 & 0 & 1 \\ 0 & 0 & 0 \end{bmatrix}
\begin{bmatrix} 0 & 1 & a \\ 0 & 0 & 0 \\ 0 & 0 & 0 \end{bmatrix},
$$

$$
\begin{bmatrix} 1 & 0 & 0 \\ 0 & 0 & 0 \\ 0 & 0 & 0 \end{bmatrix},
\begin{bmatrix} 1 & 0 & 0 \\ 0 & 1 & 0 \\ 0 & 0 & 0 \end{bmatrix}
\begin{bmatrix} 1 & 0 & 0 \\ 0 & 1 & 0 \\ 0 & 0 & 1 \end{bmatrix}
\begin{bmatrix} 1 & 0 & 0 \\ 0 & 0 & 1 \\ 0 & 0 & 0 \end{bmatrix}
\begin{bmatrix} 1 & 0 & 0 \\ 0 & 1 & a \\ 0 & 0 & 0 \end{bmatrix},
$$

$$
\begin{bmatrix} 1 & a & 0 \\ 0 & 0 & 0 \\ 0 & 0 & 0 \end{bmatrix},
\begin{bmatrix} 1 & a & 0 \\ 0 & 0 & 1 \\ 0 & 0 & 0 \end{bmatrix}
\begin{bmatrix} 1 & a & b \\ 0 & 0 & 0 \\ 0 & 0 & 0 \end{bmatrix}
\begin{bmatrix} 1 & 0 & a \\ 0 & 0 & 0 \\ 0 & 0 & 0 \end{bmatrix}
\begin{bmatrix} 1 & 0 & a \\ 0 & 1 & 0 \\ 0 & 0 & 0 \end{bmatrix}.
$$

54. (a) *False.* A 4×7 matrix has 4 rows and 7 columns.

(b) *True.* Reduced row echelon form of a given matrix is unique while row echelon form is not. (See also exercise 60 of this section.)

(c) *True.* See Theorem 1.1 on page 25.

(d) *False.* Multiplying a row by a *nonzero* constant is one of the elementary row operations. However, multiplying a row of a matrix by a constant $c = 0$ is *not* an elementary row operation. (This would change the system by eliminating the equation corresponding to this row.)

56. First of all, we need $a \neq 0$ or $c \neq 0$. If $a \neq 0$, then we have

$$\begin{bmatrix} a & b \\ c & d \end{bmatrix} \implies \begin{bmatrix} a & b \\ 0 & -\dfrac{cb}{a} + b \end{bmatrix} \implies \begin{bmatrix} a & b \\ 0 & ad - bc \end{bmatrix}.$$

Hence, $ad - bc = 0$ and $b = 0$, which implies that $d = 0$. If $c \neq 0$, then we interchange rows and proceed.

$$\begin{bmatrix} a & b \\ c & d \end{bmatrix} \implies \begin{bmatrix} c & d \\ 0 & -\dfrac{ad}{c} + b \end{bmatrix} \implies \begin{bmatrix} c & d \\ 0 & ad - bc \end{bmatrix}$$

Again, $ad - bc = 0$ and $d = 0$, which implies that $b = 0$. In conclusion, $\begin{bmatrix} a & b \\ c & d \end{bmatrix}$ is row equivalent to $\begin{bmatrix} 1 & 0 \\ 0 & 0 \end{bmatrix}$ if and only if $b = d = 0$, and $a \neq 0$ or $c \neq 0$.

58. We row reduce the augmented matrix for this system.

$$\begin{bmatrix} \lambda - 1 & 2 & 0 \\ 1 & \lambda & 0 \end{bmatrix} \implies \begin{bmatrix} 1 & \lambda & 0 \\ \lambda - 1 & 2 & 0 \end{bmatrix} \implies \begin{bmatrix} 1 & \lambda & 0 \\ 0 & (-\lambda^2 + \lambda + 2) & 0 \end{bmatrix}$$

To have a nontrivial solution we must have

$$\lambda^2 - \lambda - 2 = 0$$
$$(\lambda - 2)(\lambda + 1) = 0.$$

Thus, if $\lambda = -1$ or $\lambda = 2$, the system will have nontrivial solutions.

60. No, the echelon form is not unique. For instance, $\begin{bmatrix} 1 & 2 \\ 0 & 1 \end{bmatrix}$ and $\begin{bmatrix} 1 & 0 \\ 0 & 1 \end{bmatrix}$. The reduced row echelon form is unique.

62. $x^2 + 2y^3 = 2$
$3x^2 - y^3 = 13$

(-3) times equation 1 added to equation 2 produces

$$-7y^3 = 7 \implies y^3 = -1 \implies y = -1.$$

Hence, $x^2 = 4$ and $x = \pm 2$.

Section 1.3   Applications of Systems of Linear Equations

2. (a) Since there are three points, we choose a second-degree polynomial,
$p(x) = a_0 + a_1 x + a_2 x^2$. Then we substitute $x = 2$, 3, and 4 into $p(x)$ and
equate the results to $y = 4$, 4, and 4, respectively.

$$a_0 + a_1(2) + a_2(2)^2 = a_0 + 2a_1 + 4a_2 = 4$$
$$a_0 + a_1(3) + a_2(3)^2 = a_0 + 3a_1 + 9a_2 = 4$$
$$a_0 + a_1(4) + a_2(4)^2 = a_0 + 4a_1 + 16a_2 = 4$$

We use Gauss-Jordan elimination on the augmented matrix for this system.

$$\begin{bmatrix} 1 & 2 & 4 & 4 \\ 1 & 3 & 9 & 4 \\ 1 & 4 & 16 & 4 \end{bmatrix} \Rightarrow \begin{bmatrix} 1 & 0 & 0 & 4 \\ 0 & 1 & 0 & 0 \\ 0 & 0 & 1 & 0 \end{bmatrix}$$

Thus, $p(x) = 4$.

(b)

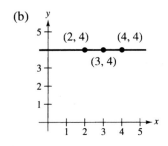

4. (a) Since there are four points, we choose a third-degree polynomial,
$p(x) = a_0 + a_1 x + a_2 x^2 + a_3 x^3$. Then we substitute $x = -1, 0, 1$, and 4
into $p(x)$ and equate the results to $y = 3, 0, 1$, and 58, respectively.

$$a_0 + a_1(-1) + a_2(-1)^2 + a_3(-1)^3 = a_0 - a_1 + a_2 - a_3 = 3$$
$$a_0 + a_1(0) + a_2(0)^2 + a_3(0)^3 = a_0 = 0$$
$$a_0 + a_1(1) + a_2(1)^2 + a_3(1)^3 = a_0 + a_1 + a_2 + a_3 = 1$$
$$a_0 + a_1(4) + a_2(4)^2 + a_3(4)^3 = a_0 + 4a_1 + 16a_2 + 64a_3 = 58$$

We use Gauss-Jordan elimination on the augmented matrix for this system.

$$\begin{bmatrix} 1 & -1 & 1 & -1 & 3 \\ 1 & 0 & 0 & 0 & 0 \\ 1 & 1 & 1 & 1 & 1 \\ 1 & 4 & 16 & 64 & 58 \end{bmatrix} \Rightarrow \begin{bmatrix} 1 & 0 & 0 & 0 & 0 \\ 0 & 1 & 0 & 0 & -\frac{3}{2} \\ 0 & 0 & 1 & 0 & 2 \\ 0 & 0 & 0 & 1 & \frac{1}{2} \end{bmatrix}$$

Thus, $p(x) = -\frac{3}{2}x + 2x^2 + \frac{1}{2}x^3$.

(b)

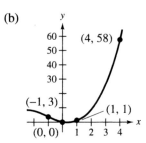

6. (a) Since there are four points, we choose a third-degree polynomial,

$p(z) = a_0 + a_1 z + a_2 z^2 + a_3 z^3$. Then we substitute $z = -1, 0, 1$ and 2 into $p(z)$ and equate the results to $y = 150, 180, 240,$ and 360, respectively.

$$a_0 + a_1(-1) + a_2(-1)^2 + a_3(-1)^3 = a_0 - a_1 + a_2 - a_3 = 150$$
$$a_0 + a_1(0) + a_2(0)^2 + a_3(0)^3 = a_0 = 180$$
$$a_0 + a_1(1) + a_2(1)^2 + a_3(1)^3 = a_0 + a_1 + a_2 + a_3 = 240$$
$$a_0 + a_1(2) + a_2(2)^2 + a_3(2)^3 = a_0 + 2a_1 + 4a_2 + 8a_3 = 360$$

We use Gauss-Jordan elimination on the augmented matrix for this system.

$$\begin{bmatrix} 1 & -1 & 1 & -1 & 150 \\ 1 & 0 & 0 & 0 & 180 \\ 1 & 1 & 1 & 1 & 240 \\ 1 & 2 & 4 & 8 & 360 \end{bmatrix} \Rightarrow \begin{bmatrix} 1 & 0 & 0 & 0 & 180 \\ 0 & 1 & 0 & 0 & 40 \\ 0 & 0 & 1 & 0 & 15 \\ 0 & 0 & 0 & 1 & 5 \end{bmatrix}$$

Thus,

$p(z) = 180 + 40z + 15z^2 + 5z^3$ and
$p(x) = 180 + 40(x - 2002) + 15(x - 2002)^2 + 5(x - 2002)^3$.

(b)

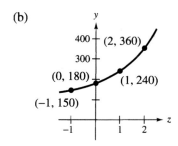

8. Letting $p(x) = a_0 + a_1 x + a_2 x^2$, we substitute $x = 0, 2,$ and 4 into $p(x)$ and equate the results to $y = 1, \frac{1}{3},$ and $\frac{1}{5}$, respectively.

$$a_0 + a_1(0) + a_2(0)^2 = a_0 = 1$$
$$a_0 + a_1(2) + a_2(2)^2 = a_0 + 2a_1 + 4a_2 = \frac{1}{3}$$
$$a_0 + a_1(4) + a_2(4)^2 = a_0 + 4a_1 + 16a_2 = \frac{1}{5}$$

We use Gauss-Jordan elimination on the augmented matrix for this system.

$$\begin{bmatrix} 1 & 0 & 0 & 1 \\ 1 & 2 & 4 & \frac{1}{3} \\ 1 & 4 & 16 & \frac{1}{5} \end{bmatrix} \Rightarrow \begin{bmatrix} 1 & 0 & 0 & 1 \\ 0 & 1 & 0 & -\frac{7}{15} \\ 0 & 0 & 1 & \frac{1}{15} \end{bmatrix}$$

Thus, $p(x) = 1 - \frac{7}{15}x + \frac{1}{15}x^2$.

10. We let $p(x) = a_0 + a_1x + a_2x^2$ be the equation of the parabola. Since the parabola passes through the points $(0, 1)$ and $(\frac{1}{2}, \frac{1}{2})$, we have

$$a_0 + a_1(0) + a_2(0)^2 = a_0 \qquad\qquad = 1$$
$$a_0 + a_1(\tfrac{1}{2}) + a_2(\tfrac{1}{2})^2 = a_0 + \tfrac{1}{2}a_1 + \tfrac{1}{4}a_2 = \tfrac{1}{2}.$$

To say that $p(x)$ has a horizontal tangent at $(\frac{1}{2}, \frac{1}{2})$ means that the derivative of $p(x)$, $p'(x) = a_1 + 2a_2x$, equals zero when $x = \frac{1}{2}$. Thus, we have a third linear equation

$$a_1 + 2a_2(\tfrac{1}{2}) = a_1 + a_2 = 0.$$

We use Gauss-Jordan elimination on the augmented matrix for this linear system.

$$\begin{bmatrix} 1 & 0 & 0 & 1 \\ 1 & \frac{1}{2} & \frac{1}{4} & \frac{1}{2} \\ 0 & 1 & 1 & 0 \end{bmatrix} \Rightarrow \begin{bmatrix} 1 & 0 & 0 & 1 \\ 0 & 1 & 0 & -2 \\ 0 & 0 & 1 & 2 \end{bmatrix}$$

Thus, $p(x) = 1 - 2x + 2x^2$.

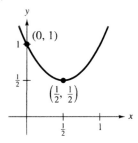

12. Let us assume that the equation of the circle is $x^2 + ax + y^2 + by - c = 0$. Since each of the given points lies on the circle, we have the following linear equations.

$$(1)^2 + a(1) + (3)^2 + b(3) - c = a + 3b - c + 10 = 0$$
$$(-2)^2 + a(-2) + (6)^2 + b(6) - c = -2a + 6b - c + 40 = 0$$
$$(4)^2 + a(4) + (2)^2 + b(2) - c = 4a + 2b - c + 20 = 0$$

We use Gauss-Jordan elimination on the system.

$$\begin{bmatrix} 1 & 3 & -1 & -10 \\ -2 & 6 & -1 & -40 \\ 4 & 2 & -1 & -20 \end{bmatrix} \Rightarrow \begin{bmatrix} 1 & 0 & 0 & -10 \\ 0 & 1 & 0 & -20 \\ 0 & 0 & 1 & -60 \end{bmatrix}$$

Hence, the equation of the circle is $x^2 - 10x + y^2 - 20y + 60 = 0$ or $(x - 5)^2 + (y - 10)^2 = 65$.

14. (a) To begin, we let

$$x = \frac{(\text{year} - 1920)}{10} \text{ and } p(x) = a_0 + a_1 x + a_2 x^2 + a_3 x^3.$$

The four data points $(0, 106)$, $(1, 123)$, $(2, 132)$, and $(3, 151)$ yield the following linear equations.

$$
\begin{aligned}
a_0 &&&&&&&&= 106 \\
a_0 &+& a_1 &+& a_2 &+& a_3 &= 123 \\
a_0 &+& 2a_1 &+& 4a_2 &+& 8a_3 &= 132 \\
a_0 &+& 3a_1 &+& 9a_2 &+& 27a_3 &= 151
\end{aligned}
$$

The solution to this system is $a_0 = 106$, $a_1 = 27$, $a_2 = -13$, $a_3 = 3$.

Hence, the cubic polynomial is $p(x) = 106 + 27x - 13x^2 + 3x^3$, where

$$x = \frac{(\text{year} - 1920)}{10}.$$

(b) To estimate the population in 1960, we let $x = 4$. $p(4) = 106 + 27(4) - 13(4)^2 + 3(4)^3 = 198$ million. The actual population was 179 million in 1960.

16. (a) Let $z = x - 2000$ and $p(z) = a_0 + a_1 z + a_2 z^2 + a_3 z^3 + a_4 z^4$. The five points $(-2, 13.414)$, $(-1, 14.406)$, $(0, 14.750)$, $(1, 15.700)$, and $(2, 16.800)$ give

$$
\begin{aligned}
a_0 &-& 2a_1 &+& 4a_2 &-& 8a_3 &+& 16a_4 &= 13.414 \\
a_0 &-& a_1 &+& a_2 &-& a_3 &+& a_4 &= 14.406 \\
a_0 &&&&&&&&&= 14.750 \\
a_0 &+& a_1 &+& a_2 &+& a_3 &+& a_4 &= 15.700 \\
a_0 &+& 2a_1 &+& 4a_2 &+& 8a_3 &+& 16a_4 &= 16.800.
\end{aligned}
$$

(b) The solution to this system is $a_0 = \frac{59}{4}$, $a_1 = \frac{137}{236}$, $a_2 = \frac{125}{334}$, $a_3 = \frac{27}{406}$, $a_4 = -\frac{29}{407}$. Hence, $p(z) = \frac{59}{4} + \frac{137}{236}z + \frac{125}{334}z^2 + \frac{27}{406}z^3 - \frac{29}{407}z^4$ or

$$p(x) = \frac{59}{4} + \frac{137}{236}(x - 2000) + \frac{125}{334}(x - 2000)^2 + \frac{27}{406}(x - 2000)^3 - \frac{29}{407}(x - 2000)^4.$$

18. Choosing a second-degree polynomial approximation $p(x) = a_0 + a_1 x + a_2 x^2$, we substitute $x = 1, 2$, and 4 into $p(x)$ and equate the results to $y = 0, 1$, and 2, respectively.

$$
\begin{aligned}
a_0 &+& a_1 &+& a_2 &= 0 \\
a_0 &+& 2a_1 &+& 4a_2 &= 1 \\
a_0 &+& 4a_1 &+& 16a_2 &= 2
\end{aligned}
$$

The solution to this system of linear equation is $a_0 = -\frac{4}{3}$, $a_1 = \frac{3}{2}$, and $a_2 = -\frac{1}{6}$. Hence, $p(x) = -\frac{4}{3} + \frac{3}{2}x - \frac{1}{6}x^2$. Finally, to estimate $\log_2 3$, we calculate $p(3) = -\frac{4}{3} + \frac{3}{2}(3) - \frac{1}{6}(3)^2 = \frac{5}{3}$.

20. Let

$$p_1(x) = a_0 + a_1 x + a_2 x^2 + \cdots + a_{n-1} x^{n-1} \text{ and}$$
$$p_2(x) = b_0 + b_1 x + b_2 x^2 + \cdots + b_{n-1} x^{n-1}$$

be two different polynomials that pass through the n given points. The polynomial

$$p_1(x) - p_2(x) = (a_0 - b_0) + (a_1 - b_1)x + (a_2 - b_2)x^2 + \cdots + (a_{n-1} - b_{n-1})x^{n-1}$$

is zero for these n values of x, and hence, we must have $a_0 = b_0, a_1 = b_1, a_2 = b_2,$ $\ldots, a_{n-1} = b_{n-1}$. Thus, there is only one polynomial function of degree $n - 1$ (or less) whose graph passes through n points in the plane with distinct x-coordinates.

22. (a) Each of the network's four junctions gives rise to a linear equation as follows

$$\textbf{input} = \textbf{output}$$
$$300 = x_1 + x_2$$
$$x_1 + x_3 = x_4 + 150$$
$$x_2 + 200 = x_3 + x_5$$
$$x_4 + x_5 = 350$$

We reorganize these equations, form the augmented matrix, and use Gauss-Jordan elimination.

$$\begin{bmatrix} 1 & 1 & 0 & 0 & 0 & 300 \\ 1 & 0 & 1 & -1 & 0 & 150 \\ 0 & 1 & -1 & 0 & -1 & -200 \\ 0 & 0 & 0 & 1 & 1 & 350 \end{bmatrix} \Rightarrow \begin{bmatrix} 1 & 0 & 1 & 0 & 1 & 500 \\ 0 & 1 & -1 & 0 & -1 & -200 \\ 0 & 0 & 0 & 1 & 1 & 350 \\ 0 & 0 & 0 & 0 & 0 & 0 \end{bmatrix}$$

Letting $x_5 = t$ and $x_3 = s$ be the free variables, we can write the solution as follows.

$$x_1 = 500 - s - t$$
$$x_2 = -200 + s + t$$
$$x_3 = s$$
$$x_4 = 350 - t$$
$$x_5 = t$$

(b) If $x_2 = 200$ and $x_3 = 50$, then we have $s = 50$ and $t = 350$. Hence, the solution is $x_1 = 100, x_2 = 200, x_3 = 50, x_4 = 0, x_5 = 350$.

(c) If $x_2 = 150$ and $x_3 = 0$, then we have $s = 0$ and $t = 350$. Hence, the solution is $x_1 = 150, x_2 = 150, x_3 = 0, x_4 = 0, x_5 = 350$.

24. (a) Each of the network's four junctions gives rise to a linear equation as follows

input = output

$400 + x_2 = x_1$

$x_1 + x_3 = x_4 + 600$

$300 = x_2 + x_3 + x_5$

$x_4 + x_5 = 100$

We reorganize these equations, form the augmented matrix, and use Gauss-Jordan elimination.

$$\begin{bmatrix} 1 & -1 & 0 & 0 & 0 & 400 \\ 1 & 0 & 1 & -1 & 0 & 600 \\ 0 & 1 & 1 & 0 & 1 & 300 \\ 0 & 0 & 0 & 1 & 1 & 100 \end{bmatrix} \Rightarrow \begin{bmatrix} 1 & 0 & 1 & 0 & 1 & 700 \\ 0 & 1 & 1 & 0 & 1 & 300 \\ 0 & 0 & 0 & 1 & 1 & 100 \\ 0 & 0 & 0 & 0 & 0 & 0 \end{bmatrix}$$

Letting $x_5 = t$ and $x_3 = s$ be the free variables, we can write the solution as follows.

$x_1 = 700 - s - t$

$x_2 = 300 - s - t$

$x_3 = s$

$x_4 = 100 - t$

$x_5 = t$

(b) If $x_3 = 0$ and $x_5 = 100$, then the solution is $x_1 = 600$, $x_2 = 200$, $x_3 = 0$, $x_4 = 0$, $x_5 = 100$.

(c) If $x_3 = x_5 = 100$, then the solution is $x_1 = 500$, $x_2 = 100$, $x_3 = 100$, $x_4 = 0$, $x_5 = 100$.

26. Applying Kirchoff's first law to either junction produces

$I_1 + I_3 = I_2$

and applying the second law to the two paths produces

$R_1I_1 + R_2I_2 = 4I_1 + I_2 = 16$

$R_2I_2 + R_3I_3 = I_2 + 4I_3 = 8.$

Rearranging these equations, forming their augmented matrix, and using Gauss-Jordan elimination yields the following.

$$\begin{bmatrix} 1 & -1 & 1 & 0 \\ 4 & 1 & 0 & 16 \\ 0 & 1 & 4 & 8 \end{bmatrix} \Rightarrow \begin{bmatrix} 1 & 0 & 0 & 3 \\ 0 & 1 & 0 & 4 \\ 0 & 0 & 1 & 1 \end{bmatrix}$$

Thus, $I_1 = 3$, $I_2 = 4$, and $I_3 = 1$.

28. Applying Kirchoff's first law to three of the four junctions produces

$$I_1 + I_3 = I_2$$
$$I_1 + I_4 = I_2$$
$$I_3 + I_6 = I_5$$

and applying the second law to th three paths produces

$$R_1I_1 + R_2I_2 = 3I_1 + 2I_2 = 14$$
$$R_2I_2 + R_4I_4 + R_5I_5 + R_3I_3 = 2I_2 + 2I_4 + I_5 + 4I_3 = 25$$
$$R_5I_5 + R_6I_6 = I_5 + I_6 = 8.$$

Rearranging these equations, forming their augmented matrix, and using Gauss-Jordan elimination yields the following.

$$\begin{bmatrix} 1 & -1 & 1 & 0 & 0 & 0 & 0 \\ 1 & -1 & 0 & 1 & 0 & 0 & 0 \\ 0 & 0 & 1 & 0 & -1 & 1 & 0 \\ 3 & 2 & 0 & 0 & 0 & 0 & 14 \\ 0 & 2 & 4 & 2 & 1 & 0 & 25 \\ 0 & 0 & 0 & 0 & 1 & 1 & 8 \end{bmatrix} \Rightarrow$$

$$\begin{bmatrix} 1 & 0 & 0 & 0 & 0 & 0 & 2 \\ 0 & 1 & 0 & 0 & 0 & 0 & 4 \\ 0 & 0 & 1 & 0 & 0 & 0 & 2 \\ 0 & 0 & 0 & 1 & 0 & 0 & 2 \\ 0 & 0 & 0 & 0 & 1 & 0 & 5 \\ 0 & 0 & 0 & 0 & 0 & 1 & 3 \end{bmatrix}$$

Thus, the solution is $I_1 = 2, I_2 = 4, I_3 = 2, I_4 = 2, I_5 = 5,$ and $I_6 = 3.$

Chapter 1 ❏ Review Exercises

2. Choosing x_2 and x_3 as the free variables and letting $x_2 = s$ and $x_3 = t$, we have

$$3x_1 + 2s - 4t = 0$$
$$3x_1 = -2s + 4t$$
$$x_1 = \tfrac{1}{3}(-2s + 4t).$$

Thus, the solution set may be described as $x_1 = -\tfrac{2}{3}s + \tfrac{4}{3}t, x_2 = s,$ and $x_3 = t$ where s and t are real numbers.

4. The matrix satisfies all three conditions in the definition of row-echelon form. Moreover, since each column that has a leading 1 (columns 1 and 4) has zeros elsewhere, the matrix is in reduced row-echelon form.

6. The matrix satisfies all three conditions in the definition of row-echelon form. Moreover, since each column that has a leading 1 (columns 2 and 3) has zeros elsewhere, the matrix is in reduced row-echelon form.

8. This matrix corresponds to the system

$$x_1 + 2x_2 + 3x_3 = 0$$
$$0 = 1.$$

Since the second equation is impossible, the system has no solution.

10. We row reduce the augmented matrix for this system.

$$\begin{bmatrix} 1 & 1 & -1 \\ 3 & 2 & 0 \end{bmatrix} \Rightarrow \begin{bmatrix} 1 & 1 & -1 \\ 0 & -1 & 3 \end{bmatrix} \Rightarrow \begin{bmatrix} 1 & 1 & -1 \\ 0 & 1 & -3 \end{bmatrix} \Rightarrow \begin{bmatrix} 1 & 0 & 2 \\ 0 & 1 & -3 \end{bmatrix}$$

Converting back to a linear system, the solution is $x = 2$ and $y = -3$.

12. Rearranging the equations, forming the augmented matrix, and row reducing, we have

$$\begin{bmatrix} 1 & -1 & 3 \\ 4 & -1 & 10 \end{bmatrix} \Rightarrow \begin{bmatrix} 1 & -1 & 3 \\ 0 & 3 & -2 \end{bmatrix} \Rightarrow \begin{bmatrix} 1 & -1 & 3 \\ 0 & 1 & -\frac{2}{3} \end{bmatrix} \Rightarrow \begin{bmatrix} 1 & 0 & \frac{7}{3} \\ 0 & 1 & -\frac{2}{3} \end{bmatrix}$$

Converting back to a linear system, we obtain the solution $x = \frac{7}{3}$ and $y = -\frac{2}{3}$.

14. Rearranging the equations forming the augmented matrix, and row reducing, we have

$$\begin{bmatrix} 4 & 1 & 0 \\ -1 & 1 & 0 \end{bmatrix} \Rightarrow \begin{bmatrix} 1 & -1 & 0 \\ 4 & 1 & 0 \end{bmatrix} \Rightarrow \begin{bmatrix} 1 & -1 & 0 \\ 0 & 5 & 0 \end{bmatrix} \Rightarrow \begin{bmatrix} 1 & 0 & 0 \\ 0 & 1 & 0 \end{bmatrix}$$

Converting back to a linear system, the solution is $x = y = 0$.

16. We row reduce the augmented matrix for this system.

$$\begin{bmatrix} 40 & 30 & 24 \\ 20 & 15 & -14 \end{bmatrix} \Rightarrow \begin{bmatrix} 1 & \frac{3}{4} & \frac{3}{5} \\ 20 & 15 & -14 \end{bmatrix} \Rightarrow \begin{bmatrix} 1 & \frac{3}{4} & \frac{3}{5} \\ 0 & 0 & -26 \end{bmatrix}$$

Since the second row corresponds to the absurd equation $0 = -26$, the system has no solution.

18. Multiplying both equations by 100 and forming the augmented matrix produces

$$\begin{bmatrix} 20 & -10 & 7 \\ 40 & -50 & -1 \end{bmatrix}.$$

Gauss-Jordan elimination yields the following.

$$\begin{bmatrix} 1 & -\frac{1}{2} & \frac{7}{20} \\ 40 & -50 & -1 \end{bmatrix} \Rightarrow \begin{bmatrix} 1 & -\frac{1}{2} & \frac{7}{20} \\ 0 & -30 & -15 \end{bmatrix}$$

$$\begin{bmatrix} 1 & -\frac{1}{2} & \frac{7}{20} \\ 0 & 1 & \frac{1}{2} \end{bmatrix} \Rightarrow \begin{bmatrix} 1 & 0 & \frac{3}{5} \\ 0 & 1 & \frac{1}{2} \end{bmatrix}$$

Hence, the solution is $x = \frac{3}{5}$ and $y = \frac{1}{2}$.

20. We use Gauss-Jordan elimination on the augmented matrix.

$$\begin{bmatrix} \frac{1}{3} & \frac{4}{7} & 3 \\ 2 & 3 & 15 \end{bmatrix} \implies \begin{bmatrix} 1 & 0 & -3 \\ 0 & 1 & 7 \end{bmatrix}$$

Thus, $x = -3$, $y = 7$.

22. We use Gauss-Jordan elimination on the augmented matrix.

$$\begin{bmatrix} 2 & 3 & 1 & 10 \\ 2 & -3 & -3 & 22 \\ 4 & -2 & 3 & -2 \end{bmatrix} \implies \begin{bmatrix} 1 & 0 & 0 & 5 \\ 0 & 1 & 0 & 2 \\ 0 & 0 & 1 & -6 \end{bmatrix}$$

Thus, $x = 5$, $y = 2$, and $z = -6$,

24. We use Gauss-Jordan elimination on the augmented matrix.

$$\begin{bmatrix} 2 & 0 & 6 & -9 \\ 3 & -2 & 11 & -16 \\ 3 & -1 & 7 & -11 \end{bmatrix} \implies \begin{bmatrix} 1 & 0 & 0 & -\frac{3}{4} \\ 0 & 1 & 0 & 0 \\ 0 & 0 & 1 & -\frac{5}{4} \end{bmatrix}$$

Thus, $x = -\frac{3}{4}$, $y = 0$, and $z = -\frac{5}{4}$.

26. We use Gauss-Jordan elimination on the augmented matrix.

$$\begin{bmatrix} 1 & 2 & 6 & 1 \\ 2 & 5 & 15 & 4 \\ 3 & 1 & 3 & -6 \end{bmatrix} \implies \begin{bmatrix} 1 & 2 & 6 & 1 \\ 0 & 1 & 3 & 2 \\ 0 & 0 & 0 & 1 \end{bmatrix}$$

Since the third row corresponds to the absurd equation $0 = 1$, there is no solution.

28. We use Gauss-Jordan elimination on the augmented matrix.

$$\begin{bmatrix} 2 & 5 & -19 & 34 \\ 3 & 8 & -31 & 54 \end{bmatrix} \implies \begin{bmatrix} 1 & 0 & 3 & 2 \\ 0 & 1 & -5 & 6 \end{bmatrix}$$

Hence, the solution is $x_1 = 2 - 3t$, $x_2 = 6 + 5t$, and $x_3 = t$, where t is any real number.

30. We use Gauss-Jordan elimination on the augmented matrix.

$$\begin{bmatrix} 1 & 5 & 3 & 0 & 0 & 14 \\ 0 & 4 & 2 & 5 & 0 & 3 \\ 0 & 0 & 3 & 8 & 6 & 16 \\ 2 & 4 & 0 & 0 & -2 & 0 \\ 2 & 0 & -1 & 0 & 0 & 0 \end{bmatrix} \implies \begin{bmatrix} 1 & 0 & 0 & 0 & 0 & 2 \\ 0 & 1 & 0 & 0 & 0 & 0 \\ 0 & 0 & 1 & 0 & 0 & 4 \\ 0 & 0 & 0 & 1 & 0 & -1 \\ 0 & 0 & 0 & 0 & 1 & 2 \end{bmatrix}$$

Hence, the solution is $x_1 = 2$, $x_2 = 0$, $x_3 = 4$, $x_4 = -1$, $x_5 = 2$.

32. We use Gauss-Jordan elimination on the augmented matrix.

$$\begin{bmatrix} 2 & 4 & -7 & 0 \\ 1 & -3 & 9 & 0 \\ 6 & 0 & 9 & 0 \end{bmatrix} \implies \begin{bmatrix} 1 & 0 & \frac{3}{2} & 0 \\ 0 & 1 & -\frac{5}{2} & 0 \\ 0 & 0 & 0 & 0 \end{bmatrix}$$

Letting $x_3 = t$ be the free variable, we have $x_1 = -\frac{3}{2}t$, $x_2 = \frac{5}{2}t$, and $x_3 = t$, where t is any real number.

34. We use Gauss-Jordan elimination on the augmented matrix.

$$\begin{bmatrix} 1 & 3 & 5 & 0 \\ 1 & 4 & \frac{1}{2} & 0 \end{bmatrix} \implies \begin{bmatrix} 1 & 0 & \frac{37}{2} & 0 \\ 0 & 1 & -\frac{9}{2} & 0 \end{bmatrix}$$

Letting $x_3 = t$ be the free variable, we have $x_1 = -\frac{37}{2}t$, $x_2 = \frac{9}{2}t$, and $x_3 = t$.

36. We use Gaussian elimination on the augmented matrix.

$$\begin{bmatrix} 1 & -1 & 2 & 0 \\ -1 & 1 & -1 & 0 \\ 1 & k & 1 & 0 \end{bmatrix} \implies \begin{bmatrix} 1 & -1 & 2 & 0 \\ 0 & 0 & 1 & 0 \\ 0 & (k+1) & -1 & 0 \end{bmatrix}$$

$$\implies \begin{bmatrix} 1 & -1 & 2 & 0 \\ 0 & (k+1) & -1 & 0 \\ 0 & 0 & 1 & 0 \end{bmatrix}$$

Hence, there will be exactly one solution (the trivial solution $x = y = z = 0$) if and only if $k \neq -1$.

38. We form the augmented matrix for the system

$$\begin{bmatrix} 2 & -1 & 1 & a \\ 1 & 1 & 2 & b \\ 0 & 3 & 3 & c \end{bmatrix}$$

and use Gaussian elimination to reduce the matrix to row-echelon form.

$$\begin{bmatrix} 1 & -\frac{1}{2} & \frac{1}{2} & \frac{a}{2} \\ 1 & 1 & 2 & b \\ 0 & 3 & 3 & c \end{bmatrix} \implies \begin{bmatrix} 1 & -\frac{1}{2} & \frac{1}{2} & \frac{a}{2} \\ 0 & \frac{3}{2} & \frac{3}{2} & \frac{2b-a}{2} \\ 0 & 3 & 3 & c \end{bmatrix} \implies$$

$$\begin{bmatrix} 1 & -\frac{1}{2} & \frac{1}{2} & \frac{a}{2} \\ 0 & 1 & 1 & \frac{2b-a}{3} \\ 0 & 3 & 3 & c \end{bmatrix} \implies \begin{bmatrix} 1 & -\frac{1}{2} & \frac{1}{2} & \frac{a}{2} \\ 0 & 1 & 1 & \frac{2b-a}{3} \\ 0 & 0 & 0 & c-2b+a \end{bmatrix}$$

(a) If $c - 2b + a \neq 0$, then the system has no solution.

(b) The system cannot have one solution.

(c) If $c - 2b + a = 0$, then the system has infinitely many solutions.

40. We begin by finding all possible first rows.

$$[0\ 0\ 0], [0\ 0\ 1], [0\ 1\ 0], [0\ 1\ a], [1\ 0\ 0], [1\ a\ 0], [1\ a\ b], [1\ 0\ a].$$

where a and b are nonzero real numbers. For each of these we examine the
possible second rows.

$$\begin{bmatrix} 0 & 0 & 0 \\ 0 & 0 & 0 \end{bmatrix}, \begin{bmatrix} 0 & 0 & 1 \\ 0 & 0 & 0 \end{bmatrix}, \begin{bmatrix} 0 & 1 & 0 \\ 0 & 0 & 0 \end{bmatrix}, \begin{bmatrix} 0 & 1 & 0 \\ 0 & 0 & 1 \end{bmatrix},$$

$$\begin{bmatrix} 0 & 1 & a \\ 0 & 0 & 0 \end{bmatrix}, \begin{bmatrix} 1 & 0 & 0 \\ 0 & 0 & 0 \end{bmatrix}, \begin{bmatrix} 1 & 0 & 0 \\ 0 & 1 & 0 \end{bmatrix}, \begin{bmatrix} 1 & 0 & 0 \\ 0 & 0 & 1 \end{bmatrix}, \begin{bmatrix} 1 & 0 & 0 \\ 0 & 1 & a \end{bmatrix},$$

$$\begin{bmatrix} 1 & a & 0 \\ 0 & 0 & 0 \end{bmatrix}, \begin{bmatrix} 1 & a & 0 \\ 0 & 0 & 1 \end{bmatrix}, \begin{bmatrix} 1 & a & b \\ 0 & 0 & 0 \end{bmatrix}, \begin{bmatrix} 1 & 0 & a \\ 0 & 0 & 0 \end{bmatrix}, \begin{bmatrix} 1 & 0 & a \\ 0 & 1 & 0 \end{bmatrix}.$$

These are all possible 2×3 reduced row-echelon matrices.

42. We use Gaussian elimination on the augmented matrix.

$$\begin{bmatrix} (\lambda + 2) & -2 & 3 & 0 \\ -2 & (\lambda - 1) & 6 & 0 \\ 1 & 2 & \lambda & 0 \end{bmatrix} \Rightarrow \begin{bmatrix} 1 & 2 & \lambda & 0 \\ 0 & \lambda + 3 & 6 + 2\lambda & 0 \\ 0 & -2\lambda - 6 & -\lambda^2 - 2\lambda + 3 & 0 \end{bmatrix}$$

$$\Rightarrow \begin{bmatrix} 1 & 2 & \lambda & 0 \\ 0 & \lambda + 3 & 6 + 2\lambda & 0 \\ 0 & 0 & (\lambda^2 - 2\lambda - 15) & 0 \end{bmatrix}$$

Hence, we need $\lambda^2 - 2\lambda - 15 = (\lambda - 5)(\lambda + 3) = 0$, which implies $\lambda = 5$ or $\lambda = -3$.

44. (a) *True.* A homogeneous system of linear equations is always consistent,
since there is always a trivial solution, *i.e.*, when all variables are equal to
zero. See Theorem 1.1 on page 25.

(b) *False.* Consider for example the following system (with three variables and
two equations).

$$x + y - z = 2$$
$$-2x - 2y + 2z = 1.$$

It is easy to see that this system has *no* solutions.

46. (a) Let x_1 = number of free-throws

x_2 = number of two-point baskets

x_3 = number of three-point baskets.

From the given information we have

$$x_1 + 2x_2 + 3x_3 = 90$$
$$x_2 = 11x_3$$
$$x_1 = 5x_3.$$

—CONTINUED—

46. —CONTINUED—

(b) Using Gauss-Jordan elimination on the augmented matrix, we obtain

$$\begin{bmatrix} 1 & 2 & 3 & 90 \\ 0 & 1 & -11 & 0 \\ 1 & 0 & -5 & 0 \end{bmatrix} \Rightarrow \begin{bmatrix} 1 & 0 & 0 & 15 \\ 0 & 1 & 0 & 33 \\ 0 & 0 & 1 & 3 \end{bmatrix}.$$

Thus, there were $x_1 = 15$ free-throws, $x_2 = 33$ two-point baskets, and $x_3 = 3$ three-point baskets.

48. (a) Since there are four points, we choose a third-degree polynomial,

$p(x) = a_0 + a_1 x + a_2 x^2 + a_3 x^3$. By substituting the values at each point into this equation, we obtain the system

$$\begin{aligned} a_0 - a_1 + a_2 - a_3 &= -1 \\ a_0 &= 0 \\ a_0 + a_1 + a_2 + a_3 &= 1 \\ a_0 + 2a_1 + 4a_2 + 8a_3 &= 4. \end{aligned}$$

Using Gauss-Jordan elimination on the augmented matrix, we obtain

$$\begin{bmatrix} 1 & -1 & 1 & -1 & -1 \\ 1 & 0 & 0 & 0 & 0 \\ 1 & 1 & 1 & 1 & 1 \\ 1 & 2 & 4 & 8 & 4 \end{bmatrix} \Rightarrow \begin{bmatrix} 1 & 0 & 0 & 0 & 0 \\ 0 & 1 & 0 & 0 & \frac{2}{3} \\ 0 & 0 & 1 & 0 & 0 \\ 0 & 0 & 0 & 1 & \frac{1}{3} \end{bmatrix}.$$

Thus, $p(x) = \frac{2}{3}x + \frac{1}{3}x^3$.

(b)

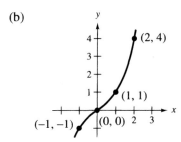

50. Substituting the points, $(1, 0)$, $(2, 0)$, $(3, 0)$, and $(4, 0)$ into the polynomial $p(x)$ yields the system

$$\begin{aligned} a_0 + a_1 + a_2 + a_3 &= 0 \\ a_0 + 2a_1 + 4a_2 + 8a_3 &= 0 \\ a_0 + 3a_1 + 9a_2 + 27a_3 &= 0 \\ a_0 + 4a_1 + 16a_2 + 64a_3 &= 0. \end{aligned}$$

Gaussian elimination shows that the only solution is $a_0 = a_1 = a_2 = a_3 = 0$.

52. We are looking for a quadratic function $y = ax^2 + bx + c$, such that the points $(0, 40)$, $(6, 73)$ and $(12, 52)$ lie on its graph. The system of equations to fit the data to a quadratic polynomial is

$$c = 40$$
$$36a + 6b + c = 73$$
$$144a + 12b + c = 52.$$

Substituting $c = 40$ into the second and the third equations, we obtain

$$36a + 6b = 33$$
$$144a + 12b = 12$$

or

$$12a + 2b = 11$$
$$12a + b = 1.$$

Adding -1 times the second equation to the first equation we obtain $b = 10$, so $a = -\frac{9}{12} = -\frac{3}{4}$. If we use the graphing utility to graph $y = -0.75x^2 + 10x + 40$ we would see that the data points $(0, 40)$, $(6, 73)$ and $(12, 52)$ lie on the graph. On page 28 it is stated that if we have n points with district x-coordinates, then there is precisely one polynomial function of degree $n - 1$ (or less) that fits these points.

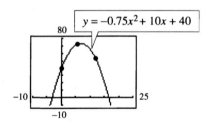

54. Applying Kirchoff's first law to either junction produces

$$I_1 + I_3 = I_2$$

and applying the second law to the two paths produces

$$R_1 I_1 + R_2 I_2 = 3I_1 + 4I_2 = 3$$
$$R_2 I_2 + R_3 I_3 = 4I_2 + 2I_3 = 2.$$

Rearranging these equations, forming the augmented matrix, and using Gauss-Jordan elimination yields the following.

$$\begin{bmatrix} 1 & -1 & 1 & 0 \\ 3 & 4 & 0 & 3 \\ 0 & 4 & 2 & 2 \end{bmatrix} \implies \begin{bmatrix} 1 & 0 & 0 & \frac{5}{13} \\ 0 & 1 & 0 & \frac{6}{13} \\ 0 & 0 & 1 & \frac{1}{13} \end{bmatrix}$$

Hence, the solution is $I_1 = \frac{5}{13}$, $I_2 = \frac{6}{13}$, and $I_3 = \frac{1}{13}$.

Chapter 1 ❑ Project Solutions

1 Graphing Linear Equations

1. $\begin{bmatrix} 2 & -1 & 3 \\ a & b & 6 \end{bmatrix} \Rightarrow \begin{bmatrix} 1 & -\frac{1}{2} & \frac{3}{2} \\ 0 & b + \frac{1}{2}a & 6 - \frac{3}{2}a \end{bmatrix}$

   (a) Unique solution if $b + \frac{1}{2}a \neq 0$. For instance, $a = b = 2$.

   (b) Infinite number of solutions if $b + \frac{1}{2}a = 6 - \frac{3}{2}a = 0 \Rightarrow a = 4$ and $b = -2$.

   (c) No solution if $b + \frac{1}{2}a = 0$ and $6 - \frac{3}{2}a \neq 0 \Rightarrow a \neq 4$ and $b = -\frac{1}{2}a$. For instance, $a = 2$, $b = -1$.

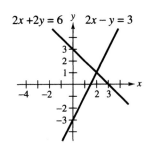 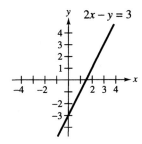 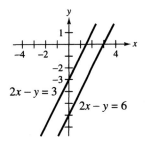

   (a) $2x - y = 3$ (b) $2x - y = 3$ (c) $2x - y = 3$
      $2x + 2y = 6$ $4x - 2y = 6$ $2x - y = 6$

   (The answers are not unique.)

2. (a) $x + y + z = 0$ (b) $x + y + z = 0$ (c) $x + y + z = 0$
      $x + y + z = 0$ $y + z = 1$ $x + y + z = 1$
      $x - y - z = 0$ $z = 2$ $x - y - z = 0$

   (The answers are not unique.)

   There are other configurations, such as three mutually parallel planes, or three planes that intersect pairwise in lines.

2 Underdetermined and Overdetermined Systems of Equations

1. Yes, $x + y = 2$ is a consistent underdetermined system.

2. Yes,

   $$\begin{aligned} x + y &= 2 \\ 2x + 2y &= 4 \\ 3x + 3y &= 6 \end{aligned}$$

   is a consistent, overdetermined system.

3. Yes,

   $$x + y + z = 1$$
   $$x + y + z = 2$$

   is an inconsistent underdetermined system.

4. Yes,

   $$x + y = 1$$
   $$x + y = 2$$
   $$x + y = 3$$

   is an inconsistent underdetermined system.

5. In general, a linear system with more equations than unknowns would probably be inconsistent. Here is an intuitive reason: Each variable represents a degree of freedom, while each equation gives a condition that in general reduces number of degrees of freedom by one. If there are more equations (conditions) than variables (degrees of freedom), then there are too many conditions for the system to be consistent. So we expect such a system to be inconsistent in general. But, as exercise 2 shows, this is not always true.

6. In general, a linear system with more unknowns than equations would probably be consistent. As in problem 5 the intuitive explanation is as follows. Each variable represents a degree of freedom, and each equation represents a condition that takes away one degree of freedom. If there are more variables than equations, in general, we would expect a solution. But, as exercise 3 shows, this is not always true.

CHAPTER 2
Matrices

Section 2.1 Operations with Matrices

2. (a) $A + B = \begin{bmatrix} 1 & 2 \\ 2 & 1 \end{bmatrix} + \begin{bmatrix} -3 & -2 \\ 4 & 2 \end{bmatrix} = \begin{bmatrix} 1-3 & 2-2 \\ 2+4 & 1+2 \end{bmatrix} = \begin{bmatrix} -2 & 0 \\ 6 & 3 \end{bmatrix}$

(b) $A - B = \begin{bmatrix} 1 & 2 \\ 2 & 1 \end{bmatrix} - \begin{bmatrix} -3 & -2 \\ 4 & 2 \end{bmatrix} = \begin{bmatrix} 1+3 & 2+2 \\ 2-4 & 1-2 \end{bmatrix} = \begin{bmatrix} 4 & 4 \\ -2 & -1 \end{bmatrix}$

(c) $2A = 2\begin{bmatrix} 1 & 2 \\ 2 & 1 \end{bmatrix} = \begin{bmatrix} 2(1) & 2(2) \\ 2(2) & 2(1) \end{bmatrix} = \begin{bmatrix} 2 & 4 \\ 4 & 2 \end{bmatrix}$

(d) $2A - B = \begin{bmatrix} 2 & 4 \\ 4 & 2 \end{bmatrix} - \begin{bmatrix} -3 & -2 \\ 4 & 2 \end{bmatrix} = \begin{bmatrix} 5 & 6 \\ 0 & 0 \end{bmatrix}$

4. (a) $A + B = \begin{bmatrix} 2 & 1 & 1 \\ -1 & -1 & 4 \end{bmatrix} + \begin{bmatrix} 2 & -3 & 4 \\ -3 & 1 & -2 \end{bmatrix} = \begin{bmatrix} 2+2 & 1-3 & 1+4 \\ -1-3 & -1+1 & 4-2 \end{bmatrix}$

$= \begin{bmatrix} 4 & -2 & 5 \\ -4 & 0 & 2 \end{bmatrix}$

(b) $A - B = \begin{bmatrix} 2 & 1 & 1 \\ -1 & -1 & 4 \end{bmatrix} - \begin{bmatrix} 2 & -3 & 4 \\ -3 & 1 & -2 \end{bmatrix} = \begin{bmatrix} 2-2 & 1+3 & 1-4 \\ -1+3 & -1-1 & 4+2 \end{bmatrix}$

$= \begin{bmatrix} 0 & 4 & -3 \\ 2 & -2 & 6 \end{bmatrix}$

(c) $2A = 2\begin{bmatrix} 2 & 1 & 1 \\ -1 & -1 & 4 \end{bmatrix} = \begin{bmatrix} 2(2) & 2(1) & 2(1) \\ 2(-1) & 2(-1) & 2(4) \end{bmatrix} = \begin{bmatrix} 4 & 2 & 2 \\ -2 & -2 & 8 \end{bmatrix}$

(d) $2A - B = \begin{bmatrix} 4 & 2 & 2 \\ -2 & -2 & 8 \end{bmatrix} - \begin{bmatrix} 2 & -3 & 4 \\ -3 & 1 & -2 \end{bmatrix} = \begin{bmatrix} 2 & 5 & -2 \\ 1 & -3 & 10 \end{bmatrix}$

6. (a) $c_{23} = 5a_{23} + 2b_{23} = 5(2) + 2(11) = 32$

(b) $c_{32} = 5a_{32} + 2b_{32} = 5(1) + 2(4) = 13$

8. Simplifying the right side of the equation produces

$$\begin{bmatrix} w & x \\ y & x \end{bmatrix} = \begin{bmatrix} -4 + 2y & 3 + 2w \\ 2 + 2z & -1 + 2x \end{bmatrix}$$

By setting corresponding entries equal to each other, we obtain four equations.

$$\begin{aligned} w &= -4 + 2y \\ x &= 3 + 2w \\ y &= 2 + 2z \\ x &= -1 + 2x \end{aligned} \implies \begin{cases} -2y + w = -4 \\ x - 2w = 3 \\ y - 2z = 2 \\ x = 1 \end{cases}$$

The solution to this linear system is $x = 1$, $y = \frac{3}{2}$, $z = -\frac{1}{4}$, and $w = -1$.

10. (a) $AB = \begin{bmatrix} 2 & -1 \\ 1 & 4 \end{bmatrix} \begin{bmatrix} 0 & 0 \\ 3 & -3 \end{bmatrix} = \begin{bmatrix} 2(0) + (-1)3 & 2(0) + (-1)(-3) \\ 1(0) + 4(3) & 1(0) + 4(-3) \end{bmatrix} = \begin{bmatrix} -3 & 3 \\ 12 & -12 \end{bmatrix}$

   (b) $BA = \begin{bmatrix} 0 & 0 \\ 3 & -3 \end{bmatrix} \begin{bmatrix} 2 & -1 \\ 1 & 4 \end{bmatrix} = \begin{bmatrix} 0(2) + 0(1) & 0(-1) + 0(4) \\ 3(2) + (-3)(1) & 3(-1) + (-3)(4) \end{bmatrix} = \begin{bmatrix} 0 & 0 \\ 3 & -15 \end{bmatrix}$

12. (a) $AB = [3 \ 2 \ 1] \begin{bmatrix} 2 \\ 3 \\ 0 \end{bmatrix} = [3(2) + 2(3) + 1(0)] = [12]$

   (b) $BA = \begin{bmatrix} 2 \\ 3 \\ 0 \end{bmatrix} [3 \ 2 \ 1] = \begin{bmatrix} 2(3) & 2(2) & 2(1) \\ 3(3) & 3(2) & 3(1) \\ 0(3) & 0(2) & 0(1) \end{bmatrix} = \begin{bmatrix} 6 & 4 & 2 \\ 9 & 6 & 3 \\ 0 & 0 & 0 \end{bmatrix}$

14. (a) $AB = \begin{bmatrix} 0 & -1 & 0 \\ 4 & 0 & 2 \\ 8 & -1 & 7 \end{bmatrix} \begin{bmatrix} 2 \\ -3 \\ 1 \end{bmatrix} = \begin{bmatrix} 0(2) + (-1)(-3) + 0(1) \\ 4(2) + 0(-3) + 2(1) \\ 8(2) + (-1)(-3) + 7(1) \end{bmatrix} = \begin{bmatrix} 3 \\ 10 \\ 26 \end{bmatrix}$

   (b) BA is not defined since B is 3×1 and A is 3×3.

16. (a) $AB = \begin{bmatrix} 5\left(\frac{1}{5}\right) & 0 & 0 \\ 0 & -8\left(-\frac{1}{8}\right) & 0 \\ 0 & 0 & 7\left(\frac{1}{7}\right) \end{bmatrix} = \begin{bmatrix} 1 & 0 & 0 \\ 0 & 1 & 0 \\ 0 & 0 & 1 \end{bmatrix}$.

   (b) Similarly, $BA = \begin{bmatrix} 1 & 0 & 0 \\ 0 & 1 & 0 \\ 0 & 0 & 1 \end{bmatrix}$.

18. (a) AB is not defined since A is 2×5 and B is 2×2.

   (b) $BA = \begin{bmatrix} 1 & 6 \\ 4 & 2 \end{bmatrix} \begin{bmatrix} 1 & 0 & 3 & -2 & 4 \\ 6 & 13 & 8 & -17 & 20 \end{bmatrix}$

   $= \begin{bmatrix} 1(1) + 6(6) & 1(0) + 6(13) & 1(3) + 6(8) & 1(-2) + 6(-17) & 1(4) + 6(20) \\ 4(1) + 2(6) & 4(0) + 2(13) & 4(3) + 2(8) & 4(-2) + 2(-17) & 4(4) + 2(20) \end{bmatrix}$

   $= \begin{bmatrix} 37 & 78 & 51 & -104 & 124 \\ 16 & 26 & 28 & -42 & 56 \end{bmatrix}$

20. Since A is 6×5 and B is 6×6, we have that

   (a) $2A + B$ is undefined.

   (b) $3B - A$ is undefined.

   (c) AB is undefined.

   (d) Using a calculator, we have that

   $BA = \begin{bmatrix} 10 & 1 & 18 & 11 & 4 \\ -5 & 3 & -25 & 4 & 11 \\ -2 & 2 & 19 & -1 & -15 \\ 10 & -15 & 8 & 1 & 6 \\ -3 & -5 & -6 & -2 & -17 \\ -18 & 9 & 2 & -8 & -11 \end{bmatrix}$.

22. In matrix form $A\mathbf{x} = \mathbf{b}$, the system is

$$\begin{bmatrix} 2 & 2 \\ -6 & -6 \end{bmatrix} \begin{bmatrix} x_1 \\ x_2 \end{bmatrix} = \begin{bmatrix} 7 \\ -21 \end{bmatrix}$$

We use Gauss-Jordan elimination on the augmented matrix.

$$\begin{bmatrix} 2 & 2 & 7 \\ -6 & -6 & -21 \end{bmatrix} \Rightarrow \begin{bmatrix} 1 & 1 & \frac{7}{2} \\ 0 & 0 & 0 \end{bmatrix}$$

Thus, the solution is

$$\mathbf{x} = \begin{bmatrix} \frac{7}{2} - t \\ t \end{bmatrix}$$

where t is any real number.

24. In the matrix for $A\mathbf{x} = \mathbf{b}$, the system is

$$\begin{bmatrix} 0 & 6 & 4 \\ 3 & 3 & 0 \\ 2 & 0 & -3 \end{bmatrix} \begin{bmatrix} x_1 \\ x_2 \\ x_3 \end{bmatrix} = \begin{bmatrix} -12 \\ 9 \\ 10 \end{bmatrix}.$$

We use Gauss-Jordan elimination on the augmented matrix

$$\begin{bmatrix} 0 & 6 & 4 & -12 \\ 3 & 3 & 0 & 9 \\ 2 & 0 & -3 & 10 \end{bmatrix} \Rightarrow \begin{bmatrix} 1 & 0 & 0 & 5 \\ 0 & 1 & 0 & -2 \\ 0 & 0 & 1 & 0 \end{bmatrix}$$

Thus, the solution is

$$\begin{bmatrix} 5 \\ -2 \\ 0 \end{bmatrix}.$$

26. In matrix form, $A\mathbf{x} = \mathbf{b}$, the system is

$$\begin{bmatrix} 1 & 0 & 2 \\ 2 & -4 & 0 \\ 3 & 2 & 5 \end{bmatrix} \begin{bmatrix} x_1 \\ x_2 \\ x_3 \end{bmatrix} = \begin{bmatrix} 4 \\ -6 \\ 10 \end{bmatrix}.$$

We use Gauss-Jordan elimination on the augmented matrix.

$$\begin{bmatrix} 1 & 0 & 2 & 4 \\ 2 & -4 & 0 & -6 \\ 3 & 2 & 5 & 10 \end{bmatrix} \Rightarrow \begin{bmatrix} 1 & 0 & 0 & -2 \\ 0 & 1 & 0 & \frac{1}{2} \\ 0 & 0 & 1 & 3 \end{bmatrix}$$

Thus, the solution is $\mathbf{x} = \begin{bmatrix} -2 \\ \frac{1}{2} \\ 3 \end{bmatrix}.$

28. Expanding the left side of the equation produces

$$\begin{bmatrix} 2 & -1 \\ 3 & -2 \end{bmatrix} A = \begin{bmatrix} 2 & -1 \\ 3 & -2 \end{bmatrix} \begin{bmatrix} a_{11} & a_{12} \\ a_{21} & a_{22} \end{bmatrix} = \begin{bmatrix} 2a_{11} - a_{21} & 2a_{12} - a_{22} \\ 3a_{11} - 2a_{21} & 3a_{12} - 2a_{22} \end{bmatrix} = \begin{bmatrix} 1 & 0 \\ 0 & 1 \end{bmatrix}$$

from which we obtain the system

$$\begin{aligned} 2a_{11} \quad - \quad a_{21} \qquad\qquad &= 1 \\ 2a_{12} \quad - \quad a_{22} &= 0 \\ 3a_{11} \quad - 2a_{21} \qquad\qquad &= 0 \\ 3a_{12} \quad - 2a_{22} &= 1 \end{aligned}$$

Solving by Gauss-Jordan elimination yields

$$a_{11} = 2, a_{12} = -1, a_{21} = 3, \text{ and } a_{22} = -2.$$

Thus, we have $A = \begin{bmatrix} 2 & -1 \\ 3 & -2 \end{bmatrix}$.

30. Expanding the left side of the matrix equation produces

$$\begin{bmatrix} a & b \\ c & d \end{bmatrix} \begin{bmatrix} 2 & 1 \\ 3 & 1 \end{bmatrix} = \begin{bmatrix} 2a + 3b & a + b \\ 2c + 3d & c + d \end{bmatrix} = \begin{bmatrix} 3 & 17 \\ 4 & -1 \end{bmatrix}.$$

We obtain two systems of linear equations (one involving a and b and the other involving c and d).

$$\begin{aligned} 2a + 3b &= 3 \\ a + b &= 17, \end{aligned}$$

and

$$\begin{aligned} 2c + 3d &= 4 \\ c + d &= -1. \end{aligned}$$

Solving by Gauss-Jordan elimination yields $a = 48, b = -31, c = -7$ and $d = 6$.

32. $AB = \begin{bmatrix} \cos\alpha & -\sin\alpha \\ \sin\alpha & \cos\alpha \end{bmatrix} \begin{bmatrix} \cos\beta & -\sin\beta \\ \sin\beta & \cos\beta \end{bmatrix}$

$\begin{bmatrix} \cos\alpha\cos\beta - \sin\alpha\sin\beta & \cos\alpha(-\sin\beta) - \sin\alpha\cos\beta \\ \sin\alpha\cos\beta + \cos\alpha\sin\beta & \sin\alpha(-\sin\beta) + \cos\alpha\cos\beta \end{bmatrix}$

$BA = \begin{bmatrix} \cos\beta & -\sin\beta \\ \sin\beta & \cos\beta \end{bmatrix} \begin{bmatrix} \cos\alpha & -\sin\alpha \\ \sin\alpha & \cos\alpha \end{bmatrix}$

$\begin{bmatrix} \cos\beta\cos\alpha - \sin\beta\sin\alpha & \cos\beta(-\sin\alpha) - \sin\beta\cos\alpha \\ \sin\beta\cos\alpha + \cos\beta\sin\alpha & \sin\beta(-\sin\alpha) + \cos\beta\cos\alpha \end{bmatrix}$

Hence, we see that $AB = BA = \begin{bmatrix} \cos(\alpha + \beta) & -\sin(\alpha + \beta) \\ \sin(\alpha + \beta) & \cos(\alpha + \beta) \end{bmatrix}$.

34. $AA = \begin{bmatrix} 2 & 0 & 0 \\ 0 & -3 & 0 \\ 0 & 0 & 0 \end{bmatrix} \begin{bmatrix} 2 & 0 & 0 \\ 0 & -3 & 0 \\ 0 & 0 & 0 \end{bmatrix} = \begin{bmatrix} 4 & 0 & 0 \\ 0 & 9 & 0 \\ 0 & 0 & 0 \end{bmatrix}$

36. $AB = \begin{bmatrix} 3 & 0 & 0 \\ 0 & -5 & 0 \\ 0 & 0 & 0 \end{bmatrix} \begin{bmatrix} -7 & 0 & 0 \\ 0 & 4 & 0 \\ 0 & 0 & 12 \end{bmatrix}$

$= \begin{bmatrix} 3(-7)+0+0 & 0+0+0 & 0+0+0 \\ 0+0+0 & 0+(-5)4+0 & 0+0+0 \\ 0+0+0 & 0+0+0 & 0+0+0 \end{bmatrix} = \begin{bmatrix} -21 & 0 & 0 \\ 0 & -20 & 0 \\ 0 & 0 & 0 \end{bmatrix}.$

Similarly,

$BA = \begin{bmatrix} -21 & 0 & 0 \\ 0 & -20 & 0 \\ 0 & 0 & 0 \end{bmatrix}.$

38. (a) $AB = \begin{bmatrix} a_{11} & 0 & 0 \\ 0 & a_{22} & 0 \\ 0 & 0 & a_{33} \end{bmatrix} \begin{bmatrix} b_{11} & b_{12} & b_{13} \\ b_{21} & b_{22} & b_{23} \\ b_{31} & b_{32} & b_{33} \end{bmatrix} = \begin{bmatrix} a_{11}b_{11} & a_{11}b_{12} & a_{11}b_{13} \\ a_{22}b_{21} & a_{22}b_{22} & a_{22}b_{23} \\ a_{33}b_{31} & a_{33}b_{32} & a_{33}b_{33} \end{bmatrix}$

We see that the ith row of B has been multiplied by a_{ii}, the ith diagonal entry of A.

(b) $BA = \begin{bmatrix} b_{11} & b_{12} & b_{13} \\ b_{21} & b_{22} & b_{23} \\ b_{31} & b_{32} & b_{33} \end{bmatrix} \begin{bmatrix} a_{11} & 0 & 0 \\ 0 & a_{22} & 0 \\ 0 & 0 & a_{33} \end{bmatrix} = \begin{bmatrix} a_{11}b_{11} & a_{22}b_{12} & a_{33}b_{13} \\ a_{11}b_{21} & a_{22}b_{22} & a_{33}b_{23} \\ a_{11}b_{31} & a_{22}b_{32} & a_{33}b_{33} \end{bmatrix}$

We see that the ith column of B has been multiplied by a_{ii}, the ith diagonal entry of A.

(c) If $a_{11} = a_{22} = a_{33}$, then $AB = a_{11}B = BA$.

40. The trace is the sum of the elements on the main diagonal.

$1 + 1 + 1 = 3.$

42. Let $AB = [c_{ij}]$, where $c_{ij} = \sum_{k=1}^{n} a_{ik}b_{kj}$. Then, $Tr(AB) = \sum_{i=1}^{n} c_{ii} = \sum_{i=1}^{n}\left(\sum_{k=1}^{n} a_{ik}b_{ki}\right).$

Similarly, if $BA = [d_{ij}]$, $d_{ij} = \sum_{k=1}^{n} b_{ik}a_{kj}$, then $Tr(BA) = \sum_{i=1}^{n} d_{ii} = \sum_{i=1}^{n}\left(\sum_{k=1}^{n} b_{ik}a_{ki}\right) = Tr(AB).$

44. Let $A = \begin{bmatrix} a_{11} & a_{12} \\ a_{21} & a_{22} \end{bmatrix}$ and $B = \begin{bmatrix} b_{11} & b_{12} \\ b_{21} & b_{22} \end{bmatrix}.$

Then the matrix equation $AB - BA = \begin{bmatrix} 1 & 0 \\ 0 & 1 \end{bmatrix}$ is equivalent to

$\begin{bmatrix} a_{11} & a_{12} \\ a_{21} & a_{22} \end{bmatrix}\begin{bmatrix} b_{11} & b_{12} \\ b_{21} & b_{22} \end{bmatrix} - \begin{bmatrix} b_{11} & b_{12} \\ b_{21} & b_{22} \end{bmatrix}\begin{bmatrix} a_{11} & a_{12} \\ a_{21} & a_{22} \end{bmatrix} = \begin{bmatrix} 1 & 0 \\ 0 & 1 \end{bmatrix}.$

This equation implies that

$a_{11}b_{11} + a_{12}b_{21} - b_{11}a_{11} - b_{12}a_{21} = a_{12}b_{21} - b_{12}a_{21} = 1$
$a_{21}b_{12} + a_{22}b_{22} - b_{21}a_{12} - b_{22}a_{22} = a_{21}b_{12} - b_{21}a_{12} = 1$

which is impossible. Hence, the original equation has no solution.

46. Assume that A is an $m \times n$ matrix and B is a $p \times q$ matrix. Because the product AB is defined, you know that $n = p$. Moreover, because AB is square, you know that $m = q$. Therefore, B must be of order $n \times m$, which implies that the product BA is defined.

48. Let rows s and t be identical in the matrix A. So, $a_{sj} = a_{tj}$ for $j = 1, \ldots, n$. Let $AB = [c_{ij}]$, where

$$c_{ij} = \sum_{k=1}^{n} a_{ik} b_{kj}.$$

Then,

$$c_{sj} = \sum_{k=1}^{n} a_{sk} b_{kj}$$

$$c_{tj} = \sum_{k=1}^{n} a_{tk} b_{kj}.$$

Because $a_{sk} = a_{tk}$ for $k = 1, \ldots, n$, rows s and t of AB are the same.

50. (a) $\quad AT = \begin{bmatrix} 0 & -1 \\ 1 & 0 \end{bmatrix} \begin{bmatrix} 1 & 2 & 3 \\ 1 & 4 & 2 \end{bmatrix} = \begin{bmatrix} -1 & -4 & -2 \\ 1 & 2 & 3 \end{bmatrix}$

$\quad AAT = \begin{bmatrix} 0 & -1 \\ 1 & 0 \end{bmatrix} \begin{bmatrix} -1 & -4 & -2 \\ 1 & 2 & 3 \end{bmatrix} = \begin{bmatrix} -1 & -2 & -3 \\ -1 & -4 & -2 \end{bmatrix}$

Triangle associated with T

Triangle associated with AT

Triangle associated with AAT

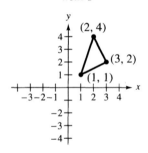
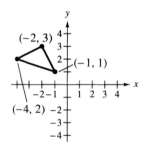
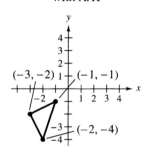

The transformation matrix A rotates the triangle about the origin in a counterclockwise direction through $90°$.

(b) Given the triangle associated with AAT, the transformation that would produce the triangle associated with AT would be a rotation about the origin of $90°$ in a clockwise direction. Another such rotation would produce the triangle associated with T.

52. (a) *True.* The number of elements in a row of the first matrix must be equal to the number of elements in a column of the second matrix. See page 50 of the text.

(b) *True.* See page 52 of the text.

54. (a) We use *scalar multiplication* to find *L*.

$$L = \tfrac{2}{3}C = \tfrac{2}{3}\begin{bmatrix} 627 & 681 \\ 135 & 150 \end{bmatrix} = \begin{bmatrix} \tfrac{2}{3}(627) & \tfrac{2}{3}(681) \\ \tfrac{2}{3}(135) & \tfrac{2}{3}(150) \end{bmatrix} = \begin{bmatrix} 418 & 454 \\ 90 & 100 \end{bmatrix}$$

(b) We use *matrix addition* to find *M*.

$$M = C - L = \begin{bmatrix} 627 & 681 \\ 135 & 150 \end{bmatrix} - \begin{bmatrix} 418 & 454 \\ 90 & 100 \end{bmatrix} = \begin{bmatrix} 627 - 418 & 681 - 454 \\ 135 - 90 & 150 - 100 \end{bmatrix} = \begin{bmatrix} 209 & 227 \\ 45 & 50 \end{bmatrix}$$

56. $PP = \begin{bmatrix} 0.75 & 0.15 & 0.10 \\ 0.20 & 0.60 & 0.20 \\ 0.30 & 0.40 & 0.30 \end{bmatrix}\begin{bmatrix} 0.75 & 0.15 & 0.10 \\ 0.20 & 0.60 & 0.20 \\ 0.30 & 0.40 & 0.30 \end{bmatrix} = \begin{bmatrix} 0.6225 & 0.2425 & 0.135 \\ 0.33 & 0.47 & 0.20 \\ 0.395 & 0.405 & 0.20 \end{bmatrix}$

This product represents the changes in party affiliation after *two* elections.

58. If $B = [b_1, b_2, \ldots, b_p]$ has columns b_i, then AB is formed by multiplying A times each column b_i. Similarly, if A has rows $a_1, \ldots, a_m$, then AB is formed by multiplying each row a_i by B.

60. $AB = \left[\begin{array}{cc|cc} 0 & 0 & 1 & 0 \\ 0 & 0 & 0 & 1 \\ \hline -1 & 0 & 0 & 0 \\ 0 & -1 & 0 & 0 \end{array}\right]\left[\begin{array}{cc|cc} 1 & 2 & 3 & 4 \\ 5 & 6 & 7 & 8 \\ \hline 1 & 2 & 3 & 4 \\ 5 & 6 & 7 & 8 \end{array}\right] = \left[\begin{array}{cc|cc} 1 & 2 & 3 & 4 \\ 5 & 6 & 7 & 8 \\ \hline -1 & -2 & -3 & -4 \\ -5 & -6 & -7 & -8 \end{array}\right]$

62. The augmented matrix row reduces as follows.

$$\begin{bmatrix} 1 & 2 & 4 & 1 \\ -1 & 0 & 2 & 3 \\ 0 & 1 & 3 & 2 \end{bmatrix} \Rightarrow \begin{bmatrix} 1 & 0 & -2 & -3 \\ 0 & 1 & 3 & 2 \\ 0 & 0 & 0 & 0 \end{bmatrix}$$

There are an infinite number of solutions. For example, $x_3 = 0$, $x_2 = 2$, $x_1 = -3$. Hence,

$$\mathbf{b} = \begin{bmatrix} 1 \\ 3 \\ 2 \end{bmatrix} = -3\begin{bmatrix} 1 \\ -1 \\ 0 \end{bmatrix} + 2\begin{bmatrix} 2 \\ 0 \\ 1 \end{bmatrix} + 0\begin{bmatrix} 4 \\ 2 \\ 3 \end{bmatrix}.$$

64. The augmented matrix row reduces as follows.

$$\begin{bmatrix} -3 & 5 & -22 \\ 3 & 4 & 4 \\ 4 & -8 & 32 \end{bmatrix} \Rightarrow \begin{bmatrix} 1 & -3 & 10 \\ 0 & 9 & -18 \\ 0 & -4 & 8 \end{bmatrix}$$

$$\Rightarrow \begin{bmatrix} 1 & -3 & 10 \\ 0 & 1 & -2 \\ 0 & 1 & -2 \end{bmatrix} \Rightarrow \begin{bmatrix} 1 & 0 & 4 \\ 0 & 1 & -2 \\ 0 & 0 & 0 \end{bmatrix}.$$

Hence,

$$\begin{bmatrix} -22 \\ 4 \\ 32 \end{bmatrix} = 4\begin{bmatrix} -3 \\ 3 \\ 4 \end{bmatrix} + (-2)\begin{bmatrix} 5 \\ 4 \\ -8 \end{bmatrix}.$$

Section 2.2   Properties of Matrix Operations

2. $A + B = \begin{bmatrix} 1 & 2 \\ 3 & 4 \end{bmatrix} + \begin{bmatrix} 0 & 1 \\ -1 & 2 \end{bmatrix} = \begin{bmatrix} 1 & 3 \\ 2 & 6 \end{bmatrix}$

4. $(a + b)B = (3 + (-4))\begin{bmatrix} 0 & 1 \\ -1 & 2 \end{bmatrix} = (-1)\begin{bmatrix} 0 & 1 \\ -1 & 2 \end{bmatrix} = \begin{bmatrix} 0 & -1 \\ 1 & -2 \end{bmatrix}$

6. $(ab)0 = (3)(-4)\begin{bmatrix} 0 & 0 \\ 0 & 0 \end{bmatrix} = (-12)\begin{bmatrix} 0 & 0 \\ 0 & 0 \end{bmatrix} = \begin{bmatrix} 0 & 0 \\ 0 & 0 \end{bmatrix}$

8. $3X = 2A - 5B = 2\begin{bmatrix} -4 & 0 \\ 1 & -5 \\ -3 & 2 \end{bmatrix} - 5\begin{bmatrix} 1 & 2 \\ -2 & 1 \\ 4 & 4 \end{bmatrix} = \begin{bmatrix} -13 & -10 \\ 12 & -15 \\ -26 & -16 \end{bmatrix}$

Hence, $X = \dfrac{1}{3}\begin{bmatrix} -13 & -10 \\ 12 & -15 \\ -26 & -16 \end{bmatrix}$.

10. $6X = 4A + 3B = 4\begin{bmatrix} -4 & 0 \\ 1 & -5 \\ -3 & 2 \end{bmatrix} + 3\begin{bmatrix} 1 & 2 \\ -2 & 1 \\ 4 & 4 \end{bmatrix} = \begin{bmatrix} -13 & 6 \\ -2 & -17 \\ 0 & 20 \end{bmatrix}$

Hence, $X = \dfrac{1}{6}\begin{bmatrix} -13 & 6 \\ -2 & -17 \\ 0 & 20 \end{bmatrix}$.

12. $C(BC) = \begin{bmatrix} 0 & 1 \\ -1 & 0 \end{bmatrix}\left(\begin{bmatrix} 1 & 3 \\ -1 & 2 \end{bmatrix}\begin{bmatrix} 0 & 1 \\ -1 & 0 \end{bmatrix}\right)$

$= \begin{bmatrix} 0 & 1 \\ -1 & 0 \end{bmatrix}\begin{bmatrix} -3 & 1 \\ -2 & -1 \end{bmatrix} = \begin{bmatrix} -2 & -1 \\ 3 & -1 \end{bmatrix}$

14. $B(C + O) = \begin{bmatrix} 1 & 3 \\ -1 & 2 \end{bmatrix}\left(\begin{bmatrix} 0 & 1 \\ -1 & 0 \end{bmatrix} + \begin{bmatrix} 0 & 0 \\ 0 & 0 \end{bmatrix}\right)$

$= \begin{bmatrix} 1 & 3 \\ -1 & 2 \end{bmatrix}\begin{bmatrix} 0 & 1 \\ -1 & 0 \end{bmatrix} = \begin{bmatrix} -3 & 1 \\ -2 & -1 \end{bmatrix}$

16. $B(cA) = \begin{bmatrix} 1 & 3 \\ -1 & 2 \end{bmatrix}\left((-2)\begin{bmatrix} 1 & 2 & 3 \\ 0 & 1 & -1 \end{bmatrix}\right)$

$= \begin{bmatrix} 1 & 3 \\ -1 & 2 \end{bmatrix}\begin{bmatrix} -2 & -4 & -6 \\ 0 & -2 & 2 \end{bmatrix} = \begin{bmatrix} -2 & -10 & 0 \\ 2 & 0 & 10 \end{bmatrix}$

18. $AB = \begin{bmatrix} 3 & 3 \\ 4 & 4 \end{bmatrix}\begin{bmatrix} 1 & -1 \\ -1 & 1 \end{bmatrix} = \begin{bmatrix} 0 & 0 \\ 0 & 0 \end{bmatrix}$, but $A \neq 0$ and $B \neq 0$.

20. $A^2 = \begin{bmatrix} 1 & 2 \\ 0 & -1 \end{bmatrix}\begin{bmatrix} 1 & 2 \\ 0 & -1 \end{bmatrix} = \begin{bmatrix} 1 & 0 \\ 0 & 1 \end{bmatrix} = I_2.$

Thus, $A^4 = (A^2)^2 = I_2^2 = I_2 = \begin{bmatrix} 1 & 0 \\ 0 & 1 \end{bmatrix}$.

22. $A + IA = \begin{bmatrix} 1 & 2 \\ 0 & -1 \end{bmatrix} + \begin{bmatrix} 1 & 0 \\ 0 & 1 \end{bmatrix}\begin{bmatrix} 1 & 2 \\ 0 & -1 \end{bmatrix}$

$\qquad\quad = \begin{bmatrix} 1 & 2 \\ 0 & -1 \end{bmatrix} + \begin{bmatrix} 1 & 2 \\ 0 & -1 \end{bmatrix} = \begin{bmatrix} 2 & 4 \\ 0 & -2 \end{bmatrix}$

24. (a) $A^T = \begin{bmatrix} -7 & 11 & 12 \\ 4 & -3 & 1 \\ 6 & -1 & 3 \end{bmatrix}^T = \begin{bmatrix} -7 & 4 & 6 \\ 11 & -3 & -1 \\ 12 & 1 & 3 \end{bmatrix}$

(b) $A^T A = \begin{bmatrix} -7 & 4 & 6 \\ 11 & -3 & -1 \\ 12 & 1 & 3 \end{bmatrix}\begin{bmatrix} -7 & 11 & 12 \\ 4 & -3 & 1 \\ 6 & -1 & 3 \end{bmatrix} = \begin{bmatrix} 101 & -95 & -62 \\ -95 & 131 & 126 \\ -62 & 126 & 154 \end{bmatrix}$

(c) $AA^T = \begin{bmatrix} -7 & 11 & 12 \\ 4 & -3 & 1 \\ 6 & -1 & 3 \end{bmatrix}\begin{bmatrix} -7 & 4 & 6 \\ 11 & -3 & -1 \\ 12 & 1 & 3 \end{bmatrix}\begin{bmatrix} 314 & -49 & -17 \\ -49 & 26 & 30 \\ -17 & 30 & 46 \end{bmatrix}$

26. (a) $A^T = \begin{bmatrix} 2 \\ -1 \\ -3 \end{bmatrix}^T = [2 \ -1 \ -3]$

(b) $A^T A = [2 \ -1 \ -3]\begin{bmatrix} 2 \\ -1 \\ -3 \end{bmatrix} = [14]$

(c) $AA^T = \begin{bmatrix} 2 \\ -1 \\ -3 \end{bmatrix}[2 \ -1 \ -3] = \begin{bmatrix} 4 & -2 & -6 \\ -2 & 1 & 3 \\ -6 & 3 & 9 \end{bmatrix}$

28. (a) $A^T = \begin{bmatrix} 4 & -3 & 2 & 0 \\ 2 & 0 & 11 & -1 \\ 14 & -2 & 12 & -9 \\ 6 & 8 & -5 & 4 \end{bmatrix}^T = \begin{bmatrix} 4 & 2 & 14 & 6 \\ -3 & 0 & -2 & 8 \\ 2 & 11 & 12 & -5 \\ 0 & -1 & -9 & 4 \end{bmatrix}$

(b) $A^T A = \begin{bmatrix} 4 & 2 & 14 & 6 \\ -3 & 0 & -2 & 8 \\ 2 & 11 & 12 & -5 \\ 0 & -1 & -9 & 4 \end{bmatrix}\begin{bmatrix} 4 & -3 & 2 & 0 \\ 2 & 0 & 11 & -1 \\ 14 & -2 & 12 & -9 \\ 6 & 8 & -5 & 4 \end{bmatrix} = \begin{bmatrix} 252 & 8 & 168 & -104 \\ 8 & 77 & -70 & 50 \\ 168 & -70 & 294 & -139 \\ -104 & 50 & -139 & 98 \end{bmatrix}$

(c) $AA^T = \begin{bmatrix} 4 & -3 & 2 & 0 \\ 2 & 0 & 11 & -1 \\ 14 & -2 & 12 & -9 \\ 6 & 8 & -5 & 4 \end{bmatrix}\begin{bmatrix} 4 & 2 & 14 & 6 \\ -3 & 0 & -2 & 8 \\ 2 & 11 & 12 & -5 \\ 0 & -1 & -9 & 4 \end{bmatrix} = \begin{bmatrix} 29 & 30 & 86 & -10 \\ 30 & 126 & 169 & -47 \\ 86 & 169 & 425 & -28 \\ -10 & -47 & -28 & 141 \end{bmatrix}$

30. In general, $AB \neq BA$ for matrices.

32. $(AB)^T = \left(\begin{bmatrix} 1 & 2 \\ 0 & -2 \end{bmatrix}\begin{bmatrix} -3 & -1 \\ 2 & 1 \end{bmatrix}\right)^T = \begin{bmatrix} 1 & 1 \\ -4 & -2 \end{bmatrix}^T = \begin{bmatrix} 1 & -4 \\ 1 & -2 \end{bmatrix}$

$\qquad B^T A^T = \begin{bmatrix} -3 & -1 \\ 2 & 1 \end{bmatrix}^T\begin{bmatrix} 1 & 2 \\ 0 & -2 \end{bmatrix}^T = \begin{bmatrix} -3 & 2 \\ -1 & 1 \end{bmatrix}\begin{bmatrix} 1 & 0 \\ 2 & -2 \end{bmatrix} = \begin{bmatrix} 1 & -4 \\ 1 & -2 \end{bmatrix}$

34. (a) *False.* In general, for $n \times n$ matrices A and B it is *not* true that $AB = BA$.
For example, let

$$A = \begin{bmatrix} 1 & 1 \\ 0 & 0 \end{bmatrix}, B = \begin{bmatrix} 1 & 0 \\ 1 & 0 \end{bmatrix}.$$

Then $AB = \begin{bmatrix} 2 & 0 \\ 0 & 0 \end{bmatrix} \neq \begin{bmatrix} 1 & 1 \\ 1 & 1 \end{bmatrix} = BA$.

(b) *True.* For any matrix A we have an additive inverse, namely $-A = (-1)A$.
See Theorem 2.2(2) on page 61.

(c) *False.* Let

$$A = \begin{bmatrix} 1 & 1 \\ 0 & 0 \end{bmatrix}, B = \begin{bmatrix} 1 & 0 \\ 1 & 0 \end{bmatrix}, C = \begin{bmatrix} 2 & 0 \\ 0 & 0 \end{bmatrix}.$$

Then $AB = \begin{bmatrix} 2 & 0 \\ 0 & 0 \end{bmatrix} = AC$, but $B \neq C$.

(d) *True.* See Theorem 2.6(2) on page 67.

36. (a) $Z = aX + bY$

$$\begin{bmatrix} 1 \\ 4 \\ 4 \end{bmatrix} = a \begin{bmatrix} 1 \\ 2 \\ 3 \end{bmatrix} + b \begin{bmatrix} 1 \\ 0 \\ 2 \end{bmatrix} = \begin{bmatrix} a + b \\ 2a \\ 3a + 2b \end{bmatrix}.$$

Solving the linear system obtained from this matrix equation, we obtained
$a = 2$ and $b = -1$. Thus, $Z = 2X - Y$.

(b) $W = aX + bY$

$$\begin{bmatrix} 0 \\ 0 \\ 1 \end{bmatrix} = a \begin{bmatrix} 1 \\ 2 \\ 3 \end{bmatrix} + b \begin{bmatrix} 1 \\ 0 \\ 2 \end{bmatrix} = \begin{bmatrix} a + b \\ 2a \\ 3a + 2b \end{bmatrix},$$

It follows from $a + b = 0$ and $2a = 0$ that a, b must both be zero, but this is
impossible since $3a + 2b$ should be 1.

(c) $aX + bY + cW = 0$

$$a \begin{bmatrix} 1 \\ 2 \\ 3 \end{bmatrix} + b \begin{bmatrix} 1 \\ 0 \\ 2 \end{bmatrix} + c \begin{bmatrix} 0 \\ 0 \\ 1 \end{bmatrix} = \begin{bmatrix} 0 \\ 0 \\ 0 \end{bmatrix}.$$

This matrix equation yields the linear system

$$\begin{aligned} a + b \quad &= 0 \\ 2a \quad &= 0 \\ 3a + 2b + c &= 0 \end{aligned}$$

which has the unique solution $a = b = c = 0$.

—CONTINUED—

36. —CONTINUED—

(d) $aX + bY + cZ = a\begin{bmatrix} 1 \\ 2 \\ 3 \end{bmatrix} + b\begin{bmatrix} 1 \\ 0 \\ 2 \end{bmatrix} + c\begin{bmatrix} 1 \\ 4 \\ 4 \end{bmatrix} = \begin{bmatrix} 0 \\ 0 \\ 0 \end{bmatrix}$

This matrix equation yields the linear system

$$\begin{aligned} a + b + c &= 0 \\ 2a \phantom{{}+ b} + 4c &= 0 \\ 3a + 2b + 4c &= 0. \end{aligned}$$

Solving this system using Gauss-Jordan elimination, we find that there are an infinite number of solutions: $a = -2t$, $b = t$, and $c = t$. For instance, $a = -2$, $b = c = 1$.

38. $A^{20} = \begin{bmatrix} (1)^{20} & 0 & 0 \\ 0 & (-1)^{20} & 0 \\ 0 & 0 & (1)^{20} \end{bmatrix} = \begin{bmatrix} 1 & 0 & 0 \\ 0 & 1 & 0 \\ 0 & 0 & 1 \end{bmatrix}$

40. Since $A^3 = \begin{bmatrix} 8 & 0 & 0 \\ 0 & -1 & 0 \\ 0 & 0 & 27 \end{bmatrix} = \begin{bmatrix} 2^3 & 0 & 0 \\ 0 & (-1)^3 & 0 \\ 0 & 0 & (3)^3 \end{bmatrix}$, we have $A = \begin{bmatrix} 2 & 0 & 0 \\ 0 & -1 & 0 \\ 0 & 0 & 3 \end{bmatrix}$.

42. $f(A) = \begin{bmatrix} 5 & 4 \\ 1 & 2 \end{bmatrix}^2 - 7\begin{bmatrix} 5 & 4 \\ 1 & 2 \end{bmatrix} + 6\begin{bmatrix} 1 & 0 \\ 0 & 1 \end{bmatrix}$

$= \begin{bmatrix} 29 & 28 \\ 7 & 8 \end{bmatrix} - \begin{bmatrix} 35 & 28 \\ 7 & 14 \end{bmatrix} + \begin{bmatrix} 6 & 0 \\ 0 & 6 \end{bmatrix} = \begin{bmatrix} 0 & 0 \\ 0 & 0 \end{bmatrix}$

44. $f(A) = \begin{bmatrix} 8 & -4 \\ 2 & 2 \end{bmatrix}^2 - 10\begin{bmatrix} 8 & -4 \\ 2 & 2 \end{bmatrix} + 24\begin{bmatrix} 1 & 0 \\ 0 & 1 \end{bmatrix}$

$= \begin{bmatrix} 56 & -40 \\ 20 & -4 \end{bmatrix} - 10\begin{bmatrix} 8 & -4 \\ 2 & 2 \end{bmatrix} + 24\begin{bmatrix} 1 & 0 \\ 0 & 1 \end{bmatrix}$

$= \begin{bmatrix} 0 & 0 \\ 0 & 0 \end{bmatrix}$

46. $(cd)A = (cd)[a_{ij}] = [(cd)a_{ij}] = [c(da_{ij})] = c[da_{ij}] = c(dA)$

48. $(c + d)A = (c + d)[a_{ij}] = [(c + d)a_{ij}] = [ca_{ij} + da_{ij}]$
$ = [ca_{ij}] + [da_{ij}] = c[a_{ij}] + d[a_{ij}] = cA + dA$

50. (a) To show that $A(BC) = (AB)C$, we compare the ijth entries in matrices on both sides of this equality. Assume that A has size $n \times p$, B has size $p \times r$ and C has size $r \times m$. Then the entry in kth row and jth column of BC is $\sum_{l=1}^{r} b_{kl}c_{lj}$. Therefore the entry in ith row and jth column of $A(BC)$ is

$$\sum_{k=1}^{p} a_{ik} \sum_{l=1}^{r} b_{kl}c_{lj} = \sum_{k,l} a_{ik}b_{kl}c_{lj}.$$

The entry in the ith row and jth column of $(AB)C$ is $\sum_{l=1}^{r} d_{il}c_{lj}$, where d_{il} is the entry of AB in ith row and lth column. Thus, $d_{il} = \sum_{k=1}^{p} a_{ik} b_{kl}$ for each $l = 1, \ldots, r$. Thus the ijth entry of $(AB)C$ is

$$\sum_{l=1}^{r} \sum_{k=1}^{p} a_{ik}b_{kl}c_{lj} = \sum_{k,l} a_{ik}b_{kl}c_{lj}.$$

Since all corresponding entries of $A(BC)$ and $(AB)C$ are equal and both matrices are of the same size $(n \times m)$ we conclude that $A(BC) = (AB)C$.

(b) The entry in the ith row and jth column of $(A + B)C$ is $(a_{i1} + b_{i1})c_{1j} + (a_{i2} + b_{i2})c_{2j} + \cdots + (a_{in} + b_{in})c_{nj}$, whereas the entry in the ith row and jth column of $AC + BC$ is $(a_{i1}c_{1j} + \cdots + a_{in}c_{nj}) + (b_{i1}c_{1j} + \cdots + b_{in}c_{nj})$, which are equal by the distributive law for real numbers.

(c) The entry in the ith row and jth column of $c(AB)$ is $c[a_{i1}b_{1j} + a_{i2}b_{2j} + \cdots + a_{in}b_{nj}]$. The corresponding entry for $(cA)B$ is $(ca_{i1})b_{1j} + (ca_{i2})b_{2j} + \cdots + (ca_{in})b_{nj}$. And the corresponding entry for $A(cB)$ is $a_{i1}(cb_{1j}) + a_{i2}(cb_{2j}) + \cdots + a_{in}(cb_{nj})$. Since these three expressions are equal, we have shown that $c(AB) = (cA)B = A(cB)$.

52. (2) $(A + B)^T = ([a_{ij}] + [b_{ij}])^T = [a_{ij} + b_{ij}]^T = [a_{ji} + b_{ji}]$

$\qquad\qquad = [a_{ji}] + [b_{ji}] = A^T + B^T$

(3) $(cA)^T = (c[a_{ij}])^T = [ca_{ij}]^T = [ca_{ji}] = c[a_{ji}] = c(A^T)$

(4) The entry in the ith row and jth column of $(AB)^T$ is $a_{j1}b_{1i} + a_{j2}b_{2i} + \cdots + a_{jn}b_{ni}$. On the other hand, the entry in the ith row and jth column of $B^T A^T$ is $b_{1i}a_{j1} + b_{2i}a_{j2} + \cdots + b_{ni}a_{jn}$, which is the same.

54. Many examples are possible. For instance, $A = \begin{bmatrix} 1 & 0 \\ 1 & -1 \end{bmatrix}$ and $B = \begin{bmatrix} 0 & 1 \\ 1 & 0 \end{bmatrix}$.

Then, $(AB)^T = \begin{bmatrix} 0 & 1 \\ -1 & 1 \end{bmatrix}^T = \begin{bmatrix} 0 & -1 \\ 1 & 1 \end{bmatrix}$,

while $A^T B^T = \begin{bmatrix} 1 & 1 \\ 0 & -1 \end{bmatrix} \begin{bmatrix} 0 & 1 \\ 1 & 0 \end{bmatrix} = \begin{bmatrix} 1 & 1 \\ -1 & 0 \end{bmatrix}$, which are not equal.

56. Since $A = A^T$, this matrix is symmetric.

58. Since $-A = A^T$, this matrix is skew-symmetric.

60. If $A^T = -A$ and $B^T = -B$, then $(A + B)^T = A^T + B^T = -A - B = -(A + B)$, which implies that $A + B$ is skew-symmetric.

62. $(A - A^T)^T = A^T - (A^T)^T = A^T - A = -(A - A^T)$, which implies that $A - A^T$ is skew-symmetric.

64. (a) An example of a 2×2 matrix of the given form is $A_2 = \begin{bmatrix} 0 & 1 \\ 0 & 0 \end{bmatrix}$.

An example of a 3×3 matrix of the given form is $A_3 = \begin{bmatrix} 0 & 1 & 2 \\ 0 & 0 & 3 \\ 0 & 0 & 0 \end{bmatrix}$.

(b) $A_2{}^2 = \begin{bmatrix} 0 & 0 \\ 0 & 0 \end{bmatrix}$

$A_3{}^2 = \begin{bmatrix} 0 & 0 & 3 \\ 0 & 0 & 0 \\ 0 & 0 & 0 \end{bmatrix}$ and $A_3{}^3 = \begin{bmatrix} 0 & 0 & 0 \\ 0 & 0 & 0 \\ 0 & 0 & 0 \end{bmatrix}$

(c) The conjecture is that if A is a 4×4 matrix of the given form, then A^4 is the 4×4 zero matrix. A graphing utility shows this to be true.

(d) If A is an $n \times n$ matrix of the given form, then A^n is the $n \times n$ zero matrix.

Section 2.3 The Inverse of a Matrix

2. $AB = \begin{bmatrix} 1 & -1 \\ 2 & 3 \end{bmatrix}\begin{bmatrix} \frac{3}{5} & \frac{1}{5} \\ -\frac{2}{5} & \frac{1}{5} \end{bmatrix} = \begin{bmatrix} 1 & 0 \\ 0 & 1 \end{bmatrix}$

$BA = \begin{bmatrix} \frac{3}{5} & \frac{1}{5} \\ -\frac{2}{5} & \frac{1}{5} \end{bmatrix}\begin{bmatrix} 1 & -1 \\ 2 & 3 \end{bmatrix} = \begin{bmatrix} 1 & 0 \\ 0 & 1 \end{bmatrix}$

4. $AB = \begin{bmatrix} 2 & -17 & 11 \\ -1 & 11 & -7 \\ 0 & 3 & -2 \end{bmatrix}\begin{bmatrix} 1 & 1 & 2 \\ 2 & 4 & -3 \\ 3 & 6 & -5 \end{bmatrix} = \begin{bmatrix} 1 & 0 & 0 \\ 0 & 1 & 0 \\ 0 & 0 & 1 \end{bmatrix}$

$BA = \begin{bmatrix} 1 & 1 & 2 \\ 2 & 4 & -3 \\ 3 & 6 & -5 \end{bmatrix}\begin{bmatrix} 2 & -17 & 11 \\ -1 & 11 & -7 \\ 3 & 6 & -2 \end{bmatrix} = \begin{bmatrix} 1 & 0 & 0 \\ 0 & 1 & 0 \\ 0 & 0 & 1 \end{bmatrix}$

6. We use the formula

$$A^{-1} = \frac{1}{ad - bc}\begin{bmatrix} d & -b \\ -c & a \end{bmatrix}, \text{ where } A = \begin{bmatrix} a & b \\ c & d \end{bmatrix} = \begin{bmatrix} 1 & -2 \\ 2 & -3 \end{bmatrix}.$$

Thus, the inverse is

$$A^{-1} = \frac{1}{(1)(-3) - (-2)(2)}\begin{bmatrix} -3 & 2 \\ -2 & 1 \end{bmatrix} = \begin{bmatrix} -3 & 2 \\ -2 & 1 \end{bmatrix}.$$

8. From the formula

$$A^{-1} = \frac{1}{ad - bc}\begin{bmatrix} d & -b \\ -c & a \end{bmatrix}, \text{ where } A = \begin{bmatrix} a & b \\ c & d \end{bmatrix} = \begin{bmatrix} -1 & 1 \\ 3 & -3 \end{bmatrix}$$

we see that $ad - bc = (-1)(-3) - (1)(3) = 0$. Thus, the matrix has no inverse.

10. We adjoin the identity matrix to form

$$[A : I] = \begin{bmatrix} 1 & 2 & 2 & \vdots & 1 & 0 & 0 \\ 3 & 7 & 9 & \vdots & 0 & 1 & 0 \\ -1 & -4 & -7 & \vdots & 0 & 0 & 1 \end{bmatrix}.$$

Using elementary row operations, we reduce the matrix as follows.

$$[I : A^{-1}] = \begin{bmatrix} 1 & 0 & 0 & \vdots & -13 & 6 & 4 \\ 0 & 1 & 0 & \vdots & 12 & -5 & -3 \\ 0 & 0 & 1 & \vdots & -5 & 2 & 1 \end{bmatrix}$$

12. We adjoin the identity matrix to form

$$[A : I] = \begin{bmatrix} 10 & 5 & -7 & \vdots & 1 & 0 & 0 \\ -5 & 1 & 4 & \vdots & 0 & 1 & 0 \\ 3 & 2 & -2 & \vdots & 0 & 0 & 1 \end{bmatrix}.$$

Using elementary row operations, we reduce the matrix as follows.

$$[I : A^{-1}] = \begin{bmatrix} 1 & 0 & 0 & \vdots & -10 & -4 & 27 \\ 0 & 1 & 0 & \vdots & 2 & 1 & -5 \\ 0 & 0 & 1 & \vdots & -13 & -5 & 35 \end{bmatrix}$$

Therefore, the inverse is

$$A^{-1} = \begin{bmatrix} -10 & -4 & 27 \\ 2 & 1 & -5 \\ -13 & -5 & 35 \end{bmatrix}.$$

14. We adjoin the identity matrix to form

$$[A : I] = \begin{bmatrix} 3 & 2 & 5 & \vdots & 1 & 0 & 0 \\ 2 & 2 & 4 & \vdots & 0 & 1 & 0 \\ -4 & 4 & 0 & \vdots & 0 & 0 & 1 \end{bmatrix}.$$

Using elementary row operations, we find that we cannot form the identity matrix on the left side. Therefore, the matrix has no inverse.

16. We adjoin the identity matrix to form

$$[I : A^{-1}] = \begin{bmatrix} 2 & 0 & 0 & \vdots & 1 & 0 & 0 \\ 0 & 3 & 0 & \vdots & 0 & 1 & 0 \\ 0 & 0 & 5 & \vdots & 0 & 0 & 1 \end{bmatrix}.$$

Using elementary row operations, we reduce the matrix as follows.

$$[A : I] = \begin{bmatrix} 1 & 0 & 0 & \vdots & \frac{1}{2} & 0 & 0 \\ 0 & 1 & 0 & \vdots & 0 & \frac{1}{3} & 0 \\ 0 & 0 & 1 & \vdots & 0 & 0 & \frac{1}{5} \end{bmatrix}$$

Therefore, the inverse is

$$A^{-1} = \begin{bmatrix} \frac{1}{2} & 0 & 0 \\ 0 & \frac{1}{3} & 0 \\ 0 & 0 & \frac{1}{5} \end{bmatrix}.$$

18. We adjoin the identity matrix to form

$$[A : I] = \begin{bmatrix} 1 & 0 & 0 & \vdots & 1 & 0 & 0 \\ 3 & 0 & 0 & \vdots & 0 & 1 & 0 \\ 2 & 5 & 5 & \vdots & 0 & 0 & 1 \end{bmatrix}.$$

Using elementary row operations, we find that we cannot form the identity matrix on the left side. Therefore, the matrix has no inverse.

20. We use the formula $A^{-1} = \dfrac{1}{ad - bc} \begin{bmatrix} d & -b \\ -c & a \end{bmatrix}$, where $A = \begin{bmatrix} a & b \\ c & d \end{bmatrix}$.

In this case, we have $A^{-1} = \dfrac{1}{\frac{1}{a}(a) - 0(a)} \begin{bmatrix} a & 0 \\ -a & \frac{1}{a} \end{bmatrix} = \begin{bmatrix} a & 0 \\ -a & \frac{1}{a} \end{bmatrix}.$

22. We adjoin the identity matrix to form

$$[A : I] = \begin{bmatrix} 4 & 8 & -7 & 14 & \vdots & 1 & 0 & 0 & 0 \\ 2 & 5 & -4 & 6 & \vdots & 0 & 1 & 0 & 0 \\ 0 & 2 & 1 & -7 & \vdots & 0 & 0 & 1 & 0 \\ 3 & 6 & -5 & 10 & \vdots & 0 & 0 & 0 & 1 \end{bmatrix}.$$

Using elementary row operations, we reduce the matrix as follows.

$$[A : I] = \begin{bmatrix} 1 & 0 & 0 & 0 & \vdots & 27 & -10 & 4 & -29 \\ 0 & 1 & 0 & 0 & \vdots & -16 & 5 & -2 & 18 \\ 0 & 0 & 1 & 0 & \vdots & -17 & 4 & -2 & 20 \\ 0 & 0 & 0 & 1 & \vdots & -7 & 2 & -1 & 8 \end{bmatrix}.$$

Therefore the inverse is

$$A^{-1} = \begin{bmatrix} 27 & -10 & 4 & -29 \\ -16 & 5 & -2 & 18 \\ -17 & 4 & -2 & 20 \\ -7 & 2 & -1 & 8 \end{bmatrix}.$$

24. We adjoin the identity matrix to form

$$[A : I] = \begin{bmatrix} 1 & 3 & -2 & 0 & \vdots & 1 & 0 & 0 & 0 \\ 0 & 2 & 4 & 6 & \vdots & 0 & 1 & 0 & 0 \\ 0 & 0 & -2 & 1 & \vdots & 0 & 0 & 1 & 0 \\ 0 & 0 & 0 & 5 & \vdots & 0 & 0 & 0 & 1 \end{bmatrix}.$$

Using elementary row operations, we reduce the matrix as follows.

$$[I : A^{-1}] = \begin{bmatrix} 1 & 0 & 0 & 0 & \vdots & 1 & -1.5 & -4 & 2.6 \\ 0 & 1 & 0 & 0 & \vdots & 0 & 0.5 & 1 & -0.8 \\ 0 & 0 & 1 & 0 & \vdots & 0 & 0 & -0.5 & 0.1 \\ 0 & 0 & 0 & 1 & \vdots & 0 & 0 & 0 & 0.2 \end{bmatrix}.$$

Therefore the inverse is

$$A^{-1} = \begin{bmatrix} 1 & -1.5 & -4 & 2.6 \\ 0 & 0.5 & 1 & -0.8 \\ 0 & 0 & -0.5 & 0.1 \\ 0 & 0 & 0 & 0.2 \end{bmatrix}.$$

26. The coefficient matrix for each system is $\begin{bmatrix} 2 & 3 \\ 1 & 4 \end{bmatrix}$, and the formula for the inverse of a matrix 2×2 matrix produces the following.

$$A^{-1} = \frac{1}{(2)(4) - (3)(1)} \begin{bmatrix} 4 & -3 \\ -1 & 2 \end{bmatrix} = \frac{1}{5} \begin{bmatrix} 4 & -3 \\ -1 & 2 \end{bmatrix}$$

(a) $\mathbf{x} = A^{-1}\mathbf{b} = \dfrac{1}{5} \begin{bmatrix} 4 & -3 \\ -1 & 2 \end{bmatrix} \begin{bmatrix} 5 \\ 10 \end{bmatrix} = \begin{bmatrix} -2 \\ 3 \end{bmatrix}$. The solution is $x = -2, y = 3$.

(b) $\mathbf{x} = A^{-1}\mathbf{b} = \dfrac{1}{5} \begin{bmatrix} 4 & -3 \\ -1 & 2 \end{bmatrix} \begin{bmatrix} 0 \\ 0 \end{bmatrix} = \begin{bmatrix} 0 \\ 0 \end{bmatrix}$. The solution is $x = y = 0$.

(c) $\mathbf{x} = A^{-1}\mathbf{b} = \dfrac{1}{5} \begin{bmatrix} 4 & -3 \\ -1 & 2 \end{bmatrix} \begin{bmatrix} 1 \\ -2 \end{bmatrix} = \begin{bmatrix} 2 \\ -1 \end{bmatrix}$. The solution is $x = 2, y = -1$.

28. The coefficient matrix A for each system is the same. Using the algorithm to invert a matrix, we have that

$$A = \begin{bmatrix} 1 & -2 & -1 \\ 3 & -5 & -2 \\ 2 & -5 & -2 \end{bmatrix} \implies A^{-1} = \begin{bmatrix} 0 & 1 & -1 \\ 2 & 0 & -1 \\ -5 & 1 & 1 \end{bmatrix}.$$

(a) $x = A^{-1}b = A^{-1} \begin{bmatrix} 0 \\ 1 \\ -1 \end{bmatrix} = \begin{bmatrix} 2 \\ 1 \\ 0 \end{bmatrix}$

The solution is $x_1 = 2, x_2 = 1, x_3 = 0$.

(b) $x = A^{-1}b = A^{-1} \begin{bmatrix} 1 \\ -2 \\ 0 \end{bmatrix} = \begin{bmatrix} -2 \\ 2 \\ -7 \end{bmatrix}.$

The solution is $x_1 = -2, x_2 = 2, x_3 = -7$.

30. Using a graphing calculator, we have

$$Ax = B$$

$$x = A^{-1}B = \begin{bmatrix} -1 \\ 2 \\ 1 \\ 3 \\ 0 \\ 1 \end{bmatrix}$$

where

$$A = \begin{bmatrix} 4 & -2 & 4 & 2 & -5 & -1 \\ 3 & 6 & -5 & -6 & 3 & 3 \\ 2 & -3 & 1 & 3 & -1 & -2 \\ -1 & 4 & -4 & -6 & 2 & 4 \\ 3 & -1 & 5 & 2 & -3 & -5 \\ -2 & 3 & -4 & -6 & 1 & 2 \end{bmatrix}, \quad x = \begin{bmatrix} x_1 \\ x_2 \\ x_3 \\ x_4 \\ x_5 \\ x_6 \end{bmatrix}, \text{ and } B = \begin{bmatrix} 1 \\ -11 \\ 0 \\ -9 \\ 1 \\ -12 \end{bmatrix}.$$

The solution is $x_1 = -1, x_2 = 2, x_3 = 1, x_4 = 3, x_5 = 0, x_6 = 1$.

32. (a) $(AB)^{-1} = B^{-1}A^{-1} = \begin{bmatrix} \frac{5}{11} & \frac{2}{11} \\ \frac{3}{11} & -\frac{1}{11} \end{bmatrix}\begin{bmatrix} -\frac{2}{7} & \frac{1}{7} \\ \frac{3}{7} & \frac{2}{7} \end{bmatrix} = \frac{1}{77}\begin{bmatrix} -4 & 9 \\ -9 & 1 \end{bmatrix}$

(b) $(A^T)^{-1} = (A^{-1})^T = \begin{bmatrix} -\frac{2}{7} & \frac{1}{7} \\ \frac{3}{7} & \frac{2}{7} \end{bmatrix}^T = \begin{bmatrix} -\frac{2}{7} & \frac{3}{7} \\ \frac{1}{7} & \frac{2}{7} \end{bmatrix}$

(c) $(A)^{-2} = (A^{-1})^2 = \begin{bmatrix} -\frac{2}{7} & \frac{1}{7} \\ \frac{3}{7} & \frac{2}{7} \end{bmatrix}\begin{bmatrix} -\frac{2}{7} & \frac{3}{7} \\ \frac{1}{7} & \frac{2}{7} \end{bmatrix} = \begin{bmatrix} \frac{1}{7} & 0 \\ 0 & \frac{1}{7} \end{bmatrix}$

(d) $(2A)^{-1} = \frac{1}{2}A^{-1} = \frac{1}{2}\begin{bmatrix} -\frac{2}{7} & \frac{1}{7} \\ \frac{3}{7} & \frac{2}{7} \end{bmatrix} = \begin{bmatrix} -\frac{1}{7} & \frac{1}{14} \\ \frac{3}{14} & \frac{1}{7} \end{bmatrix}$

34. (a) $(AB)^{-1} = B^{-1}A^{-1} = \begin{bmatrix} 6 & 5 & -3 \\ -2 & 4 & -1 \\ 1 & 3 & 4 \end{bmatrix}\begin{bmatrix} 1 & -4 & 2 \\ 0 & 1 & 3 \\ 4 & 2 & 1 \end{bmatrix} = \begin{bmatrix} -6 & -25 & 24 \\ -6 & 10 & 7 \\ 17 & 7 & 15 \end{bmatrix}$

(b) $(A^T)^{-1} = (A^{-1})^T = \begin{bmatrix} 1 & -4 & 2 \\ 0 & 1 & 3 \\ 4 & 2 & 1 \end{bmatrix}^T = \begin{bmatrix} 1 & 0 & 4 \\ -4 & 1 & 2 \\ 2 & 3 & 1 \end{bmatrix}$

(c) $A^{-2} = (A^{-1})^2 = \begin{bmatrix} 1 & -4 & 2 \\ 0 & 1 & 3 \\ 4 & 2 & 1 \end{bmatrix}\begin{bmatrix} 1 & -4 & 2 \\ 0 & 1 & 3 \\ 4 & 2 & 1 \end{bmatrix} = \begin{bmatrix} 9 & -4 & -8 \\ 12 & 7 & 6 \\ 8 & -12 & 15 \end{bmatrix}$

(d) $(2A)^{-1} = \frac{1}{2}A^{-1} = \frac{1}{2}\begin{bmatrix} 1 & -4 & 2 \\ 0 & 1 & 3 \\ 4 & 2 & 1 \end{bmatrix} = \begin{bmatrix} \frac{1}{2} & -2 & 1 \\ 0 & \frac{1}{2} & \frac{3}{2} \\ 2 & 1 & \frac{1}{2} \end{bmatrix}$

36. The matrix $\begin{bmatrix} 4 & x \\ -2 & -3 \end{bmatrix}$ will be singular if $ad - bc = (4)(-3) - (x)(-2) = 0$, which implies that $2x = 12$ or $x = 6$.

38. Using the formula for the inverse of a 2×2 matrix, we have

$$A^{-1} = \frac{1}{ad - bc}\begin{bmatrix} d & -b \\ -c & a \end{bmatrix} = \frac{1}{\sin^2 \theta + \cos^2 \theta}\begin{bmatrix} \sin \theta & -\cos \theta \\ \cos \theta & \sin \theta \end{bmatrix} = \begin{bmatrix} \sin \theta & -\cos \theta \\ \cos \theta & \sin \theta \end{bmatrix}.$$

40. (a) *True.* If A_1, A_2, A_3, A_4 are invertible 7×7 matrices, then $B = A_1 A_2 A_3 A_4$ is also invertible 7×7 matrix with inverse $B^{-1} = A_4^{-1} A_3^{-1} A_2^{-1} A_1^{-1}$, by Theorem 2.9 on page 80 and induction.

(b) *True.* $(A^{-1})^T = (A^T)^{-1}$ by Theorem 2.8(4) on page 78.

(c) *False.* For example consider the matrix $\begin{bmatrix} 1 & 1 \\ 0 & 0 \end{bmatrix}$ which is not invertible, but $1 \cdot 1 - 0 \cdot 0 = 1 \neq 0$.

(d) *False.* If A is a square matrix then the system $A\mathbf{x} = \mathbf{b}$ has a unique solution if and only if A is a *nonsingular* matrix.

42. $A^T(A^{-1})^T = (A^{-1}A)^T = I_n{}^T = I_n$, and $(A^{-1})^T A^T = (AA^{-1})^T = I_n{}^T = I_n$. Hence, $(A^{-1})^T = (A^T)^{-1}$.

44. Since C is invertible, we can multiply both sides of the equation $CA = CB$ by C^{-1} on the left to obtain the following.

$$C^{-1}(CA) = C^{-1}(CB)$$
$$(C^{-1}C)A = (C^{-1}C)B$$
$$IA = IB$$
$$A = B$$

46. Since $ABC = I$, A is invertible and $A^{-1} = BC$. Thus, $ABCA = A$ and $BCA = I$. Thus, $B^{-1} = CA$.

48. Let $A^2 = A$ and suppose A is nonsingular. Then, A^{-1} exists, and we have the following.

$$A^{-1}(A^2) = A^{-1}A$$
$$(A^{-1}A)A = I$$
$$A = I$$

50. A has an inverse if $a_{ii} \neq 0$ for all $i = 1 \ldots n$ and

$$A^{-1} = \begin{bmatrix} \frac{1}{a_{11}} & 0 & 0 & \cdots & 0 \\ 0 & \frac{1}{a_{22}} & 0 & \cdots & 0 \\ \vdots & \vdots & \vdots & & \vdots \\ 0 & 0 & 0 & \cdots & \frac{1}{a_{nn}} \end{bmatrix}.$$

52. $A = \begin{bmatrix} 1 & 2 \\ -2 & 1 \end{bmatrix}$

(a) $A^2 - 2A + 5I = \begin{bmatrix} -3 & 4 \\ -4 & -3 \end{bmatrix} - \begin{bmatrix} 2 & 4 \\ -4 & 2 \end{bmatrix} + \begin{bmatrix} 5 & 0 \\ 0 & 5 \end{bmatrix} = \begin{bmatrix} 0 & 0 \\ 0 & 0 \end{bmatrix}$

(b) $A\left(\frac{1}{5}(2I - A)\right) = \frac{1}{5}(2A - A^2) = \frac{1}{5}(5I) = I$

Similarly, $\left(\frac{1}{5}(2I - A)\right)A = I$. Or, $\frac{1}{5}(2I - A) = \frac{1}{5}\begin{bmatrix} 1 & -2 \\ 2 & 1 \end{bmatrix} = A^{-1}$ directly.

(c) The calculation in part (b) did not depend on the entries of A.

54. Let C be the inverse of $(I - AB)$, i.e., $C = (I - AB)^{-1}$. Then $C(I - AB) = (I - AB)C = I$. Consider the matrix $I + BCA$. We claim that this matrix is the inverse of $I - BA$. To check this claim we need to show that

$$(I + BCA)(I - BA) = (I - BA)(I + BCA) = I.$$

We check that

$$(I - BA)(I + BCA) = I - BA + BCA - BABCA = I - BA + B(C - ABC)A$$
$$= I - BA + B(\underbrace{(I - AB)C}_{I})A = I - BA + BA = I$$

Similarly, we check that $(I + BCA)(I - BA) = I$.

56. Let A, D, P be $n \times n$ matrices. Suppose $P^{-1}AP = D$. Then $P(P^{-1}AP)P^{-1} = PDP^{-1}$, so $A = PDP^{-1}$. It is not necessary that $A = D$. For example, let

$$A = \begin{bmatrix} 2 & 1 \\ 0 & 1 \end{bmatrix}, D = \begin{bmatrix} 2 & 0 \\ 0 & 1 \end{bmatrix}, P = \begin{bmatrix} 1 & 1 \\ 0 & -1 \end{bmatrix}.$$

It is easy to check that

$$AP = PD = \begin{bmatrix} 2 & 1 \\ 0 & -1 \end{bmatrix},$$

so we have $P^{-1}AP = D$, but $A \neq D$.

Section 2.4   Elementary Matrices

2. This matrix is *not* elementary, because it is not square.

4. This matrix *is* elementary. It can be obtained by interchanging the two rows of I_2.

6. This matrix *is* elementary. It can be obtained by multiplying the first row of I_3 by 2, and adding the result to the third row.

8. This matrix is *not* elementary, because two elementary row operations are required to obtain it from I_4.

10. C is obtained by adding the third row of A to the first row. Thus,

$$E = \begin{bmatrix} 1 & 0 & 1 \\ 0 & 1 & 0 \\ 0 & 0 & 1 \end{bmatrix}.$$

12. A is obtained by adding (-1) times the third row of C to the first row. Thus,

$$E = \begin{bmatrix} 1 & 0 & -1 \\ 0 & 1 & 0 \\ 0 & 0 & 1 \end{bmatrix}.$$

14. To obtain the inverse matrix, we reverse the elementary row operation that produced it. Thus,

$$E^{-1} = \begin{bmatrix} \frac{1}{5} & 0 \\ 0 & 1 \end{bmatrix}.$$

16. To obtain the inverse matrix, we reverse the elementary row operation that produced it. Thus, we add 3 times row two to the third row to obtain

$$E^{-1} = \begin{bmatrix} 1 & 0 & 0 \\ 0 & 1 & 0 \\ 0 & 3 & 1 \end{bmatrix}.$$

18. To obtain the inverse matrix, we reverse the elementary row operation that produced it. Thus, we interchange the second and third row to obtain

$$E^{-1} = \begin{bmatrix} 1 & 0 & 0 \\ 0 & 0 & 1 \\ 0 & 1 & 0 \end{bmatrix}.$$

20. To obtain the inverse matrix, we reverse the elementary row operation that produced it. Thus,

$$E^{-1} = \begin{bmatrix} 1 & 0 & 0 & 0 \\ 0 & 1 & 0 & 0 \\ 0 & 0 & k & 0 \\ 0 & 0 & 0 & 1 \end{bmatrix}.$$

22. The matrix $A = \begin{bmatrix} 0 & 1 \\ 1 & 0 \end{bmatrix}$ is itself an elementary matrix, and hence the factorization is

$$A = \begin{bmatrix} 0 & 1 \\ 1 & 0 \end{bmatrix}.$$

24. We reduce the matrix $A = \begin{bmatrix} 1 & 1 \\ 2 & 1 \end{bmatrix}$ as follows.

Matrix	Elementary Row Operation	Elementary Matrix
$\begin{bmatrix} 1 & 1 \\ 0 & -1 \end{bmatrix}$	-2 times row one to row two	$E_1 = \begin{bmatrix} 1 & 0 \\ -2 & 1 \end{bmatrix}$
$\begin{bmatrix} 1 & 1 \\ 0 & 1 \end{bmatrix}$	-1 times row two	$E_2 = \begin{bmatrix} 1 & 0 \\ 0 & -1 \end{bmatrix}$
$\begin{bmatrix} 1 & 0 \\ 0 & 1 \end{bmatrix}$	-1 times row two to row one	$E_3 = \begin{bmatrix} 1 & -1 \\ 0 & 1 \end{bmatrix}$

Thus, one way to factor A is

$$A = E_1^{-1}E_2^{-1}E_3^{-1} = \begin{bmatrix} 1 & 0 \\ 2 & 1 \end{bmatrix} \begin{bmatrix} 1 & 0 \\ 0 & -1 \end{bmatrix} \begin{bmatrix} 1 & 1 \\ 0 & 1 \end{bmatrix}.$$

26. We reduce the matrix $A = \begin{bmatrix} 1 & 2 & 3 \\ 2 & 5 & 6 \\ 1 & 3 & 4 \end{bmatrix}$ as follows.

Matrix	Elementary Row Operation	Elementary Matrix
$\begin{bmatrix} 1 & 2 & 3 \\ 0 & 1 & 0 \\ 1 & 3 & 4 \end{bmatrix}$	-2 times row one to row two	$E_1 = \begin{bmatrix} 1 & 0 & 0 \\ -2 & 1 & 0 \\ 0 & 0 & 1 \end{bmatrix}$
$\begin{bmatrix} 1 & 2 & 3 \\ 0 & 1 & 0 \\ 0 & 1 & 1 \end{bmatrix}$	-1 times row one to row three	$E_2 = \begin{bmatrix} 1 & 0 & 0 \\ 0 & 1 & 0 \\ -1 & 0 & 1 \end{bmatrix}$
$\begin{bmatrix} 1 & 2 & 3 \\ 0 & 1 & 0 \\ 0 & 0 & 1 \end{bmatrix}$	-1 times row two to row three	$E_3 = \begin{bmatrix} 1 & 0 & 0 \\ 0 & 1 & 0 \\ 0 & -1 & 1 \end{bmatrix}$
$\begin{bmatrix} 1 & 2 & 0 \\ 0 & 1 & 0 \\ 0 & 0 & 1 \end{bmatrix}$	-3 times row three to row one	$E_4 = \begin{bmatrix} 1 & 0 & -3 \\ 0 & 1 & 0 \\ 0 & 0 & 1 \end{bmatrix}$
$\begin{bmatrix} 1 & 0 & 0 \\ 0 & 1 & 0 \\ 0 & 0 & 1 \end{bmatrix}$	-2 times row two to row one	$E_5 = \begin{bmatrix} 1 & -2 & 0 \\ 0 & 1 & 0 \\ 0 & 0 & 1 \end{bmatrix}$

Thus, one way to factor A is

$$A = E_1^{-1}E_2^{-1}E_3^{-1}E_4^{-1}E_5^{-1} =$$

$$\begin{bmatrix} 1 & 0 & 0 \\ 2 & 1 & 0 \\ 0 & 0 & 1 \end{bmatrix} \begin{bmatrix} 1 & 0 & 0 \\ 0 & 1 & 0 \\ 1 & 0 & 1 \end{bmatrix} \begin{bmatrix} 1 & 0 & 0 \\ 0 & 1 & 0 \\ 0 & 1 & 1 \end{bmatrix} \begin{bmatrix} 1 & 0 & 3 \\ 0 & 1 & 0 \\ 0 & 0 & 1 \end{bmatrix} \begin{bmatrix} 1 & 2 & 0 \\ 0 & 1 & 0 \\ 0 & 0 & 1 \end{bmatrix}.$$

28. We reduce the matrix $A = \begin{bmatrix} -1 & 2 & 0 \\ 0 & 2 & 0 \\ 1 & 0 & 1 \end{bmatrix}$ as follows.

Matrix	Elementary Row Operation	Elementary Matrix
$\begin{bmatrix} 1 & -2 & 0 \\ 0 & 2 & 0 \\ 1 & 0 & 1 \end{bmatrix}$	-1 times row one	$E_1 = \begin{bmatrix} -1 & 0 & 0 \\ 0 & 1 & 0 \\ 0 & 0 & 1 \end{bmatrix}$
$\begin{bmatrix} 1 & 0 & 0 \\ 0 & 2 & 0 \\ 1 & 0 & 1 \end{bmatrix}$	Row two added to row one	$E_2 = \begin{bmatrix} 1 & 1 & 0 \\ 0 & 1 & 0 \\ 0 & 0 & 1 \end{bmatrix}$
$\begin{bmatrix} 1 & 0 & 0 \\ 0 & 1 & 0 \\ 1 & 0 & 1 \end{bmatrix}$	$\frac{1}{2}$ times row two	$E_3 = \begin{bmatrix} 1 & 0 & 0 \\ 0 & \frac{1}{2} & 0 \\ 0 & 0 & 1 \end{bmatrix}$
$\begin{bmatrix} 1 & 0 & 0 \\ 0 & 1 & 0 \\ 0 & 0 & 1 \end{bmatrix}$	-1 times row one to row three	$E_4 = \begin{bmatrix} 1 & 0 & 0 \\ 0 & 1 & 0 \\ -1 & 0 & 1 \end{bmatrix}$

Thus, one way to factor A is

$$A = E_1^{-1}E_2^{-1}E_3^{-1}E_4^{-1} = \begin{bmatrix} -1 & 0 & 0 \\ 0 & 1 & 0 \\ 0 & 0 & 1 \end{bmatrix} \begin{bmatrix} 1 & -1 & 0 \\ 0 & 1 & 0 \\ 0 & 0 & 1 \end{bmatrix} \begin{bmatrix} 1 & 0 & 0 \\ 0 & 2 & 0 \\ 0 & 0 & 1 \end{bmatrix} \begin{bmatrix} 1 & 0 & 0 \\ 0 & 1 & 0 \\ 1 & 0 & 1 \end{bmatrix}.$$

30. (a) *False.* It is impossible to obtain the zero matrix by applying any elementary row operation to the identity matrix.

(b) *True.* See the definition of row equivalence on page 89.

(c) *True.* If $A = E_1E_2 \ldots E_k$, where each E_i is an elementary matrix, then A is invertible (since every elemenraty matrix is) and $A^{-1} = E_k^{-1} \ldots E_2^{-1} E_1^{-1}$.

(d) *True.* See equivalent conditions (2) and (3) of Theorem 2.15 on page 92.

32. (a) EA and A have the same rows, except that the corresponding row in A is multiplied by c.

(b) E^2 is obtained by multiplying the corresponding row in I by c^2.

34. We can first factor A as a product of elementary matrices.

$$A = E_1^{-1}E_2^{-1}E_3^{-1} = \begin{bmatrix} 1 & 0 & 0 \\ 0 & 1 & 0 \\ a & 0 & 1 \end{bmatrix}\begin{bmatrix} 1 & 0 & 0 \\ 0 & 1 & 0 \\ 0 & b & 1 \end{bmatrix}\begin{bmatrix} 1 & 0 & 0 \\ 0 & 1 & 0 \\ 0 & 0 & c \end{bmatrix}$$

Hence, $A^{-1} = (E_1^{-1}E_2^{-1}E_3^{-1})^{-1} = E_3E_2E_1$.

$$\begin{bmatrix} 1 & 0 & 0 \\ 0 & 1 & 0 \\ 0 & 0 & \frac{1}{c} \end{bmatrix}\begin{bmatrix} 1 & 0 & 0 \\ 0 & 1 & 0 \\ 0 & -b & 1 \end{bmatrix}\begin{bmatrix} 1 & 0 & 0 \\ 0 & 1 & 0 \\ -a & 0 & 1 \end{bmatrix} = \begin{bmatrix} 1 & 0 & 0 \\ 0 & 1 & 0 \\ -\frac{a}{c} & \frac{b}{c} & \frac{1}{c} \end{bmatrix}.$$

36. No. For example $\begin{bmatrix} 1 & 2 \\ 0 & 1 \end{bmatrix} + \begin{bmatrix} 1 & 0 \\ 2 & 1 \end{bmatrix} = \begin{bmatrix} 2 & 2 \\ 2 & 2 \end{bmatrix}$ is not elementary.

38.   Matrix   Elementary Matrix

$$\begin{bmatrix} -2 & 1 \\ -6 & 4 \end{bmatrix} = A$$

$$\begin{bmatrix} -2 & 1 \\ 0 & 1 \end{bmatrix} = U \qquad \begin{bmatrix} 1 & 0 \\ -3 & 1 \end{bmatrix} = E_1$$

$$E_1A = U \implies A = E_1^{-1}U = \begin{bmatrix} 1 & 0 \\ 3 & 1 \end{bmatrix}\begin{bmatrix} -2 & 1 \\ 0 & 1 \end{bmatrix} = LU$$

40.   Matrix   Elementary Matrix

$$\begin{bmatrix} 2 & 0 & 0 \\ 0 & -3 & 1 \\ 10 & 12 & 3 \end{bmatrix} = A$$

$$\begin{bmatrix} 2 & 0 & 0 \\ 0 & -3 & 1 \\ 0 & 12 & 3 \end{bmatrix} \qquad \begin{bmatrix} 1 & 0 & 0 \\ 0 & 1 & 0 \\ -5 & 0 & 1 \end{bmatrix} = E_1$$

$$\begin{bmatrix} 2 & 0 & 0 \\ 0 & -3 & 1 \\ 0 & 0 & 7 \end{bmatrix} = U \qquad \begin{bmatrix} 1 & 0 & 0 \\ 0 & 1 & 0 \\ 0 & 4 & 1 \end{bmatrix} = E_2$$

$$E_2 E_1 A = U \quad \Rightarrow \quad A = E_1^{-1} E_2^{-1} U = \begin{bmatrix} 1 & 0 & 0 \\ 0 & 1 & 0 \\ 5 & -4 & 1 \end{bmatrix} \begin{bmatrix} 2 & 0 & 0 \\ 0 & -3 & 1 \\ 0 & 0 & 7 \end{bmatrix} = LU$$

42. (a) Matrix   Elementary Matrix

$$\begin{bmatrix} 2 & 0 & 0 & 0 \\ -2 & 1 & -1 & 0 \\ 6 & 2 & 1 & 0 \\ 0 & 0 & 0 & -1 \end{bmatrix} = A$$

$$\begin{bmatrix} 2 & 0 & 0 & 0 \\ 0 & 1 & -1 & 0 \\ 6 & 2 & 1 & 0 \\ 0 & 0 & 0 & -1 \end{bmatrix} \qquad \begin{bmatrix} 1 & 0 & 0 & 0 \\ 1 & 1 & 0 & 0 \\ 0 & 0 & 1 & 0 \\ 0 & 0 & 0 & 1 \end{bmatrix} = E_1$$

$$\begin{bmatrix} 2 & 0 & 0 & 0 \\ 0 & 1 & -1 & 0 \\ 0 & 2 & 1 & 0 \\ 0 & 0 & 0 & -1 \end{bmatrix} \qquad \begin{bmatrix} 1 & 0 & 0 & 0 \\ 0 & 1 & 0 & 0 \\ -3 & 0 & 1 & 0 \\ 0 & 0 & 0 & 1 \end{bmatrix} = E_2$$

$$\begin{bmatrix} 2 & 0 & 0 & 0 \\ 0 & 1 & -1 & 0 \\ 0 & 0 & 3 & 0 \\ 0 & 0 & 0 & -1 \end{bmatrix} = U \qquad \begin{bmatrix} 1 & 0 & 0 & 0 \\ 0 & 1 & 0 & 0 \\ 0 & -2 & 1 & 0 \\ 0 & 0 & 0 & 1 \end{bmatrix} = E_3$$

$$E_3 E_2 E_1 A = U \quad \Rightarrow \quad A = E_1^{-1} E_2^{-1} E_3^{-1} U = \begin{bmatrix} 1 & 0 & 0 & 0 \\ -1 & 1 & 0 & 0 \\ 3 & 2 & 1 & 0 \\ 0 & 0 & 0 & 1 \end{bmatrix} \begin{bmatrix} 2 & 0 & 0 & 0 \\ 0 & 1 & -1 & 0 \\ 0 & 0 & 3 & 0 \\ 0 & 0 & 0 & -1 \end{bmatrix} = LU$$

(b) $Ly = b$: $\begin{bmatrix} 1 & 0 & 0 & 0 \\ -1 & 1 & 0 & 0 \\ 3 & 2 & 1 & 0 \\ 0 & 0 & 0 & 1 \end{bmatrix} \begin{bmatrix} y_1 \\ y_2 \\ y_3 \\ y_4 \end{bmatrix} = \begin{bmatrix} 4 \\ -4 \\ 15 \\ -1 \end{bmatrix}$

$y_1 = 4, \; -y_1 + y_2 = -4 \quad \Rightarrow \quad y_2 = 0,$

$3y_1 + 2y_2 + y_3 = 15 \quad \Rightarrow \quad y_3 = 3, \text{ and } y_4 = -1.$

—CONTINUED—

42. —CONTINUED—

(c) $U\mathbf{x} = \mathbf{y}$:
$$\begin{bmatrix} 2 & 0 & 0 & 0 \\ 0 & 1 & -1 & 0 \\ 0 & 0 & 3 & 0 \\ 0 & 0 & 0 & -1 \end{bmatrix}\begin{bmatrix} x_1 \\ x_2 \\ x_3 \\ x_4 \end{bmatrix} = \begin{bmatrix} 4 \\ 0 \\ 3 \\ -1 \end{bmatrix}$$

$x_4 = 1, x_3 = 1, x_2 - x_3 = 0 \implies x_2 = 1$, and $x_1 = 2$.

Thus, the solution to the system $A\mathbf{x} = \mathbf{b}$ is $x_1 = 2, x_2 = x_3 = x_4 = 1$.

44. (a) Suppose $A = \begin{bmatrix} 0 & 1 \\ 1 & 0 \end{bmatrix} = \begin{bmatrix} a & 0 \\ b & c \end{bmatrix}\begin{bmatrix} d & e \\ 0 & f \end{bmatrix} = \begin{bmatrix} ad & ae \\ bd & be + cf \end{bmatrix}$.

Since $0 = ad$, either $a = 0$ or $d = 0$.

If $a = 0$, then $ae = 0 = 1$, which is impossible.

If $d = 0$, then $bd = 0 = 1$, which is impossible.

(b) Consider the following *LU*-factorization.

$$A = \begin{bmatrix} a & b \\ c & d \end{bmatrix} = \begin{bmatrix} 1 & 0 \\ x & 1 \end{bmatrix}\begin{bmatrix} y & z \\ 0 & w \end{bmatrix} = LU$$

Then $y = a, xy = xa = c \implies x = \dfrac{c}{a}$.

Also, $z = b$ and $xz + w = d \implies w = d - \left(\dfrac{c}{a}\right)b$.

The factorization is

$$\begin{bmatrix} a & b \\ c & d \end{bmatrix} = \begin{bmatrix} a & 0 \\ \dfrac{c}{a} & 1 \end{bmatrix}\begin{bmatrix} a & b \\ 0 & d - \dfrac{cb}{a} \end{bmatrix}, \quad a \neq 0.$$

46. $A^2 = \begin{bmatrix} 0 & 1 \\ 1 & 0 \end{bmatrix}\begin{bmatrix} 0 & 1 \\ 1 & 0 \end{bmatrix} = \begin{bmatrix} 1 & 0 \\ 0 & 1 \end{bmatrix} \neq A$.

Because $A^2 \neq A$, A is *not* idempotent.

48. $A^2 = \begin{bmatrix} 2 & 3 \\ 1 & 2 \end{bmatrix}\begin{bmatrix} 2 & 3 \\ 1 & 2 \end{bmatrix} = \begin{bmatrix} 7 & 12 \\ 4 & 7 \end{bmatrix}$.

Because $A^2 \neq A$, A is *not* idempotent.

50. $A^2 = \begin{bmatrix} 0 & 1 & 0 \\ 1 & 0 & 0 \\ 0 & 0 & 1 \end{bmatrix}\begin{bmatrix} 0 & 1 & 0 \\ 1 & 0 & 0 \\ 0 & 0 & 1 \end{bmatrix} = \begin{bmatrix} 1 & 0 & 0 \\ 0 & 1 & 0 \\ 0 & 0 & 1 \end{bmatrix}$.

Because $A^2 \neq A$, A is *not* idempotent.

52. $A^2 = \begin{bmatrix} a & 0 \\ b & c \end{bmatrix} \begin{bmatrix} a & 0 \\ b & c \end{bmatrix} = \begin{bmatrix} a^2 & 0 \\ ab + bc & c^2 \end{bmatrix}.$

In order for A^2 to equal A, we need $a = a^2$ and $c = c^2$. If $a = a^2$, there two cases to consider.

(*i*) $a = 0$: If $c = 0$, then $b = 0$ $\Rightarrow$ $a = b = c = 0$ is a solution.

If $c = 1$, then b can be any number $\Rightarrow$ $a = 0, c = 1, b$ *free* is a solution.

(*ii*) $a = 1$: If $c = 0$, then b can be any number $\Rightarrow$ $a = 1, c = 0, b$ *free* is a solution.

If $c = 1$, then $b = 0$ $\Rightarrow$ $a = c = 1, b = 0$ is a solution.

Hence, the possible matrices are

$$\begin{bmatrix} 0 & 0 \\ 0 & 0 \end{bmatrix}, \begin{bmatrix} 0 & 0 \\ b & 1 \end{bmatrix}, \begin{bmatrix} 1 & 0 \\ b & 0 \end{bmatrix}, \begin{bmatrix} 1 & 0 \\ 0 & 1 \end{bmatrix}.$$

54. Assume A is idempotent. Then we have

$$A^2 = A$$
$$(A^2)^T = A^T$$
$$(A^T A^T) = A^T$$

which means that A^T is idempotent.

Now assume A^T is idempotent. Then we have

$$A^T A^T = A^T$$
$$(A^T A^T)^T = (A^T)^T$$
$$AA = A$$

which means that A is idempotent.

56. If A is row equivalent to B, then

$$A = E_k \cdots E_2 E_1 B$$

where $E_1, \ldots, E_k$ are elementary matrices.

Hence,

$$B = E_1{}^{-1} E_2{}^{-1} \cdots E_k{}^{-1} A$$

which shows that B is row equivalent to A.

58. If B is row equivalent to A, then

$$B = E_k \cdots E_2 E_1 A$$

where $E_1, \ldots, E_k$ are elementary matrices. Since elementary matrices are nonsingular,

$$B^{-1} = (E_k \cdots E_1 A)^{-1} = A^{-1} E_1{}^{-1} \cdots E_k{}^{-1}$$

which shows that B is also nonsingular.

Section 2.5   Applications of Matrix Operations

2. This matrix is *not* stochastic because every entry in a stochastic matrix must satisfy $0 \leq a_{ij} \leq 1$.

4. This matrix *is* stochastic because each entry is between 0 and 1, and each column adds up to 1.

6. This matrix *is* stochastic because each entry is between 0 and 1, and each column adds up to 1.

8. We form the matrix representing the given transition probabilities. [*A* represents infected mice and *B* noninfected.]

$$P = \begin{bmatrix} 0.2 & 0.1 \\ 0.8 & 0.9 \end{bmatrix} \begin{matrix} A \\ B \end{matrix} \Big\} \text{ To}$$

$$\overbrace{}^{\text{From}}$$
$$A \quad B$$

The state matrix representing the current population is

$$X = \begin{bmatrix} 100 \\ 900 \end{bmatrix} \begin{matrix} A \\ B \end{matrix} .$$

The state matrix for next week is

$$PX = \begin{bmatrix} 0.2 & 0.1 \\ 0.8 & 0.9 \end{bmatrix} \begin{bmatrix} 100 \\ 900 \end{bmatrix} = \begin{bmatrix} 110 \\ 890 \end{bmatrix}.$$

The state matrix for the week after next is

$$P(PX) = \begin{bmatrix} 0.2 & 0.1 \\ 0.8 & 0.9 \end{bmatrix} \begin{bmatrix} 110 \\ 890 \end{bmatrix} = \begin{bmatrix} 111 \\ 889 \end{bmatrix}.$$

Thus, next week 110 will be infected, while in 2 weeks 111 will be infected.

10. We form the matrix representing the given transition probabilities. [*A* represents users of brand *A*, *B* users of brand *B*, and *N* users of neither brands.]

$$\overbrace{}^{\text{From}}$$

$$P = \begin{array}{c}\begin{matrix}A & B & N\end{matrix}\\ \begin{bmatrix} 0.75 & 0.15 & 0.10 \\ 0.20 & 0.75 & 0.15 \\ 0.05 & 0.10 & 0.75 \end{bmatrix}\begin{matrix}A \\ B \\ N\end{matrix}\end{array}\left.\phantom{\begin{matrix}A\\B\\N\end{matrix}}\right\}\text{To}$$

The state matrix representing the current product usage is

$$X = \begin{bmatrix} 20{,}000 \\ 30{,}000 \\ 50{,}000 \end{bmatrix}\begin{matrix}A \\ B \\ N\end{matrix}$$

The state matrix for next month is

$$PX = \begin{bmatrix} 0.75 & 0.15 & 0.10 \\ 0.20 & 0.75 & 0.15 \\ 0.05 & 0.10 & 0.75 \end{bmatrix}\begin{bmatrix} 20{,}000 \\ 30{,}000 \\ 50{,}000 \end{bmatrix} = \begin{bmatrix} 24{,}500 \\ 34{,}000 \\ 41{,}500 \end{bmatrix}.$$

Similarly, the state matrices for the following two months are

$$P(PX) = P\begin{bmatrix} 24{,}500 \\ 34{,}000 \\ 41{,}500 \end{bmatrix} = \begin{bmatrix} 27{,}625 \\ 36{,}625 \\ 35{,}750 \end{bmatrix} \text{ and } P(P(PX)) = \begin{bmatrix} 29{,}788 \\ 38{,}356 \\ 31{,}856 \end{bmatrix}.$$

Thus, the next month's users will be grouped as follows: 24,500 for brand *A*, 34,000 brand *B*, and 41,500 neither. In two months the distribution will be 27,625 brand *A*, 36,625 brand *B*, and 35,750 neither. Finally, in three months the distribution will be 29,788 brand *A*, 38,356 brand *B*, and 31,856 neither.

12. We find that

$$PX = \begin{bmatrix} 0.6 & 0.1 & 0.1 \\ 0.2 & 0.7 & 0.1 \\ 0.2 & 0.2 & 0.8 \end{bmatrix}\begin{bmatrix} 100 \\ 100 \\ 800 \end{bmatrix} = \begin{bmatrix} 150 \\ 170 \\ 680 \end{bmatrix}, \quad \text{and} \quad P^2X = P(PX) = \begin{bmatrix} 175 \\ 217 \\ 608 \end{bmatrix}.$$

Continuing, we have $P^3X = \begin{bmatrix} 187.5 \\ 247.7 \\ 564.8 \end{bmatrix}$.

Finally, the steady state matrix for *P* is $\begin{bmatrix} 200 \\ 300 \\ 500 \end{bmatrix}$ since

$$\begin{bmatrix} 0.6 & 0.1 & 0.1 \\ 0.2 & 0.7 & 0.1 \\ 0.2 & 0.2 & 0.8 \end{bmatrix}\begin{bmatrix} 200 \\ 300 \\ 500 \end{bmatrix} = \begin{bmatrix} 200 \\ 300 \\ 500 \end{bmatrix}.$$

14. Let

$$P = \begin{bmatrix} a & b \\ 1-a & 1-b \end{bmatrix}$$

be a 2×2 stochastic matrix, and consider the system of equations $PX = X$.

$$\begin{bmatrix} a & b \\ 1-a & 1-b \end{bmatrix} \begin{bmatrix} x_1 \\ x_2 \end{bmatrix} = \begin{bmatrix} x_1 \\ x_2 \end{bmatrix}$$

We have

$$ax_1 + bx_2 = x_1$$
$$(1-a)x_1 + (1-b)x_2 = x_2$$

or

$$(a-1)x_1 + bx_2 = 0$$
$$(1-a)x_1 - bx_2 = 0.$$

Letting $x_1 = b$ and $x_2 = 1 - a$, we have 2×1 state matrix X satisfying $PX = X$

$$X = \begin{bmatrix} b \\ 1-a \end{bmatrix}.$$

16. Dividing the message into groups of three and form the uncoded matrices.

P L E	A S E	_ S E	N D _	M O N	E Y _
[16 12 5]	[1 19 5]	[0 19 5]	[14 4 0]	[13 15 14]	[5 25 0]

Multiplying each uncoded row matrix on the right by A yields the following coded row matrices.

$$[16 \quad 12 \quad 5]A = [16 \quad 12 \quad 5] \begin{bmatrix} 4 & 2 & 1 \\ -3 & -3 & -1 \\ 3 & 2 & 1 \end{bmatrix} = [43 \quad 6 \quad 9]$$

$$[1 \quad 19 \quad 5]A = [-38 \quad -45 \quad -13]$$
$$[0 \quad 19 \quad 5]A = [-42 \quad -47 \quad -14]$$
$$[14 \quad 4 \quad 0]A = [44 \quad 16 \quad 10]$$
$$[13 \quad 15 \quad 14]A = [49 \quad 9 \quad 12]$$
$$[5 \quad 25 \quad 0]A = [-55 \quad -65 \quad -20]$$

Thus, the coded message is

$$43, 6, 9, -38, -45, -13, -42, 47, -14, 44, 16, 10, 49, 9, 12, -55, -65, -20.$$

18. Divide the message into groups of four and form the uncoded matrices.

H	E	L	P			_	I	S	_			C	O	M	I			N	G	_	_
[8	5	12	16]			[0	9	19	0]			[3	15	13	9]			[14	7	0	0]

Multiplying each uncoded row matrix on the right by A yields the coded row matrices

$$[8 \quad 5 \quad 12 \quad 16]A = [8 \quad 5 \quad 12 \quad 16]\begin{bmatrix} -2 & 3 & -1 & -1 \\ -1 & 1 & 1 & 1 \\ -1 & -1 & 1 & 2 \\ 3 & 1 & -2 & -4 \end{bmatrix}$$

$$= [15 \quad 33 \quad -23 \quad -43]$$

$$[0 \quad 9 \quad 19 \quad 0]A = [-28 \quad -10 \quad 28 \quad 47]$$

$$[3 \quad 15 \quad 13 \quad 9]A = [-7 \quad 20 \quad 7 \quad 2]$$

$$[14 \quad 7 \quad 0 \quad 0]A = [-35 \quad 49 \quad -7 \quad -7].$$

Thus, the coded message is

$$15, 33, -23, -43, -28, -10, 28, 47, -7, 20, 7, 2, -35, 49, -7, -7.$$

20. We find $A^{-1} = \begin{bmatrix} -4 & 3 \\ 3 & -2 \end{bmatrix}$, and multiplying each coded row matrix on the right by A^{-1} to find the associated uncoded row matrix.

$$[85 \quad 120]\begin{bmatrix} -4 & 3 \\ 3 & -2 \end{bmatrix} = [20 \quad 15] \quad \Rightarrow \quad T, O$$

$$[6 \quad 8]A^{-1} = [0 \quad 2] \quad \Rightarrow \quad \_, B$$

$$[10 \quad 15]A^{-1} = [5 \quad 0] \quad \Rightarrow \quad E, \_$$

$$[84 \quad 117]A^{-1} = [15 \quad 18] \quad \Rightarrow \quad O, R$$

$$[42 \quad 56]A^{-1} = [0 \quad 14] \quad \Rightarrow \quad \_, N$$

$$[90 \quad 125]A^{-1} = [15 \quad 20] \quad \Rightarrow \quad O, T$$

$$[60 \quad 80]A^{-1} = [0 \quad 20] \quad \Rightarrow \quad \_, T$$

$$[30 \quad 45]A^{-1} = [15 \quad 0] \quad \Rightarrow \quad O, \_$$

$$[19 \quad 26]A^{-1} = [2 \quad 5] \quad \Rightarrow \quad B, E$$

Thus, the message is TO __ BE __ OR __NOT __ TO __ BE.

22. We find $A^{-1} = \begin{bmatrix} -2 & -3 & -1 \\ -3 & -3 & -1 \\ -2 & -4 & -1 \end{bmatrix}$

and multiplying each coded row matrix on the right by A^{-1} to find the associated uncoded row matrix.

$$[9 \quad -1 \quad -9]A^{-1} = [9 \quad -1 \quad -9]\begin{bmatrix} -2 & -3 & -1 \\ -3 & -3 & -1 \\ -2 & -4 & -1 \end{bmatrix} = [3 \quad 12 \quad 1] \Rightarrow C, L, A$$

$$[38 \quad -19 \quad -19]A^{-1} = [19 \quad 19 \quad 0] \Rightarrow S, S, \_\_$$
$$[28 \quad -9 \quad -19]A^{-1} = [9 \quad 19 \quad 0] \Rightarrow I, S, \_\_$$
$$[-80 \quad 25 \quad 41]A^{-1} = [3 \quad 1 \quad 14] \Rightarrow C, A, N$$
$$[-64 \quad 21 \quad 31]A^{-1} = [3 \quad 5 \quad 12] \Rightarrow C, E, L$$
$$[-7 \quad -4 \quad 7]A^{-1} = [12 \quad 5 \quad 4] \Rightarrow L, E, D$$

Thus, the message is CLASS __ IS __ CANCELLED.

24. We let $A^{-1} = \begin{bmatrix} a & b \\ c & d \end{bmatrix}$ and find that

$$\overset{\_\_ \quad\quad S}{[-19 \quad -19]\begin{bmatrix} a & b \\ c & d \end{bmatrix} = [0 \quad 19]}$$

$$\overset{U \quad\quad E}{[37 \quad 16]\begin{bmatrix} a & b \\ c & d \end{bmatrix} = [21 \quad 5].}$$

This produces a system of 4 equations.

$$
\begin{aligned}
-19a \quad\quad -19c \quad\quad &= 0 \\
-19b \quad\quad -19d &= 19 \\
37a \quad\quad +16c \quad\quad &= 21 \\
37b \quad\quad +16d &= 5.
\end{aligned}
$$

Solving this system, we find $a = 1$, $b = 1$, $c = -1$, and $d = -2$. Thus,

$$A^{-1} = \begin{bmatrix} 1 & 1 \\ -1 & -2 \end{bmatrix}.$$

Using A^{-1} we multiply each coded row matrix to yield the uncoded row matrices.

$$[3 \ 1], [14 \ 3], [5 \ 12], [0 \ 15], [18 \ 4], [5 \ 18], [19 \ 0], [0 \ 19], [21 \ 5].$$

This corresponds to the message

CANCEL __ ORDERS __ SUE.

26. (a) We have

$$[45 \ -35]\begin{bmatrix} w & x \\ y & z \end{bmatrix} = [10 \quad 15] \text{ and } [38 \ -30]\begin{bmatrix} w & x \\ y & z \end{bmatrix} = [8 \quad 14].$$

So, $45w - 35y = 10$ and $45x - 35z = 15$
     $38w - 30y = 8$ $38x - 30z = 14.$

Solving these two systems gives $w = y = 1$ and $x = -2, z = -3$. Thus,

$$A^{-1} = \begin{bmatrix} 1 & -2 \\ 1 & -3 \end{bmatrix}.$$

(b) Decoding we have:

$$[45 \ -35]A^{-1} = [10 \quad 15] \implies J, O$$
$$[38 \ -30]A^{-1} = [8 \quad 14] \implies H, N$$
$$[18 \ -18]A^{-1} = [0 \quad 18] \implies \_\_, R$$
$$[35 \ -30]A^{-1} = [5 \quad 20] \implies E, T$$
$$[81 \ -60]A^{-1} = [21 \quad 18] \implies U, R$$
$$[42 \ -28]A^{-1} = [14 \quad 0] \implies N, \_\_$$
$$[75 \ -55]A^{-1} = [20 \quad 15] \implies T, O$$
$$[2 \ -2]A^{-1} = [0 \quad 2] \implies \_\_, B$$
$$[22 \ -21]A^{-1} = [1 \quad 19] \implies A, S$$
$$[15 \ -10]A^{-1} = [5 \quad 0] \implies E, \_\_$$

The message is JOHN__RETURN__TO__BASE__.

28. We use the given information to find D.

$$\begin{array}{cc} & \begin{array}{cc} A & B \end{array} \\ D = & \begin{bmatrix} 0.3 & 0.4 \\ 0.4 & 0.2 \end{bmatrix} \begin{array}{c} A \\ B \end{array} \end{array}$$

The equation $X = DX + E$ may be written in the form $(I - D)X = E$; that is,

$$\begin{bmatrix} 0.7 & -0.4 \\ -0.4 & 0.8 \end{bmatrix} X = \begin{bmatrix} 50{,}000 \\ 30{,}000 \end{bmatrix}.$$

Solving the system, we find $X = \begin{bmatrix} 130{,}000 \\ 102{,}500 \end{bmatrix}.$

30. From the given matrix D, we form the linear system $X = DX + E$, which can be written as $(I - D)X = E$

$$\begin{bmatrix} 0.8 & -0.4 & -0.4 \\ -0.4 & 0.8 & -0.2 \\ 0 & -0.2 & 0.8 \end{bmatrix} X = \begin{bmatrix} 5000 \\ 2000 \\ 8000 \end{bmatrix}.$$

Solving this system, we find $X = \begin{bmatrix} 21{,}875 \\ 17{,}000 \\ 14{,}250 \end{bmatrix}.$

32. (a) The line that best fits the given points is shown on the graph.

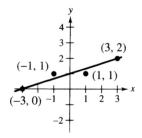

(b) Using the matrices

$$X = \begin{bmatrix} 1 & -3 \\ 1 & -1 \\ 1 & 1 \\ 1 & 3 \end{bmatrix} \quad \text{and} \quad Y = \begin{bmatrix} 0 \\ 1 \\ 1 \\ 2 \end{bmatrix}$$

we have

$$X^TX = \begin{bmatrix} 4 & 0 \\ 0 & 20 \end{bmatrix} \quad \text{and} \quad X^TY = \begin{bmatrix} 4 \\ 6 \end{bmatrix}$$

$$A = (X^TX)^{-1}X^TY = \begin{bmatrix} \frac{1}{4} & 0 \\ 0 & \frac{1}{20} \end{bmatrix}\begin{bmatrix} 4 \\ 6 \end{bmatrix} = \begin{bmatrix} 1 \\ \frac{3}{10} \end{bmatrix}.$$

Thus, the least squares regression line is $y = \frac{3}{10}x + 1$.

(c) Solving $Y = XA + E$ for E, we have

$$E = Y - XA = \begin{bmatrix} -0.1 \\ 0.3 \\ -0.3 \\ 0.1 \end{bmatrix}.$$

Thus, the sum of the squares error is $E^TE = 0.2$.

34. (a) The line that best fits the given points is shown on the graph.

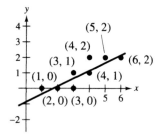

—CONTINUED—

34. **—CONTINUED—**

(b) Using the matrices

$$X = \begin{bmatrix} 1 & 1 \\ 1 & 2 \\ 1 & 3 \\ 1 & 3 \\ 1 & 4 \\ 1 & 4 \\ 1 & 5 \\ 1 & 6 \end{bmatrix} \quad \text{and} \quad Y = \begin{bmatrix} 0 \\ 0 \\ 0 \\ 1 \\ 1 \\ 2 \\ 2 \\ 2 \end{bmatrix}$$

we have

$$X^T X = \begin{bmatrix} 8 & 28 \\ 28 & 116 \end{bmatrix} \quad X^T Y = \begin{bmatrix} 8 \\ 37 \end{bmatrix}$$

$$A = (X^T X)^{-1}(X^T Y) = \begin{bmatrix} -\frac{3}{4} \\ \frac{1}{2} \end{bmatrix}.$$

Thus, the least squares regression line is $y = \frac{1}{2}x - \frac{3}{4}$.

(c) Solving $Y = XA + E$ for E, we have

$$E = Y - XA = \begin{bmatrix} \frac{1}{4} & -\frac{1}{4} & -\frac{3}{4} & \frac{1}{4} & -\frac{1}{4} & \frac{3}{4} & \frac{1}{4} & -\frac{1}{4} \end{bmatrix}^T$$

and the sum of the squares error is $E^T E = 1.5$.

36. Using the matrices

$$X = \begin{bmatrix} 1 & 1 \\ 1 & 3 \\ 1 & 5 \end{bmatrix} \quad \text{and} \quad Y = \begin{bmatrix} 0 \\ 3 \\ 6 \end{bmatrix}$$

we have

$$X^T X = \begin{bmatrix} 1 & 1 & 1 \\ 1 & 3 & 5 \end{bmatrix} \begin{bmatrix} 1 & 1 \\ 1 & 3 \\ 1 & 5 \end{bmatrix} = \begin{bmatrix} 3 & 9 \\ 9 & 35 \end{bmatrix}$$

$$X^T Y = \begin{bmatrix} 1 & 1 & 1 \\ 1 & 3 & 5 \end{bmatrix} \begin{bmatrix} 0 \\ 3 \\ 6 \end{bmatrix} = \begin{bmatrix} 9 \\ 39 \end{bmatrix}$$

$$A = (X^T X)^{-1}(X^T Y) = \begin{bmatrix} -\frac{3}{2} \\ \frac{3}{2} \end{bmatrix}.$$

Thus, the least squares regression line is $y = \frac{3}{2}x - \frac{3}{2}$.

38. Using matrices

$$X = \begin{bmatrix} 1 & -4 \\ 1 & -2 \\ 1 & 2 \\ 1 & 4 \end{bmatrix} \text{ and } Y = \begin{bmatrix} -1 \\ 0 \\ 4 \\ 5 \end{bmatrix}$$

we have

$$X^T X = \begin{bmatrix} 4 & 0 \\ 0 & 40 \end{bmatrix}, \quad X^T Y = \begin{bmatrix} 8 \\ 32 \end{bmatrix}$$

$$A = (X^T X)^{-1}(X^T Y) = \begin{bmatrix} \frac{1}{4} & 0 \\ 0 & \frac{1}{40} \end{bmatrix} \begin{bmatrix} 8 \\ 32 \end{bmatrix} = \begin{bmatrix} 2 \\ 0.8 \end{bmatrix}.$$

Thus, the least squares regression line is $y = 0.8x + 2$.

40. Using matrices

$$X = \begin{bmatrix} 1 & -3 \\ 1 & -1 \\ 1 & 1 \\ 1 & 3 \end{bmatrix} \text{ and } Y = \begin{bmatrix} 4 \\ 2 \\ 1 \\ 0 \end{bmatrix}$$

we have

$$X^T X = \begin{bmatrix} 4 & 0 \\ 0 & 20 \end{bmatrix}, \quad X^T Y = \begin{bmatrix} 7 \\ -13 \end{bmatrix}$$

$$A = (X^T X)^{-1}(X^T Y) = \begin{bmatrix} \frac{1}{4} & 0 \\ 0 & \frac{1}{20} \end{bmatrix} \begin{bmatrix} 7 \\ -13 \end{bmatrix} = \begin{bmatrix} \frac{7}{4} \\ -\frac{13}{20} \end{bmatrix}$$

Thus, the least squares regression line is $y = -0.65x + 1.75$.

42. Using matrices

$$X = \begin{bmatrix} 1 & 0 \\ 1 & 4 \\ 1 & 5 \\ 1 & 8 \\ 1 & 10 \end{bmatrix}, \quad Y = \begin{bmatrix} 6 \\ 3 \\ 0 \\ -4 \\ -5 \end{bmatrix}$$

we have

$$X^T X = \begin{bmatrix} 1 & 1 & 1 & 1 & 1 \\ 0 & 4 & 5 & 8 & 10 \end{bmatrix} \begin{bmatrix} 1 & 0 \\ 1 & 4 \\ 1 & 5 \\ 1 & 8 \\ 1 & 10 \end{bmatrix} = \begin{bmatrix} 5 & 27 \\ 27 & 205 \end{bmatrix}$$

$$X^T Y = \begin{bmatrix} 1 & 1 & 1 & 1 & 1 \\ 0 & 4 & 5 & 8 & 10 \end{bmatrix} \begin{bmatrix} 6 \\ 3 \\ 0 \\ -4 \\ -5 \end{bmatrix} = \begin{bmatrix} 0 \\ -70 \end{bmatrix}.$$

$$A = (X^T X)^{-1}(X^T Y) = \frac{1}{296} \begin{bmatrix} 205 & -27 \\ -27 & 5 \end{bmatrix} \begin{bmatrix} 0 \\ -70 \end{bmatrix} = \frac{1}{296} \begin{bmatrix} 1890 \\ -350 \end{bmatrix}.$$

Thus, the least squares regression line is $y = -\frac{175}{148}x + \frac{945}{148}$.

44. (a) Using the matrices

$$X = \begin{bmatrix} 1 & 25 \\ 1 & 30 \\ 1 & 35 \\ 1 & 40 \end{bmatrix}, \quad Y = \begin{bmatrix} 82 \\ 75 \\ 67 \\ 55 \end{bmatrix}$$

we have

$$X^TX = \begin{bmatrix} 4 & 130 \\ 130 & 4350 \end{bmatrix}, \quad X^TY = \begin{bmatrix} 279 \\ 8845 \end{bmatrix}$$

and

$$A = (X^TX)^{-1}X^TY = \begin{bmatrix} 127.6 \\ -1.78 \end{bmatrix}.$$

Thus, the least squares regression line is $y = -1.78x + 127.6$.

(b) When $x = 32.95$, $y = -1.78(32.95) + 127.6 = 68.95 \approx 69$.

46. (a) Using the matrices

$$X = \begin{bmatrix} 1 & 100 \\ 1 & 120 \\ 1 & 140 \end{bmatrix}, \quad Y = \begin{bmatrix} 75 \\ 68 \\ 55 \end{bmatrix}$$

we have

$$X^TX = \begin{bmatrix} 1 & 1 & 1 \\ 100 & 120 & 140 \end{bmatrix} \begin{bmatrix} 1 & 100 \\ 1 & 120 \\ 1 & 140 \end{bmatrix} = \begin{bmatrix} 3 & 360 \\ 360 & 44{,}000 \end{bmatrix}$$

$$X^TY = \begin{bmatrix} 198 \\ 23{,}360 \end{bmatrix}$$

$$A = (X^TX)^{-1}(X^TY) = \frac{1}{2400} \begin{bmatrix} 44{,}000 & -360 \\ -360 & 3 \end{bmatrix} \begin{bmatrix} 198 \\ 23{,}360 \end{bmatrix}$$

$$= \frac{1}{2400} \begin{bmatrix} 302{,}400 \\ -1200 \end{bmatrix} = \begin{bmatrix} 126 \\ -0.5 \end{bmatrix}.$$

Thus, the least squares regression line is $y = -0.5x + 126$.

(b)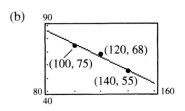

(c)

Number (x)	100	120	140
Percent (y)	75	68	55
Model percent (y)	76	66	56

(d) When $x = 170$, $y = -0.5(170) + 126 = 41\%$.

(e) When $y = 40\%$, we have $40 = -0.5x + 126$ and, therefore, $x = 172$.

Chapter 2 ❑ Review Exercises

2. $-2\begin{bmatrix} 1 & 2 \\ 5 & -4 \\ 6 & 0 \end{bmatrix} + 8\begin{bmatrix} 7 & 1 \\ 1 & 2 \\ 1 & 4 \end{bmatrix} = \begin{bmatrix} -2 & -4 \\ -10 & 8 \\ -12 & 0 \end{bmatrix} + \begin{bmatrix} 56 & 8 \\ 8 & 16 \\ 8 & 32 \end{bmatrix} = \begin{bmatrix} 54 & 4 \\ -2 & 24 \\ -4 & 32 \end{bmatrix}$

4. $\begin{bmatrix} 1 & 5 \\ 2 & -4 \end{bmatrix}\begin{bmatrix} 6 & -2 & 8 \\ 4 & 0 & 0 \end{bmatrix} = \begin{bmatrix} 1(6) + 5(4) & 1(-2) + 5(0) & 1(8) + 5(0) \\ 2(6) - 4(4) & 2(-2) - 4(0) & 2(8) - 4(0) \end{bmatrix}$

$\qquad\qquad = \begin{bmatrix} 26 & -2 & 8 \\ -4 & -4 & 16 \end{bmatrix}$

6. $\begin{bmatrix} 2 & 1 \\ 6 & 0 \end{bmatrix}\begin{bmatrix} 4 & 2 \\ -3 & 1 \end{bmatrix} + \begin{bmatrix} -2 & 4 \\ 0 & 4 \end{bmatrix} = \begin{bmatrix} 5 & 5 \\ 24 & 12 \end{bmatrix} + \begin{bmatrix} -2 & 4 \\ 0 & 4 \end{bmatrix} = \begin{bmatrix} 3 & 9 \\ 24 & 16 \end{bmatrix}$

8. Multiplying the left side of the equation yields

$$\begin{bmatrix} x_2 - 2x_3 \\ -x_1 + 3x_2 + x_3 \\ 2x_1 - 2x_2 + 4x_3 \end{bmatrix} = \begin{bmatrix} -1 \\ 0 \\ 2 \end{bmatrix}.$$

Thus, the corresponding system of linear equations is

$$\begin{aligned} x_2 - 2x_3 &= -1 \\ -x_1 + 3x_2 + x_3 &= 0 \\ 2x_1 - 2x_2 + 4x_3 &= 2 \end{aligned}$$

10. Letting

$$A = \begin{bmatrix} -3 & -1 & 1 \\ 2 & 4 & -5 \\ 1 & -2 & 3 \end{bmatrix}, \ X = \begin{bmatrix} x_1 \\ x_2 \\ x_3 \end{bmatrix} \text{ and } B = \begin{bmatrix} 0 \\ -3 \\ 1 \end{bmatrix}$$

the given system can be written in matrix form

$$AX = B.$$

12. $A^T = \begin{bmatrix} 1 & 3 & -1 \end{bmatrix}$

$A^T A = \begin{bmatrix} 1 & 3 & -1 \end{bmatrix}\begin{bmatrix} 1 \\ 3 \\ -1 \end{bmatrix} = \begin{bmatrix} 11 \end{bmatrix}$

$AA^T = \begin{bmatrix} 1 \\ 3 \\ -1 \end{bmatrix}\begin{bmatrix} 1 & 3 & -1 \end{bmatrix} = \begin{bmatrix} 1 & 3 & -1 \\ 3 & 9 & -3 \\ -1 & -3 & 1 \end{bmatrix}$

14. From the formula

$$A^{-1} = \frac{1}{ad - bc}\begin{bmatrix} d & -b \\ -c & a \end{bmatrix}$$

we see that $ad - bc = 4(2) - (-1)(-8) = 0$, and thus the matrix has no inverse.

16. We begin by adjoining the identity matrix to the given matrix.

$$[A \vdots I] = \begin{bmatrix} 1 & 1 & 1 & 1 & \vdots & 1 & 0 & 0 & 0 \\ 0 & 1 & 1 & 1 & \vdots & 0 & 1 & 0 & 0 \\ 0 & 0 & 1 & 1 & \vdots & 0 & 0 & 1 & 0 \\ 0 & 0 & 0 & 1 & \vdots & 0 & 0 & 0 & 1 \end{bmatrix}$$

This matrix reduces to

$$[I \vdots A^{-1}] = \begin{bmatrix} 1 & 0 & 0 & 0 & \vdots & 1 & -1 & 0 & 0 \\ 0 & 1 & 0 & 0 & \vdots & 0 & 1 & -1 & 0 \\ 0 & 0 & 1 & 0 & \vdots & 0 & 0 & 1 & -1 \\ 0 & 0 & 0 & 1 & \vdots & 0 & 0 & 0 & 1 \end{bmatrix}.$$

Thus, the inverse matrix is

$$A^{-1} = \begin{bmatrix} 1 & -1 & 0 & 0 \\ 0 & 1 & -1 & 0 \\ 0 & 0 & 1 & -1 \\ 0 & 0 & 0 & 1 \end{bmatrix}.$$

18.
$$\overset{A}{\begin{bmatrix} -1 & 1 & 2 \\ 2 & 3 & 1 \\ 5 & 4 & 2 \end{bmatrix}} \overset{\mathbf{x}}{\begin{bmatrix} x_1 \\ x_2 \\ x_3 \end{bmatrix}} = \overset{\mathbf{b}}{\begin{bmatrix} 1 \\ -2 \\ 4 \end{bmatrix}}$$

Using Gauss-Jordan elimination, we find that

$$A^{-1} = \begin{bmatrix} -\frac{2}{15} & -\frac{2}{5} & \frac{1}{3} \\ -\frac{1}{15} & \frac{4}{5} & -\frac{1}{3} \\ \frac{7}{15} & -\frac{3}{5} & \frac{1}{3} \end{bmatrix}.$$

Hence, we solve the equation $A\mathbf{x} = \mathbf{b}$ as follows.

$$\mathbf{x} = A^{-1}\mathbf{b} = \begin{bmatrix} -\frac{2}{15} & -\frac{2}{5} & \frac{1}{3} \\ -\frac{1}{15} & \frac{4}{5} & -\frac{1}{3} \\ \frac{7}{15} & -\frac{3}{5} & \frac{1}{3} \end{bmatrix}\begin{bmatrix} 1 \\ -2 \\ 4 \end{bmatrix} = \begin{bmatrix} 2 \\ -3 \\ 3 \end{bmatrix}$$

20. A is nonsingular if and only if the second row is not a multiple of the first. That is, A is nonsingular if and only if $x \neq -3$.

Alternatively, we could use the formula for the inverse of a 2×2 matrix to show that A is nonsingular if $ad - bc = 3(-1) - 1(x) \neq 0$. That is, $x \neq -3$.

22. Because the given matrix represents 6 times the second row, the inverse will be $\frac{1}{6}$ times the second row.

$$\begin{bmatrix} 1 & 0 & 0 \\ 0 & \frac{1}{6} & 0 \\ 0 & 0 & 1 \end{bmatrix}$$

24. We begin by finding a sequence of elementary row operations to write A in reduced row-echelon form.

Matrix	Elementary Row Operation	Elementary Matrix
$\begin{bmatrix} 1 & -4 \\ -3 & 13 \end{bmatrix}$	Interchange 2 rows.	$E_1 = \begin{bmatrix} 0 & 1 \\ 1 & 0 \end{bmatrix}$
$\begin{bmatrix} 1 & -4 \\ 0 & 1 \end{bmatrix}$	Add 3 times row 1 to row 2.	$E_2 = \begin{bmatrix} 1 & 0 \\ 3 & 1 \end{bmatrix}$
$\begin{bmatrix} 1 & 0 \\ 0 & 1 \end{bmatrix}$	Add 4 times row 2 to row 1.	$E_3 = \begin{bmatrix} 1 & 4 \\ 0 & 1 \end{bmatrix}$

Then, we can factor A as follows.

$$A = E_1^{-1}E_2^{-1}E_3^{-1} = \begin{bmatrix} 0 & 1 \\ 1 & 0 \end{bmatrix}\begin{bmatrix} 1 & 0 \\ -3 & 1 \end{bmatrix}\begin{bmatrix} 1 & -4 \\ 0 & 1 \end{bmatrix}$$

26. We begin by finding a sequence of elementary row operations to write A in reduced row-echelon form.

Matrix	Elementary Row Operation	Elementary Matrix
$\begin{bmatrix} 1 & 0 & 2 \\ 0 & 2 & 0 \\ 1 & 0 & 3 \end{bmatrix}$	$\frac{1}{3}$ times row one.	$E_1 = \begin{bmatrix} \frac{1}{3} & 0 & 0 \\ 0 & 1 & 0 \\ 0 & 0 & 1 \end{bmatrix}$
$\begin{bmatrix} 1 & 0 & 2 \\ 0 & 2 & 0 \\ 0 & 0 & 1 \end{bmatrix}$	Add -1 times row one to row three.	$E_2 = \begin{bmatrix} 1 & 0 & 0 \\ 0 & 1 & 0 \\ -1 & 0 & 1 \end{bmatrix}$
$\begin{bmatrix} 1 & 0 & 0 \\ 0 & 2 & 0 \\ 0 & 0 & 1 \end{bmatrix}$	Add -2 times row three to row one.	$E_3 = \begin{bmatrix} 1 & 0 & -2 \\ 0 & 1 & 0 \\ 0 & 0 & 1 \end{bmatrix}$
$\begin{bmatrix} 1 & 0 & 0 \\ 0 & 1 & 0 \\ 0 & 0 & 1 \end{bmatrix}$	$\frac{1}{2}$ times row two.	$E_4 = \begin{bmatrix} 1 & 0 & 0 \\ 0 & \frac{1}{2} & 0 \\ 0 & 0 & 1 \end{bmatrix}$

Thus, we can factor A as follows.

$$A = E_1^{-1}E_2^{-1}E_3^{-1}E_4^{-1} = \begin{bmatrix} 3 & 0 & 0 \\ 0 & 1 & 0 \\ 0 & 0 & 1 \end{bmatrix}\begin{bmatrix} 1 & 0 & 0 \\ 0 & 1 & 0 \\ 1 & 0 & 1 \end{bmatrix}\begin{bmatrix} 1 & 0 & 2 \\ 0 & 1 & 0 \\ 0 & 0 & 1 \end{bmatrix}\begin{bmatrix} 1 & 0 & 0 \\ 0 & 2 & 0 \\ 0 & 0 & 1 \end{bmatrix}$$

28. Letting $A = \begin{bmatrix} a & b \\ c & d \end{bmatrix}$, we have

$$A^2 = \begin{bmatrix} a & b \\ c & d \end{bmatrix}\begin{bmatrix} a & b \\ c & d \end{bmatrix} = \begin{bmatrix} a^2 + bc & ab + bd \\ ac + dc & cb + d^2 \end{bmatrix} = \begin{bmatrix} 0 & 0 \\ 0 & 0 \end{bmatrix}$$

Hence, many answers are possible.

$$\begin{bmatrix} 0 & 0 \\ 0 & 0 \end{bmatrix}, \begin{bmatrix} 0 & 1 \\ 0 & 0 \end{bmatrix}, \text{etc.}$$

30. There are many possible answers.

$$A = \begin{bmatrix} 0 & 1 \\ 0 & 0 \end{bmatrix}, \quad B = \begin{bmatrix} 1 & 0 \\ 0 & 0 \end{bmatrix} \implies AB = \begin{bmatrix} 0 & 1 \\ 0 & 0 \end{bmatrix}\begin{bmatrix} 1 & 0 \\ 0 & 0 \end{bmatrix} = \begin{bmatrix} 0 & 0 \\ 0 & 0 \end{bmatrix} = O$$

But, $BA = \begin{bmatrix} 1 & 0 \\ 0 & 0 \end{bmatrix}\begin{bmatrix} 0 & 1 \\ 0 & 0 \end{bmatrix} = \begin{bmatrix} 0 & 1 \\ 0 & 0 \end{bmatrix} \neq O$.

32. If $aX + bY + cZ = 0$, then we have

$$a\begin{bmatrix} 1 \\ 2 \\ 0 \\ 1 \end{bmatrix} + b\begin{bmatrix} -1 \\ 0 \\ 3 \\ 2 \end{bmatrix} + c\begin{bmatrix} 3 \\ 4 \\ -1 \\ 2 \end{bmatrix} = \begin{bmatrix} 0 \\ 0 \\ 0 \\ 0 \end{bmatrix},$$

which yields the system of equations

$$\begin{aligned} a - b + 3c &= 0 \\ 2a \quad\;\; + 4c &= 0 \\ 3b - c &= 0 \\ a + 2b + 2c &= 0. \end{aligned}$$

Solving this homogeneous system, the only solution is $a = b = c = 0$.

34. No, this is not true. For example, let

$$A = \begin{bmatrix} 2 & -3 \\ 2 & -5 \end{bmatrix}, \quad B = \begin{bmatrix} 1 & 0 \\ 0 & -4 \end{bmatrix} \quad \text{and} \quad C = \begin{bmatrix} 3 & 1 \\ 1 & 2 \end{bmatrix}.$$

Then, $AC = \begin{bmatrix} 3 & -4 \\ 1 & -8 \end{bmatrix} = CB$, but $A \neq B$.

36.   Matrix   Elementary Matrix

$$\begin{bmatrix} 1 & 1 & 1 \\ 1 & 2 & 2 \\ 1 & 2 & 3 \end{bmatrix} = A$$

$$\begin{bmatrix} 1 & 1 & 1 \\ 0 & 1 & 1 \\ 1 & 2 & 3 \end{bmatrix} \qquad \begin{bmatrix} 1 & 0 & 0 \\ -1 & 1 & 0 \\ 0 & 0 & 1 \end{bmatrix} = E_1$$

$$\begin{bmatrix} 1 & 1 & 1 \\ 0 & 1 & 1 \\ 0 & 1 & 2 \end{bmatrix} \qquad \begin{bmatrix} 1 & 0 & 0 \\ 0 & 1 & 0 \\ -1 & 0 & 1 \end{bmatrix} = E_2$$

$$\begin{bmatrix} 1 & 1 & 1 \\ 0 & 1 & 1 \\ 0 & 0 & 1 \end{bmatrix} = U \qquad \begin{bmatrix} 1 & 0 & 0 \\ 0 & 1 & 0 \\ 0 & -1 & 1 \end{bmatrix} = E_3$$

$$E_3 E_2 E_1 A = U \quad \Rightarrow \quad A = E_1^{-1} E_2^{-1} E_3^{-1} U = \begin{bmatrix} 1 & 0 & 0 \\ 1 & 1 & 0 \\ 1 & 1 & 1 \end{bmatrix} \begin{bmatrix} 1 & 1 & 1 \\ 0 & 1 & 1 \\ 0 & 0 & 1 \end{bmatrix} = LU$$

38.   Matrix   Elementary Matrix

$$\begin{bmatrix} 2 & 1 & 1 & -1 \\ 0 & 3 & 1 & -1 \\ 0 & 0 & -2 & 0 \\ 2 & 1 & 1 & -2 \end{bmatrix} = A$$

$$\begin{bmatrix} 2 & 1 & 1 & -1 \\ 0 & 3 & 1 & -1 \\ 0 & 0 & -2 & 0 \\ 0 & 0 & 0 & -1 \end{bmatrix} = U \qquad \begin{bmatrix} 1 & 0 & 0 & 0 \\ 0 & 1 & 0 & 0 \\ 0 & 0 & 1 & 0 \\ -1 & 0 & 0 & 0 \end{bmatrix} = E$$

$$EA = U \Rightarrow A = \begin{bmatrix} 1 & 0 & 0 & 0 \\ 0 & 1 & 0 & 0 \\ 0 & 0 & 1 & 0 \\ 1 & 0 & 0 & 1 \end{bmatrix} \begin{bmatrix} 2 & 1 & 1 & -1 \\ 0 & 3 & 1 & -1 \\ 0 & 0 & -2 & 0 \\ 0 & 0 & 0 & -1 \end{bmatrix} = LU$$

$$Ly = b: \begin{bmatrix} 1 & 0 & 0 & 0 \\ 0 & 1 & 0 & 0 \\ 0 & 0 & 1 & 0 \\ 1 & 0 & 0 & 1 \end{bmatrix} \begin{bmatrix} y_1 \\ y_2 \\ y_3 \\ y_4 \end{bmatrix} = \begin{bmatrix} 7 \\ -3 \\ 2 \\ 8 \end{bmatrix} \quad \Rightarrow \quad y = \begin{bmatrix} 7 \\ -3 \\ 2 \\ 1 \end{bmatrix}$$

$$Ux = y: \begin{bmatrix} 2 & 1 & 1 & -1 \\ 0 & 3 & 1 & -1 \\ 0 & 0 & -2 & 0 \\ 0 & 0 & 0 & -1 \end{bmatrix} \begin{bmatrix} x_1 \\ x_2 \\ x_3 \\ x_4 \end{bmatrix} = \begin{bmatrix} 7 \\ -3 \\ 2 \\ 1 \end{bmatrix} \quad \Rightarrow \quad x = \begin{bmatrix} 4 \\ -1 \\ -1 \\ -1 \end{bmatrix}$$

40. (a) *False.* The product of a 2 × 3 matrix and a 3 × 5 matrix is a 2 × 5 matrix.

(b) *True.* See Theorem 2.6(4) on page 67.

42. (a) *True.*

$$(ABA^{-1})^2 = (ABA^{-1})(ABA^{-1}) = AB(A^{-1}A)BA^{-1} = ABIBA^{-1} = AB^2A^{-1}.$$

(b) *False.* Let

$$A = \begin{bmatrix} 1 & 0 \\ 0 & 1 \end{bmatrix} \quad \text{and} \quad B = \begin{bmatrix} -1 & 0 \\ 0 & -1 \end{bmatrix}.$$

Then

$$A + B = \begin{bmatrix} 0 & 0 \\ 0 & 0 \end{bmatrix}.$$

$A + B$ is a *singular* matrix, while both A and B are *nonsingular* matrices.

44. This matrix *is* stochastic because $0 \le a_{ij} \le 1$ and each column adds up to 1.

46. $$PX = \begin{bmatrix} 0.6 & 0.2 & 0.0 \\ 0.2 & 0.7 & 0.1 \\ 0.2 & 0.1 & 0.9 \end{bmatrix} \begin{bmatrix} 1000 \\ 1000 \\ 1000 \end{bmatrix} = \begin{bmatrix} 800 \\ 1000 \\ 1200 \end{bmatrix}$$

$$P^2X = P\begin{bmatrix} 800 \\ 1000 \\ 1200 \end{bmatrix} = \begin{bmatrix} 680 \\ 980 \\ 1340 \end{bmatrix};$$

$$P^3X = P\begin{bmatrix} 680 \\ 980 \\ 1340 \end{bmatrix} = \begin{bmatrix} 604 \\ 956 \\ 1440 \end{bmatrix}.$$

48. If we continue the computation in Exercise 47, we find that the steady state is

$$X = \begin{bmatrix} 140,000 \\ 100,000 \\ 60,000 \end{bmatrix}$$

which can be verified by calculating

$$PX = X.$$

50. The uncoded row matrices are

B E A	M __ M	E __ U	P __ S	C O T	T Y __
[2 5 1]	[13 0 13]	[5 0 21]	[16 0 19]	[3 15 20]	[20 25 0]

Multiplying each 1 × 3 matrix on the right by A yields the coded row matrices.

$$[17 \ 6 \ 20] \ [0 \ 0 \ 13] \ [-32 \ -16 \ -43] \ [-6 \ -3 \ 7] \ [11 \ -2 \ -3] [115 \ 45 \ 155]$$

Thus, the coded message is

17, 6, 20, 0, 0, 13, −32, −16, −43, −6, −3, 7, 11, −2, −3, 115, 45, 155.

52. We find A^{-1} to be

$$A^{-1} = \begin{bmatrix} -3 & -4 \\ 1 & 1 \end{bmatrix}$$

and the coded row matrices are

$$[11 \quad 52], [-8 \quad -9], [-13 \quad -39], [5 \quad 20], [12 \quad 56], [5 \quad 20], [-2 \quad 7], [9 \quad 41], [25 \quad 100].$$

Multiplying each coded row matrix on the right by A^{-1} yields the uncoded row matrices:

$$\begin{array}{ccccccccccccccccc} \text{S} & \text{H} & \text{O} & \text{W} & \_\_ & \text{M} & \text{E} & \_\_ & \text{T} & \text{H} & \text{E} & \_\_ & \text{M} & \text{O} & \text{N} & \text{E} & \text{Y} & \_\_ \end{array}$$
$$[19 \quad 8], \quad [15 \quad 23], \quad [0 \quad 13], \quad [5 \quad 0], \quad [20 \quad 8], \quad [5 \quad 0], \quad [13 \quad 15], \quad [14 \quad 5], \quad [25 \quad 0]$$

Thus, the message is SHOW__ME__THE__MONEY__.

54. We find A^{-1} to be

$$A^{-1} = \begin{bmatrix} -40 & 16 & 9 \\ 13 & -5 & -3 \\ 5 & -2 & -1 \end{bmatrix}$$

and the coded row matrices are

$$[23 \quad 20 \quad 132], [54 \quad 128 \quad 102], [32 \quad 21 \quad 203], [6 \quad 10 \quad 23], [21 \quad 15 \quad 129], [36 \quad 46 \quad 173], [29 \quad 72 \quad 45].$$

Multiplying each coded row matrix on the right by A^{-1} yields the uncoded row matrices

$$\begin{array}{ccccccccccccccccccccc} \_\_ & \text{D} & \text{O} & \text{N} & \text{T} & \_\_ & \text{H} & \text{A} & \text{V} & \text{E} & \_\_ & \text{A} & \_\_ & \text{C} & \text{O} & \text{W} & \_\_ & \text{M} & \text{A} & \text{N} & \_\_ \end{array}$$
$$[0 \quad 4 \quad 15], \quad [14 \quad 20 \quad 0], \quad [8 \quad 1 \quad 22], \quad [5 \quad 0 \quad 1], \quad [0 \quad 3 \quad 15], \quad [23 \quad 0 \quad 15], \quad [1 \quad 14 \quad 0]$$

Thus, the message is __DONT__HAVE__A__COW__MAN__.

56. We solve the equation $X = DX + E$ for X to obtain$(I - D)X = E$, which corresponds to solving the augmented matrix.

$$\begin{bmatrix} 0.9 & -0.3 & -0.2 & \vdots & 3000 \\ 0 & 0.8 & -0.3 & \vdots & 3500 \\ -0.4 & -0.1 & 0.9 & \vdots & 8500 \end{bmatrix}$$

The solution to this system is

$$X = \begin{bmatrix} 10000 \\ 10000 \\ 15000 \end{bmatrix}.$$

58. Using the matrices

$$X = \begin{bmatrix} 1 & 2 \\ 1 & 3 \\ 1 & 4 \\ 1 & 5 \\ 1 & 6 \end{bmatrix} \quad \text{and} \quad Y = \begin{bmatrix} 1 \\ 3 \\ 2 \\ 4 \\ 4 \end{bmatrix}$$

we have

$$X^T X = \begin{bmatrix} 5 & 20 \\ 20 & 90 \end{bmatrix}, \quad X^T Y = \begin{bmatrix} 14 \\ 63 \end{bmatrix}$$

$$A = (X^T X)^{-1} X^T Y = \begin{bmatrix} 1.8 & -0.4 \\ -0.4 & 0.1 \end{bmatrix} \begin{bmatrix} 14 \\ 63 \end{bmatrix} = \begin{bmatrix} 0 \\ 0.7 \end{bmatrix}.$$

Thus, the least squares regression line is $y = 0.7x$.

60. Using the matrices

$$X = \begin{bmatrix} 1 & 1 \\ 1 & 1 \\ 1 & 1 \\ 1 & 1 \\ 1 & 2 \end{bmatrix} \quad \text{and} \quad Y = \begin{bmatrix} 1 \\ 3 \\ 2 \\ 4 \\ 5 \end{bmatrix}$$

we have

$$X^T X = \begin{bmatrix} 5 & 6 \\ 6 & 8 \end{bmatrix}, \quad X^T Y = \begin{bmatrix} 15 \\ 20 \end{bmatrix}$$

$$A = (X^T X)^{-1} X^T Y = \begin{bmatrix} 2 & -1.5 \\ -1.5 & 1.25 \end{bmatrix} \begin{bmatrix} 15 \\ 20 \end{bmatrix} = \begin{bmatrix} 0 \\ 2.5 \end{bmatrix}.$$

Thus, the least squares regression line is $y = 2.5x$.

62. (a) (Note: $x = 6$ represents 1996.) Using matrices

$$X = \begin{bmatrix} 1 & 6 \\ 1 & 7 \\ 1 & 8 \\ 1 & 9 \\ 1 & 10 \end{bmatrix} \quad \text{and} \quad Y = \begin{bmatrix} 156.9 \\ 160.5 \\ 163.0 \\ 166.6 \\ 172.2 \end{bmatrix}$$

we have

$$X^T X = \begin{bmatrix} 5 & 40 \\ 4 & 330 \end{bmatrix} \quad \text{and} \quad X^T Y = \begin{bmatrix} 819.2 \\ 6590.3 \end{bmatrix}.$$

So, $A = (X^T X)^{-1} (X^T Y) = \dfrac{1}{10} \begin{bmatrix} 66 & -8 \\ -8 & 1 \end{bmatrix} \begin{bmatrix} 819.2 \\ 6590.3 \end{bmatrix} = \begin{bmatrix} 134.48 \\ 3.67 \end{bmatrix}.$

Thus, the least squares regression line is $y = 3.67x + 134.48$.

(b) To estimate the CPI for 2005, we let $x = 15$ and then $y(15) = 3.67(15) + 134.48 = 189.53$.

To estimate the CPI for 2010, we let $x = 2$ and then $y(20) = 3.67(20) + 134.48 = 207.88$.

Chapter 2 ❑ Project Solutions

1 Exploring Matrix Multiplication

1. Test 1 seems to be the more difficult. The averages were:

    Test 1 average = 75
    Test 2 average = 85.5

2. Anna, David, Chris, Bruce

3. $M\begin{bmatrix} 1 \\ 0 \end{bmatrix}$ gives scores on first test. $M\begin{bmatrix} 0 \\ 1 \end{bmatrix}$ gives scores on second test.

4. $[1\ 0\ 0\ 0]M$ gives Anna's scores.

    $[0\ 0\ 1\ 0]M$ gives Chris's scores.

5. $M\begin{bmatrix} 1 \\ 1 \end{bmatrix}$ gives the sum of the test scores for each student, and $\frac{1}{2}M\begin{bmatrix} 1 \\ 1 \end{bmatrix}$ gives each students' average.

6. $[1\ 1\ 1\ 1]M$ gives the sum of scores on each test; $\frac{1}{4}[1\ 1\ 1\ 1]M$ gives the average on each test.

7. $[1\ 1\ 1\ 1]M\begin{bmatrix} 1 \\ 1 \end{bmatrix}$ gives the overall point total for all students on all tests.

8. $\frac{1}{8}[1\ 1\ 1\ 1]M\begin{bmatrix} 1 \\ 1 \end{bmatrix} = 80.25$

9. $M\begin{bmatrix} 1.1 \\ 1.0 \end{bmatrix}$

2 Nilpotent Matrices

1. $A^2 \neq 0$ and $A^3 = 0$, the index is 3.

2. (a) Nilpotent of index 2   (b) not nilpotent   (c) nilpotent of index 2

    (d) not nilpotent   (e) nilpotent of index 2   (f) nilpotent of index 3

3. $\begin{bmatrix} 0 & 0 & 1 \\ 0 & 0 & 0 \\ 0 & 0 & 0 \end{bmatrix}$ index 2; $\begin{bmatrix} 0 & 1 & 1 \\ 0 & 0 & 1 \\ 0 & 0 & 0 \end{bmatrix}$ index 3

4. $\begin{bmatrix} 0 & 0 & 0 & 1 \\ 0 & 0 & 0 & 0 \\ 0 & 0 & 0 & 0 \\ 0 & 0 & 0 & 0 \end{bmatrix}$ index 2; $\begin{bmatrix} 0 & 0 & 1 & 1 \\ 0 & 0 & 0 & 1 \\ 0 & 0 & 0 & 0 \\ 0 & 0 & 0 & 0 \end{bmatrix}$ index 3; $\begin{bmatrix} 0 & 1 & 1 & 1 \\ 0 & 0 & 1 & 1 \\ 0 & 0 & 0 & 1 \\ 0 & 0 & 0 & 0 \end{bmatrix}$ index 4

5. $\begin{bmatrix} 0 & 1 & 1 & 1 & 1 \\ 0 & 0 & 1 & 1 & 1 \\ 0 & 0 & 0 & 1 & 1 \\ 0 & 0 & 0 & 0 & 1 \\ 0 & 0 & 0 & 0 & 0 \end{bmatrix}$

6. No. If A is nilpotent and invertible, then $A^k = O$ for some k and $A^{k-1} \neq O$. Thus,

$$A^{-1}A = I \implies O = A^{-1}A^k = (A^{-1}A)A^{k-1} = IA^{k-1} \neq O$$

which is impossible.

7. If A is nilpotent, then $(A^k)^T = (A^T)^k = O$, But $(A^T)^{k-1} = (A^{k-1})^T \neq O$ which shows that A^T is nilpotent with the same index.

8. Let A be nilpotent of index k. Then,

$$(I - A)(A^{k-1} + A^{k-2} + \cdots + A^2 + A + I) = I - A^k = I$$

which shows that

$$(A^{k-1} + A^{k-2} + \cdots + A^2 + A + I)$$

is the inverse of $I - A$.

CHAPTER 3
Determinants

Section 3.1　　The Determinant of a Matrix

2. The determinant of a matrix of order 1 is the entry in the matrix. Thus,
$\det[-3] = -3$.

4. $\begin{vmatrix} -3 & 1 \\ 5 & 2 \end{vmatrix} = -3(2) - 5(1) = -11$

6. $\begin{vmatrix} 2 & -2 \\ 4 & 3 \end{vmatrix} = 2(3) - 4(-2) = 14$

8. $\begin{vmatrix} \frac{1}{3} & 5 \\ 4 & -9 \end{vmatrix} = \frac{1}{3} \cdot (-9) - 5 \cdot 4 = -23.$

10. $\begin{vmatrix} 2 & -3 \\ -6 & 9 \end{vmatrix} = 2(9) - (-6)(-3) = 0$

12. $\begin{vmatrix} \lambda - 2 & 0 \\ 4 & \lambda - 4 \end{vmatrix} = (\lambda - 2)(\lambda - 4) - 4(0) = \lambda^2 - 6\lambda + 8$

14. (a) The minors of the matrix are as follows.

$$M_{11} = \ |1| = \ \ 1$$
$$M_{12} = \ |2| = \ \ 2$$
$$M_{21} = \ |0| = \ \ 0$$
$$M_{22} = |-1| = -1$$

(b) The cofactors of the matrix are as follows.

$$C_{11} = (-1)^2 M_{11} = 1 \qquad C_{12} = (-1)^3 M_{12} = -2$$
$$C_{21} = (-1)^3 M_{21} = 0 \qquad C_{22} = (-1)^4 M_{22} = -1$$

16. (a) The minors of the matrix are as follows.

$$M_{11} = \begin{vmatrix} 3 & 1 \\ -7 & -8 \end{vmatrix} = -17$$

$$M_{12} = \begin{vmatrix} 6 & 1 \\ 4 & -8 \end{vmatrix} = -52$$

$$M_{13} = \begin{vmatrix} 6 & 3 \\ 4 & -7 \end{vmatrix} = -54$$

$$M_{21} = \begin{vmatrix} 4 & 2 \\ -7 & -8 \end{vmatrix} = -18$$

$$M_{22} = \begin{vmatrix} -3 & 2 \\ 4 & -8 \end{vmatrix} = 16$$

$$M_{23} = \begin{vmatrix} -3 & 4 \\ 4 & -7 \end{vmatrix} = 5$$

$$M_{31} = \begin{vmatrix} 4 & 2 \\ 3 & 1 \end{vmatrix} = -2$$

$$M_{32} = \begin{vmatrix} -3 & 2 \\ 6 & 1 \end{vmatrix} = -15$$

$$M_{33} = \begin{vmatrix} -3 & 4 \\ 6 & 3 \end{vmatrix} = -33$$

(b) The cofactors of the matrix are as follows.

$$C_{11} = (-1)^2 M_{11} = -17 \qquad C_{12} = (-1)^3 M_{12} = 52 \qquad C_{13} = (-1)^4 M_{13} = -54$$

$$C_{21} = (-1)^3 M_{21} = 18 \qquad C_{22} = (-1)^4 M_{22} = 16 \qquad C_{23} = (-1)^5 M_{23} = -5$$

$$C_{31} = (-1)^4 M_{31} = -2 \qquad C_{32} = (-1)^5 M_{32} = 15 \qquad C_{33} = (-1)^6 M_{33} = -33$$

18. (a) We found the cofactors of the matrix in Exercise 16. Now we find the determinant by expanding along the third row.

$$\begin{vmatrix} -3 & 4 & 2 \\ 6 & 3 & 1 \\ 4 & -7 & -8 \end{vmatrix} = 4C_{31} - 7C_{32} - 8C_{33}$$

$$= 4(-2) - 7(15) - 8(-33) = 151.$$

(b) Expanding along the first column we have

$$\begin{vmatrix} -3 & 4 & 2 \\ 6 & 3 & 1 \\ 4 & -7 & -8 \end{vmatrix} = -3C_{11} + 6C_{21} + 4C_{31}$$

$$= -3(-17) + 6(18) + 4(-2) = 151.$$

20. We choose to expand along the third row because it has a zero.

$$\begin{vmatrix} 2 & -1 & 3 \\ 1 & 4 & 4 \\ 1 & 0 & 2 \end{vmatrix} = 1\begin{vmatrix} -1 & 3 \\ 4 & 4 \end{vmatrix} - 0\begin{vmatrix} 2 & 3 \\ 1 & 4 \end{vmatrix} + 2\begin{vmatrix} 2 & -1 \\ 1 & 4 \end{vmatrix}$$

$$= 1(-16) + 2(9) = 2$$

22. We choose to expand along the first row because it has two zeros.

$$\begin{vmatrix} -3 & 0 & 0 \\ 7 & 11 & 0 \\ 1 & 2 & 2 \end{vmatrix} = -3 \begin{vmatrix} 11 & 0 \\ 2 & 2 \end{vmatrix} - 0 \begin{vmatrix} 7 & 0 \\ 1 & 2 \end{vmatrix} + 0 \begin{vmatrix} 7 & 11 \\ 1 & 2 \end{vmatrix}$$

$$= -3(22) = -66$$

24. We expand along the first row.

$$\begin{vmatrix} -0.4 & 0.4 & 0.3 \\ 0.2 & 0.2 & 0.2 \\ 0.3 & 0.2 & 0.2 \end{vmatrix} = -0.4 \begin{vmatrix} 0.2 & 0.2 \\ 0.2 & 0.2 \end{vmatrix} - 0.4 \begin{vmatrix} 0.2 & 0.2 \\ 0.3 & 0.2 \end{vmatrix} + 0.3 \begin{vmatrix} 0.2 & 0.2 \\ 0.3 & 0.2 \end{vmatrix}$$

$$= -0.4(0) - 0.4(-0.02) + 0.3(-0.02)$$

$$= 0.002$$

26. We expand along the first row.

$$\begin{vmatrix} x & y & 1 \\ -2 & -2 & 1 \\ 1 & 5 & 1 \end{vmatrix} = x \begin{vmatrix} -2 & 1 \\ 5 & 1 \end{vmatrix} - y \begin{vmatrix} -2 & 1 \\ 1 & 1 \end{vmatrix} + 1 \begin{vmatrix} -2 & -2 \\ 1 & 5 \end{vmatrix}$$

$$= x(-7) - y(-3) + (-8)$$

$$= -7x + 3y - 8$$

28. We choose to expand along the third row since it has all zeros. Hence, the determinant of the matrix is zero.

30. We choose to expand along the first row, since it has two zeroes.

$$\begin{vmatrix} 3 & 0 & 7 & 0 \\ 2 & 6 & 11 & 12 \\ 4 & 1 & -1 & 2 \\ 1 & 5 & 2 & 10 \end{vmatrix} = 3 \cdot \begin{vmatrix} 6 & 11 & 12 \\ 1 & -1 & 2 \\ 5 & 2 & 10 \end{vmatrix} + 7 \cdot \begin{vmatrix} 2 & 6 & 12 \\ 4 & 1 & 2 \\ 1 & 5 & 10 \end{vmatrix}$$

The determinants of the 3×3 matrices are

$$\begin{vmatrix} 6 & 11 & 12 \\ 1 & -1 & 2 \\ 5 & 2 & 10 \end{vmatrix} = 6 \cdot \begin{vmatrix} -1 & 2 \\ 2 & 10 \end{vmatrix} - 11 \cdot \begin{vmatrix} 1 & 2 \\ 5 & 10 \end{vmatrix} + 12 \cdot \begin{vmatrix} 1 & -1 \\ 5 & 2 \end{vmatrix}$$

$$= 6(-10 - 4) - 11(10 - 10) + 12(2 + 5) = -84 + 84 = 0$$

$$\begin{vmatrix} 2 & 6 & 12 \\ 4 & 1 & 2 \\ 1 & 5 & 10 \end{vmatrix} = 2 \cdot \begin{vmatrix} 1 & 2 \\ 5 & 10 \end{vmatrix} - 6 \cdot \begin{vmatrix} 4 & 2 \\ 1 & 10 \end{vmatrix} + 12 \cdot \begin{vmatrix} 4 & 1 \\ 1 & 5 \end{vmatrix}$$

$$= 2(10 - 10) - 6(40 - 2) + 12(20 - 1) = 0.$$

Thus, determinant of the original matrix is $3 \cdot 0 + 7 \cdot 0 = 0$.

32. We expand along the first row.

$$\begin{vmatrix} w & x & y & z \\ 10 & 15 & -25 & 30 \\ -30 & 20 & -15 & -10 \\ 30 & 35 & -25 & -40 \end{vmatrix}$$

$$= w\begin{vmatrix} 15 & -25 & 30 \\ 20 & -15 & -10 \\ 35 & -25 & -40 \end{vmatrix} - x\begin{vmatrix} 10 & -25 & 30 \\ -30 & -15 & -10 \\ 30 & -25 & -40 \end{vmatrix} + y\begin{vmatrix} 10 & 15 & 30 \\ -30 & 20 & -10 \\ 30 & 35 & -40 \end{vmatrix} - z\begin{vmatrix} 10 & 15 & -25 \\ -30 & 20 & -15 \\ 30 & 35 & -25 \end{vmatrix}$$

The determinants of the 3×3 matrices are:

$$\begin{vmatrix} 15 & -25 & 30 \\ 20 & -15 & -10 \\ 35 & -25 & -40 \end{vmatrix} = 15\begin{vmatrix} -15 & -10 \\ -25 & -40 \end{vmatrix} + 25\begin{vmatrix} 20 & -10 \\ 35 & -40 \end{vmatrix} + 30\begin{vmatrix} 20 & -15 \\ 35 & -25 \end{vmatrix}$$

$$= 15(600 - 250) + 25(-800 + 350) + 30(-500 + 525)$$

$$= 5250 - 11{,}250 + 750$$

$$= -5250$$

$$\begin{vmatrix} 10 & -25 & 30 \\ -30 & -15 & -10 \\ 30 & -25 & -40 \end{vmatrix} = 10\begin{vmatrix} -15 & -10 \\ -25 & -40 \end{vmatrix} + 25\begin{vmatrix} -30 & -10 \\ 30 & -40 \end{vmatrix} + 30\begin{vmatrix} -30 & -15 \\ 30 & -25 \end{vmatrix}$$

$$= 10(600 - 250) + 25(1200 + 300) + 30(750 + 450)$$

$$= 3500 + 37{,}500 + 36{,}000$$

$$= 77{,}000$$

$$\begin{vmatrix} 10 & 15 & 30 \\ -30 & 20 & -10 \\ 30 & 35 & -40 \end{vmatrix} = 10\begin{vmatrix} 20 & -10 \\ 35 & -40 \end{vmatrix} - 15\begin{vmatrix} -30 & -10 \\ 30 & -40 \end{vmatrix} + 30\begin{vmatrix} -30 & 20 \\ 30 & 35 \end{vmatrix}$$

$$= 10(-800 + 350) - 15(1200 + 300) + 30(-1050 - 600)$$

$$= -4500 - 22{,}500 - 49{,}500$$

$$= -76{,}500$$

$$\begin{vmatrix} 10 & 15 & -25 \\ -30 & 20 & -15 \\ 30 & 35 & -25 \end{vmatrix} = 10\begin{vmatrix} 20 & -15 \\ 35 & -25 \end{vmatrix} - 15\begin{vmatrix} -30 & -15 \\ 30 & -25 \end{vmatrix} - 25\begin{vmatrix} -30 & 20 \\ 30 & 35 \end{vmatrix}$$

$$= 10(-500 + 525) - 15(750 + 450) - 25(-1050 - 600)$$

$$= 250 - 18{,}000 + 41{,}250$$

$$= 23{,}500$$

So, the determinant is $-5250w - 77{,}000x - 76{,}500y - 23{,}500z$.

34. We choose to expand along the second row since it has all zeros. Hence, the determinant of the matrix is zero.

36. Using a graphing utility (TI-86), we find that

$$\begin{vmatrix} 0.25 & -1 & 0.6 \\ 0.5 & 0.8 & -0.2 \\ 0.75 & 0.9 & -0.4 \end{vmatrix} = -0.175.$$

38. Using a graphing utility (software package Maple), we find that

$$\begin{vmatrix} 1 & 2 & 4 & -1 \\ 6 & 2 & 3 & -2 \\ 4 & -1 & 4 & 3 \\ 5 & -2 & 2 & 4 \end{vmatrix} = -45.$$

40. Using a graphing utility (TI-86), we find that

$$\begin{vmatrix} 8 & 5 & 1 & -2 & 0 & 3 \\ -1 & 0 & 7 & 1 & 6 & -5 \\ 0 & 8 & 6 & 5 & -3 & 1 \\ 1 & 2 & 5 & -8 & 4 & 3 \\ 2 & 6 & -2 & 0 & 6 & 7 \\ 8 & -3 & 1 & 2 & -5 & 1 \end{vmatrix} = 420{,}246.$$

42. The determinant of a triangular matrix is the product of the elements on the main diagonal.

$$\begin{vmatrix} 5 & 0 & 0 \\ 0 & 6 & 0 \\ 0 & 0 & -3 \end{vmatrix} = 5(6)(-3) = -90$$

44. The determinant of a triangular matrix is the product of the elements on the main diagonal.

$$\begin{vmatrix} 4 & 0 & 0 & 0 \\ -1 & \frac{1}{2} & 0 & 0 \\ 3 & 5 & 3 & 0 \\ -8 & 7 & 0 & -2 \end{vmatrix} = 4\left(\tfrac{1}{2}\right)(3)(-2) = -12$$

46. The determinant of a triangular matrix is the product of the elements on the main diagonal.

$$\begin{vmatrix} 7 & 0 & 0 & 0 & 0 \\ -8 & \frac{1}{4} & 0 & 0 & 0 \\ 4 & 5 & 2 & 0 & 0 \\ 3 & -3 & 5 & -1 & 0 \\ 1 & 13 & 4 & 1 & -2 \end{vmatrix} = (7)\left(\tfrac{1}{4}\right)(2)(-1)(-2) = 7$$

48. (a) *False.* The determinant of a triangular matrix is equal to the *product* of the entries on the main diagonal. For example, if

$$A = \begin{bmatrix} 1 & 0 \\ 0 & 2 \end{bmatrix},$$

then $\det(A) = 2 \neq 3 = 1 + 2$.

(b) *True.* See Theorem 3.1 on page 115.

(c) *True.* This is because in a cofactor expansion each cofactor gets multiplied by the corresponding entry. If this entry is zero, the product would be zero independent of the value of the cofactor.

50. $\begin{vmatrix} \lambda - 2 & -2 \\ -6 & \lambda + 2 \end{vmatrix} = (\lambda - 2)(\lambda + 2) - 12 = \lambda^2 - 16 = 0$

So, $\lambda = \pm 4$.

52. $\begin{vmatrix} \lambda + 2 & -2 & 4 \\ 0 & \lambda & -2 \\ 0 & -1 & \lambda - 1 \end{vmatrix} = (\lambda + 2) \begin{vmatrix} \lambda & -2 \\ -1 & \lambda - 1 \end{vmatrix} = (\lambda + 2)[\lambda(\lambda - 1) - 2]$

$$= (\lambda + 2)(\lambda^2 - \lambda - 2)$$

$$= (\lambda + 2)(\lambda - 2)(\lambda + 1) = 0$$

So, $\lambda = \pm 2$, or -1.

54. The system of linear equations will have a unique solution if and only if the coefficient matrix is invertible. Using the formula for the inverse of a 2×2 matrix, we see that this is equivalent to $ad - bc \neq 0$. Thus,

$$ad - bc = \begin{vmatrix} a & b \\ c & d \end{vmatrix} \neq 0$$

is the required condition for the system to have a unique solution.

56. Expanding the left side of the equation along the first row yields:

$$\begin{vmatrix} 1 & 1 & 1 \\ a & b & c \\ a^3 & b^3 & c^3 \end{vmatrix} = 1 \begin{vmatrix} b & c \\ b^3 & c^3 \end{vmatrix} - 1 \begin{vmatrix} a & c \\ a^3 & c^3 \end{vmatrix} + 1 \begin{vmatrix} a & b \\ a^3 & b^3 \end{vmatrix}$$

$$= bc^3 - b^3c - ac^3 + a^3c + ab^3 - a^3b$$

$$= b(c^3 - a^3) + b^3(a - c) + ac(a^2 - c^2)$$

$$= (c - a)[bc^2 + abc + ba^2 - b^3 - a^2c - ac^2]$$

$$= (c - a)[c^2(b - a) + ac(b - a) + b(a - b)(a + b)]$$

$$= (c - a)(b - a)[c^2 + ac - ab - b^2]$$

$$= (c - a)(b - a)[(c - b)(c + b) + a(c - b)]$$

$$= (c - a)(b - a)(c - b)(c + b + a)$$

$$= (a - b)(b - c)(c - a)(a + b + c).$$

58. Using Exercise 57 as a model, we observe that the right column contains the coefficients a, b, c. Hence,

$$\begin{vmatrix} x & 0 & 0 & d \\ -1 & x & 0 & c \\ 0 & -1 & x & b \\ 0 & 0 & -1 & a \end{vmatrix} = x \begin{vmatrix} x & 0 & c \\ -1 & x & b \\ 0 & -1 & a \end{vmatrix} + 1 \begin{vmatrix} 0 & 0 & d \\ -1 & x & b \\ 0 & -1 & a \end{vmatrix}$$

$$= x(ax^2 + bx + c) + d$$

$$= ax^3 + bx^2 + cx + d.$$

Section 3.2 Evaluation of a Determinant Using Elementary Operations

2. Because the second row is a multiple of the first row, the determinant is zero.

4. Because the first and third rows are the same, the determinant is zero.

6. Because the first and third rows are interchanged, the sign of the determinant is changed.

8. Because 4 has been factored out of the second column, and 3 factored out of the third column, the first determinant is 12 times the second one.

10. Because 6 has been factored out of each row, the first determinant is 6^4 times the second one.

12. Because a multiple of the first row of the matrix on the left was added to the second row to produce the matrix on the right, the determinants are equal.

14. Because the second row of the matrix on the left was multiplied by (-1), the sign of the determinant is changed.

16. Because the sixth column is a multiple of the second column, the determinant is zero.

18.
$$\begin{vmatrix} 1 & 1 & 1 \\ 2 & -1 & -2 \\ 1 & -2 & -1 \end{vmatrix} = \begin{vmatrix} 1 & 1 & 1 \\ 0 & -3 & -4 \\ 0 & -3 & -2 \end{vmatrix}$$

$$= \begin{vmatrix} 1 & 1 & 1 \\ 0 & -3 & -4 \\ 0 & 0 & 2 \end{vmatrix} = 1(-3)(2) = -6$$

20.
$$\begin{vmatrix} 3 & -1 & -3 \\ -1 & -4 & -2 \\ 3 & -1 & -1 \end{vmatrix} = - \begin{vmatrix} -1 & -4 & -2 \\ 3 & -1 & -3 \\ 3 & -1 & -1 \end{vmatrix}$$

$$= - \begin{vmatrix} -1 & -4 & -2 \\ 0 & -13 & -9 \\ 0 & -13 & -7 \end{vmatrix}$$

$$= - \begin{vmatrix} -1 & -4 & -2 \\ 0 & -13 & -9 \\ 0 & 0 & 2 \end{vmatrix} = (-1)(26) = -26$$

22. $\begin{vmatrix} 3 & 8 & -7 \\ 0 & -5 & 4 \\ 6 & 1 & 6 \end{vmatrix} = \begin{vmatrix} 3 & 8 & -7 \\ 0 & -5 & 4 \\ 0 & -15 & 20 \end{vmatrix}$

$\qquad = \begin{vmatrix} 3 & 8 & -7 \\ 0 & -5 & 4 \\ 0 & 0 & 8 \end{vmatrix} = 3(-5)(8) = -120$

24. $\begin{vmatrix} 4 & -8 & 5 \\ 8 & -5 & 3 \\ 8 & 5 & 2 \end{vmatrix} = \begin{vmatrix} 4 & -8 & 5 \\ 0 & 11 & -7 \\ 0 & 21 & -8 \end{vmatrix} = 4(-88 + 147) = 236$

26. $\begin{vmatrix} 9 & -4 & 2 & 5 \\ 2 & 7 & 6 & -5 \\ 4 & 1 & -2 & 0 \\ 7 & 3 & 4 & 10 \end{vmatrix} = \begin{vmatrix} 9 & -4 & 2 & 5 \\ 11 & 3 & 8 & 0 \\ 4 & 1 & -2 & 0 \\ -11 & 11 & 0 & 0 \end{vmatrix}$

$\qquad = \begin{vmatrix} 9 & -4 & 2 & 5 \\ 27 & 7 & 0 & 0 \\ 4 & 1 & -2 & 0 \\ -11 & 11 & 0 & 0 \end{vmatrix}$

$\qquad = (-5) \begin{vmatrix} 27 & 7 & 0 \\ 4 & 1 & -2 \\ -11 & 11 & 0 \end{vmatrix}$

$\qquad = (-5)(2) \begin{vmatrix} 27 & 7 \\ -11 & 11 \end{vmatrix}$

$\qquad = (-10)(11) \begin{vmatrix} 27 & 7 \\ -1 & 1 \end{vmatrix} = (-110)(27 + 7) = -3740$

28. $\begin{vmatrix} 0 & -3 & 8 & 2 \\ 8 & 1 & -1 & 6 \\ -4 & 6 & 0 & 9 \\ -7 & 0 & 0 & 14 \end{vmatrix} = \begin{vmatrix} 0 & -3 & 8 & 2 \\ 8 & 1 & -1 & 22 \\ -4 & 6 & 0 & 1 \\ -7 & 0 & 0 & 0 \end{vmatrix}$

$\qquad = 7 \begin{vmatrix} -3 & 8 & 2 \\ 1 & -1 & 22 \\ 6 & 0 & 1 \end{vmatrix}$

$\qquad = 7 \begin{vmatrix} -15 & 8 & 2 \\ -131 & -1 & 22 \\ 0 & 0 & 1 \end{vmatrix} = 7(15 + 1048) = 7441$

30.
$$\begin{vmatrix} 3 & -2 & 4 & 3 & 1 \\ -1 & 0 & 2 & 1 & 0 \\ 5 & -1 & 0 & 3 & 2 \\ 4 & 7 & -8 & 0 & 0 \\ 1 & 2 & 3 & 0 & 2 \end{vmatrix} = \begin{vmatrix} 3 & -2 & 4 & 3 & 1 \\ -1 & 0 & 2 & 1 & 0 \\ -1 & 3 & -8 & -3 & 0 \\ 4 & 7 & -8 & 0 & 0 \\ -5 & 6 & -5 & -6 & 0 \end{vmatrix}$$

$$= \begin{vmatrix} -1 & 0 & 2 & 1 \\ -1 & 3 & -8 & -3 \\ 4 & 7 & -8 & 0 \\ -5 & 6 & -5 & -6 \end{vmatrix}$$

$$= \begin{vmatrix} -1 & 0 & 2 & 1 \\ -4 & 3 & -2 & 0 \\ 4 & 7 & -8 & 0 \\ -11 & 6 & 7 & 0 \end{vmatrix}$$

$$= -\begin{vmatrix} -4 & 3 & -2 \\ 4 & 7 & -8 \\ -11 & 6 & 7 \end{vmatrix}$$

$$= -\begin{vmatrix} 0 & 10 & -10 \\ 4 & 7 & -8 \\ -11 & 6 & 7 \end{vmatrix}$$

$$= -10\begin{vmatrix} 0 & 1 & -1 \\ 4 & 7 & -8 \\ -11 & 6 & 7 \end{vmatrix} = -10[(-1)(28 - 88) - 1(24 + 77)] = 410$$

32. (a) *False.* Adding a multiple of one row to another does not change the value of the determinant.

(b) *True.* See page 132.

(c) *True.* In this case we can transform a matrix into a matrix with a row of zeros, which has zero deteriminant as can be seen by expanding by cofactors along that row. We achieve this transformation by adding a multiple of one row to another (which does not change the determinant of a matrix).

34.
$$\begin{vmatrix} 1 & 0 & 0 \\ 0 & 1 & 0 \\ 0 & 0 & k \end{vmatrix} = k\begin{vmatrix} 1 & 0 & 0 \\ 0 & 1 & 0 \\ 0 & 0 & 1 \end{vmatrix} = k$$

36.
$$\begin{vmatrix} 0 & 0 & 1 \\ 0 & 1 & 0 \\ 1 & 0 & 0 \end{vmatrix} = -\begin{vmatrix} 1 & 0 & 0 \\ 0 & 1 & 0 \\ 0 & 0 & 1 \end{vmatrix} = -1$$

38.
$$\begin{vmatrix} 1 & 0 & 0 \\ 0 & 1 & 0 \\ 0 & k & 1 \end{vmatrix} = \begin{vmatrix} 1 & 0 & 0 \\ 0 & 1 & 0 \\ 0 & 0 & 1 \end{vmatrix} = 1$$

40. $\begin{vmatrix} 1+a & 1 & 1 \\ 1 & 1+b & 1 \\ 1 & 1 & 1+c \end{vmatrix} = \begin{vmatrix} 0 & -a & -a-c-ac \\ 0 & b & -c \\ 1 & 1 & 1+c \end{vmatrix} = ac - b(-a-c-ac)$

$$= ac + ab + bc + abc = \frac{abc(ac + ab + bc + abc)}{abc}$$

$$= abc\left(1 + \frac{1}{b} + \frac{1}{c} + \frac{1}{a}\right)$$

42. $\begin{vmatrix} \sec\theta & \tan\theta \\ \tan\theta & \sec\theta \end{vmatrix} = \sec^2\theta - \tan^2\theta = 1$

44. Suppose B is obtained from A by adding a multiple of a row of A to another row of A. More specifically, suppose c times the jth row of A is added to the ith row of A.

$$B = \begin{bmatrix} a_{11} & \cdots & a_{1n} \\ \vdots & & \\ (a_{i1} + ca_{j1}) & \cdots & (a_{in} + ca_{jn}) \\ \vdots & & \\ a_{n1} & \cdots & a_{nn} \end{bmatrix}$$

Expand along this row.

$$\det B = (a_{i1} + ca_{j1})C_{i1} + \cdots + (a_{in} + ca_{jn})C_{in}$$
$$= [a_{i1}C_{i1} + \cdots + a_{in}C_{in}] + [ca_{j1}C_{i1} + \cdots + ca_{jn}C_{in}]$$

The first bracketed expression is $\det A$, so prove that the second bracketed expression is zero. Use mathematical induction. For $n = 2$ (assuming $i = 2$ and $j = 1$),

$$ca_{11}C_{21} + ca_{12}C_{22} = \det\begin{bmatrix} a_{11} & a_{12} \\ ca_{11} & ca_{12} \end{bmatrix} = 0 \text{ (because row 2 is a multiple of row 1).}$$

Assuming the expression is true for $n - 1$,

$$ca_{j1}C_{i1} + \cdots + ca_{jn}C_{in} = 0$$

by expanding along any row different from c and j and applying the induction hypothesis.

46. Use the information given in Table 3.1 on page 134. Cofactor expansion would cost:

$$(3,628,799)(0.001) + (6,235,300)(0.003) = \$22,334.70.$$

Row reduction would cost much less.

$$(288)(0.001) + 339(0.003) = \$1.30$$

Section 3.3   Properties of Determinants

2. (a) $|A| = \begin{vmatrix} 1 & 2 \\ 2 & 4 \end{vmatrix} = 0$

(b) $|B| = \begin{vmatrix} -1 & 2 \\ 3 & 0 \end{vmatrix} = -6$

(c) $AB = \begin{bmatrix} 1 & 2 \\ 2 & 4 \end{bmatrix} \begin{bmatrix} -1 & 2 \\ 3 & 0 \end{bmatrix} = \begin{bmatrix} 5 & 2 \\ 10 & 4 \end{bmatrix}$

(d) $|AB| = \begin{vmatrix} 5 & 2 \\ 10 & 4 \end{vmatrix} = 0$

Note that $|A||B| = 0(-6) = 0 = |AB|$.

4. (a) $|A| = \begin{vmatrix} 2 & 0 & 1 \\ 1 & -1 & 2 \\ 3 & 1 & 0 \end{vmatrix} = 0$

(b) $|B| = \begin{vmatrix} 2 & -1 & 4 \\ 0 & 1 & 3 \\ 3 & -2 & 1 \end{vmatrix} = -7$

(c) $AB = \begin{bmatrix} 2 & 0 & 1 \\ 1 & -1 & 2 \\ 3 & 1 & 0 \end{bmatrix} \begin{bmatrix} 2 & -1 & 4 \\ 0 & 1 & 3 \\ 3 & -2 & 1 \end{bmatrix} = \begin{bmatrix} 7 & -4 & 9 \\ 8 & -6 & 3 \\ 6 & -2 & 15 \end{bmatrix}$

(d) $|AB| = \begin{vmatrix} 7 & -4 & 9 \\ 8 & -6 & 3 \\ 6 & -2 & 15 \end{vmatrix} = 0$

Note that $|A||B| = 0(-7) = 0 = |AB|$.

6. $|A| = \begin{vmatrix} 5 & 15 \\ 10 & -20 \end{vmatrix} = 5^2 \begin{vmatrix} 1 & 3 \\ 2 & -4 \end{vmatrix} = 5^2(-10) = -250$

8. $|A| = \begin{vmatrix} 4 & 16 & 0 \\ 12 & -8 & 8 \\ 16 & 20 & -4 \end{vmatrix} = 4^3 \begin{vmatrix} 1 & 4 & 0 \\ 3 & -2 & 2 \\ 4 & 5 & -1 \end{vmatrix}$

$= 4^3 \begin{vmatrix} 1 & 4 & 0 \\ 11 & 8 & 0 \\ 4 & 5 & -1 \end{vmatrix} = (-64)(-36) = 2304$

10. (a) $|A| = \begin{vmatrix} 1 & -2 \\ 1 & 0 \end{vmatrix} = 2$

(b) $|B| = \begin{vmatrix} 3 & -2 \\ 0 & 0 \end{vmatrix} = 0$

(c) $|A + B| = \left| \begin{bmatrix} 1 & -2 \\ 1 & 0 \end{bmatrix} + \begin{bmatrix} 3 & -2 \\ 0 & 0 \end{bmatrix} \right| = \begin{vmatrix} 4 & -4 \\ 1 & 0 \end{vmatrix} = 4$

Note that $|A| + |B| = 2 + 0 = 2 \neq |A + B|$

12. First we observe that $|A| = \begin{vmatrix} -4 & 10 \\ 5 & 6 \end{vmatrix} = -74.$

(a) $|A^T| = |A| = -74$

(b) $|A^2| = |A|\,|A| = (-74)^2 = 5476$

(c) $|AA^T| = |A|\,|A^T| = (-74)(-74) = 5476$

(d) $|2A| = 2^2|A| = 4(-74) = -296$

(e) $|A^{-1}| = \dfrac{1}{|A|} = \dfrac{1}{(-74)} = -\dfrac{1}{74}.$

14. First we observe that $|A| = \begin{vmatrix} 1 & 5 & 4 \\ 0 & -6 & 2 \\ 0 & 0 & -3 \end{vmatrix} = 18.$

(a) $|A^T| = |A| = 18$

(b) $|A^2| = |A|\,|A| = 18^2 = 324$

(c) $|AA^T| = |A|\,|A^T| = (18)(18) = 324$

(d) $|2A| = 2^3|A| = 8(18) = 144$

(e) $|A^{-1}| = \dfrac{1}{|A|} = \dfrac{1}{18}.$

16. (a) $\begin{vmatrix} -2 & 4 \\ 6 & 8 \end{vmatrix} = -16 - 24 = -40$

(b) $|A^T| = |A| = -40$

(c) $|A^2| = |A|\,|A| = |A|^2 = 1600$

(d) $|2A| = 2^2|A| = -160$

(e) $|A^{-1}| = \dfrac{1}{|A|} = -\dfrac{1}{40}$

18. (a) $|A| = \begin{vmatrix} 6 & 5 & 1 & -1 \\ -2 & 4 & 3 & 5 \\ 6 & 1 & -4 & -2 \\ 2 & 2 & 1 & 3 \end{vmatrix} = -312$

(b) $|A^T| = |A| = -312$

(c) $|A^2| = |A|\,|A| = |A|^2 = 97,344$

(d) $|2A| = 2^4|A| = -4992$

(e) $|A^{-1}| = \dfrac{1}{|A|} = -\dfrac{1}{312}$

20. (a) $|AB| = |A|\,|B| = 10(12) = 120$

(b) $|A^4| = |A|^4 = (10)^4 = 1000$

(c) $|2B| = 2^3|B| = 2^3(12) = 96$

(d) $|(AB)^T| = |AB| = 120$

(e) $|A^{-1}| = \dfrac{1}{|A|} = \dfrac{1}{10}$

22. (a) $|BA| = |B|\,|A| = 5(-2) = -10$

(b) $|B^4| = |B|^4 = 5^4 = 625$

(c) $|2A| = 2^3|A| = 2^3(-2) = -16$

(d) $|(AB)^T| = |AB| = |A|\,|B| = -10$

(e) $|B^{-1}| = |B|^{-1} = \dfrac{1}{5}$

24. Because

$$\begin{vmatrix} 3 & -6 \\ 4 & 2 \end{vmatrix} = 30 \neq 0,$$

the matrix is nonsingular.

26. Because

$$\begin{vmatrix} 1 & 0 & 4 \\ 0 & 6 & 3 \\ 2 & -1 & 4 \end{vmatrix} = -21 \neq 0,$$

the matrix is nonsingular.

28. Because

$$\begin{vmatrix} 2 & -\frac{1}{2} & 8 \\ 1 & -\frac{1}{4} & 4 \\ -\frac{5}{2} & \frac{3}{2} & 8 \end{vmatrix} = 0,$$

the matrix is singular.

30. Because

$$\begin{vmatrix} 0.8 & 0.2 & -0.6 & 0.1 \\ -1.2 & 0.6 & 0.6 & 0 \\ 0.7 & -0.3 & 0.1 & 0 \\ 0.2 & -0.3 & 0.6 & 0 \end{vmatrix} = 0.015 \neq 0,$$

the matrix is nonsingular.

32. The coefficient matrix of the system is

$$\begin{bmatrix} 1 & 1 & -1 \\ 2 & -1 & 1 \\ 3 & -2 & 2 \end{bmatrix}.$$

Because the determinant of this matrix is zero, the system does not have a unique solution.

34. The coefficient matrix of the system is

$$\begin{bmatrix} 1 & -1 & -1 & -1 \\ 1 & 1 & -1 & -1 \\ 1 & 1 & 1 & -1 \\ 1 & 1 & 1 & 1 \end{bmatrix}.$$

Because the determinant of this matrix is 8, and hence nonzero, the system has a unique solution.

36. We find the values of k that make A singular by setting $|A| = 0$.

$$|A| = \begin{vmatrix} k-1 & 2 \\ 2 & k+2 \end{vmatrix} = (k-1)(k+2) - 4 = k^2 + k - 6 = (k+3)(k-2) = 0$$

which implies that $k = -3$ or $k = 2$.

38. We find the values of k that make A singular by setting $|A| = 0$. Using the second column in the cofactor expansion, we have

$$\begin{aligned} |A| = \begin{vmatrix} 1 & k & 2 \\ -2 & 0 & -k \\ 3 & 1 & -4 \end{vmatrix} &= -k\begin{vmatrix} -2 & -k \\ 3 & -4 \end{vmatrix} - 1\begin{vmatrix} 1 & 2 \\ -2 & -k \end{vmatrix} \\ &= -k(8 + 3k) - (-k + 4) \\ &= -3k^2 - 7k - 4 \\ &= -(3k + 4)(k + 1). \end{aligned}$$

So, $|A| = 0$ implies that $k = -\frac{4}{3}$ or $k = -1$.

40. Given that AB is singular, then $|AB| = |A||B| = 0$. Hence, either $|A|$ or $|B|$ must be zero, which implies that either A or B is singular.

42. We expand the determinant on the left

$$\begin{vmatrix} a+b & a & a \\ a & a+b & a \\ a & a & a+b \end{vmatrix} = (a+b)((a+b)^2 - a^2) - a((a+b)a - a^2) + a(a^2 - a(a+b))$$

$$= (a+b)(2ab + b^2) - a(ab) + a(-ab)$$

$$= 2a^2b + ab^2 + 2ab^2 + b^3 - 2a^2b$$

$$= b^2(3a + b).$$

44. Since the rows of A all add up to zero, we have

$$|A| = \begin{vmatrix} 2 & -1 & -1 \\ -3 & 1 & 2 \\ 0 & -2 & 2 \end{vmatrix} = \begin{vmatrix} 2 & -1 & 0 \\ -3 & 1 & 0 \\ 0 & -2 & 0 \end{vmatrix} = 0.$$

46. Calculating the determinant of A by expanding along the first row is equivalent to calculating the determinant of A^T by expanding along the first column. Since the determinant of a matrix can be found by expanding along any row or column, we see that $|A| = |A^T|$.

48. $|A^{10}| = |A|^{10} = 0 \Rightarrow |A| = 0 \Rightarrow A$ is singular.

50. (a) *False.* Let

$$A = \begin{bmatrix} 1 & 0 \\ 0 & 1 \end{bmatrix} \quad \text{and} \quad B = \begin{bmatrix} -1 & 0 \\ 0 & -1 \end{bmatrix}.$$

Then $\det(A) = \det(B) = 1 \neq 0 = \det(A + B)$

(b) *True.* See Theorem 3.9 and exercise 46 of this section for the proof.

(c) *True.* See page 144 for equivalent conditions for nonsingular matrices and Theorem 3.7 on page 142.

52. If the order of A is odd, then $(-1)^n = -1$, and the result of exercise 51 implies that $|A| = -|A|$ or $|A| = 0$.

54. Since

$$A^{-1} = \begin{bmatrix} \frac{1}{2} & -\frac{1}{2} \\ -\frac{1}{2} & -\frac{1}{2} \end{bmatrix} \text{ and } A^T = \begin{bmatrix} 1 & -1 \\ -1 & -1 \end{bmatrix}, A^T \neq A^{-1} \text{ and this matrix is } not \text{ orthogonal.}$$

56. Since

$$A^{-1} = \begin{bmatrix} \frac{1}{\sqrt{2}} & -\frac{1}{\sqrt{2}} \\ -\frac{1}{\sqrt{2}} & -\frac{1}{\sqrt{2}} \end{bmatrix} = A^T,$$

this matrix *is* orthogonal.

58. Since

$$A^{-1} = \begin{bmatrix} \frac{1}{\sqrt{2}} & 0 & -\frac{1}{\sqrt{2}} \\ 0 & 1 & 0 \\ -\frac{1}{\sqrt{2}} & 0 & \frac{1}{\sqrt{2}} \end{bmatrix} = A^T,$$

this matrix *is* orthogonal.

60. $A = \begin{bmatrix} \frac{3}{5} & 0 & -\frac{4}{5} \\ 0 & 1 & 0 \\ \frac{4}{5} & 0 & \frac{3}{5} \end{bmatrix}$

Using a graphing calculator (TI-86), we have

(a), (b) $A^{-1} = \begin{bmatrix} \frac{3}{5} & 0 & \frac{4}{5} \\ 0 & 1 & 0 \\ -\frac{4}{5} & 0 & \frac{3}{5} \end{bmatrix} = A^T.$

(c) As shown in exercise 59, if A is an orthogonal matrix, then $|A| = \pm 1$. For this given A, we have $|A| = 1$.

Since $A^{-1} = A^T$, A is an orthogonal matrix.

62. Let A be an idempotent matrix, and let $x = \det(A)$. Then $A^2 = A$ so $\det(A^2) = \det(A)$. We also have that $\det(A^2) = \det(A \cdot A) = \det(A) \cdot \det(A) = \det(A)^2$. Thus, $x = \det(A)$ is a real number such that $x^2 = x$. Solving the last equation for x we obtain $x = 0$ or $x = 1$.

64. $\det \begin{bmatrix} A_{11} & A_{12} \\ 0 & A_{22} \end{bmatrix} = (\det A_{11})(\det A_{22})$

Section 3.4   Introduction to Eigenvalues

2. $A\mathbf{x}_1 = \begin{bmatrix} 4 & 3 \\ 1 & 2 \end{bmatrix}\begin{bmatrix} 3 \\ 1 \end{bmatrix} = \begin{bmatrix} 15 \\ 5 \end{bmatrix} = 5\begin{bmatrix} 3 \\ 1 \end{bmatrix}$

$A\mathbf{x}_2 = \begin{bmatrix} 4 & 3 \\ 1 & 2 \end{bmatrix}\begin{bmatrix} -1 \\ 1 \end{bmatrix} = \begin{bmatrix} -1 \\ 1 \end{bmatrix}$

4. $A\mathbf{x}_1 = \begin{bmatrix} 1 & -2 & 1 \\ 0 & 1 & 4 \\ 0 & 0 & 2 \end{bmatrix}\begin{bmatrix} 1 \\ 0 \\ 0 \end{bmatrix} = \begin{bmatrix} 1 \\ 0 \\ 0 \end{bmatrix}$

$A\mathbf{x}_2 = \begin{bmatrix} 1 & -2 & 1 \\ 0 & 1 & 4 \\ 0 & 0 & 2 \end{bmatrix}\begin{bmatrix} -7 \\ 4 \\ 1 \end{bmatrix} = \begin{bmatrix} -14 \\ 8 \\ 2 \end{bmatrix} = 2\begin{bmatrix} -7 \\ 4 \\ 1 \end{bmatrix}$

6. $|\lambda I - A| = \begin{vmatrix} \lambda - 2 & -2 \\ -2 & \lambda - 2 \end{vmatrix} = \lambda^2 - 4\lambda = \lambda(\lambda - 4)$

$\lambda = 0: \begin{bmatrix} -2 & -2 \\ -2 & -2 \end{bmatrix} \to \begin{bmatrix} 1 & 1 \\ 0 & 0 \end{bmatrix} \Rightarrow \mathbf{x} = \begin{bmatrix} 1 \\ -1 \end{bmatrix}$

$\lambda = 4: \begin{bmatrix} 2 & -2 \\ -2 & 2 \end{bmatrix} \to \begin{bmatrix} 1 & -1 \\ 0 & 0 \end{bmatrix} \Rightarrow \mathbf{x} = \begin{bmatrix} 1 \\ 1 \end{bmatrix}.$

8. $\begin{vmatrix} \lambda - 2 & -5 \\ -4 & \lambda - 3 \end{vmatrix} = \lambda^2 - 5\lambda - 14 = (\lambda - 7)(\lambda + 2) = 0$

$\lambda = 7: \qquad \begin{bmatrix} 5 & -5 \\ -4 & 4 \end{bmatrix} \Rightarrow \begin{bmatrix} 1 & -1 \\ 0 & 0 \end{bmatrix} \Rightarrow \mathbf{x} = \begin{bmatrix} 1 \\ 1 \end{bmatrix}.$

$\lambda = -2: \qquad \begin{bmatrix} -4 & -5 \\ -4 & -5 \end{bmatrix} \Rightarrow \begin{bmatrix} -4 & -5 \\ 0 & 0 \end{bmatrix} \Rightarrow \mathbf{x} = \begin{bmatrix} 5 \\ -4 \end{bmatrix}.$

10. Let

$$A = \begin{bmatrix} 3 & -1 \\ 5 & -3 \end{bmatrix}.$$

To find eigenvalues for A we need to solve

$$\begin{vmatrix} \lambda - 3 & 1 \\ -5 & \lambda + 3 \end{vmatrix} = \lambda^2 - 9 + 5 = (\lambda - 2)(\lambda + 2) = 0.$$

Thus, eigenvalues are $\lambda = 2$ and $\lambda = -2$.

$$\lambda = 2: \qquad \begin{bmatrix} -1 & 1 \\ -5 & 5 \end{bmatrix} \Rightarrow \begin{bmatrix} -1 & 1 \\ 0 & 0 \end{bmatrix} \Rightarrow \mathbf{x} = \begin{bmatrix} 1 \\ 1 \end{bmatrix}$$

$$\lambda = -2: \qquad \begin{bmatrix} -5 & 1 \\ -5 & 1 \end{bmatrix} \Rightarrow \begin{bmatrix} -5 & 1 \\ 0 & 0 \end{bmatrix} \Rightarrow \mathbf{x} = \begin{bmatrix} 1 \\ 5 \end{bmatrix}.$$

12. $|\lambda I - A| = \begin{vmatrix} \lambda - 2 & 0 & -1 \\ 0 & \lambda - 3 & -4 \\ 0 & 0 & \lambda - 1 \end{vmatrix} = (\lambda - 2)(\lambda - 3)(\lambda - 1)$

$$\lambda = 2: \begin{bmatrix} 0 & 0 & -1 \\ 0 & -1 & -4 \\ 0 & 0 & 1 \end{bmatrix} \rightarrow \begin{bmatrix} 0 & 1 & 0 \\ 0 & 0 & 1 \\ 0 & 0 & 0 \end{bmatrix} \Rightarrow \mathbf{x} = \begin{bmatrix} 1 \\ 0 \\ 0 \end{bmatrix}$$

$$\lambda = 3: \begin{bmatrix} 1 & 0 & -1 \\ 0 & 0 & -4 \\ 0 & 0 & 2 \end{bmatrix} \rightarrow \begin{bmatrix} 1 & 0 & 0 \\ 0 & 0 & 1 \\ 0 & 0 & 0 \end{bmatrix} \Rightarrow \mathbf{x} = \begin{bmatrix} 0 \\ 1 \\ 0 \end{bmatrix}$$

$$\lambda = 1: \begin{bmatrix} -1 & 0 & -1 \\ 0 & -2 & -4 \\ 0 & 0 & 0 \end{bmatrix} \rightarrow \begin{bmatrix} 1 & 0 & 1 \\ 0 & 1 & 2 \\ 0 & 0 & 0 \end{bmatrix} \Rightarrow \mathbf{x} = \begin{bmatrix} -1 \\ -2 \\ 1 \end{bmatrix}.$$

14. Using a graphing calculator (TI-86) for

$$A = \begin{bmatrix} 4 & 3 \\ -3 & -2 \end{bmatrix}$$

gives $\{1 \quad 1\}$. So, the characteristic equation yields eigenvalues $\lambda_1 = \lambda_2 = 1$.

$$\lambda = 1: \begin{bmatrix} -3 & -3 \\ 3 & 3 \end{bmatrix} \Rightarrow \begin{bmatrix} 1 & 1 \\ 0 & 0 \end{bmatrix} \Rightarrow x = \begin{bmatrix} 1 \\ -1 \end{bmatrix}$$

16. Using a graphing calculator (TI-86) for

$$A = \begin{bmatrix} 4 & 0 & 0 \\ 0 & 0 & -3 \\ 0 & -2 & 1 \end{bmatrix}$$

gives the eigenvalues $\{3 \quad -2 \quad 4\}$. So, $\lambda_1 = 3$, $\lambda_2 = -2$, and $\lambda_3 = 4$.

—CONTINUED—

16. —CONTINUED—

$$\lambda_1 = 3: \quad \begin{bmatrix} -1 & 0 & 0 \\ 0 & 3 & 3 \\ 0 & 2 & 2 \end{bmatrix} \Rightarrow \begin{bmatrix} 1 & 0 & 0 \\ 0 & 1 & 1 \\ 0 & 0 & 0 \end{bmatrix} \Rightarrow x = \begin{bmatrix} 0 \\ 1 \\ -1 \end{bmatrix}$$

$$\lambda_2 = -2: \quad \begin{bmatrix} -6 & 0 & 0 \\ 0 & -2 & 3 \\ 0 & 2 & -3 \end{bmatrix} \Rightarrow \begin{bmatrix} 1 & 0 & 0 \\ 0 & 1 & -1.5 \\ 0 & 0 & 0 \end{bmatrix} \Rightarrow x = \begin{bmatrix} 0 \\ 3 \\ 2 \end{bmatrix}$$

$$\lambda_3 = 4: \quad \begin{bmatrix} 0 & 0 & 0 \\ 0 & 4 & 3 \\ 0 & 2 & 3 \end{bmatrix} \Rightarrow \begin{bmatrix} 0 & 1 & 0 \\ 0 & 0 & 1 \\ 0 & 0 & 0 \end{bmatrix} \Rightarrow x = \begin{bmatrix} 1 \\ 0 \\ 0 \end{bmatrix}$$

18. Using a graphing calculator (TI-86) for

$$A = \begin{bmatrix} 1 & 0 & 2 & 3 \\ 0 & 2 & 0 & 0 \\ 0 & 0 & 1 & 3 \\ 0 & -1 & 3 & 1 \end{bmatrix}$$

gives eigenvalues $\{1 \quad 4 \quad -2 \quad 2\}$.

So, $\lambda_1 = 1, \lambda_2 = 4, \lambda_3 = -2, \lambda_4 = 2$.

$$\lambda_1 = 1: \quad \begin{bmatrix} 0 & 0 & -2 & -3 \\ 0 & -1 & 0 & 0 \\ 0 & 0 & 0 & -3 \\ 0 & 1 & -3 & 0 \end{bmatrix} \Rightarrow \begin{bmatrix} 0 & 1 & 0 & 0 \\ 0 & 0 & 1 & 0 \\ 0 & 0 & 0 & 1 \\ 0 & 0 & 0 & 0 \end{bmatrix} \Rightarrow x_1 = \begin{bmatrix} 1 \\ 0 \\ 0 \\ 0 \end{bmatrix}$$

$$\lambda_2 = 4: \quad \begin{bmatrix} 3 & 0 & -2 & -3 \\ 0 & 2 & 0 & 0 \\ 0 & 0 & 3 & -3 \\ 0 & 1 & -3 & 3 \end{bmatrix} \Rightarrow \begin{bmatrix} 1 & 0 & 0 & -\frac{5}{3} \\ 0 & 1 & 0 & 0 \\ 0 & 0 & 1 & -1 \\ 0 & 0 & 0 & 0 \end{bmatrix} \Rightarrow x_2 = \begin{bmatrix} 5 \\ 0 \\ 3 \\ 3 \end{bmatrix}$$

$$\lambda_3 = -2: \quad \begin{bmatrix} -3 & 0 & -2 & -3 \\ 0 & -4 & 0 & 0 \\ 0 & 0 & -3 & -3 \\ 0 & 1 & -3 & -3 \end{bmatrix} \Rightarrow \begin{bmatrix} 1 & 0 & 0 & \frac{1}{3} \\ 0 & 1 & 0 & 0 \\ 0 & 0 & 1 & 1 \\ 0 & 0 & 0 & 0 \end{bmatrix} \Rightarrow x_3 = \begin{bmatrix} -1 \\ 0 \\ 3 \\ -3 \end{bmatrix}$$

$$\lambda_4 = 2: \quad \begin{bmatrix} 1 & 0 & -2 & -3 \\ 0 & 0 & 0 & 0 \\ 0 & 0 & 1 & -3 \\ 0 & 1 & -3 & 1 \end{bmatrix} \Rightarrow \begin{bmatrix} 1 & 0 & 0 & -9 \\ 0 & 1 & 0 & -8 \\ 0 & 0 & 1 & -3 \\ 0 & 0 & 0 & 0 \end{bmatrix} \Rightarrow x_4 = \begin{bmatrix} 9 \\ 8 \\ 3 \\ 1 \end{bmatrix}$$

20. (a) True. The characteristic equation is

$$|\lambda I - A| = \begin{vmatrix} \lambda - 2 & 1 \\ -1 & \lambda \end{vmatrix} = \lambda(\lambda - 2) + 1 = \lambda^2 - 2\lambda + 1 = (\lambda - 1)^2$$

which implies that $\lambda_1 = \lambda_2 = 1$.

(b) True. The characteristic equation is

$$|\lambda I - A| = \begin{vmatrix} \lambda - 4 & 2 \\ 1 & \lambda \end{vmatrix} = \lambda(\lambda - 4) - 2 = \lambda^2 - 4\lambda - 2$$

which implies that $\lambda_1 = 2 + \sqrt{6}$ and $\lambda_2 = 2 - \sqrt{6}$.

Section 3.5   Applications of Determinants

2. The matrix of cofactors is

$$\begin{bmatrix} |4| & -|0| \\ -|0| & |-1| \end{bmatrix} = \begin{bmatrix} 4 & 0 \\ 0 & -1 \end{bmatrix}.$$

Thus, the adjoint of A is

$$\text{adj}(A) = \begin{bmatrix} 4 & 0 \\ 0 & -1 \end{bmatrix}^T = \begin{bmatrix} 4 & 0 \\ 0 & -1 \end{bmatrix}.$$

Since $|A| = -4$, the inverse of A is

$$A^{-1} = \frac{1}{|A|}\,\text{adj}(A) = -\tfrac{1}{4}\begin{bmatrix} 4 & 0 \\ 0 & -1 \end{bmatrix} = \begin{bmatrix} -1 & 0 \\ 0 & \frac{1}{4} \end{bmatrix}.$$

4. The matrix of cofactors is

$$\begin{bmatrix} \begin{vmatrix} 1 & -1 \\ 2 & 2 \end{vmatrix} & -\begin{vmatrix} 0 & -1 \\ 2 & 2 \end{vmatrix} & \begin{vmatrix} 0 & 1 \\ 2 & 2 \end{vmatrix} \\ -\begin{vmatrix} 2 & 3 \\ 2 & 2 \end{vmatrix} & \begin{vmatrix} 1 & 3 \\ 2 & 2 \end{vmatrix} & -\begin{vmatrix} 1 & 2 \\ 2 & 2 \end{vmatrix} \\ \begin{vmatrix} 2 & 3 \\ 1 & -1 \end{vmatrix} & -\begin{vmatrix} 1 & 3 \\ 0 & -1 \end{vmatrix} & \begin{vmatrix} 1 & 2 \\ 0 & 1 \end{vmatrix} \end{bmatrix} = \begin{bmatrix} 4 & -2 & -2 \\ 2 & -4 & 2 \\ -5 & 1 & 1 \end{bmatrix}.$$

Thus, the adjoint of A is

$$\text{adj}(A) = \begin{bmatrix} 4 & 2 & -5 \\ -2 & -4 & 1 \\ -2 & 2 & 1 \end{bmatrix}.$$

Since $|A| = -6$, the inverse of A is

$$A^{-1} = \frac{1}{|A|}\,\text{adj}(A) = \begin{bmatrix} -\frac{2}{3} & -\frac{1}{3} & \frac{5}{6} \\ \frac{1}{3} & \frac{2}{3} & -\frac{1}{6} \\ \frac{1}{3} & -\frac{1}{3} & -\frac{1}{6} \end{bmatrix}.$$

6. The matrix of cofactors is

$$\begin{bmatrix} \begin{vmatrix} 2 & 3 \\ -1 & -2 \end{vmatrix} & -\begin{vmatrix} 1 & 3 \\ -1 & -2 \end{vmatrix} & \begin{vmatrix} 1 & 2 \\ -1 & -1 \end{vmatrix} \\ -\begin{vmatrix} 1 & 1 \\ 1 & -2 \end{vmatrix} & \begin{vmatrix} 0 & 1 \\ -1 & -2 \end{vmatrix} & -\begin{vmatrix} 0 & 1 \\ -1 & -1 \end{vmatrix} \\ \begin{vmatrix} 1 & 1 \\ 2 & 3 \end{vmatrix} & -\begin{vmatrix} 0 & 1 \\ 1 & 3 \end{vmatrix} & \begin{vmatrix} 0 & 1 \\ 0 & 2 \end{vmatrix} \end{bmatrix} = \begin{bmatrix} -1 & -1 & 1 \\ 1 & 1 & -1 \\ 1 & 1 & -1 \end{bmatrix}.$$

Thus, the adjoint of A is

$$\text{adj}(A) = \begin{bmatrix} -1 & 1 & 1 \\ -1 & 1 & 1 \\ 1 & -1 & -1 \end{bmatrix}.$$

Since $\det(A) = 0$, the matrix A has no inverse.

8. The matrix of cofactors is

$$
\begin{bmatrix}
\begin{vmatrix}1&0&1\\0&1&1\\1&1&1\end{vmatrix} & -\begin{vmatrix}1&0&1\\1&1&1\\0&1&1\end{vmatrix} & \begin{vmatrix}1&1&1\\1&0&1\\0&1&1\end{vmatrix} & -\begin{vmatrix}1&1&0\\1&0&1\\0&1&1\end{vmatrix} \\[6pt]
-\begin{vmatrix}1&1&0\\0&1&1\\1&1&1\end{vmatrix} & \begin{vmatrix}1&1&0\\1&1&1\\0&1&1\end{vmatrix} & -\begin{vmatrix}1&1&0\\1&0&1\\0&1&1\end{vmatrix} & \begin{vmatrix}1&1&1\\1&0&1\\0&1&1\end{vmatrix} \\[6pt]
\begin{vmatrix}1&1&0\\1&0&1\\1&1&1\end{vmatrix} & -\begin{vmatrix}1&1&0\\1&0&1\\0&1&1\end{vmatrix} & \begin{vmatrix}1&1&0\\1&1&1\\0&1&1\end{vmatrix} & -\begin{vmatrix}1&1&1\\1&1&0\\0&1&1\end{vmatrix} \\[6pt]
-\begin{vmatrix}1&1&0\\1&0&1\\0&1&1\end{vmatrix} & \begin{vmatrix}1&1&0\\1&0&1\\1&1&1\end{vmatrix} & -\begin{vmatrix}1&1&0\\1&1&1\\1&0&1\end{vmatrix} & \begin{vmatrix}1&1&1\\1&1&0\\1&0&1\end{vmatrix}
\end{bmatrix}
=
\begin{bmatrix}
-1 & -1 & -1 & 2 \\
-1 & -1 & 2 & -1 \\
-1 & 2 & -1 & -1 \\
2 & -1 & -1 & -1
\end{bmatrix}.
$$

Thus, the adjoint of A is

$$
\text{adj}(A) = \begin{bmatrix}
-1 & -1 & -1 & 2 \\
-1 & -1 & 2 & -1 \\
-1 & 2 & -1 & -1 \\
2 & -1 & -1 & -1
\end{bmatrix}.
$$

Since $\det(A) = -3$, the inverse of A is

$$
A^{-1} = \frac{1}{|A|}\,\text{adj}(A) = \begin{bmatrix}
\frac13 & \frac13 & \frac13 & -\frac23 \\
\frac13 & \frac13 & -\frac23 & \frac13 \\
\frac13 & -\frac23 & \frac13 & \frac13 \\
-\frac23 & \frac13 & \frac13 & \frac13
\end{bmatrix}.
$$

10. Following the proof of Theorem 3.10, we have

$$A\,\text{adj}(A) = |A|\,I.$$

Now, if A is not invertible, then $|A| = 0$, and $A\,\text{adj}(A)$ is the zero matrix.

12. We have

$$
\text{adj}(\text{adj}(A)) = \text{adj}(|A|A^{-1}) = \det(|A|A^{-1})(|A|A^{-1})^{-1}
$$
$$
= |A|^n|A^{-1}|\frac{1}{|A|}A = |A|^{n-2}A.
$$

14. $A = \begin{bmatrix} -1 & 3 \\ 1 & 2 \end{bmatrix} \Rightarrow \text{adj}(A) = \begin{bmatrix} 2 & -1 \\ -3 & -1 \end{bmatrix} \Rightarrow$

$$
\text{adj}(\text{adj}(A)) = \begin{bmatrix} -1 & 3 \\ 1 & 2 \end{bmatrix} = |A|^0 \begin{bmatrix} -1 & 3 \\ 1 & 2 \end{bmatrix}
$$

Thus, $\text{adj}(\text{adj}(A)) = |A|^{n-2}A.$

16. We illustrate the formula $\mathrm{adj}(A^{-1}) = [\mathrm{adj}(A)]^{-1}$ in case $A = \begin{bmatrix} 1 & 3 \\ 1 & 2 \end{bmatrix}$.

$$A = \begin{bmatrix} 1 & 3 \\ 1 & 2 \end{bmatrix} \implies A^{-1} = \begin{bmatrix} -2 & 3 \\ 1 & -1 \end{bmatrix} \text{ and } \mathrm{adj}(A^{-1}) = \begin{bmatrix} -1 & -1 \\ -3 & -2 \end{bmatrix}.$$

On the other hand, $\mathrm{adj}(A) = \begin{bmatrix} 2 & -1 \\ -3 & 1 \end{bmatrix}$ and $(\mathrm{adj}(A))^{-1} = \begin{bmatrix} -1 & -1 \\ -3 & -2 \end{bmatrix}.$

18. The coefficient matrix is

$$A = \begin{bmatrix} 2 & -1 \\ 3 & 2 \end{bmatrix}, \qquad \text{where } |A| = 7.$$

Because $|A| \neq 0$, we can use Cramer's Rule. We replace each column with the column of constants to obtain

$$A_1 = \begin{bmatrix} -10 & -1 \\ -1 & 2 \end{bmatrix}, \qquad |A_1| = -21$$

$$A_2 = \begin{bmatrix} 2 & -10 \\ 3 & -1 \end{bmatrix}, \qquad |A_2| = 28.$$

Thus, we solve for x_1 and x_2.

$$x_1 = \frac{|A_1|}{|A|} = -\frac{21}{7} = -3$$

$$x_2 = \frac{|A_2|}{|A|} = \frac{28}{7} = 4$$

20. The coefficient matrix is

$$A = \begin{bmatrix} 18 & 12 \\ 30 & 24 \end{bmatrix}, \qquad \text{where } |A| = 72.$$

Because $|A| \neq 0$, we can use Cramer's Rule.

$$A_1 = \begin{bmatrix} 13 & 12 \\ 23 & 24 \end{bmatrix}, \qquad |A_1| = 36$$

$$A_2 = \begin{bmatrix} 18 & 13 \\ 30 & 23 \end{bmatrix}, \qquad |A_2| = 24$$

The solution is

$$x_1 = \frac{|A_1|}{|A|} = \frac{36}{72} = \frac{1}{2}$$

$$x_2 = \frac{|A_2|}{|A|} = \frac{24}{72} = \frac{1}{3}.$$

22. The coefficient matrix is

$$A = \begin{bmatrix} 13 & -6 \\ 26 & -12 \end{bmatrix}, \qquad \text{where } |A| = 0.$$

Because $|A| = 0$, Cramer's Rule cannot be applied. (The system does not have a solution.)

24. The coefficient matrix is

$$A = \begin{bmatrix} -0.4 & 0.8 \\ 0.2 & 0.3 \end{bmatrix}, \qquad \text{where} \quad |A| = -0.28.$$

Because $|A| \neq 0$, we can use Cramer's Rule.

$$A_1 = \begin{bmatrix} 1.6 & 0.8 \\ 0.6 & 0.3 \end{bmatrix}, \qquad |A_1| = 0$$

$$A_2 = \begin{bmatrix} -0.4 & 1.6 \\ 0.2 & 0.6 \end{bmatrix}, \qquad |A_2| = -0.56$$

The solution is

$$x_1 = \frac{|A_1|}{|A|} = \frac{0}{-0.28} = 0$$

$$x_2 = \frac{|A_2|}{|A|} = \frac{-0.56}{-0.28} = 2.$$

26. The coefficient matrix of the system is

$$A = \begin{bmatrix} 3 & 2 \\ 2 & 10 \end{bmatrix}, \qquad \text{where} \quad |A| = 26.$$

Because $|A| \neq 0$, we can use Cramer's Rule.

$$A_1 = \begin{bmatrix} 1 & 2 \\ 6 & 10 \end{bmatrix}, \qquad |A_1| = -2$$

$$A_2 = \begin{bmatrix} 3 & 1 \\ 2 & 6 \end{bmatrix}, \qquad |A_2| = 16$$

The solution is

$$x_1 = \frac{|A_1|}{|A|} = \frac{-2}{26} = -\frac{1}{13}$$

$$x_2 = \frac{|A_2|}{|A|} = \frac{16}{26} = \frac{8}{13}.$$

28. The coefficient matrix is

$$A = \begin{bmatrix} 4 & -2 & 3 \\ 2 & 2 & 5 \\ 8 & -5 & -2 \end{bmatrix}, \quad \text{where} \quad |A| = -82.$$

Because $|A| \neq 0$, we can use Cramer's Rule.

$$A_1 = \begin{bmatrix} -2 & -2 & 3 \\ 16 & 2 & 5 \\ 4 & -5 & -2 \end{bmatrix}, \qquad |A_1| = -410$$

$$A_2 = \begin{bmatrix} 4 & -2 & 3 \\ 2 & 16 & 5 \\ 8 & 4 & -2 \end{bmatrix}, \qquad |A_2| = -656$$

$$A_3 = \begin{bmatrix} 4 & -2 & -2 \\ 2 & 2 & 16 \\ 8 & -5 & 4 \end{bmatrix}, \qquad |A_3| = 164$$

—CONTINUED—

28. **—CONTINUED—**

The solution is

$$x_1 = \frac{|A_1|}{|A|} = \frac{-410}{-82} = 5$$

$$x_2 = \frac{|A_2|}{|A|} = \frac{-656}{-82} = 8$$

$$x_3 = \frac{|A_3|}{|A|} = \frac{164}{-82} = -2.$$

30. The coefficient matrix is

$$A = \begin{bmatrix} 14 & -21 & -7 \\ -4 & 2 & -2 \\ 56 & -21 & 7 \end{bmatrix}, \quad \text{where } |A| = 1568.$$

Because $|A| \neq 0$, we can use Cramer's Rule.

$$A_1 = \begin{bmatrix} -21 & -21 & -7 \\ 2 & 2 & -2 \\ 7 & -21 & 7 \end{bmatrix}, \quad |A_1| = 1568$$

$$A_2 = \begin{bmatrix} 14 & -21 & -7 \\ -4 & 2 & -2 \\ 56 & 7 & 7 \end{bmatrix}, \quad |A_2| = 3136$$

$$A_3 = \begin{bmatrix} 14 & -21 & -21 \\ -4 & 2 & 2 \\ 56 & -21 & 7 \end{bmatrix}, \quad |A_3| = -1568$$

The solution is

$$x_1 = \frac{|A_1|}{|A|} = \frac{1568}{1568} = 1$$

$$x_2 = \frac{|A_2|}{|A|} = \frac{3136}{1568} = 2$$

$$x_3 = \frac{|A_3|}{|A|} = -\frac{1568}{1568} = -1.$$

32. The coefficient matrix is

$$A = \begin{bmatrix} 2 & 3 & 5 \\ 3 & 5 & 9 \\ 5 & 9 & 17 \end{bmatrix}, \quad \text{where } |A| = 0.$$

Because $|A| = 0$, Cramer's Rule cannot be applied.

34. The coefficient matrix is

$$A = \begin{bmatrix} 2 & 5 & 0 & 1 \\ 1 & 4 & 2 & -2 \\ 2 & -2 & 5 & 1 \\ 1 & 0 & 0 & -3 \end{bmatrix}, \quad \text{where } |A| = -213.$$

To solve for x_1, we compute the determinant of A_1.

$$A_1 = \begin{bmatrix} 11 & 5 & 0 & 1 \\ -7 & 4 & 2 & -2 \\ 3 & -2 & 5 & 1 \\ 1 & 0 & 0 & -3 \end{bmatrix}, \quad |A_1| = -1491.$$

Then, $x_1 = |A_1|/|A| = -1491/(-213) = 7.$

36. The coefficient matrix is

$$A = \begin{bmatrix} 3 & 2 & 5 \\ 4 & -3 & -4 \\ -8 & 2 & 3 \end{bmatrix}, \quad \text{where } |A| = -43.$$

To solve for x_1, we compute the determinant of A_1.

$$A_1 = \begin{bmatrix} 4 & 2 & 5 \\ 1 & -3 & -4 \\ 0 & 2 & 3 \end{bmatrix}, \quad |A_1| = 0.$$

Then, $x_1 = |A_1|/|A| = 0/(-43) = 0.$

38. If we draw the altitude from vertex C to side c, then from trigonometry we see that

$$c = a \cos B + b \cos A.$$

Similarly, the other two equations follow by using the other altitudes. We now use Cramer's Rule to solve for $\cos C$ in this system of three equations.

$$\cos C = \frac{\begin{vmatrix} 0 & c & a \\ c & 0 & b \\ b & a & c \end{vmatrix}}{\begin{vmatrix} 0 & c & b \\ c & 0 & a \\ b & a & 0 \end{vmatrix}} = \frac{-c(c^2 - b^2) + a(ac)}{-c(-ba) + b(ac)} = \frac{a^2 + b^2 - c^2}{2ab}.$$

Solving for c^2 we obtain

$$2ab \cos C = a^2 + b^2 - c^2$$

$$c^2 = a^2 + b^2 - 2ab \cos C.$$

40. We use the formula for area as follows.

$$\text{Area} = \pm\frac{1}{2} \begin{vmatrix} x_1 & y_1 & 1 \\ x_2 & y_2 & 1 \\ x_3 & y_3 & 1 \end{vmatrix} = \pm\frac{1}{2} \begin{vmatrix} 1 & 1 & 1 \\ 2 & 4 & 1 \\ 4 & 2 & 1 \end{vmatrix} = \pm\frac{1}{2}(-8) = 4.$$

42. We use the formula for area as follows.

$$\text{Area} = \pm\tfrac{1}{2}\begin{vmatrix} x_1 & y_1 & 1 \\ x_2 & y_2 & 1 \\ x_3 & y_3 & 1 \end{vmatrix} = \pm\tfrac{1}{2}\begin{vmatrix} 1 & 1 & 1 \\ -1 & 1 & 1 \\ 0 & -2 & 1 \end{vmatrix} = \pm\tfrac{1}{2}(6) = 3$$

44. We use the fact that

$$\begin{vmatrix} x_1 & y_1 & 1 \\ x_2 & y_2 & 1 \\ x_3 & y_3 & 1 \end{vmatrix} = \begin{vmatrix} -1 & 0 & 1 \\ 1 & 1 & 1 \\ 3 & 3 & 1 \end{vmatrix} = 2$$

to determine that the three points are not collinear.

46. We use the fact that

$$\begin{vmatrix} x_1 & y_1 & 1 \\ x_2 & y_2 & 1 \\ x_3 & y_3 & 1 \end{vmatrix} = \begin{vmatrix} -1 & -3 & 1 \\ -4 & 7 & 1 \\ 2 & -13 & 1 \end{vmatrix} = 0$$

to determine that the three points are collinear.

48. We find the equation as follows

$$0 = \begin{vmatrix} x & y & 1 \\ x_1 & y_1 & 1 \\ x_2 & y_2 & 1 \end{vmatrix} = \begin{vmatrix} x & y & 1 \\ -4 & 7 & 1 \\ 2 & 4 & 1 \end{vmatrix} = 3x + 6y - 30$$

Thus, an equation for the line is $2y + x = 10$.

50. We find the equation as follows

$$0 = \begin{vmatrix} x & y & 1 \\ x_1 & y_1 & 1 \\ x_2 & y_2 & 1 \end{vmatrix} = \begin{vmatrix} x & y & 1 \\ 1 & 4 & 1 \\ 3 & 4 & 1 \end{vmatrix} = 2y - 8$$

Thus, an equation for the line is $y = 4$.

52. We use the formula for volume as follows

$$\text{Volume} = \pm\tfrac{1}{6}\begin{vmatrix} x_1 & y_1 & z_1 & 1 \\ x_2 & y_2 & z_2 & 1 \\ x_3 & y_3 & z_3 & 1 \\ x_4 & y_4 & z_4 & 1 \end{vmatrix} = \pm\tfrac{1}{6}\begin{vmatrix} 1 & 1 & 1 & 1 \\ 0 & 0 & 0 & 1 \\ 2 & 1 & -1 & 1 \\ -1 & 1 & 2 & 1 \end{vmatrix} = \tfrac{1}{6}(3) = \tfrac{1}{2}$$

54. We use the formula for volume as follows

$$\text{Volume} = \pm\tfrac{1}{6}\begin{vmatrix} x_1 & y_1 & z_1 & 1 \\ x_2 & y_2 & z_2 & 1 \\ x_3 & y_3 & z_3 & 1 \\ x_4 & y_4 & z_4 & 1 \end{vmatrix} = \pm\tfrac{1}{6}\begin{vmatrix} 0 & 0 & 0 & 1 \\ 0 & 2 & 0 & 1 \\ 3 & 0 & 0 & 1 \\ 1 & 1 & 4 & 1 \end{vmatrix} = \pm\tfrac{1}{6}(24) = 4$$

56. We use the fact that

$$\begin{vmatrix} x_1 & y_1 & z_1 & 1 \\ x_2 & y_2 & z_2 & 1 \\ x_3 & y_3 & z_3 & 1 \\ x_4 & y_4 & z_4 & 1 \end{vmatrix} = \begin{vmatrix} 1 & 2 & 3 & 1 \\ -1 & 0 & 1 & 1 \\ 0 & -2 & -5 & 1 \\ 2 & 6 & 11 & 1 \end{vmatrix} = 0$$

to determine that the four points are coplanar.

58. We use the fact that

$$\begin{vmatrix} x_1 & y_1 & z_1 & 1 \\ x_2 & y_2 & z_2 & 1 \\ x_3 & y_3 & z_3 & 1 \\ x_4 & y_4 & z_4 & 1 \end{vmatrix} = \begin{vmatrix} 1 & 2 & 7 & 1 \\ -3 & 6 & 6 & 1 \\ 4 & 4 & 2 & 1 \\ 3 & 3 & 4 & 1 \end{vmatrix} = -1$$

to determine that the four points are not coplanar.

60. We find the equation as follows

$$0 = \begin{vmatrix} x & y & z & 1 \\ x_1 & y_1 & z_1 & 1 \\ x_2 & y_2 & z_2 & 1 \\ x_3 & y_3 & z_3 & 1 \end{vmatrix} = \begin{vmatrix} x & y & z & 1 \\ 0 & -1 & 0 & 1 \\ 1 & 1 & 0 & 1 \\ 2 & 1 & 2 & 1 \end{vmatrix}$$

$$= x\begin{vmatrix} -1 & 0 & 1 \\ 1 & 0 & 1 \\ 1 & 2 & 1 \end{vmatrix} - y\begin{vmatrix} 0 & 0 & 1 \\ 1 & 0 & 1 \\ 2 & 2 & 1 \end{vmatrix} + z\begin{vmatrix} 0 & -1 & 1 \\ 1 & 1 & 1 \\ 2 & 1 & 1 \end{vmatrix} - \begin{vmatrix} 0 & -1 & 0 \\ 1 & 1 & 0 \\ 2 & 1 & 2 \end{vmatrix}$$

$$= 4x - 2y - 2z - 2, \quad \text{or} \quad 2x - y - z = 1$$

62. We find the equation as follows

$$0 = \begin{vmatrix} x & y & z & 1 \\ x_1 & y_1 & z_1 & 1 \\ x_2 & y_2 & z_2 & 1 \\ x_3 & y_3 & z_3 & 1 \end{vmatrix} = \begin{vmatrix} x & y & z & 1 \\ 1 & 2 & 7 & 1 \\ 4 & 4 & 2 & 1 \\ 3 & 3 & 4 & 1 \end{vmatrix}$$

$$= x\begin{vmatrix} 2 & 7 & 1 \\ 4 & 2 & 1 \\ 3 & 4 & 1 \end{vmatrix} - y\begin{vmatrix} 1 & 7 & 1 \\ 4 & 2 & 1 \\ 3 & 4 & 1 \end{vmatrix} + z\begin{vmatrix} 1 & 2 & 1 \\ 4 & 4 & 1 \\ 3 & 3 & 1 \end{vmatrix} - \begin{vmatrix} 1 & 2 & 7 \\ 4 & 4 & 2 \\ 3 & 3 & 4 \end{vmatrix}$$

$$= -x - y - z + 10, \quad \text{or} \quad x + y + z = 10$$

64. Cramer's Rule was not used correctly to solve for z. The given setup solves for x not z.

Chapter 3 ❏ Review Exercises

2. Using the formula for the determinant of a 2 × 2 matrix, we have

$$\begin{vmatrix} 0 & -3 \\ 1 & 2 \end{vmatrix} = 0(2) - (1)(-3)$$

$$= 3.$$

4. Using the formula for the determinant of a 2 × 2 matrix, we have

$$\begin{vmatrix} -2 & 0 \\ 0 & 3 \end{vmatrix} = (-2)(3) - (0)(0)$$

$$= -6.$$

6. The determinant of a triangular matrix is the product of the entries along the main diagonal.

$$\begin{vmatrix} 5 & 0 & 2 \\ 0 & -1 & 3 \\ 0 & 0 & 1 \end{vmatrix} = 5(-1)(1)$$

$$= -5$$

8. The determinant is 0, since the matrix has a column of zeros.

10. $$\begin{vmatrix} -15 & 0 & 3 \\ 3 & 9 & -6 \\ 12 & -3 & 6 \end{vmatrix} = 3^3 \begin{vmatrix} -5 & 0 & 1 \\ 1 & 3 & -2 \\ 4 & -1 & 2 \end{vmatrix} = 27 \begin{vmatrix} -5 & 0 & 1 \\ -9 & 3 & 0 \\ 14 & -1 & 0 \end{vmatrix} = 27 \begin{vmatrix} -9 & 3 \\ 14 & -1 \end{vmatrix}$$

$$= 27(9 - 42)$$

$$= -891$$

12. The determinant of a triangular matrix is the product of its diagonal entries. Thus, the determinant equals $2(1)(3)(-1) = -6$.

14. $$\begin{vmatrix} 3 & -1 & 2 & 1 \\ -2 & 0 & 1 & -3 \\ -1 & 2 & -3 & 4 \\ -2 & 1 & -2 & 1 \end{vmatrix} = \begin{vmatrix} 3 & -1 & 2 & 1 \\ -2 & 0 & 1 & -3 \\ 5 & 0 & 1 & 6 \\ 1 & 0 & 0 & 2 \end{vmatrix}$$

$$= -(-1) \begin{vmatrix} -2 & 1 & -3 \\ 5 & 1 & 6 \\ 1 & 0 & 2 \end{vmatrix}$$

$$= 1 \begin{vmatrix} 1 & -3 \\ 1 & 6 \end{vmatrix} + 2 \begin{vmatrix} -2 & 1 \\ 5 & 1 \end{vmatrix}$$

$$= 9 + 2(-7) = -5$$

16.
$$\begin{vmatrix} 1 & 2 & -1 & 3 & 4 \\ 2 & 3 & -1 & 2 & -2 \\ 1 & 2 & 0 & 1 & -1 \\ 1 & 0 & 2 & -1 & 0 \\ 0 & -1 & 1 & 0 & 2 \end{vmatrix} = \begin{vmatrix} 1 & 2 & -1 & 3 & 4 \\ 0 & -1 & 1 & -4 & -10 \\ 0 & 0 & 1 & -2 & -5 \\ 0 & -2 & 3 & -4 & -4 \\ 0 & -1 & 1 & 0 & 2 \end{vmatrix}$$

$$= -\begin{vmatrix} 1 & -1 & 4 & 10 \\ 0 & 1 & -2 & -5 \\ 0 & 1 & 4 & 16 \\ 0 & 0 & 4 & 12 \end{vmatrix}$$

$$= -\begin{vmatrix} 1 & -2 & -5 \\ 0 & 6 & 21 \\ 0 & 4 & 12 \end{vmatrix} = -(72 - 84) = 12$$

18.
$$\begin{vmatrix} 0 & 0 & 0 & 0 & 2 \\ 0 & 0 & 0 & 2 & 0 \\ 0 & 0 & 2 & 0 & 0 \\ 0 & 2 & 0 & 0 & 0 \\ 2 & 0 & 0 & 0 & 0 \end{vmatrix} = 2\begin{vmatrix} 0 & 0 & 0 & 2 \\ 0 & 0 & 2 & 0 \\ 0 & 2 & 0 & 0 \\ 2 & 0 & 0 & 0 \end{vmatrix}$$

$$= 2(-2)\begin{vmatrix} 0 & 0 & 2 \\ 0 & 2 & 0 \\ 2 & 0 & 0 \end{vmatrix}$$

$$= -4(2)\begin{vmatrix} 0 & 2 \\ 2 & 0 \end{vmatrix} = (-8)(-4) = 32$$

20. (a) $|A| = \begin{vmatrix} 1 & 2 & 3 \\ 4 & 5 & 6 \\ 7 & 8 & 0 \end{vmatrix} = 27$

(b) $|B| = \begin{vmatrix} 1 & 2 & 1 \\ 0 & -1 & 1 \\ 0 & 2 & 3 \end{vmatrix} = -5$

(c) $AB = \begin{bmatrix} 1 & 6 & 12 \\ 4 & 15 & 27 \\ 7 & 6 & 15 \end{bmatrix}$

(d) $|AB| = -135$

Note that $|A|\,|B| = |AB| = -135$.

22. First we find

$$|A| = \begin{vmatrix} 3 & 0 & 1 \\ -1 & 0 & 0 \\ 2 & 1 & 2 \end{vmatrix} = -1$$

(a) $|A^T| = |A| = -1$

(b) $|A^3| = |A|^3 = (-1)^3 = -1$

(c) $|A^T A| = |A^T|\,|A| = (-1)(-1) = 1$

(d) $|5A| = 5^3|A| = 125(-1) = -125$

24. (a) $|A| = \begin{vmatrix} 2 & -1 & 4 \\ 5 & 0 & 3 \\ 1 & -2 & 0 \end{vmatrix} = \begin{vmatrix} 2 & -1 & 4 \\ 5 & 0 & 3 \\ -3 & 0 & -8 \end{vmatrix} = 1\begin{vmatrix} 5 & 3 \\ -3 & -8 \end{vmatrix} = -31$

(b) $|A^{-1}| = \dfrac{1}{|A|} = -\dfrac{1}{31}$

26. • *Gaussian elimination with back substitution.* First we use Gaussian elimination on the augmented matrix for this system.

$$
\begin{bmatrix} 1 & 3 & 2 & 5 \\ 2 & -1 & -1 & 0 \\ 1 & 4 & 1 & 3 \end{bmatrix} \Rightarrow \begin{bmatrix} 1 & 3 & 2 & 5 \\ 0 & -7 & -5 & -10 \\ 0 & 1 & -1 & -2 \end{bmatrix} \Rightarrow
$$

$$
\Rightarrow \begin{bmatrix} 1 & 3 & 2 & 5 \\ 0 & 1 & -1 & -2 \\ 0 & 0 & -12 & -24 \end{bmatrix} \Rightarrow \begin{bmatrix} 1 & 3 & 2 & 5 \\ 0 & 1 & -1 & -2 \\ 0 & 0 & 1 & 2 \end{bmatrix}.
$$

Thus, $x_3 = 2$, $x_2 = -2 + x_3 = -2 + 2 = 0$ and $x_1 = -3x_2 - 2x_3 + 5 = -2(2) + 5 = 1$. The solution to this system is $x_1 = 1$, $x_2 = 0$ and $x_3 = 2$.

• *Gauss-Jordan elimination.* We continue applying elementary row operation to the row echelon form of the augmented matrix to obtain reduced row echelon form.

$$
\begin{bmatrix} 1 & 3 & 2 & 5 \\ 0 & 1 & -1 & -2 \\ 0 & 0 & 1 & 2 \end{bmatrix} \Rightarrow \begin{bmatrix} 1 & 0 & 5 & 11 \\ 0 & 1 & -1 & -2 \\ 0 & 0 & 1 & 2 \end{bmatrix} \Rightarrow \begin{bmatrix} 1 & 0 & 0 & 1 \\ 0 & 1 & 0 & 0 \\ 0 & 0 & 1 & 2 \end{bmatrix}.
$$

The last column gives the solution of this system.

• *Cramer's Rule.* The coefficient matrix of this system is

$$
A = \begin{bmatrix} 1 & 3 & 2 \\ 2 & -1 & -1 \\ 1 & 4 & 1 \end{bmatrix}.
$$

$$
A_1 = \begin{bmatrix} 5 & 3 & 2 \\ 0 & -1 & -1 \\ 3 & 4 & 1 \end{bmatrix}, \quad A_2 = \begin{bmatrix} 1 & 5 & 2 \\ 2 & 0 & -1 \\ 1 & 3 & 1 \end{bmatrix}, \quad A_3 = \begin{bmatrix} 1 & 3 & 5 \\ 2 & -1 & 0 \\ 1 & 4 & 3 \end{bmatrix}.
$$

By Cramer's Rule,

$$
x_1 = \frac{\det(A_1)}{\det(A)} = \frac{12}{12} = 1,
$$

$$
x_2 = \frac{\det(A_2)}{\det(A)} = \frac{0}{12} = 0,
$$

$$
x_3 = \frac{\det(A_3)}{\det(A)} = \frac{24}{12} = 2.
$$

28. • *Gaussian elimination with back substitution.* First we use Gaussian elimination on the augmented matrix for this system.

$$\begin{bmatrix} 1 & -1 & 2 & 3 \\ 3 & -2 & 1 & 1 \\ 2 & 1 & 1 & 0 \end{bmatrix} \Rightarrow \begin{bmatrix} 1 & -1 & 2 & 3 \\ 0 & 1 & -5 & -8 \\ 0 & 3 & -3 & -6 \end{bmatrix} \Rightarrow$$

$$\Rightarrow \begin{bmatrix} 1 & -1 & 2 & 3 \\ 0 & 1 & -5 & -8 \\ 0 & 1 & -1 & -2 \end{bmatrix} \Rightarrow \begin{bmatrix} 1 & -1 & 2 & 3 \\ 0 & 1 & -1 & -2 \\ 0 & 0 & 2 & 3 \end{bmatrix}.$$

Thus, $x_3 = \frac{3}{2}$,

$$x_2 = -2 + x_3 = -2 + \frac{3}{2} = -\frac{1}{2},$$

$$x_1 = 3 - 2x_3 + x_2 = 3 - 3 + \left(-\frac{1}{2}\right) = -\frac{1}{2}.$$

The solution to this system is $x_1 = -\frac{1}{2}$, $x_2 = -\frac{1}{2}$ and $x_3 = \frac{3}{2}$.

• *Gauss-Jordan elimination.* We continue applying elementary row operation to the row echelon form of the augmented matrix to obtain reduced row echelon form.

$$\begin{bmatrix} 1 & -1 & 2 & 3 \\ 0 & 1 & -1 & -2 \\ 0 & 0 & 1 & \frac{3}{2} \end{bmatrix} \Rightarrow \begin{bmatrix} 1 & 0 & 1 & 1 \\ 0 & 1 & -1 & -2 \\ 0 & 0 & 1 & \frac{3}{2} \end{bmatrix} \Rightarrow \begin{bmatrix} 1 & 0 & 0 & -\frac{1}{2} \\ 0 & 1 & 0 & -\frac{1}{2} \\ 0 & 0 & 1 & \frac{3}{2} \end{bmatrix}.$$

The last column gives the solution of this system.

• *Cramer's Rule.* The coefficient matrix of this system is

$$A = \begin{bmatrix} 1 & -1 & 2 \\ 3 & -2 & 1 \\ 2 & 1 & 1 \end{bmatrix}.$$

$$A_1 = \begin{bmatrix} 3 & -1 & 2 \\ 1 & -2 & 1 \\ 0 & 1 & 1 \end{bmatrix}, \quad A_2 = \begin{bmatrix} 1 & 3 & 2 \\ 3 & 1 & 1 \\ 2 & 0 & 1 \end{bmatrix}, \quad A_3 = \begin{bmatrix} 1 & -1 & 3 \\ 3 & -2 & 1 \\ 2 & 1 & 0 \end{bmatrix}.$$

By Cramer's Rule,

$$x_1 = \frac{\det(A_1)}{\det(A)} = \frac{-6}{12} = -\frac{1}{2},$$

$$x_2 = \frac{\det(A_2)}{\det(A)} = \frac{-6}{12} = -\frac{1}{2},$$

$$x_3 = \frac{\det(A_3)}{\det(A)} = \frac{18}{12} = \frac{3}{2}.$$

30. Because the determinant of the coefficient matrix is

$$\begin{vmatrix} 2 & -5 \\ 3 & -7 \end{vmatrix} = 1 \neq 0,$$

the system has a unique solution.

32. Because the determinant of the coefficient matrix is

$$\begin{vmatrix} 2 & 3 & 1 \\ 2 & -3 & -3 \\ 8 & 6 & 0 \end{vmatrix} = 0.$$

the system does not have a unique solution.

34. Because the determinant of the coefficient matrix is

$$\begin{vmatrix} 1 & 5 & 3 & 0 & 0 \\ 4 & 2 & 5 & 0 & 0 \\ 0 & 0 & 3 & 8 & 6 \\ 2 & 4 & 0 & 0 & -2 \\ 2 & 0 & -1 & 0 & 0 \end{vmatrix} = -896 \neq 0,$$

the system has a unique solution.

36. (a) *True.* If either A or B is singular, then $\det(A)$ or $\det(B)$ is zero
(Theorem 3.7), but then $\det(AB) = \det(A)\det(B) = 0 \neq -1$, which
leads to contradiction.

(b) *False.* $\det(2A) = 2^3\det(A) = 8 \cdot 5 = 40 \neq 10.$

(c) *False.* Let A and B be 3×3 identity matrix I_3. Then $\det(A) = \det(B) = \det(I_3) = 1$, but $\det(A + B) = \det(2I_3) = 2^3 \cdot 1 = 8$ while
$\det(A) + \det(B) = 1 + 1 = 2.$

38. Using the fact that $|cA| = c^n|A|$, where A is an $n \times n$ matrix, we obtain

$$|2A| = 2^4|A| = 16(-1) = -16.$$

40.
$$\begin{vmatrix} 1 & 0 & 2 \\ 1 & -1 & 2 \\ 5 & 1 & 0 \end{vmatrix} = \begin{vmatrix} 1 & 0 & 2 \\ 1 & -1 & 2 \\ 2 & 1 & -1 \end{vmatrix} + \begin{vmatrix} 1 & 0 & 2 \\ 1 & -1 & 2 \\ 3 & 0 & 1 \end{vmatrix}$$
$$10 = 5 + 5$$

42.
$$\begin{vmatrix} a & 1 & 1 & 1 \\ 1 & a & 1 & 1 \\ 1 & 1 & a & 1 \\ 1 & 1 & 1 & a \end{vmatrix} = \begin{vmatrix} 0 & 1-a^2 & 1-a & 1-a \\ 1 & a & 1 & 1 \\ 0 & 1-a & a-1 & 0 \\ 0 & 1-a & 0 & a-1 \end{vmatrix}$$
$$= -\begin{vmatrix} 1-a^2 & 1-a & 1-a \\ 1-a & a-1 & 0 \\ 1-a & 0 & a-1 \end{vmatrix}$$
$$= (1-a)^3 \begin{vmatrix} 1+a & 1 & 1 \\ 1 & -1 & 0 \\ 1 & 0 & -1 \end{vmatrix} \quad \text{(factoring out } (1-a) \text{ from each row)}$$
$$= (1-a)^3(1(1) - 1(-1 - a - 1)) \quad \text{(expanding along the third row)}$$
$$= (1-a)^3(a+3)$$

44. $|\lambda I - A| = \begin{vmatrix} \lambda - 5 & -2 \\ -4 & \lambda - 1 \end{vmatrix} = (\lambda - 5)(\lambda - 1) - 8 = \lambda^2 - 6\lambda - 3$

$\lambda_1 = 3 + 2\sqrt{3}$ and $\lambda_2 = 3 - 2\sqrt{3}$

$\lambda_1 = 3 + 2\sqrt{3}: \begin{bmatrix} -2 + 2\sqrt{3} & -2 \\ -4 & 2 + 2\sqrt{3} \end{bmatrix} \rightarrow \begin{bmatrix} 1 & -\frac{1}{2} - \frac{1}{2}\sqrt{3} \\ -4 & 2 + 2\sqrt{3} \end{bmatrix}$

$\rightarrow \begin{bmatrix} 1 & -\frac{1}{2} - \frac{1}{2}\sqrt{3} \\ 0 & 0 \end{bmatrix} \Rightarrow x = \begin{bmatrix} 1 + \sqrt{3} \\ 2 \end{bmatrix}$

$\lambda_2 = 3 - 2\sqrt{3}: \begin{bmatrix} -2 - 2\sqrt{3} & -2 \\ -4 & 2 - 2\sqrt{3} \end{bmatrix} \rightarrow \begin{bmatrix} 1 & -\frac{1}{2} + \frac{1}{2}\sqrt{3} \\ -4 & 2 - 2\sqrt{3} \end{bmatrix}$

46. $|\lambda I - A| = \begin{vmatrix} \lambda + 3 & 0 & -4 \\ -2 & \lambda - 1 & -1 \\ 1 & 0 & \lambda - 1 \end{vmatrix} = (\lambda + 3)(\lambda - 1)^2 + 4(\lambda - 1)$

$= (\lambda - 1)(\lambda^2 + 2\lambda + 1)$

$= (\lambda - 1)(\lambda + 1)^2$

$\lambda_1 = 1, \lambda_2 = -1, \lambda_3 = -1$

$\lambda_1 = 1: \quad \begin{bmatrix} 4 & 0 & -4 \\ -2 & 0 & -1 \\ 1 & 0 & 0 \end{bmatrix} \begin{bmatrix} 1 & 0 & 0 \\ 0 & 0 & 1 \\ 0 & 0 & 0 \end{bmatrix} \Rightarrow x = \begin{bmatrix} 0 \\ 1 \\ 0 \end{bmatrix}$

$\lambda_2, \lambda_3 = -1: \begin{bmatrix} 2 & 0 & -4 \\ -2 & -2 & -1 \\ 1 & 0 & -2 \end{bmatrix} \begin{bmatrix} 1 & 0 & -2 \\ 0 & 1 & 2.5 \\ 0 & 0 & 0 \end{bmatrix} \Rightarrow x = \begin{bmatrix} 2 \\ -2.5 \\ 1 \end{bmatrix}$

48. $J(u, v) = \begin{vmatrix} \dfrac{\partial x}{\partial u} & \dfrac{\partial x}{\partial v} \\ \dfrac{\partial y}{\partial u} & \dfrac{\partial y}{\partial v} \end{vmatrix}$

$= \begin{vmatrix} a & b \\ c & d \end{vmatrix}$

$= ad - bc$

50. $J(u, v, w) = \begin{vmatrix} 1 & -1 & 1 \\ 2v & 2u & 0 \\ 1 & 1 & 1 \end{vmatrix} = 1(2u) + 1(2v) + 1(2v - 2u) = 4v$

52. Since $|B| \neq 0$, B^{-1} exists, and we can let $C = AB^{-1}$, then

$A = CB$ and $|C| = |AB^{-1}| = |A| \, |B^{-1}| = |A|\dfrac{1}{|B|} = 1.$

54. The matrix of cofactors is given by

$$\begin{bmatrix} 0 & 2 \\ -2 & 1 \end{bmatrix}.$$

Thus, the adjoint is

$$\text{adj} \begin{bmatrix} 1 & 2 \\ -2 & 0 \end{bmatrix} = \begin{bmatrix} 0 & -2 \\ 2 & 1 \end{bmatrix}.$$

56. The determinant of the coefficient matrix is

$$\begin{vmatrix} 2 & 1 \\ 3 & -1 \end{vmatrix} = -5 \neq 0.$$

Thus, the system has a unique solution. Using Cramer's Rule,

$$A_1 = \begin{bmatrix} 0.3 & 1 \\ -1.3 & -1 \end{bmatrix}, \ |A_1| = 1.0$$

$$A_2 = \begin{bmatrix} 2 & 0.3 \\ 3 & -1.3 \end{bmatrix}, \ |A_2| = -3.5.$$

Thus,

$$x = \frac{|A_1|}{|A|} = \frac{1}{-5} = -0.2$$

$$y = \frac{|A_2|}{|A|} = \frac{-3.5}{-5} = 0.7.$$

58. The determinant of the coefficient matrix is

$$\begin{vmatrix} 4 & 4 & 4 \\ 4 & -2 & -8 \\ 8 & 2 & -4 \end{vmatrix} = 0.$$

Thus, Cramer's Rule does not apply.

60. The formula for area yields

$$\text{Area} = \pm\tfrac{1}{2} \begin{vmatrix} x_1 & y_1 & 1 \\ x_2 & y_2 & 1 \\ x_3 & y_3 & 1 \end{vmatrix} = \pm\tfrac{1}{2} \begin{vmatrix} -4 & 0 & 1 \\ 4 & 0 & 1 \\ 0 & 6 & 1 \end{vmatrix}$$

$$= \pm\tfrac{1}{2}(-6)(-4-4) = 24.$$

62. We use the equation

$$\begin{vmatrix} x & y & 1 \\ x_1 & y_1 & 1 \\ x_2 & y_2 & 1 \end{vmatrix}$$

to find the equation of the line.

$$\begin{vmatrix} x & y & 1 \\ 2 & 5 & 1 \\ 6 & -1 & 1 \end{vmatrix} = x(6) - y(-4) - 32 = 0, \quad \text{or} \quad 2y + 3x = 16.$$

64. The equation of the plane is given by

$$\begin{vmatrix} x & y & z & 1 \\ x_1 & y_1 & z_1 & 1 \\ x_2 & y_2 & z_2 & 1 \\ x_3 & y_3 & z_3 & 1 \end{vmatrix} = 0$$

Thus, we have

$$\begin{vmatrix} x & y & z & 1 \\ 0 & 0 & 0 & 1 \\ 2 & -1 & 1 & 1 \\ -3 & 2 & 5 & 1 \end{vmatrix} = 1 \begin{vmatrix} x & y & z \\ 2 & -1 & 1 \\ -3 & 2 & 5 \end{vmatrix}$$

$$= x(-7) - y(13) + z(1) = 0$$

Hence, the equation of the plane is $7x + 13y - z = 0$.

66. (a) *False.* The *transpose* of the matrix of cofactors of A is called the adjoint matrix of A.

(b) *False.* Cramer's Rule requires the determinant of this matrix to be in the *numerator.* The denominator is always $\det(A)$ where A is the coefficient matrix of the system. (assuming, of course, that it is nonsingular).

Chapter 3 ❏ Project Solutions

1 Eigenvalues and Stochastic Matrices

1. $P\mathbf{x}_1 = P\begin{bmatrix} 7 \\ 10 \\ 4 \end{bmatrix} = \begin{bmatrix} 7 \\ 10 \\ 4 \end{bmatrix}$

$P\mathbf{x}_2 = P\begin{bmatrix} 0 \\ -1 \\ 1 \end{bmatrix} = \begin{bmatrix} 0 \\ -.65 \\ .65 \end{bmatrix}$

$P\mathbf{x}_3 = P\begin{bmatrix} -2 \\ 1 \\ 1 \end{bmatrix} = \begin{bmatrix} -1.1 \\ .55 \\ .55 \end{bmatrix}$

2. $S = \begin{bmatrix} 7 & 0 & -2 \\ 10 & -1 & 1 \\ 4 & 1 & 1 \end{bmatrix}$ $S^{-1}PS = \begin{bmatrix} 1 & 0 & 0 \\ 0 & .65 & 0 \\ 0 & 0 & .55 \end{bmatrix} = D$

The entries along D are the corresponding eigenvalues of P.

3. $S^{-1}PS = D \Rightarrow PS = SD \Rightarrow P = SDS^{-1}$. Then

$$P^n = (SDS^{-1})^n = (SDS^{-1})(SDS^{-1}) \cdots (SDS^{-1})$$
$$= SD^n S^{-1}$$

For $n = 10$, $D^n = \begin{bmatrix} 1 & 0 & 0 \\ 0 & (.65)^{10} & 0 \\ 0 & 0 & (.55)^{10} \end{bmatrix} \Rightarrow P^{10} = SD^{10}S^{-1} \approx \begin{bmatrix} .335 & .332 & .332 \\ .473 & .481 & .468 \\ .192 & .186 & .200 \end{bmatrix} \Rightarrow$

$$\Rightarrow P^{10}X \approx \begin{bmatrix} 33287 \\ 47147 \\ 19566 \end{bmatrix}$$

2 The Cayley-Hamilton Theorem

1. $|\lambda I - A| = \begin{vmatrix} \lambda - 2 & 2 \\ 2 & \lambda + 1 \end{vmatrix} = \lambda^2 - \lambda - 6$

$A^2 - A - 6I = \begin{bmatrix} 2 & -2 \\ -2 & -1 \end{bmatrix}\begin{bmatrix} 2 & -2 \\ -2 & -1 \end{bmatrix} - \begin{bmatrix} 2 & -2 \\ -2 & -1 \end{bmatrix} - 6\begin{bmatrix} 1 & 0 \\ 0 & 1 \end{bmatrix}$

$= \begin{bmatrix} 8 & -2 \\ -2 & 5 \end{bmatrix} - \begin{bmatrix} 8 & -2 \\ -2 & 5 \end{bmatrix} = \begin{bmatrix} 0 & 0 \\ 0 & 0 \end{bmatrix}$

2. $|\lambda I - A| = \begin{vmatrix} \lambda - 6 & 0 & -4 \\ 2 & \lambda - 1 & -3 \\ -2 & 0 & \lambda - 4 \end{vmatrix} = \lambda^3 - 11\lambda^2 + 26\lambda - 16$

$A^3 - 11A^2 + 26A - 16I = \begin{bmatrix} 344 & 0 & 336 \\ -36 & 1 & -1 \\ 168 & 0 & 176 \end{bmatrix} - 11\begin{bmatrix} 44 & 0 & 40 \\ -8 & 1 & 7 \\ 20 & 0 & 24 \end{bmatrix}$

$+ 26\begin{bmatrix} 6 & 0 & 4 \\ -2 & 1 & 3 \\ 2 & 0 & 4 \end{bmatrix} - 16\begin{bmatrix} 1 & 0 & 0 \\ 0 & 1 & 0 \\ 0 & 0 & 1 \end{bmatrix} = \begin{bmatrix} 0 & 0 & 0 \\ 0 & 0 & 0 \\ 0 & 0 & 0 \end{bmatrix}$.

3. $|\lambda I - A| = \begin{vmatrix} \lambda - a & -b \\ -c & \lambda - d \end{vmatrix} = \lambda^2 - (a + d)\lambda + (ad - bc)$

$A^2 - (a + d)A + (ad - bc)I = \begin{bmatrix} a^2 + bc & ab + bd \\ ac + dc & bc + d^2 \end{bmatrix} - (a + d)\begin{bmatrix} a & b \\ c & d \end{bmatrix}$

$+ (ad - bc)\begin{bmatrix} 1 & 0 \\ 0 & 1 \end{bmatrix} = \begin{bmatrix} 0 & 0 \\ 0 & 0 \end{bmatrix}$

4. $\left(\dfrac{1}{c_0}\right)(-A^{n-1} - c_{n-1}A^{n-2} - \cdots - c_2 A - c_1 I)A$

$= \dfrac{1}{c_0}(-A^n - c_{n-1}A^{n-1} - \cdots - c_2 A^2 - c_1 A) = \dfrac{1}{c_0}(c_0 I) = I$

Since $c_0 I = -A^n - c_{n-1}A^{n-1} - \cdots - c_2 A^2 - c_1 A$ from the equation $p(A) = 0$.

$$|\lambda I - A| = \begin{vmatrix} \lambda - 1 & -2 \\ -3 & \lambda - 5 \end{vmatrix} = \lambda^2 - 6\lambda - 1$$

$$A^{-1} = \dfrac{1}{(-1)}(-A + 6I) = A - 6I = \begin{bmatrix} -5 & 2 \\ 3 & -1 \end{bmatrix}.$$

5. (a) Since $A^2 = 2A + I$ we have $A^3 = 2A^2 + A = 2(2A + I) + A = 5A + 2I$.

$$A^3 = 5\begin{bmatrix} 3 & -1 \\ 2 & -1 \end{bmatrix} + 2\begin{bmatrix} 1 & 0 \\ 0 & 1 \end{bmatrix} = \begin{bmatrix} 17 & -5 \\ 10 & -3 \end{bmatrix}.$$

Similarly, $A^4 = 2A^3 + A^2 = 2(5A + 2I) + (2A + I) = 12A + 5I$. Therefore,

$$A^4 = 12\begin{bmatrix} 3 & -1 \\ 2 & -1 \end{bmatrix} + 5\begin{bmatrix} 1 & 0 \\ 0 & 1 \end{bmatrix} = \begin{bmatrix} 41 & -12 \\ 24 & -7 \end{bmatrix}.$$

Note: This approach is a lot more efficient, since we can calculate A^n without calculating all the previous powers of A.

(b) First we calculate the characteristic polynomial of A.

$$|\lambda I - A| = \begin{vmatrix} \lambda & 0 & -1 \\ -2 & \lambda - 2 & 1 \\ -1 & 0 & \lambda - 2 \end{vmatrix} = \lambda^3 - 4\lambda^2 + 3\lambda + 2.$$

By Cayley-Hamilton Theorem $A^3 - 4A^2 + 3A + 2I = O$ or $A^3 = 4A^2 - 3A - 2I$. Now we can express any positive power A^n as a linear combination of A^2, A and I. For example,

$$A^4 = 4A^3 - 3A^2 - 2A = 4(4A^2 - 3A - 2I) - 3A^2 - 2A = 13A^2 - 14A - 8I,$$

$$A^5 = 4A^4 - 3A^3 - 2A^2 = 4(13A^2 - 14A - 8I) - 3(4A^2 - 3A - 2I) - 2A^2$$

$$= 38A^2 - 47A - 26I.$$

Here

$$A = \begin{bmatrix} 0 & 0 & 1 \\ 2 & 2 & -1 \\ 1 & 0 & 2 \end{bmatrix}, \quad A^2 = AA = \begin{bmatrix} 0 & 0 & 1 \\ 2 & 2 & -1 \\ 1 & 0 & 2 \end{bmatrix}\begin{bmatrix} 0 & 0 & 1 \\ 2 & 2 & -1 \\ 1 & 0 & 2 \end{bmatrix} = \begin{bmatrix} 1 & 0 & 2 \\ 3 & 4 & -2 \\ 2 & 0 & 5 \end{bmatrix}.$$

—CONTINUED—

5. —CONTINUED—

With this method we can calculate A^5 directly without calculating A^3 and A^4 first.

$$A^5 = 38A^2 - 47A - 26I = 38 \begin{bmatrix} 1 & 0 & 2 \\ 3 & 4 & -2 \\ 2 & 0 & 5 \end{bmatrix} - 47 \begin{bmatrix} 0 & 0 & 1 \\ 2 & 2 & -1 \\ 1 & 0 & 2 \end{bmatrix} - 26 \begin{bmatrix} 1 & 0 & 0 \\ 0 & 1 & 0 \\ 0 & 0 & 1 \end{bmatrix}$$

$$= \begin{bmatrix} 12 & 0 & 29 \\ 20 & 32 & -29 \\ 29 & 0 & 70 \end{bmatrix}$$

Similarly,

$$A^4 = 13A^2 - 14A - 8I = 13 \begin{bmatrix} 1 & 0 & 2 \\ 3 & 4 & -2 \\ 2 & 0 & 5 \end{bmatrix} - 14 \begin{bmatrix} 0 & 0 & 1 \\ 2 & 2 & -1 \\ 1 & 0 & 2 \end{bmatrix} - 8 \begin{bmatrix} 1 & 0 & 0 \\ 0 & 1 & 0 \\ 0 & 0 & 1 \end{bmatrix}$$

$$= \begin{bmatrix} 5 & 0 & 12 \\ 11 & 16 & -12 \\ 12 & 0 & 29 \end{bmatrix}$$

$$A^3 = 4A^2 - 3A - 2I = \begin{bmatrix} 2 & 0 & 5 \\ 6 & 8 & -5 \\ 5 & 0 & 12 \end{bmatrix}.$$

CHAPTER 4
Vector Spaces

Section 4.1   Vectors in R^n

2. $\mathbf{v} = \mathbf{u} + \mathbf{w} = (-2, 3) + (-3, -2) = (-5, 1)$

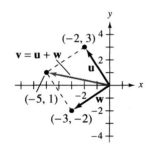

4. $\mathbf{v} = -\mathbf{u} + \mathbf{w}$

$$= -(-2, 3) + (-3, -2) = (-1, -5)$$

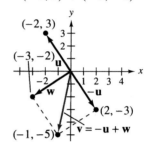

6. $\mathbf{v} = \mathbf{u} - 2\mathbf{w} = (-2, 3) - 2(-3, -2) = (4, 7)$

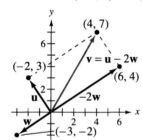

8. (a) $4\mathbf{v} = 4(3, -2) = (12, -8)$

(b) $-\frac{1}{2}\mathbf{v} = -\frac{1}{2}(3, -2) = \left(-\frac{3}{2}, 1\right)$

(c) $0\mathbf{v} = 0(3, -2) = (0, 0)$

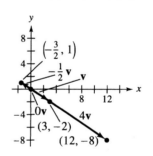

10. $\mathbf{u} - \mathbf{v} + 2\mathbf{w} = (1, 2, 3) - (2, 2, -1) + 2(4, 0, -4)$

$$= (-1, 0, 4) + (8, 0, -8) = (7, 0, -4)$$

12. $5\mathbf{u} - 3\mathbf{v} - \frac{1}{2}\mathbf{w} = 5(1, 2, 3) - 3(2, 2, -1) - \frac{1}{2}(4, 0, -4)$

$$= (5, 10, 15) - (6, 6, -3) - (2, 0, -2)$$

$$= (-3, 4, 20)$$

14. $2\mathbf{u} + \mathbf{v} - \mathbf{w} + 3\mathbf{z} = \mathbf{0}$ implies that $3\mathbf{z} = -2\mathbf{u} - \mathbf{v} + \mathbf{w}$.

Hence,

$$3\mathbf{z} = -2(1, 2, 3) - (2, 2, -1) + (4, 0, -4)$$
$$= (-2, -4, -6) - (2, 2, -1) + (4, 0, -4) = (0, -6, -9).$$

Finally, $\mathbf{z} = \frac{1}{3}(0, -6, -9) = (0, -2, -3)$.

16. (a) $-\mathbf{v} = -(2, 0, 1) = (-2, 0, -1)$

    (b) $2\mathbf{v} = 2(2, 0, 1) = (\ 4, 0,\ \ 2)$

    (c) $\frac{1}{2}\mathbf{v} = \frac{1}{2}(2, 0, 1) = (\ 1, 0,\ \ \frac{1}{2})$

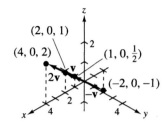

18. (a) Since $(6, -4, 9) \neq c\left(\frac{1}{2}, -\frac{2}{3}, \frac{3}{4}\right)$ for any c, $\mathbf{u}$ is *not* a scalar multiple of $\mathbf{z}$.

    (b) Since $\left(-1, \frac{4}{3}, -\frac{3}{2}\right) = -2\left(\frac{1}{2}, -\frac{2}{3}, \frac{3}{4}\right)$, $\mathbf{v}$ is a scalar multiple of $\mathbf{z}$.

    (c) Since $(12, 0, 9) \neq c\left(\frac{1}{2}, -\frac{2}{3}, \frac{3}{4}\right)$ for any c, $\mathbf{w}$ is *not* a scalar multiple of $\mathbf{z}$.

20. (a) $\mathbf{u} - \mathbf{v} = (0, 4, 3, 4, 4) - (6, 8, -3, 3, -5) = (-6, -4, 6, 1, 9)$

    (b) $2(\mathbf{u} + 3\mathbf{v}) = 2[(0, 4, 3, 4, 4) + 3(6, 8, -3, 3, -5)]$

$$= 2[(0, 4, 3, 4, 4) + (18, 24, -9, 9, -15)]$$

$$= 2(18, 28, -6, 13, -11)$$

$$= (36, 56, -12, 26, -22)$$

22. (a) $\mathbf{u} - \mathbf{v} = (6, -5, 4, 3) - \left(-2, \frac{5}{3}, -\frac{4}{3}, -1\right) = \left(8, -\frac{20}{3}, \frac{16}{3}, 4\right)$

    (b) $2(\mathbf{u} + 3\mathbf{v}) = 2\left[(6, -5, 4, 3) + 3\left(-2, \frac{5}{3}, -\frac{4}{3}, -1\right)\right]$

$$= 2[(6, -5, 4, 3) + (-6, 5, -4, -3)]$$

$$= 2(0, 0, 0, 0)$$

$$= (0, 0, 0, 0)$$

24. Using a TI-86 calculator with $\mathbf{u} = (1, 2, -3, 1)$, $\mathbf{v} = (0, 2, -1, -2)$, and $\mathbf{w} = (2, -2, 1, 3)$ we have:

    (a) $\mathbf{v} + 3\mathbf{w} = (6, -4, 2, 7)$

    (b) $2\mathbf{w} - \frac{1}{2}\mathbf{u} = \left(\frac{7}{2}, -5, \frac{7}{2}, \frac{11}{2}\right)$

    (c) $2\mathbf{u} + \mathbf{w} - 3\mathbf{v} = (4, -4, -2, 11)$

    (d) $\frac{1}{2}(4\mathbf{v} - 3\mathbf{u} + \mathbf{w}) = \left(-\frac{1}{2}, 0, 3, -4\right)$

26. $\mathbf{w} + \mathbf{u} = -\mathbf{v}$

$$\mathbf{w} = -\mathbf{v} - \mathbf{u}$$

$$= -(0, 2, 3, -1) - (1, -1, 0, 1)$$

$$= (-1, -1, -3, 0)$$

28. The equation

$$a\mathbf{u} + b\mathbf{w} = \mathbf{v}$$
$$a(1, 2) + b(1, -1) = (0, 3)$$

yields the system

$$a + b = 0$$
$$2a - b = 3.$$

Solving this system produces $a = 1$ and $b = -1$. Thus, $\mathbf{v} = \mathbf{u} - \mathbf{w}$.

30. The equation

$$a\mathbf{u} + b\mathbf{w} = \mathbf{v}$$
$$a(1, 2) + b(1, -1) = (1, -1)$$

yields the system

$$a + b = 1$$
$$2a - b = -1.$$

Solving this system produces $a = 0$ and $b = 1$. Thus, $\mathbf{v} = \mathbf{w} = 0\mathbf{u} + 1\mathbf{w}$.

32. The equation

$$a\mathbf{u} + b\mathbf{w} = \mathbf{v}$$
$$a(1, 2) + b(1, -1) = (1, -4)$$

yields the system

$$a + b = 1$$
$$2a - b = -4.$$

Solving this system produces $a = -1$ and $b = 2$. Thus, $\mathbf{v} = -\mathbf{u} + 2\mathbf{w}$.

34. $2\mathbf{u} + \mathbf{v} - 3\mathbf{w} = 0$

$$\mathbf{w} = \tfrac{2}{3}\mathbf{u} + \tfrac{1}{3}\mathbf{v}$$
$$= \tfrac{2}{3}(0, 0, -8, 1) + \tfrac{1}{3}(1, -8, 0, 7)$$
$$= \left(0, 0, -\tfrac{16}{3}, \tfrac{2}{3}\right) + \left(\tfrac{1}{3}, -\tfrac{8}{3}, 0, \tfrac{7}{3}\right)$$
$$= \left(\tfrac{1}{3}, -\tfrac{8}{3}, -\tfrac{16}{3}, 3\right)$$

36. The equation

$$a\mathbf{u}_1 + b\mathbf{u}_2 + c\mathbf{u}_3 = \mathbf{v}$$
$$a(1, 3, 5) + b(2, -1, 3) + c(-3, 2, -4) = (-1, 7, 2)$$

yields the system

$$a + 2b - 3c = -1$$
$$3a - b + 2c = 7$$
$$5a + 3b - 4c = 2$$

Solving this system we discover that there is no solution, Thus, $\mathbf{v}$ cannot be written as a linear combination of $\mathbf{u}_1$, $\mathbf{u}_2$ and $\mathbf{u}_3$.

38. The equation

$$a\mathbf{u}_1 + b\mathbf{u}_2 + c\mathbf{u}_3 = \mathbf{v}$$

$$a(1, 3, 2, 1) + b(2, -2, -5, 4) + c(2, -1, 3, 6) = (2, 5, -4, 0)$$

yields the system

$$
\begin{aligned}
a + 2b + 2c &= 2 \\
3a - 2b - c &= 5 \\
2a - 5b + 3c &= -4 \\
a + 4b + 6c &= 0
\end{aligned}
$$

Solving this system produces $a = 2$, $b = 1$ and $c = -1$. Thus, $\mathbf{v} = 2\mathbf{u}_1 + \mathbf{u}_2 - \mathbf{u}_3$.

40. Write a matrix using the given $\mathbf{u}_1, \mathbf{u}_2, \ldots, \mathbf{u}_6$ as columns and augment this matrix with $\mathbf{v}$ as a column. That gives us

$$
A = \begin{bmatrix}
1 & 3 & 1 & 3 & 1 & 4 & 8 \\
-3 & -2 & 1 & -1 & -2 & 2 & 17 \\
4 & 4 & 1 & 3 & 1 & -1 & -16 \\
-5 & -3 & -1 & -4 & 5 & 3 & 26 \\
2 & -2 & 4 & 2 & -3 & -1 & 0 \\
-1 & 1 & -1 & 3 & 4 & 1 & -4
\end{bmatrix}.
$$

The reduced row-echelon form for A is

$$
\begin{bmatrix}
1 & 0 & 0 & 0 & 0 & 0 & -1 \\
0 & 1 & 0 & 0 & 0 & 0 & -1 \\
0 & 0 & 1 & 0 & 0 & 0 & 2 \\
0 & 0 & 0 & 1 & 0 & 0 & -2 \\
0 & 0 & 0 & 0 & 1 & 0 & 0 \\
0 & 0 & 0 & 0 & 0 & 1 & 4
\end{bmatrix}.
$$

So, $\mathbf{v} = (8, 17, -16, 26, 0, -4) = -\mathbf{u}_1 - 1\mathbf{u}_2 + 2\mathbf{u}_3 - 2\mathbf{u}_4 + 4\mathbf{u}_6$. We verify the solution by showing that

$$
\begin{aligned}
-1(1, -3, 4, -5, 2, -1) &- 1(3, -2, 4, -3, -2, 1) + 2(1, 1, 1, -1, 4, -1) \\
&- 2(3, -1, 3, -4, 2, 3) + 4(4, 2, -1, 3, -1, 1)
\end{aligned}
$$

equals $(8, 17, -16, 26, 0, -4)$.

42. (a) *True.* See page 179.

(b) *False.* The zero vector is defined as an additive identity.

44. The equation

$$a\mathbf{v}_1 + b\mathbf{v}_2 + c\mathbf{v}_3 = \mathbf{0}$$

$$a(1, 0, 1) + b(-1, 1, 2) + c(0, 1, 3) = (0, 0, 0)$$

yields the homogeneous system

$$
\begin{aligned}
a - b &= 0 \\
b + c &= 0 \\
a + 2b + 3c &= 0.
\end{aligned}
$$

Solving this system we find that $a = -t$, $b = -t$ and $c = t$, where t is any real number. For instance, taking $t = -1$, we obtain $a = 1$, $b = 1$, $c = -1$, and hence, $\mathbf{v}_1 + \mathbf{v}_2 - \mathbf{v}_3 = \mathbf{0}$.

46. (1) $\mathbf{u} + \mathbf{v} = (2, -1, 3) + (3, 4, 0) = (5, 3, 3)$ is a vector in R^3.

(2) $\mathbf{u} + \mathbf{v} = (2, -1, 3) + (3, 4, 0) = (5, 3, 3) = (3, 4, 0) + (2, -1, 3) = \mathbf{v} + \mathbf{u}$

(3) $(\mathbf{u} + \mathbf{v}) + \mathbf{w} = [(2, -1, 3) + (3, 4, 0)] + (7, 8, -4)$

$$= (5, 3, 3) + (7, 8, -4) = (12, 11, -1)$$

$\mathbf{u} + (\mathbf{v} + \mathbf{w}) = (2, -1, 3) + [(3, 4, 0) + (7, 8, -4)]$

$$= (2, -1, 3) + (10, 12, -4) = (12, 11 - 1)$$

Hence, $(\mathbf{u} + \mathbf{v}) + \mathbf{w} = \mathbf{u} + (\mathbf{v} + \mathbf{w})$.

(4) $\mathbf{u} + \mathbf{0} = (2, -1, 3) + (0, 0, 0) = (2, -1, 3) = \mathbf{u}$

(5) $\mathbf{u} + (-\mathbf{u}) = (2, -1, 3) + (-2, 1, -3) = (0, 0, 0) = \mathbf{0}$

(6) $c\mathbf{u} = 2(2, -1, 3) = (4, -2, 6)$ is a vector in R^3.

(7) $c(\mathbf{u} + \mathbf{v}) = 2[(2, -1, 3) + (3, 4, 0)] = 2(5, 3, 3) = (10, 6, 6)$

$c\mathbf{u} + c\mathbf{v} = 2(2, -1, 3) + 2(3, 4, 0) = (4, -2, 6) + (6, 8, 0) = (10, 6, 6)$

Hence, $c(\mathbf{u} + \mathbf{v}) = c\mathbf{u} + c\mathbf{v}$.

(8) $(c + d)\mathbf{u} = (2 + (-1))(2, -1, 3) = 1(2, -1, 3) = (2, -1, 3)$

$c\mathbf{u} + d\mathbf{u} = 2(2, -1, 3) + (-1)(2, -1, 3)$

$$= (4, -2, 6) + (-2, 1, -3) = (2, -1, 3)$$

Hence, $(c + d)\mathbf{u} = c\mathbf{u} + d\mathbf{u}$.

(9) $c(d\mathbf{u}) = 2((-1)(2, -1, 3)) = 2(-2, 1, -3) = (-4, 2, -6)$

$(cd)\mathbf{u} = (2(-1))(2, -1, 3) = (-2)(2, -1, 3) = (-4, 2, -6)$

Hence, $c(d\mathbf{u}) = (cd)\mathbf{u}$.

(10) $1\mathbf{u} = 1(2, -1, 3) = (2, -1, 3) = \mathbf{u}$

48. We prove each of the ten properties.

(1) $\mathbf{u} + \mathbf{v} = (u_1, \ldots, u_n) + (v_1, \ldots, v_n) = (u_1 + v_1, \ldots, u_n + v_n)$ is a vector in R^n.

(2) $\mathbf{u} + \mathbf{v} = (u_1, \ldots, u_n) + (v_1, \ldots, v_n) = (u_1 + v_1, \ldots, u_n + v_n)$

$$= (v_1 + u_1, \ldots, v_n + u_n)$$

$$= (v_1, \ldots, v_n) + (u_1, \ldots, u_n) = \mathbf{v} + \mathbf{u}$$

(3) $(\mathbf{u} + \mathbf{v}) + \mathbf{w} = [(u_1, \ldots, u_n) + (v_1, \ldots, v_n)] + (w_1, \ldots, w_n)$

$$= (u_1 + v_1, \ldots, u_n + v_n) + (w_1, \ldots, w_n)$$

$$= ((u_1 + v_1) + w_1, \ldots, (u_n + v_n) + w_n)$$

$$= (u_1 + (v_1 + w_1), \ldots, u_n + (v_n + w_n))$$

$$= (u_1, \ldots, u_n) + (v_1 + w_1, \ldots, v_n + w_n)$$

$$= (u_1, \ldots, u_n) + [(v_1, \ldots, v_n) + (w_1, \ldots, w_n)]$$

$$= \mathbf{u} + (\mathbf{v} + \mathbf{w})$$

(4) $\mathbf{u} + \mathbf{0} = (u_1, \ldots, u_n) + (0, \ldots, 0) = (u_1 + 0, \ldots, u_n + 0) = (u_1, \ldots, u_n) = \mathbf{u}$

(5) $\mathbf{u} + (-\mathbf{u}) = (u_1, \ldots, u_n) + (-u_1, \ldots, -u_n)$

$$= (u_1 - u_1, \ldots, u_n - u_n) = (0, \ldots, 0) = \mathbf{0}$$

(6) $c\mathbf{u} = c(u_1, \ldots, u_n) = (cu_1, \ldots, cu_n)$ is a vector in R^n.

—CONTINUED—

48. —CONTINUED—

(7) $c(\mathbf{u} + \mathbf{v}) = c[(u_1, \ldots, u_n) + (v_1, \ldots, v_n)] = c(u_1 + v_1, \ldots, u_n + v_n)$

$\qquad = (c(u_1 + v_1), \ldots, c(u_n + v_n)) = (cu_1 + cv_1, \ldots, cu_n + cv_n)$

$\qquad = (cu_1, \ldots, cu_n) + (cv_1, \ldots, cv_n)$

$\qquad = c(u_1, \ldots, u_n) + c(v_1, \ldots, cv_n) = c\mathbf{u} + c\mathbf{v}$

(8) $(c + d)\mathbf{u} = (c + d)(u_1, \ldots, u_n) = ((c + d)u_1, \ldots, (c + d)u_n)$

$\qquad = (cu_1 + du_1, \ldots, cu_n + du_n)$

$\qquad = (cu_1, \ldots, cu_n) + (du_1, \ldots du_n)$

$\qquad = c\mathbf{u} + d\mathbf{u}$

(9) $c(d\mathbf{u}) = c(d(u_1, \ldots, u_n)) = c(du_1, \ldots, du_n) = (c(du_1), \ldots, c(du_n))$

$\qquad = ((cd)u_1, \ldots, (cd)u_n) = (cd)(u_1, \ldots, u_n) = (cd)\mathbf{u}$

(10) $1\mathbf{u} = 1(u_1, \ldots, u_n) = (1u_1, \ldots, 1u_1) = (u_1, \ldots, u_n) = \mathbf{u}$

50. *Justification for each step:*

(a) Use the fact that $c + 0 = 0$ for any real number c, thus, in particular, $0 = 0 + 0$.

(b) Use property 8 of Theorem 4.2.

(c) The fact that an equality remains an equality if we add the same vector to both sides. We also used property 6 of Theorem 4.2 to conclude that $0\mathbf{v}$ is a vector in R^n, thus, $-0\mathbf{v}$ is a vector in R^n.

(d) Property 5 of Theorem 4.2 is applied to the left hand side. Property 3 of Theorem 4.2 is applied to the right hand side.

(e) Use properties 5 and 6 of Theorem 4.2

(f) Use properties 4 of Theorem 4.2.

52. *Justification for each step.*

(a) Equality remains if both sides are multiplied by a non-zero constant. Property 6 of Theorem 4.2 assures us that the results are still in R^n.

(b) Use property 9 of Theorem 4.2 on the left side and property 4 of Theorem 4.3 (proved in exercise 51) on the right side.

(c) Use the property of reals that states that the product of multiplicative inverses is 1.

(d) Use property 10 of Theorem 4.2.

54. (a) $\begin{bmatrix} 1 & 2 & 3 \\ 7 & 8 & 9 \\ 4 & 5 & 6 \end{bmatrix} \Rightarrow \begin{bmatrix} 1 & 0 & -1 \\ 0 & 1 & 2 \\ 0 & 0 & 0 \end{bmatrix}$

Yes. $\begin{bmatrix} 3 \\ 9 \\ 6 \end{bmatrix} = (-1)\begin{bmatrix} 1 \\ 7 \\ 4 \end{bmatrix} + 2\begin{bmatrix} 2 \\ 8 \\ 5 \end{bmatrix}$

(b) $\begin{bmatrix} 1 & 2 & 3 \\ 7 & 8 & 9 \\ 4 & 5 & 7 \end{bmatrix} \Rightarrow \begin{bmatrix} 1 & 0 & 0 \\ 0 & 1 & 0 \\ 0 & 0 & 1 \end{bmatrix}$

No.

56. You could describe vector subtraction $\mathbf{u} - \mathbf{v}$ as follows

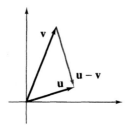

Or, write subtraction in terms of addition, $\mathbf{u} - \mathbf{v} = \mathbf{u} + (-1)\mathbf{v}$.

Section 4.2   Vector Spaces

2. The additive identity of $C(-\infty, \infty)$ is the zero function, $f(x) = 0$.

4. The additive identity of $M_{1,4}$ is the 1×4 zero matrix

$[0 \quad 0 \quad 0 \quad 0]$.

6. The additive identity of $M_{2,2}$ is the 2×2 zero matrix

$\begin{bmatrix} 0 & 0 \\ 0 & 0 \end{bmatrix}$.

8. In $C(-\infty, \infty)$, the additive inverse of $f(x)$ is $-f(x)$.

10. In $M_{1,4}$, the additive inverse of $[v_1 \quad v_2 \quad v_3 \quad v_4]$ is $[-v_1 \quad -v_2 \quad -v_3 \quad -v_4]$.

12. In $M_{2,2}$, the additive inverse of

$\begin{bmatrix} a & b \\ c & d \end{bmatrix}$ is $\begin{bmatrix} -a & -b \\ -c & -d \end{bmatrix}$.

14. $M_{1,1}$ with the standard operations is a vector space. All ten vector space axioms hold.

16. *P*, the set of all polynomials with the standard operations, is a vector space. All ten vector space axioms hold.

18. This set is *not* a vector space. The set is not closed under scalar multiplication. For example, $(-1)(3, 2) = (-3, -2)$ is not in the set.

20. This set is *not* a vector space. The set is not closed under addition nor scalar multiplication. A counterexample is

$$\begin{bmatrix} 1 & 1 \\ 1 & 1 \end{bmatrix} + \begin{bmatrix} 1 & 1 \\ 1 & 1 \end{bmatrix} = \begin{bmatrix} 2 & 2 \\ 2 & 2 \end{bmatrix}.$$

Each matrix on the left is in the set, while their sum is not.

22. This set is *not* a vector space. The set is not closed under addition nor scalar multiplication. A counterexample is

$$\begin{bmatrix} 1 & 0 \\ 0 & 1 \end{bmatrix} + \begin{bmatrix} 1 & 0 \\ 0 & -1 \end{bmatrix} = \begin{bmatrix} 2 & 0 \\ 0 & 0 \end{bmatrix}.$$

Each matrix on the left is nonsingular, while their sum is not.

24. $C[0, 1]$ is a vector space. All ten vector space axioms hold.

26. (a) Axiom 10 fails. For example,

$$1(2, 3, 4) = (2, 3, 0) \neq (2, 3, 4).$$

(b) Axiom 4 fails because there is no zero vector. For instance,
$(2, 3, 4) + (x, y, z) = (0, 0, 0) \neq (2, 3, 4)$ for all choices of (x, y, z).

(c) Axiom 7 fails. For example,

$$2[(1, 1, 1) + (1, 1, 1)] = 2(3, 3, 3) = (6, 6, 6)$$
$$2(1, 1, 1) + 2(1, 1, 1) = (2, 2, 2) + (2, 2, 2) = (5, 5, 5)$$

Hence, $c(\mathbf{u} + \mathbf{v}) \neq c\mathbf{u} + c\mathbf{v}$.

(d) $(x_1, y_1, z_1) + (x_2, y_2, z_2) = (x_1 + x_2 + 1, y_1 + y_2 + 1, z_1 + z_2 + 1)$
$\qquad\qquad c(x, y, z) = (cx + c - 1, cy + c - 1, cz + c - 1)$

This is a vector space. We verify the 10 axioms.

(1) $(x_1, y_1, z_1) + (x_2, y_2, z_2) \in R^3$

(2) $(x_1, y_1, z_1) + (x_2, y_2, z_2) = (x_1 + x_2 + 1, y_1 + y_2 + 1, z_1 + z_2 + 1)$
$\qquad\qquad = (x_2 + x_1 + 1, y_2 + y_1 + 1, z_2 + z_1 + 1)$
$\qquad\qquad = (x_2, y_2, z_2) + (x_1, y_1, z_1)$

(3) $(x_1, y_1, z_1) + [(x_2, y_2, z_2) + (x_3, y_3, z_3)]$
$\qquad = (x_1, y_1, z_1) + (x_2 + x_3 + 1, y_2 + y_3 + 1, z_2 + z_3 + 1)$
$\qquad = (x_1 + (x_2 + x_3 + 1) + 1, y_1 + (y_2 + y_3 + 1) + 1, z_1 + (z_2 + z_3 + 1) + 1)$
$\qquad = ((x_1 + x_2 + 1) + x_3 + 1, (y_1 + y_2 + 1) + y_3 + 1, (z_1 + z_2 + 1) + z_3 + 1)$
$\qquad = (x_1 + x_2 + 1, y_1 + y_2 + 1, z_1 + z_2 + 1) + (x_3, y_3, z_3)$
$\qquad = [(x_1, y_1, z_1) + (x_2, y_2, z_2)] + (x_3, y_3, z_3)$

—CONTINUED—

26. —CONTINUED—

(4) $\mathbf{0} = (-1, -1, -1)$: $(x, y, z) + (-1, -1, -1) = (x - 1 + 1, y - 1 + 1, z - 1 + 1)$
$$= (x, y, z)$$

(5) $-(x, y, z) = (-x - 2, -y - 2, -z - 2)$:

$(x, y, z) + (-(x, y, z)) = (x, y, z) + (-x - 2, -y - 2, -z - 2)$
$$= (x - x - 2 + 1, y - y - 2 + 1, z - z - 2 + 1)$$
$$= (-1, -1, -1)$$
$$= \mathbf{0}$$

(6) $c(x, y, z) \in R^3$

(7) $c((x_1, y_1, z_1) + (x_2, y_2, z_2)) =$
$$= c(x_1 + x_2 + 1, y_1 + y_2 + 1, z_1 + z_2 + 1)$$
$$= (c(x_1 + x_2 + 1) + c - 1, c(y_1 + y_2 + 1) + c - 1, c(z_1 + z_2 + 1) + c - 1)$$
$$= (cx_1 + c - 1 + cx_2 + c - 1 + 1, cy_1 + c - 1 + cy_2 + c - 1 + 1,$$
$$cz_1 + c - 1 + cz_2 + c - 1 + 1)$$
$$= (cx_1 + c - 1, cy_1 + c - 1, cz_1 + c - 1) + (cx_2 + c - 1, cy_2 + c - 1, cz_2 + c - 1)$$
$$= c(x_1, y_1, z_1) + c(x_2, y_2, z_2)$$

(8) $(c + d)(x, y, z) = ((c + d)x + c + d - 1, (c + d)y + c + d - 1, (c + d)z + c + d - 1)$
$$= (cx + c - 1 + dx + d - 1 + 1, cy + c - 1 + dy + d - 1 + 1,$$
$$cz + c - 1 + dz + d - 1 + 1)$$
$$= (cx + c - 1, cy + c - 1, cz + c - 1) + (dx + d - 1, dy + d - 1, dz + d - 1)$$
$$= c(x, y, z) + d(x, y, z)$$

(9) $c(d(x, y, z) = c(dx + d - 1, dy + d - 1, dz + d - 1)$
$$= (c(dx + d - 1) + c - 1, c(dy + d - 1) + c - 1, c(dz + d - 1) + c - 1)$$
$$= ((cd)x + cd - 1, (cd)y + cd - 1, (cd)z + cd - 1)$$
$$= (cd)(x, y, z)$$

(10) $1(x, y, z) = (1x + 1 - 1, 1y + 1 - 1, 1z + 1 - 1)$
$$= (x, y, z)$$

Note: In general, if V is a vector space and a is a constant vector, then the set V together with the operations
$$u \oplus v = (u + a) + (v + a) - a$$
$$c * u = c(u + a) - a$$
is also a vector space. Letting $a = (1, 1, 1) \in R^3$ gives the above example.

28. We verify the ten axioms in the definition of vector space.

(1) $\mathbf{u} + \mathbf{v} = (u, 2u) + (v, 2v) = (u + v, 2u + 2v)$
$$= (u + v, 2(u + v)) \text{ is in the set.}$$

(2) $\mathbf{u} + \mathbf{v} = (u, 2u) + (v, 2v) = (u + v, 2u + 2v)$
$$= (v + u, 2v + 2u) = (v, 2v) + (u, 2u) = \mathbf{v} + \mathbf{u}.$$

—CONTINUED—

28. —CONTINUED—

(3) $\mathbf{u} + (\mathbf{v} + \mathbf{w}) = (u, 2u) + [(v, 2v) + (w, 2w)] = (u, 2u) + (v + w, 2v + 2w)$

$\qquad = (u + (v + w), 2u + (2v + 2w)) = ((u + v) + w, (2u + 2v) + 2w)$

$\qquad = (u + v, 2u + 2v) + (w, 2w) = [(u, 2u) + (v, 2v)] + (w, 2w)$

$\qquad = (\mathbf{u} + \mathbf{v}) + \mathbf{w}$

(4) The zero vector is

$\qquad \mathbf{0} = (0, 0)$

$\qquad \mathbf{u} + \mathbf{0} = (u, 2u) + (0, 0) = (u, 2u) = \mathbf{u}.$

(5) The additive inverse of $(u, 2u)$ is

$\qquad (-u, -2u) = (-u, 2(-u)).$

$\qquad \mathbf{u} + (-\mathbf{u}) = (u, 2u) + (-u, 2(-u)) = (0, 0) = \mathbf{0}$

(6) $c\mathbf{u} = c(u, 2u) = (cu, 2(cu))$ is in the set.

(7) $c(\mathbf{u} + \mathbf{v}) = c[(u, 2u) + (v, 2v)] = c(u + v, 2u + 2v)$

$\qquad = (c(u + v), c(2u + 2v)) = (cu + cv, c(2u) + c(2v))$

$\qquad = (cu, c(2u)) + (cv, c(2v)) = c(u, 2u) + c(v, 2v)$

$\qquad = c\mathbf{u} + c\mathbf{v}$

(8) $(c + d)\mathbf{u} = (c + d)(u, 2u) = ((c + d)u, (c + d)2u) = (cu + du, c(2u) + d(2u))$

$\qquad = (cu, c(2u)) + (du, d(2u)) = c(u, 2u) + d(u, 2u)$

$\qquad = c\mathbf{u} + d\mathbf{u}$

(9) $c(d\mathbf{u}) = c(d(u, 2u)) = c(du, d(2u)) = (c(du), c(d(2u)))$

$\qquad = ((cd)u, (cd)(2u)) = (cd)(u, 2u) = (cd)\mathbf{u}$

(10) $1(\mathbf{u}) = 1(u, 2u) = (u, 2u) = \mathbf{u}$

30. Yes, V is a vector space. We verify the 10 axioms

(1) $x, y \in V \Rightarrow x + y = xy \in V$ $\quad$ (V = positive real numbers)

(2) $x + y = xy = yx = y + x$

(3) $x + (y + z) = x + (yz) = x(yz) = (xy)z = (x + y)z = (x + y) + z$

(4) $x + 1 = x1 = x = 1x = 1 + x$ $\quad$ (Zero vector is 1)

(5) $x + \dfrac{1}{x} = x\left(\dfrac{1}{x}\right) = 1$ $\quad \left(\text{additive inverse of } x \text{ is } \dfrac{1}{x}\right)$

(6) For $c \in R$, $x \in V$, $cx = x^c \in V$.

(7) $c(x + y) = (x + y)^c = (xy)^c = x^c y^c = x^c + y^c = cx + cy$

(8) $(c + d)x = x^{c+d} = x^c x^d = x^c + x^d = cx + dx$

(9) $c(dx) = (dx)^c = (x^d)^c = x^{(dc)} = (dc)x = (cd)x$

(10) $1x = x^1 = x.$

32. (a) *True.* For a set with two operations to be a vector space, *all* ten axioms must be satisfied. Therefore, if one of the axioms fails than this set cannot be a vector space.

(b) *False.* The first axiom is not satisfied, since $x + (1 - x) = 1$ is not a polynomial of degree 1, but is a sum of polynomials of degree 1.

(c) *True.* This set is a vector space, because all ten vector space axioms hold.

34. We prove that $0\mathbf{v} = \mathbf{0}$ for any element $\mathbf{v}$ of a vector space V. First we note that $0\mathbf{v}$ is a vector in V by property 6 of the definition of a vector space. Since $0 = 0 + 0$, we have $0\mathbf{v} = (0 + 0)\mathbf{v} = 0\mathbf{v} + 0\mathbf{v}$. The last equality holds by property 8 of the definition of a vector space. Add $(-0\mathbf{v})$ to both sides of the last equality to obtain

$$0\mathbf{v} + (-0\mathbf{v}) = (0\mathbf{v} + 0\mathbf{v}) + (-0\mathbf{v}).$$

Apply property 3 of the definition of a vector space to the right hand side to obtain

$$0\mathbf{v} + (-0\mathbf{v}) = 0\mathbf{v} + (0\mathbf{v} + (-0\mathbf{v}))$$

By property 5 of the definition of a vector space applied to both sides we see that

$$\mathbf{0} = 0\mathbf{v} + \mathbf{0}.$$

But the right hand side is equal to $0\mathbf{v}$ by property 4 of the definition of a vector space, and so we see that $\mathbf{0} = 0\mathbf{v}$, as required.

36. Suppose, by way of contradiction, that there are two distinct additive identities $\mathbf{0}$ and $\mathbf{u}_0$. Consider the vector $\mathbf{0} + \mathbf{u}_0$. On one hand this vector is equal to $\mathbf{u}_0$ since $\mathbf{0}$ is an additive identity. On the other hand, this vector is also equal to $\mathbf{0}$ since $\mathbf{u}_0$ is an additive identity. So in contradiction to our assumption that $\mathbf{0}$ and $\mathbf{u}_0$ are distinct we obtain $\mathbf{0} = \mathbf{u}_0$. This proves that the additive identity in a vector space is unique.

Section 4.3   Subspaces of Vector Spaces

2. Because W is nonempty and $W \subset R^3$, we need only check that W is closed under addition and scalar multiplication. Given

$$(x_1, y_1, 2x_1 - 3y_1) \quad \text{and} \quad (x_2, y_2, 2x_2 - 3y_2),$$

it follows that

$$(x_1, y_1, 2x_1 - 3y_1) + (x_2, y_2, 2x_2 - 3y_2) = (x_1 + x_2, y_1 + y_2, 2(x_1 + x_2) - 3(y_1 + y_2)) \in W.$$

Furthermore, for any real number c and $(x, y, 2x - 3y) \in W$, it follows that

$$c(x, y, 2x - 3y) = (cx, cy, 2(cx) - 3(cy)) \in W.$$

4. Because W is nonempty and $W \subset M_{3,2}$, we need only check that W is closed under addition and scalar multiplication. Given

$$\begin{bmatrix} a_1 & b_1 \\ a_1 + b_1 & 0 \\ 0 & c_1 \end{bmatrix} \in W \quad \text{and} \quad \begin{bmatrix} a_2 & b_2 \\ a_2 + b_2 & 0 \\ 0 & c_2 \end{bmatrix} \in W$$

it follows that

$$\begin{bmatrix} a_1 & b_1 \\ a_1 + b_1 & 0 \\ 0 & c_1 \end{bmatrix} + \begin{bmatrix} a_2 & b_2 \\ a_2 + b_2 & 0 \\ 0 & c_2 \end{bmatrix} = \begin{bmatrix} a_1 + a_2 & b_1 + b_2 \\ (a_1 + a_2) + (b_1 + b_2) & 0 \\ 0 & c_1 + c_2 \end{bmatrix} \in W.$$

Furthermore, for any real number d,

$$d \begin{bmatrix} a & b \\ a + b & 0 \\ 0 & c \end{bmatrix} = \begin{bmatrix} da & db \\ da + db & 0 \\ 0 & dc \end{bmatrix} \in W.$$

6. Recall from calculus that differentiability implies continuity. Thus, $W \subset V$. Furthermore, because W is nonempty, we need only check that W is closed under addition and scalar multiplication. Given differentiable functions $\mathbf{f}$ and $\mathbf{g}$ on $[0, 1]$, it follows that $\mathbf{f} + \mathbf{g}$ is differentiable on $[0, 1]$, and thus $\mathbf{f} + \mathbf{g} \in W$. Also, for any real number c and for any differentiable function $\mathbf{f} \in W$, $c\mathbf{f}$ is differentiable, and hence $c\mathbf{f} \in W$.

8. This set is not closed under scalar multiplication. For example,

$$\sqrt{2}, (1, 1) = \left(\sqrt{2}, \sqrt{2}\right) \notin W.$$

10. This set is not closed under scalar multiplication. For example,

$$(-2)(1, 1, 1) = (-2, -2, -2) \notin W.$$

12. This set is not closed under addition or scalar multiplication. For example,

$$\begin{bmatrix} 1 & 0 \\ 0 & 1 \end{bmatrix} + \begin{bmatrix} 1 & 0 \\ 0 & 1 \end{bmatrix} = \begin{bmatrix} 2 & 0 \\ 0 & 2 \end{bmatrix} \notin W$$

$$2\begin{bmatrix} 1 & 0 \\ 0 & 1 \end{bmatrix} = \begin{bmatrix} 2 & 0 \\ 0 & 2 \end{bmatrix} \notin W.$$

14. (a) This set is a subspace of $M_{m,n}$, because it is closed under addition and scalar multiplication.

   (b) This set is *not* a subspace, because it is not closed under scalar multiplication.

   (c) This set is a subspace of $M_{m,n}$ because it is closed under addition and scalar multiplication.

   (d) This set is *not* a subspace, because it is not closed under addition.

   (e) This set is *not* a subspace because it is not closed under addition or scalar multiplication.

   (f) This set is a subspace of $M_{m,n}$ because it is closed under addition and scalar multiplication.

16. W is not a subspace of R^3. For example, $(0, 0, 4) \in W$ and $(1, 1, 4) \in W$, but $(0, 0, 4) + (1, 1, 4) = (1, 1, 8) \notin W$, so W is not closed under addition.

18. W is a subspace of R^3. Note first that $W \subset R^3$ and W is nonempty. If $(s_1, s_1 - t_1, t_1)$ and $(s_2, s_2 - t_2, t_2)$ are in W, then their sum is also in W.

$$(s_1, s_1 - t_1, t_1) + (s_2, s_2 - t_2, t_2) = (s_1 + s_2, (s_1 + s_2) - (t_1 + t_2), t_1 + t_2) \in W.$$

   Furthermore, if c is any real number,

$$c(s_1, s_1 - t_1, t_1) = (cs_1, cs_1 - ct_1, ct_1) \in W.$$

20. W is not a subspace of R^3. For example, $(1, 1, 1) \in W$ and $(1, 1, 1) \in W$, but their sum, $(2, 2, 2) \notin W$. Hence, W is not closed under addition.

22. (a) *False.* Zero subspace and the whole vector space are not *proper* subspaces, even though they are subspaces.

(b) *True.* Because W must itself be a vector space under inherited operations, it must contain an additive identity.

(c) *False.* Let

$$W = \{(x, 0)|x \in R\} \subset R^2,$$

$$U = \{(0, y)|y \in R\} \subset R^2.$$

Then the set $W \cup U$ is not closed under addition, since $(1, 0), (0, 1) \in W \cup U$, but $(1, 0) + (0, 1) = (1, 1)$ is not.

24. Because W is not empty (for example, $\mathbf{x} \in W$) we need only check that W is closed under addition and scalar multiplication. Let

$$a_1\mathbf{x} + b_1\mathbf{y} + c_1\mathbf{z} \in W,$$

$$a_2\mathbf{x} + b_2\mathbf{y} + c_2\mathbf{z} \in W.$$

Then

$$(a_1\mathbf{x} + b_1\mathbf{y} + c_1\mathbf{z}) + (a_2\mathbf{x} + b_2\mathbf{y} + c_2\mathbf{z}) =$$

$$(a_1\mathbf{x} + a_2\mathbf{x}) + (b_1\mathbf{y} + b_2\mathbf{y}) + (c_1\mathbf{z} + c_2\mathbf{z}) =$$

$$(a_1 + a_2)\mathbf{x} + (b_1 + b_2)\mathbf{y} + (c_1 + c_2)\mathbf{z} \in W.$$

Similarly, if $a\mathbf{x} + b\mathbf{y} + c\mathbf{z} \in W$ and $d \in R$, then

$$d(a\mathbf{x} + b\mathbf{y} + c\mathbf{z}) = da\mathbf{x} + db\mathbf{y} + dc\mathbf{z} \in W.$$

26. Because W is not empty we need only check that W is closed under addition and scalar multiplication. Let $c \in R$ and $\mathbf{x}, \mathbf{y}, \in W$. Then $A\mathbf{x} = \mathbf{0}$ and $A\mathbf{y} = \mathbf{0}$.

Thus,

$$A(\mathbf{x} + \mathbf{y}) = A\mathbf{x} + A\mathbf{y} = \mathbf{0} + \mathbf{0} = \mathbf{0},$$

$$A(c\mathbf{x}) = cA\mathbf{x} = c\mathbf{0} = \mathbf{0}.$$

Therefore, $\mathbf{x} + \mathbf{y} \in W$ and $c\mathbf{x} \in W$.

28. Let $V = R^2$. Consider

$$W = \{(x, 0)|x \in R\}, \quad U = \{(0, y)|y \in R\}.$$

Then $W \cup U$ is *not* a subspace of V, because it is not closed under addition. Indeed, $(1, 0), (0, 1) \in W \cup U$, but $(1, 1)$ (which is the sum of these two vectors) is not.

30. S is a subspace of $C[0, 1]$. S is nonempty since the zero function is in S.

If $f_1, f_2 \in S$, then

$$\int_0^1 (f_1 + f_2)(x)dx = \int_0^1 [f_1(x) + f_2(x)]dx$$

$$= \int_0^1 f_1(x)\,dx + \int_0^1 f_2(x)\,dx$$

$$= 0 + 0 = 0 \implies f_1 + f_2 \in S$$

If $f \in S$ and $c \in R$, then

$$\int_0^1 (cf)(x)dx = \int_0^1 cf(x)dx = c\int_0^1 f(x)dx = c0 = 0 \implies cf \in S.$$

Thus, S is closed under addition and scalar multiplication.

32. Let c be scalar and $\mathbf{u} \in V \cap W$. Then $\mathbf{u} \in V$ and $\mathbf{u} \in W$, which are both subspaces. Hence, $c\mathbf{u} \in V$ and $c\mathbf{u} \in W$, which implies that $c\mathbf{u} \in V \cap W$.

Section 4.4   Spanning Sets and Linear Independence

2. (a) Solving the equation

$$c_1(1, 2, -2) + c_2(2, -1, 1) = (1, -5, -5)$$

for c_1 and c_2 yields the system

$$\begin{aligned} c_1 + 2c_2 &= 1 \\ 2c_1 - c_2 &= -5 \\ -2c_1 + c_2 &= -5. \end{aligned}$$

This system has no solution. Thus, **u** cannot be written as a linear combination of the vectors in S.

(b) We proceed as in (a), substituting $(-2, -6, 6)$ for $(1, -5, -5)$. So, the system to be solved is

$$\begin{aligned} c_1 + 2c_2 &= -2 \\ 2c_1 - c_2 &= -6 \\ -2c_1 + c_2 &= 6. \end{aligned}$$

The solution to this system is $c_1 = -\frac{14}{5}$ and $c_2 = \frac{2}{5}$. Thus, **v** can be written as a linear combination of the vectors in S.

—CONTINUED—

2. —CONTINUED—

(c) We proceed as in (a), substituting $(-1, -22, 22)$ for $(1, -5, -5)$. So, the system to be solved is

$$\begin{aligned} c_1 + 2c_2 &= -1 \\ 2c_1 - c_2 &= -22 \\ -2c_1 + c_2 &= 22. \end{aligned}$$

The solution to this system is $c_1 = -9$ and $c_2 = 4$. Thus, **w** can be written as a linear combination of the vectors in S.

4. (a) Solving the equation

$$c_1(6, -7, 8, 6) + c_2(4, 6, -4, 1) = (-42, 113, -112, -60)$$

for c_1 and c_2 yields the system

$$\begin{aligned} 6c_1 + 4c_2 &= -42 \\ -7c_1 + 6c_2 &= 113 \\ 8c_1 - 4c_2 &= -112 \\ 6c_1 + c_2 &= -60 \end{aligned}$$

The solution to this system is $c_1 = -11$ and $c_2 = 6$. Thus, **u** can be written as a linear combination of the vectors in S.

(b) We proceed as in (a), substituting $\left(\frac{49}{2}, \frac{99}{4}, -14, \frac{19}{2}\right)$ for $(-42, 113, -112, -60)$, which yields the system

$$\begin{aligned} 6c_1 + 4c_2 &= \tfrac{49}{2} \\ -7c_1 + 6c_2 &= \tfrac{99}{4} \\ 8c_1 - 4c_2 &= -14 \\ 6c_1 + c_2 &= \tfrac{19}{2} \end{aligned}$$

The solution to this system is $c_1 = \frac{3}{4}$ and $c_2 = 5$. Thus, **v** can be written as a linear combination of the vectors in S.

(c) We proceed as in (a), substituting $\left(-4, -14, \frac{27}{2}, \frac{53}{8}\right)$ for $(-42, 113, -112, -60)$, which yields the system

$$\begin{aligned} 6c_1 + 4c_2 &= -4 \\ -7c_1 + 6c_2 &= -14 \\ 8c_1 - 4c_2 &= \tfrac{27}{2} \\ 6c_1 + c_2 &= \tfrac{53}{8} \end{aligned}$$

This system has no solution. Thus, **w** cannot be written as a linear combination of the vectors in S.

6. Let $\mathbf{u} = (u_1, u_2)$ be any vector in R^2. Solving the equation

$$c_1(5, 0) + c_2(5, -4) = (u_1, u_2)$$

for c_1 and c_2 yields the system

$$\begin{aligned} 5c_1 + 5c_2 &= u_1 \\ -4c_2 &= u_2. \end{aligned}$$

This system has a unique solution because the determinant of the coefficient matrix is nonzero. Thus, S spans R^2.

8. S does not span R^2 since only vectors of the form $t(1, 3)$ are in span(S). For example, $(0, 1)$ is not in span(S). S spans a line in R^2.

10. S spans R^2. Let $\mathbf{u} = (u_1, u_2)$ be any vector in R^2. Solving the equation

$$c_1(-1, 4) + c_2(4, -1) + c_3(1, 1) = (u_1, u_2)$$

for c_1, c_2 and c_3 yields the system

$$-c_1 + 4c_2 + c_3 = u_1$$
$$4c_1 - c_2 + c_3 = u_2.$$

This system is equivalent to

$$c_1 - 4c_2 - c_3 = -u_1$$
$$15c_2 - 5c_3 = 4u_1 + u_2.$$

Hence, for any $\mathbf{u} = (u_1, u_2)$ in R^2, we can take $c_3 = 0$, $c_2 = (4u_1 + u_2)/15$ and $c_1 = 4c_2 - u_1 = (u_1 + 4u_2)/15$.

12. Let $\mathbf{u} = (u_1, u_2, u_3)$ be any vector in R^3. Solving the equation

$$c_1(6, 7, 6) + c_2(3, 2, -4) + c_3(1, -3, 2) = (u_1, u_2, u_3)$$

for c_1, c_2 and c_3 yields the system

$$6c_1 + 3c_2 + c_3 = u_1$$
$$7c_1 + 2c_2 - 3c_3 = u_2$$
$$6c_1 - 4c_2 + 2c_3 = u_3.$$

This system has a unique solution since the determinant of the coefficient matrix is nonzero. Thus, S spans R^3.

14. Let $\mathbf{u} = (u_1, u_2, u_3)$ be any vector in R^3. Solving the equation

$$c_1(1, 0, 1) + c_2(1, 1, 0) + c_3(0, 1, 1) = (u_1, u_2, u_3)$$

for c_1, c_2 and c_3 yields the system

$$c_1 + c_2 = u_1$$
$$c_2 + c_3 = u_2$$
$$c_1 + c_3 = u_3.$$

This system has a unique solution since the determinant of the coefficient matrix is nonzero. Thus, S spans R^3.

16. This set does not span R^3. Notice that the third and fourth vectors are spanned by the first two.

$$(4, 0, 5) = 2(1, 0, 3) + (2, 0, -1)$$
$$(2, 0, 6) = 2(1, 0, 3)$$

Hence, S spans a plane in R^3.

18. This set is linearly dependent since

$$(-2, 4) + 2(1, -2) = (0, 0).$$

20. This set is linearly dependent since

$$-3(1, 0) + (1, 1) + (2, -1) = (0, 0).$$

22. Since $(-1, 3, 2)$ is not a scalar multiple of $(6, 2, 1)$, the set S is linearly independent.

24. From the vector equation

$$c_1\left(\tfrac{3}{4}, \tfrac{5}{2}, \tfrac{3}{2}\right) + c_2\left(3, 4, \tfrac{7}{2}\right) + c_3\left(-\tfrac{3}{2}, 6, 2\right) = (0, 0, 0)$$

we obtain the homogeneous system

$$\tfrac{3}{4}c_1 + 3c_2 - \tfrac{3}{2}c_3 = 0$$

$$\tfrac{5}{2}c_1 + 4c_2 + 6c_3 = 0$$

$$\tfrac{3}{2}c_1 + \tfrac{7}{2}c_2 + 2c_3 = 0.$$

This system has only the trivial solution $c_1 = c_2 = c_3 = 0$. Hence, the set S is linearly independent.

26. Since the fourth vector is a linear combination of the first three, this set is linearly dependent.

$$(1, 5, -3) = (1, 0, 0) + \tfrac{5}{4}(0, 4, 0) + \tfrac{1}{2}(0, 0, -6)$$

28. From the vector equation

$$c_1(0, 0, 0, 1) + c_2(0, 0, 1, 1) + c_3(0, 1, 1, 1) + c_4(1, 1, 1, 1) = (0, 0, 0, 0)$$

we obtain the homogeneous system

$$c_4 = 0$$

$$c_3 + c_4 = 0$$

$$c_2 + c_3 + c_4 = 0$$

$$c_1 + c_2 + c_3 + c_4 = 0.$$

This system has only the trivial solution $c_1 = c_2 = c_3 = c_4 = 0$. Hence, the set S is linearly independent.

30. One example of a nontrivial linear combination of vectors in S whose sum is the zero vector is

$$(2, 4) + 2(-1, -2) + 0(0, 6) = (0, 0).$$

Solving this equation for $(2, 4)$ yields

$$(2, 4) = -2(-1, -2) + 0(0, 6).$$

32. One example of a nontrivial linear combination of vectors in S whose sum is the zero vector is

$$2(1, 2, 3, 4) - (1, 0, 1, 2) - (1, 4, 5, 6) = (0, 0, 0, 0).$$

Solving this equation for $(1, 4, 5, 6)$ yields

$$(1, 4, 5, 6) = 2(1, 2, 3, 4) - (1, 0, 1, 2).$$

34. (a) From the vector equation

$$c_1(t, 0, 0) + c_2(0, 1, 0) + c_3(0, 0, 1) = (0, 0, 0)$$

we obtain the homogeneous system

$$\begin{aligned} tc_1 \quad &= 0 \\ c_2 \quad &= 0 \\ c_3 &= 0. \end{aligned}$$

Since $c_2 = c_3 = 0$, the set will be linearly independent if $t \neq 0$.

(b) Proceeding as in (a), we obtain the homogeneous system

$$\begin{aligned} tc_1 + tc_2 + tc_3 &= 0 \\ tc_1 + c_2 \quad &= 0 \\ tc_1 \quad + c_3 &= 0. \end{aligned}$$

The coefficient matrix will have nonzero determinant if $2t^2 - t \neq 0$. That is, the set will be linearly independent if $t \neq 0$ or $t \neq \frac{1}{2}$.

36. From the vector equation

$$c_1\begin{bmatrix} 1 & -1 \\ 4 & 5 \end{bmatrix} + c_2\begin{bmatrix} 4 & 3 \\ -2 & 3 \end{bmatrix} + c_3\begin{bmatrix} 1 & -8 \\ 22 & 23 \end{bmatrix} = \begin{bmatrix} 0 & 0 \\ 0 & 0 \end{bmatrix}$$

we obtain the homogeneous system

$$\begin{aligned} c_1 + 4c_2 + \quad c_3 &= 0 \\ -c_1 + 3c_2 - \quad 8c_3 &= 0 \\ 4c_1 - 2c_2 + 22c_3 &= 0 \\ 5c_1 + 3c_2 + 23c_3 &= 0. \end{aligned}$$

Since this system has only the trivial solution $c_1 = c_2 = c_3 = 0$, the set of vectors is linearly independent.

38. Let $a_0 + a_1x + a_2x^2 + a_3x^3$ be any vector in P_3. Solving the equation

$$c_1(x^2 - 2x) + c_2(x^3 + 8) + c_3(x^3 - x^2) + c_4(x^2 - 4) = a_0 + a_1x + a_2x^2 + a_3x^3$$

for c_1, c_2, c_3 and c_4 yields the system

$$\begin{aligned} c_2 + c_3 \quad &= a_3 \\ c_1 \quad - c_3 + c_4 &= a_2 \\ -2c_1 \quad &= a_1 \\ 8c_2 \quad - 4c_4 &= a_0. \end{aligned}$$

This system has a unique solution because the determinant of the coefficient matrix is nonzero. Thus, S, spans P_3.

40. Let **U** be another subspace of **V** that contains S. To show that span $(S) \subset$ **U**, let $\mathbf{u} \in \text{span}(S)$. Then $\mathbf{u} = \sum_{i=1}^{k} c_i \mathbf{v}_i$, where $\mathbf{v}_i \in S$. Hence, $\mathbf{v}_i \in$ **U**, since **U** contains S. Because **U** is a subspace, $\mathbf{u} \in$ **U**.

42. The matrix $\begin{bmatrix} 0 & 0 & 2 \\ 0 & 1 & 1 \\ 1 & 1 & 1 \end{bmatrix}$ row reduces to $\begin{bmatrix} 1 & 0 & 0 \\ 0 & 1 & 0 \\ 0 & 0 & 1 \end{bmatrix}$ and $\begin{bmatrix} 1 & 1 & 2 \\ 1 & 1 & 1 \\ 1 & 2 & 1 \end{bmatrix}$

row reduces to $\begin{bmatrix} 1 & 0 & 0 \\ 0 & 1 & 0 \\ 0 & 0 & 1 \end{bmatrix}$ as well. Thus, both sets of vectors span R^3.

44. (a) *False.* A set is *linearly dependent* if and only if one of the vactors of this set can be written as a linear combination of the others.

(b) *True.* See the definition of spanning set of a vector space on page 188.

46. The matrix $\begin{bmatrix} 1 & 3 & 0 \\ 2 & 2 & 0 \\ 3 & 1 & 1 \end{bmatrix}$ row reduces to $\begin{bmatrix} 1 & 0 & 0 \\ 0 & 1 & 0 \\ 0 & 0 & 1 \end{bmatrix}$ which shows that the

equation

$$c_1(1, 2, 3) + c_2(3, 2, 1) + c_3(0, 0, 1)$$

only has the trivial solution. Thus, the three vectors are linearly independent. Furthermore, the vectors span R^3 because the coefficient matrix of the linear system

$$\begin{bmatrix} 1 & 3 & 0 \\ 2 & 2 & 0 \\ 3 & 1 & 1 \end{bmatrix} \begin{bmatrix} c_1 \\ c_2 \\ c_3 \end{bmatrix} = \begin{bmatrix} u_1 \\ u_2 \\ u_3 \end{bmatrix}$$

is nonsingular.

48. If S_1 is linearly dependent, then for some $\mathbf{u}_1, \ldots, \mathbf{u}_n, \mathbf{v} \in S_1$, $\mathbf{v} = c_1\mathbf{u}_1 + \cdots + c_n\mathbf{u}_n$. Hence, in S_2, we have $\mathbf{v} = c_1\mathbf{u}_1 + \cdots + c_n\mathbf{u}_n$, which implies that S_2 is linearly dependent.

50. Since $\{\mathbf{u}_1, \ldots, \mathbf{u}_n, \mathbf{v}\}$ is linearly dependent, there exist scalars $c_1, \ldots, c_n, c$ not all zero, such that

$$c_1\mathbf{u}_1 + \ldots + c_n\mathbf{u}_n + c\mathbf{v} = \mathbf{0}.$$

But, $c \neq 0$ because $\{\mathbf{u}_1, \ldots, \mathbf{u}_n\}$ are linearly independent. Thus,

$$c\mathbf{v} = -c_1\mathbf{u}_1 - \cdots - c_n\mathbf{u}_n \Rightarrow \mathbf{v} = \frac{-c_1}{c}\mathbf{u}_1 - \cdots - \frac{c_n}{c}\mathbf{u}_n$$

52. Suppose that $\mathbf{v}_k = c_1\mathbf{v}_1 + \cdots + c_{k-1}\mathbf{v}_{k-1}$. For any vector $\mathbf{u} \in V$,

$$\mathbf{u} = d_1\mathbf{v}_1 + \cdots + d_{k-1}\mathbf{v}_{k-1} + d_k\mathbf{v}_k$$
$$= d_1\mathbf{v}_1 + \cdots + d_{k-1}\mathbf{v}_{k-1} + d_k(c_1\mathbf{v}_1 + \cdots + c_{k-1}\mathbf{v}_{k-1})$$
$$= (d_1 + c_1 d_k)\mathbf{v}_1 + \cdots + (d_{k-1} + c_{k-1}d_k)\mathbf{v}_{k-1}$$

which shows that $\mathbf{u} \in \text{span}(\mathbf{v}_1, \ldots, \mathbf{v}_{k-1})$.

54. A set consisting of just one vector is linearly independent if it is not the zero vector.

56. The vectors are linearly dependent because

$$(\mathbf{v} - \mathbf{u}) + (\mathbf{w} - \mathbf{v}) + (\mathbf{u} - \mathbf{w}) = \mathbf{0}$$

58. Consider

$$c_1 A\mathbf{v}_1 + c_2 A\mathbf{v}_2 + c_3 A\mathbf{v}_3 = \mathbf{0}$$
$$A(c_1\mathbf{v}_1 + c_2\mathbf{v}_2 + c_3\mathbf{v}_3) = \mathbf{0}$$
$$A^{-1}A(c_1\mathbf{v}_1 + c_2\mathbf{v}_2 + c_3\mathbf{v}_3) = A^{-1}\mathbf{0}$$
$$c_1\mathbf{v}_1 + c_2\mathbf{v}_2 + c_3\mathbf{v}_3 = \mathbf{0}$$

Since $\{\mathbf{v}_1, \mathbf{v}_2, \mathbf{v}_3\}$ are linearly independent, $c_1 = c_2 = c_3 = 0$, proving that $\{A\mathbf{v}_1, A\mathbf{v}_2, A\mathbf{v}_3\}$ are linearly independent.

If $A = \mathbf{0}$, then $\{A\mathbf{v}_1, A\mathbf{v}_2, A\mathbf{v}_3\} = \{\mathbf{0}\}$ is linearly dependent.

Section 4.5   Basis and Dimension

2. There are four vectors in the standard basis for $M_{4,1}$.

$$\left\{ \begin{bmatrix} 1 \\ 0 \\ 0 \\ 0 \end{bmatrix}, \begin{bmatrix} 0 \\ 1 \\ 0 \\ 0 \end{bmatrix}, \begin{bmatrix} 0 \\ 0 \\ 1 \\ 0 \end{bmatrix}, \begin{bmatrix} 0 \\ 0 \\ 0 \\ 1 \end{bmatrix} \right\}$$

4. There are five vectors in the standard basis for P_4.

$$\{1, x, x^2, x^3, x^4\}$$

6. S is linearly dependent $((0, 0) \in S)$ and does not span $R^2 ((1, 1) \notin \text{span}(S))$.

8. S does not span R^2, although it is linearly independent. For instance, $(1, 1) \notin \text{span}(S)$.

10. S does not span R^3, although it is linearly independent. For instance, $(0, 1, 0) \notin \text{span}(S)$.

12. S is not a basis, because it has too many vectors. A basis for R^3 can only have three vectors.

14. S is not a basis because it has too many vectors. A basis for P_2 can only have three vectors.

16. S is not a basis because the vectors are linearly dependent.

$$1(6x - 3) + 1(3x^2) + 3(1 - 2x - x^2) = 0$$

18. S is not a basis because the vectors are linearly dependent.

$$5\begin{bmatrix} 1 & 0 \\ 0 & 0 \end{bmatrix} - 4\begin{bmatrix} 0 & 1 \\ 1 & 0 \end{bmatrix} + 3\begin{bmatrix} 1 & 0 \\ 0 & 1 \end{bmatrix} - \begin{bmatrix} 8 & -4 \\ -4 & 3 \end{bmatrix} = \begin{bmatrix} 0 & 0 \\ 0 & 0 \end{bmatrix}$$

Also, S does not span $M_{2,2}$.

20. Because v_1 and v_2 are multiplies of each other, they do not form a basis for R^2.

22. Because $\{v_1, v_2\}$ consists of exactly two linearly independent vectors, it is a basis for R^2.

24. To determine if the vectors in S are linearly independent, we find the solution to

$$c_1(1, 5, 3) + c_2(0, 1, 2) + c_3(0, 0, 6) = (0, 0, 0)$$

which corresponds to the solution of

$$c_1 = 0$$
$$5c_1 + c_2 = 0$$
$$3c_1 + 2c_2 + 6c_3 = 0.$$

This system has only the trivial solution. Thus S consists of exactly three linearly independent vectors, and is, therefore, a basis for R^3.

26. This set contains the zero vector, and is, therefore, linearly dependent.

$$1(0, 0, 0) + 0(1, 5, 6) + 0(6, 2, 1) = (0, 0, 0)$$

Thus, S is not a basis for R^3.

28. To determine if the vectors of S are linearly independent, we find the solution to

$$c_1(1, 0, 0, 1) + c_2(0, 2, 0, 2) + c_3(1, 0, 1, 0) + c_4(0, 2, 2, 0) = (0, 0, 0, 0).$$

Since the corresponding linear system has nontrivial solutions (for instance, $c_1 = 2, c_2 = -1, c_3 = -2, c_4 = 1$, the vectors are linearly dependent, and S is not a basis for R^4.

30. We form the equation

$$c_1\begin{bmatrix} 1 & 2 \\ -5 & 4 \end{bmatrix} + c_2\begin{bmatrix} 2 & -7 \\ 6 & 2 \end{bmatrix} + c_3\begin{bmatrix} 4 & -9 \\ 11 & 12 \end{bmatrix} + c_4\begin{bmatrix} 12 & -16 \\ 17 & 42 \end{bmatrix} = \begin{bmatrix} 0 & 0 \\ 0 & 0 \end{bmatrix}$$

which yields the homogeneous system

$$c_1 + 2c_2 + 4c_3 + 12c_4 = 0$$
$$2c_1 - 7c_2 - 9c_3 - 16c_4 = 0$$
$$-5c_1 + 6c_2 + 11c_3 + 17c_4 = 0$$
$$4c_1 + 2c_2 + 12c_3 + 42c_4 = 0.$$

Since this system has nontrivial solutions (for instance, $c_1 = 2, c_2 = -1, c_3 = 3$ and $c_4 = -1$), the set is linearly dependent, and is not a basis for $M_{2,2}$.

32. We form the equation

$$c_1(4t - t^2) + c_2(5 + t^3) + c_3(3t + 5) + c_4(2t^3 - 3t^2) = 0$$

which yields the homogeneous system

$$
\begin{aligned}
c_2 \quad\quad + 2c_4 &= 0 \\
-c_1 \quad\quad\quad - 3c_4 &= 0 \\
4c_1 \quad + 3c_3 \quad\quad &= 0 \\
5c_2 + 5c_3 \quad\quad &= 0.
\end{aligned}
$$

This system has only the trivial solution. Thus S consists of exactly four linearly independent vectors, and is, therefore, a basis for P_3.

34. We form the equation

$$c_1(t^3 - 1) + c_2(2t^2) + c_3(t + 3) + c_4(5 + 2t + 2t^2 + t^3) = 0$$

which yields the homogeneous system

$$
\begin{aligned}
c_1 \quad\quad\quad + c_4 &= 0 \\
2c_2 \quad\quad + 2c_4 &= 0. \\
c_3 + 2c_4 &= 0 \\
-c_1 \quad + 3c_3 + 5c_4 &= 0.
\end{aligned}
$$

This system has nontrivial solutions (for instance, $c_1 = 1, c_2 = 1, c_3 = 2$, and $c_4 = -1$). Therefore, S is not a basis for P_3 since the vectors are linearly dependent.

36. The set S contains the zero vector, and is, therefore, linearly dependent.

$$1(0, 0, 0) + 0(1, 3, 4) + 0(6, 1, -2) = (0, 0, 0).$$

Thus, S is not a basis for R^3.

38. We form the equation

$$c_1(1, 4, 7) + c_2(3, 0, 1) + c_3(2, 1, 2) = (0, 0, 0)$$

which yields the homogeneous system

$$
\begin{aligned}
c_1 + 3c_2 + 2c_3 &= 0 \\
4c_1 \quad\quad + 2c_3 &= 0 \\
7c_1 + c_2 + 2c_3 &= 0
\end{aligned}
$$

This system has only the trivial solution, so S is a basis for R^3. Solving the system

$$
\begin{aligned}
c_1 + 3c_2 + 2c_3 &= 8 \\
4c_1 \quad\quad + c_3 &= 3 \\
7c_1 + c_2 + 2c_3 &= 8
\end{aligned}
$$

yields $c_1 = 1, c_2 = 3$ and $c_3 = -1$. Thus

$$\mathbf{u} = (8, 3, 8) = 1(1, 4, 7) + 3(3, 0, 1) - 1(2, 1, 2).$$

40. Because a basis for R has one linearly independent vector, the dimension of R is 1.

42. Because a basis for $M_{2,3}$ has six linearly independent vectors, the dimension of $M_{2,3}$ is 6.

44. One basis for the space of all 3×3 symmetric matrices is

$$\left\{ \begin{bmatrix} 1 & 0 & 0 \\ 0 & 0 & 0 \\ 0 & 0 & 0 \end{bmatrix}, \begin{bmatrix} 0 & 1 & 0 \\ 1 & 0 & 0 \\ 0 & 0 & 0 \end{bmatrix}, \begin{bmatrix} 0 & 0 & 1 \\ 0 & 0 & 0 \\ 1 & 0 & 0 \end{bmatrix}, \begin{bmatrix} 0 & 0 & 0 \\ 0 & 1 & 0 \\ 0 & 0 & 0 \end{bmatrix}, \begin{bmatrix} 0 & 0 & 0 \\ 0 & 0 & 1 \\ 0 & 1 & 0 \end{bmatrix}, \begin{bmatrix} 0 & 0 & 0 \\ 0 & 0 & 0 \\ 0 & 0 & 1 \end{bmatrix} \right\}.$$

Since this basis has 6 vectors, the dimension is 6.

46. Although there are four subsets of S that contain three vectors, only three of them are bases for R^3.

$$\{(1, 3, -2), (-4, 1, 1), (2, 1, 1)\}, \ \{(1, 3, -2), (-2, 7, -3), (2, 1, 1)\},$$
$$\{(-4, 1, 1), (-2, 7, -3), (2, 1, 1)\}$$

The set $\{(1, 3, -2), (-4, 1, 1), (-2, 7, -3)\}$ is linearly dependent.

48. We can add any vector that is not in the span of $S = \{(1, 0, 2), (0, 1, 1)\}$. For instance, the set $\{(1, 0, 2), (0, 1, 1), (1, 0, 0)\}$ is a basis for R^3.

50. (a) W is a line through the origin (the y-axis)
  (b) A basis for W is $\{(0, 1)\}$.
  (c) The dimension of W is 1.

52. (a) W is a plane through the origin.
  (b) A basis for W is $\{(2, 1, 0), (-1, 0, 1)\}$, obtained by letting $s = 1, t = 0$, and then $s = 0, t = 1$.
  (c) The dimension of W is 2.

54. (a) A basis for $W \{(5, -3, 1, 1)\}$.
  (b) The dimension of W is 1.

56. (a) A basis for W is $\{(1, 0, 1, 2), (4, 1, 0, -1)\}$.
  (b) The dimension of W is 2.

58. (a) *True.* See Theorem 4.10 and definition of dimension on page 219.
  (b) *False.* A set of $n - 1$ vectors could be linearly dependent, for instance, they can all be multiples of each other.

60. Suppose that P had a finite basis $B = \{p_1, \ldots, p_n\}$. Let m be the maximum degree of all polynomials in B. Then the polynomial x^{m+1} is not in the span of B, and hence, P is not finite-dimensional.

62. (1) Let $S = \{\mathbf{v}_1, \ldots, \mathbf{v}_n\}$ be a linearly independent set of vectors. Suppose, by way of contradiction, that S does not span V. Then there exists $\mathbf{v} \in V$ such that $\mathbf{v} \notin \text{span}(\mathbf{v}_1, \ldots, \mathbf{v}_n)$. Thus, the set $\{\mathbf{v}_1, \ldots, \mathbf{v}_n, \mathbf{v}\}$ is linearly independent, which is impossible by Theorem 4.10. Thus, S does span V, and hence is a basis.

  (2) Let $S = \{\mathbf{v}_1, \ldots, \mathbf{v}_n\}$ span V. Suppose, by way of contradiction, that S is linearly dependent. Then, some $\mathbf{v}_i \in S$ is a linear combination of the other vectors in S. Without loss of generality, we can assume that $\mathbf{v}_n$ is a linear combination of $\mathbf{v}_1, \ldots, \mathbf{v}_{n-1}$, and hence, $\{\mathbf{v}_1, \ldots, \mathbf{v}_{n-1}\}$ spans V. But, $n - 1$ vectors span a vector space of at most dimension $n - 1$, a contradiction. Thus, S is linearly independent, and hence a basis.

64. Let the number of vectors in S be n. If S is linearly independent, then we are done. If not, some $\mathbf{v} \in S$ is a linear combination of other vectors in S. Let $S_1 = S - \mathbf{v}$. Note that $\text{span}(S) = \text{span}(S_1)$ because $\mathbf{v}$ is a linear combination of vectors in S_1. We now consider spanning set S_1. If S_1 is linearly independent, we are done. If not we repeat the process of removing a vector which is a linear combination of other vectors in S_1 to obtain spanning set S_2. Continue this process with S_2. Note that this process would terminate because the original set S is a finite set and each removal produces a spanning set with fewer vectors than the previous spanning set. Thus, in at most $n - 1$ steps the process would terminate leaving us with minimal spanning set, which is linearly independent and is contained in S.

66. If a set $\{\mathbf{v}_1, \ldots, \mathbf{v}_m\}$ spans V where $m < n$, then by Exercise 64, you could reduce this set to an independent spanning set of less than n vectors. But then $\dim V \neq n$.

Section 4.6 Rank of a Matrix and Systems of Linear Equations

2. (a) Because this matrix is row-reduced already, the rank is 1.

(b) A basis for the row space is $\{(1, 2, 3)\}$.

(c) A basis for the column space is $\{(1)\}$.

4. (a) Because this matrix row reduces to

$$\begin{bmatrix} 1 & 0 & \frac{1}{2} \\ 0 & 1 & -\frac{1}{2} \end{bmatrix}$$

the rank of the matrix is 2.

(b) A basis for the row space is $\left\{ \left(1, 0, \frac{1}{2}\right), \left(0, 1, -\frac{1}{2}\right) \right\}$

(c) Row-reducing the transpose of the original matrix produces

$$\begin{bmatrix} 1 & 0 \\ 0 & 1 \\ 0 & 0 \end{bmatrix}.$$

Thus, a basis for the column space of the matrix is $\{(1, 0), (0, 1)\}$.

6. (a) Because this matrix row reduces to

$$\begin{bmatrix} 1 & 0 & \frac{4}{5} \\ 0 & 1 & \frac{1}{5} \\ 0 & 0 & 0 \end{bmatrix}$$

the rank of the matrix is 2.

(b) A basis for the row space is $\left\{ \left(1, 0, \frac{4}{5}\right), \left(0, 1, \frac{1}{5}\right) \right\}$.

(c) Row-reducing the transpose of the original matrix produces

$$\begin{bmatrix} 1 & 0 & \frac{23}{7} \\ 0 & 1 & \frac{2}{7} \\ 0 & 0 & 0 \end{bmatrix}.$$

Hence, a basis for the column space of the matrix is $\left\{ \left(1, 0, \frac{23}{7}\right), \left(0, 1, \frac{2}{7}\right) \right\}$, or the first 2 columns of the original matrix.

8. (a) Because this matrix row reduces to

$$\begin{bmatrix} 1 & 2 & 0 & 3 \\ 0 & 0 & 1 & 4 \\ 0 & 0 & 0 & 0 \\ 0 & 0 & 0 & 0 \end{bmatrix}$$

the rank of the matrix is 2.

(b) A basis for the row space is $\{(1, 2, 0, 3), (0, 0, 1, 4)\}$.

(c) Row-reducing the transpose of the original matrix produces

$$\begin{bmatrix} 1 & 0 & \frac{5}{9} & \frac{2}{9} \\ 0 & 1 & -\frac{4}{9} & \frac{2}{9} \\ 0 & 0 & 0 & 0 \\ 0 & 0 & 0 & 0 \end{bmatrix}.$$

Hence, a basis for the column space is $\left\{\left(1, 0, \frac{5}{9}, \frac{2}{9}\right), \left(0, 1, -\frac{4}{9}, \frac{2}{9}\right)\right\}$, or, the first and third columns of the original matrix.

10. We begin by forming the matrix whose rows are vectors in S.

$$\begin{bmatrix} 6 & -3 & 6 & 34 \\ 3 & -2 & 3 & 19 \\ 8 & 3 & -9 & 6 \\ -2 & 0 & 6 & -5 \end{bmatrix}$$

This matrix reduces to

$$\begin{bmatrix} 1 & 0 & 0 & 0 \\ 0 & 1 & 0 & 0 \\ 0 & 0 & 1 & 0 \\ 0 & 0 & 0 & 1 \end{bmatrix}$$

Thus, a basis for span(S) is

$$\{(1, 0, 0, 0), (0, 1, 0, 0), (0, 0, 1, 0), (0, 0, 0, 1)\}. \quad (\text{span}(S) = R^4)$$

12. We form the matrix whose rows are the vectors in S, and then row-reduce.

$$\begin{bmatrix} 2 & 5 & -3 & -2 \\ -2 & -3 & 2 & -5 \\ 1 & 3 & -2 & 2 \\ -1 & -5 & 3 & 5 \end{bmatrix} \Rightarrow \begin{bmatrix} 1 & 0 & 0 & 3 \\ 0 & 1 & 0 & -13 \\ 0 & 0 & 1 & -19 \\ 0 & 0 & 0 & 0 \end{bmatrix}$$

Thus, a basis for span(S) is

$$\{(1, 0, 0, 3), (0, 1, 0, -13), (0, 0, 1, -19)\}.$$

14. Solving the system $A\mathbf{x} = \mathbf{0}$ yields solutions of the form $(t, 2t)$, where t is any real number. The dimension of the solution space is 1, and a basis is $\{(1, 2)\}$.

16. Solving the system $A\mathbf{x} = \mathbf{0}$ yields solutions of the form $(-3t, 0, t)$, where t is any real number. The dimension of the solution space is 1, and a basis is $\{(-3, 0, 1)\}$.

18. Solving the system $A\mathbf{x} = \mathbf{0}$ yields solutions of the form $(2s - t, s, t)$ where s and t are any real numbers. The dimension of the solution space is 2, and a basis is $\{(-1, 0, 1), (2, 1, 0)\}$.

20. The only solution to the system $A\mathbf{x} = \mathbf{0}$ is the trivial solution. So, the solution space is $\{(0, 0, 0, 0)\}$ whose dimension is 0.

22. The only solution to this system is the trivial solution $x = y = z = 0$. Thus, the solution space is $\{(0, 0, 0)\}$ whose dimension is 0.

24. This system yields solutions of the form $\left(-4s - 3t, -s - \frac{2}{3}t, s, t\right)$, where s and t is any real numbers. The dimension of the solution space is 2, and a basis is $\left\{(-4, -1, 1, 0), \left(-3, -\frac{2}{3}, 0, 1\right)\right\}$.

26. This system yields solutions of the form $\left(-t + 2s - r, -4t - 8s - \frac{1}{3}r, r, s, t\right)$, where r, s and t are any real numbers. The dimension of the solution space is 3, and a basis is

$$\left\{(-1, -4, 0, 0, 1), (2, -8, 0, 1, 0), \left(-1, -\tfrac{1}{3}, 1, 0, 0\right)\right\}.$$

28. (a) The system $A\mathbf{x} = \mathbf{b}$ is inconsistent since its augmented matrix reduces to

$$\begin{bmatrix} 1 & 0 & 0 & -2 & 0 \\ 0 & 1 & 0 & -\frac{1}{2} & 0 \\ 0 & 0 & 1 & \frac{1}{2} & 0 \\ 0 & 0 & 0 & 0 & 1 \end{bmatrix}.$$

30. (a) The system $A\mathbf{x} = \mathbf{b}$ is consistent since its augmented matrix reduces to

$$\begin{bmatrix} 1 & -2 & 0 & 4 \\ 0 & 0 & 1 & 0 \\ 0 & 0 & 0 & 0 \end{bmatrix}.$$

(b) The solutions of $A\mathbf{x} = \mathbf{b}$ are of the form $(4 + 2t, t, 0)$, where t is any real number. That is,

$$\mathbf{x} = t\begin{bmatrix} 2 \\ 1 \\ 0 \end{bmatrix} + \begin{bmatrix} 4 \\ 0 \\ 0 \end{bmatrix},$$

where

$$\mathbf{x}_h = t\begin{bmatrix} 2 \\ 1 \\ 0 \end{bmatrix} \quad \text{and} \quad \mathbf{x}_p = \begin{bmatrix} 4 \\ 0 \\ 0 \end{bmatrix}.$$

32. (a) The system $A\mathbf{x} = \mathbf{b}$ is consistent since its augmented matrix reduces to

$$\begin{bmatrix} 1 & 0 & 4 & -5 & 6 & 0 \\ 0 & 1 & 2 & 2 & 4 & 1 \\ 0 & 0 & 0 & 0 & 0 & 0 \end{bmatrix}.$$

(b) The solutions of the system are of the form

$$(-6t + 5s - 4r, 1 - 4t - 2s - 2r, r, s, t),$$

where r, s and t are any real numbers. That is,

$$\mathbf{x} = r\begin{bmatrix} -4 \\ -2 \\ 1 \\ 0 \\ 0 \end{bmatrix} + s\begin{bmatrix} 5 \\ -2 \\ 0 \\ 1 \\ 0 \end{bmatrix} + t\begin{bmatrix} -6 \\ -4 \\ 0 \\ 0 \\ 1 \end{bmatrix} + \begin{bmatrix} 0 \\ 1 \\ 0 \\ 0 \\ 0 \end{bmatrix},$$

where

$$\mathbf{x}_h = r\begin{bmatrix} -4 \\ -2 \\ 1 \\ 0 \\ 0 \end{bmatrix} + s\begin{bmatrix} 5 \\ -2 \\ 0 \\ 1 \\ 0 \end{bmatrix} + t\begin{bmatrix} -6 \\ -4 \\ 0 \\ 0 \\ 1 \end{bmatrix} \quad \text{and} \quad \mathbf{x}_p = \begin{bmatrix} 0 \\ 1 \\ 0 \\ 0 \\ 0 \end{bmatrix}.$$

34. The vector $\mathbf{b}$ is not in the column space of A since the linear system $A\mathbf{x} = \mathbf{b}$ is inconsistent.

36. The vector $\mathbf{b}$ is not in the column space of A since the linear system $A\mathbf{x} = \mathbf{b}$ is inconsistent.

38. The rank of the matrix is at most 3. Thus, the dimension of the column space is at most 3, and any four vectors in the column space must form a linearly dependent set.

40. Many examples are possible. For instance,

$$\underbrace{\begin{bmatrix} 1 & 0 \\ 0 & 0 \end{bmatrix}}_{\text{rank } 1} \underbrace{\begin{bmatrix} 0 & 0 \\ 0 & 1 \end{bmatrix}}_{\text{rank } 1} = \underbrace{\begin{bmatrix} 0 & 0 \\ 0 & 0 \end{bmatrix}}_{\text{rank } 0}.$$

42. Let $[a_{ij}] = A$ be an $m \times n$ matrix in row-echelon form. The nonzero row vectors $\mathbf{r}_1, \ldots, \mathbf{r}_k$ of A have the form (if the first column of A is not all zero)

$$\mathbf{r}_1 = (e_{11}, \ldots, e_{1p}, \ldots, e_{1q}, \ldots)$$
$$\mathbf{r}_2 = (0, \ldots, 0, e_{2p}, \ldots, e_{2q}, \ldots)$$
$$\mathbf{r}_3 = (0, \ldots, 0, 0, \ldots, 0, e_{3q}, \ldots),$$

and so forth, where e_{11}, e_{2p}, e_{3q} denote leading ones. Then the equation

$$c_1\mathbf{r}_1 + c_2\mathbf{r}_2 + \cdots + c_k\mathbf{r}_k = \mathbf{0}$$

implies that $c_1 e_{11} = 0$, $c_1 e_{1p} + c_2 e_{2p} = 0$, $c_1 e_{1q} + c_2 e_{2q} + c_3 e_{3q} = 0$, and so forth. We can conclude in turn that $c_1 = 0$, $c_2 = 0$, $\ldots$, $c_k = 0$, and thus the row vectors are linearly independent.

44. Suppose that the three points are collinear. If they are on the same vertical line, then $x_1 = x_2 = x_3$. Thus, the matrix has two equal columns, and its rank is less than 3. Similarly, if the three points lie on the nonvertical line $y = mx + b$, we have

$$\begin{bmatrix} x_1 & y_1 & 1 \\ x_2 & y_2 & 1 \\ x_3 & y_3 & 1 \end{bmatrix} = \begin{bmatrix} x_1 & mx_1 + b & 1 \\ x_2 & mx_2 + b & 1 \\ x_3 & mx_3 + b & 1 \end{bmatrix}.$$

Since the second column is a linear combination of the first and third columns, this determinant is zero, and the rank is less than 3.

On the other hand, if the rank of the matrix

$$\begin{bmatrix} x_1 & y_1 & 1 \\ x_2 & y_2 & 1 \\ x_3 & y_3 & 1 \end{bmatrix}$$

is less than three, then the determinant is zero, which implies that the three points are collinear.

46. For $n = 2$, $\begin{bmatrix} 1 & 2 \\ 3 & 4 \end{bmatrix}$ has rank 2.

For $n = 3$, $\begin{bmatrix} 1 & 2 & 3 \\ 4 & 5 & 6 \\ 7 & 8 & 9 \end{bmatrix}$ has rank 2.

In general, for $n \geq 2$, the rank is 2, since rows $3, \ldots, n$, are linear combinations of the first two rows.

For example, $R_3 = 2R_2 - R_1$.

48. (a) *True.* See Theorem 4.13 on page 227.
   (b) *False.* The dimension of the solution space of $A\mathbf{x} = \mathbf{0}$ for $m \times n$ matrix of rank r is $n - r$. See Theorem 4.17 on page 235.

50. (a) *True.* The columns of A become the rows of the transpose A^T, so the columns of A span the same space as the rows of A^T.
   (b) *False.* The elementary row operations on A do *not* change linear dependency relations of the columns of A but may change the column space of A.

52. (a) rank$(A) = $ rank$(B) = 3$.
       nullity$(A) = n - r = 5 - 3 = 2$.

   (b) Choosing $x_3 = s$ and $x_5 = t$ as the free variables, we have

$x_1 = -s - t$
$x_2 = 2s - 3t$
$x_3 = s$
$x_4 = 5t$
$x_5 = t$

A basis for nullspace is $\{(-1, 2, 1, 0, 0), (-1, -3, 0, 5, 1)\}$.

—CONTINUED—

52. **—CONTINUED—**

(c) A basis for the row space of A (which is equal to the row space of B) is

$$\{(1, 0, 1, 0, 1), (0, 1, -2, 0, 3), (0, 0, 0, 1, -5)\}.$$

(d) A basis for the column space of A (which is *not* the same as the column space of B) is

$$\{(-2, 1, 3, 1), (-5, 3, 11, 7), (0, 1, 7, 5)\}.$$

(e) linearly dependent

(f) (i) and (iii) are linearly independent, while (ii) is linearly dependent.

54. (a) $A\mathbf{x} = B\mathbf{x} \Rightarrow (A - B)(\mathbf{x}) = \mathbf{0}$ for all $\mathbf{x} \in R^n \Rightarrow$ nullity of $A - B = n$
and rank $(A - B) = 0$

(b) Thus, $A - B = \mathbf{0} \Rightarrow A = B$.

56. Let A and B be 2 $m \times n$ row equivalent matrices. The dependency relationships among the columns of A can be expressed in the form $A\mathbf{x} = 0$, while those of B in the form $B\mathbf{x} = 0$. Since A and B are row equivalent, $A\mathbf{x} = 0$ and $B\mathbf{x} = 0$ have the same solution sets, and hence the same dependency relationships.

Section 4.7   Coordinates and Change of Basis

2. Since $[\mathbf{x}]_B = \begin{bmatrix} -2 \\ 3 \end{bmatrix}$, we can write

$$\mathbf{x} = -2(-1, 4) + 3(4, -1) = (14, -11),$$

which implies that the coordinates of $\mathbf{x}$ relative to the standard basis S are

$$[\mathbf{x}]_S = \begin{bmatrix} 14 \\ -11 \end{bmatrix}.$$

4. Since $[\mathbf{x}]_B = \begin{bmatrix} 2 \\ 0 \\ 4 \end{bmatrix}$, we can write

$$\mathbf{x} = 2\left(\tfrac{3}{4}, \tfrac{5}{2}, \tfrac{3}{2}\right) + 0\left(3, 4, \tfrac{7}{2}\right) + 4\left(-\tfrac{3}{2}, 6, 2\right) = \left(-\tfrac{9}{2}, 29, 11\right),$$

which implies that the coordinates of $\mathbf{x}$ relative to the standard basis S are

$$[\mathbf{x}_S] = \begin{bmatrix} -\tfrac{9}{2} \\ 29 \\ 11 \end{bmatrix}.$$

6. Since $[\mathbf{x}]_B = \begin{bmatrix} -2 \\ 3 \\ 4 \\ 1 \end{bmatrix}$, we can write

$$\mathbf{x} = -2(4, 0, 7, 3) + 3(0, 5, -1, -1) + 4(-3, 4, 2, 1) + 1(0, 1, 5, 0) = (-20, 32, -4, -5),$$

which implies that the coordinates of $\mathbf{x}$ relative to the standard basis S are

$$[\mathbf{x}]_S = \begin{bmatrix} -20 \\ 32 \\ -4 \\ -5 \end{bmatrix}.$$

8. We begin by writing $\mathbf{x}$ as a linear combination of the vectors in B.

$$\mathbf{x} = (-26, 32) = c_1(-6, 7) + c_2(4, -3)$$

Equating corresponding components yields the following system of linear equations.

$$\begin{aligned} -6c_1 + 4c_2 &= -26 \\ 7c_1 - 3c_2 &= 32 \end{aligned}$$

The solution of this system is $c_1 = 5$ and $c_2 = 1$. Thus, $\mathbf{x} = 5(-6, 7) + 1(4, -3)$ and $[\mathbf{x}]_B = \begin{bmatrix} 5 \\ 1 \end{bmatrix}$.

10. We begin by writing $\mathbf{x}$ as a linear combination of the vectors in B.

$$\mathbf{x} = \left(3, -\tfrac{1}{2}, 8\right) = c_1\left(\tfrac{3}{2}, 4, 1\right) + c_2\left(\tfrac{3}{4}, \tfrac{5}{2}, 0\right) + c_3\left(1, \tfrac{1}{2}, 2\right)$$

Equating corresponding components yields the following system of linear equations.

$$\begin{aligned} \tfrac{3}{2}c_1 + \tfrac{3}{4}c_2 + c_3 &= 3 \\ 4c_1 + \tfrac{5}{2}c_2 + \tfrac{1}{2}c_3 &= -\tfrac{1}{2} \\ c_1 \qquad\quad + 2c_3 &= 8 \end{aligned}$$

The solution of this system is $c_1 = 2$, $c_2 = -4$ and $c_3 = 3$. Thus,

$$\mathbf{x} = 2\left(\tfrac{3}{2}, 4, 1\right) - 4\left(\tfrac{3}{4}, \tfrac{5}{2}, 0\right) + 3\left(1, \tfrac{1}{2}, 2\right) \text{ and } [\mathbf{x}]_B = \begin{bmatrix} 2 \\ -4 \\ 3 \end{bmatrix}.$$

12. We begin by writing $\mathbf{x}$ as a linear combination of the vectors in B.

$$\mathbf{x} = (0, -20, 7, 15) = c_1(9, -3, 15, 4) + c_2(3, 0, 0, 1) + c_3(0, -5, 6, 8) + c_4(3, -4, 2, -3)$$

Equating corresponding components yields the following system of linear equations.

$$\begin{aligned} 9c_1 + 3c_2 \qquad\quad + 3c_4 &= 0 \\ -3c_1 \qquad\quad - 5c_3 - 4c_4 &= -20 \\ 15c_1 \qquad\quad + 6c_3 + 2c_4 &= 7 \\ 4c_1 + c_2 + 8c_3 - 3c_4 &= 15 \end{aligned}$$

—CONTINUED—

12. —CONTINUED—

The solution of this system is $c_1 = -1$, $c_2 = 1$, $c_3 = 3$ and $c_4 = 2$. Thus,

$(0, -20, 7, 15) = -1(9, -3, 15, 4) + 1(3, 0, 0, 1) + 3(0, -5, 6, 8) + 2(3, -4, 2, -3)$, and

$$[\mathbf{x}]_B = \begin{bmatrix} -1 \\ 1 \\ 3 \\ 2 \end{bmatrix}.$$

14. We begin by forming the matrix

$$[B' \;\vdots\; B] = \begin{bmatrix} 1 & 5 & \vdots & 1 & 0 \\ 1 & 6 & \vdots & 0 & 1 \end{bmatrix}$$

and then use Gauss-Jordan elimination to produce

$$[I_2 \;\vdots\; P^{-1}] = \begin{bmatrix} 1 & 0 & \vdots & 6 & -5 \\ 0 & 1 & \vdots & -1 & 1 \end{bmatrix}.$$

Thus, the transition matrix from B to B' is

$$P^{-1} = \begin{bmatrix} 6 & -5 \\ -1 & 1 \end{bmatrix}.$$

16. We begin by forming the matrix

$$[B' \;\vdots\; B] = \begin{bmatrix} 1 & 0 & \vdots & 1 & 1 \\ 0 & 1 & \vdots & 1 & 0 \end{bmatrix}.$$

Since this matrix is already in the form $[I_2 \;\vdots\; P^{-1}]$, we see that the transition matrix from B to B' is

$$P^{-1} = \begin{bmatrix} 1 & 1 \\ 1 & 0 \end{bmatrix}.$$

18. We begin by forming the matrix

$$[B' \;\vdots\; B] = \begin{bmatrix} 1 & 2 & 2 & \vdots & 1 & 0 & 0 \\ 3 & 7 & 9 & \vdots & 0 & 1 & 0 \\ -1 & -4 & -7 & \vdots & 0 & 0 & 1 \end{bmatrix}$$

and then use Gauss-Jordan elimination to produce

$$[I_3 \;\vdots\; P^{-1}] = \begin{bmatrix} 1 & 0 & 0 & \vdots & -13 & 6 & 4 \\ 0 & 1 & 0 & \vdots & 12 & -5 & -3 \\ 0 & 0 & 1 & \vdots & -5 & 2 & 1 \end{bmatrix}.$$

Thus, the transition matrix from B to B' is

$$P^{-1} = \begin{bmatrix} -13 & 6 & 4 \\ 12 & -5 & -3 \\ -5 & 2 & 1 \end{bmatrix}.$$

20. We begin by forming the matrix

$$[B' \quad \vdots \quad B] = \begin{bmatrix} 1 & 0 & 0 & \vdots & 2 & 0 & -3 \\ 0 & 1 & 0 & \vdots & -1 & 2 & 2 \\ 0 & 0 & 1 & \vdots & 4 & 1 & 1 \end{bmatrix}.$$

Since this matrix is already in the form $[I_3 \quad \vdots \quad P^{-1}]$, we see that the transition matrix from B to B' is

$$P^{-1} = \begin{bmatrix} 2 & 0 & -3 \\ -1 & 2 & 2 \\ 4 & 1 & 1 \end{bmatrix}.$$

22. We begin by forming the matrix

$$[B' \quad \vdots \quad B] = \begin{bmatrix} 1 & 0 & 0 & 0 & \vdots & 1 & 0 & 0 & 0 \\ 0 & 1 & 0 & 0 & \vdots & 1 & 1 & 0 & 0 \\ 0 & 0 & 1 & 0 & \vdots & 1 & 1 & 1 & 0 \\ 0 & 0 & 0 & 1 & \vdots & 1 & 1 & 1 & 1 \end{bmatrix}.$$

Since this matrix is already in the form $[I_4 \quad \vdots \quad P^{-1}]$, we see that the transition matrix from B to B' is

$$P^{-1} = \begin{bmatrix} 1 & 0 & 0 & 0 \\ 1 & 1 & 0 & 0 \\ 1 & 1 & 1 & 0 \\ 1 & 1 & 1 & 1 \end{bmatrix}.$$

24. (a) $[B' \quad \vdots \quad B] = \begin{bmatrix} 1 & 32 & \vdots & 2 & 6 \\ 1 & 31 & \vdots & -2 & 3 \end{bmatrix} \Rightarrow \begin{bmatrix} 1 & 0 & \vdots & -126 & -90 \\ 0 & 1 & \vdots & 4 & 3 \end{bmatrix} = [I \quad \vdots \quad P^{-1}]$

$$\Rightarrow P^{-1} = \begin{bmatrix} -126 & -90 \\ 4 & 3 \end{bmatrix}$$

(b) $[B \quad \vdots \quad B'] = \begin{bmatrix} 2 & 6 & \vdots & 1 & 32 \\ -2 & 3 & \vdots & 1 & 31 \end{bmatrix} \Rightarrow \begin{bmatrix} 1 & 0 & \vdots & -\frac{1}{6} & -5 \\ 0 & 1 & \vdots & \frac{2}{9} & 7 \end{bmatrix} = [I \quad \vdots \quad P]$

$$\Rightarrow P = \begin{bmatrix} -\frac{1}{6} & -5 \\ \frac{2}{9} & 7 \end{bmatrix}.$$

(c) $PP^{-1} = \begin{bmatrix} -\frac{1}{6} & -5 \\ \frac{2}{9} & 7 \end{bmatrix} \begin{bmatrix} -126 & -90 \\ 4 & 3 \end{bmatrix} = \begin{bmatrix} 1 & 0 \\ 0 & 1 \end{bmatrix}$

(d) $[\mathbf{x}]_B = P[\mathbf{x}]_{B'} = \begin{bmatrix} -\frac{1}{6} & -5 \\ \frac{2}{9} & 7 \end{bmatrix} \begin{bmatrix} 2 \\ -1 \end{bmatrix} = \begin{bmatrix} \frac{14}{3} \\ -\frac{59}{9} \end{bmatrix}$

26. (a) $[B' \quad \vdots \quad B] = \begin{bmatrix} 2 & 0 & 1 & \vdots & 1 & 1 & 0 \\ 2 & 1 & 0 & \vdots & 1 & -1 & 0 \\ 0 & 1 & 1 & \vdots & 1 & 1 & 1 \end{bmatrix} \Rightarrow \begin{bmatrix} 1 & 0 & 0 & \vdots & \frac{1}{4} & -\frac{1}{4} & -\frac{1}{4} \\ 0 & 1 & 0 & \vdots & \frac{1}{2} & -\frac{1}{2} & \frac{1}{2} \\ 0 & 0 & 1 & \vdots & \frac{1}{2} & \frac{3}{2} & \frac{1}{2} \end{bmatrix} =$

$$[I \quad \vdots \quad P^{-1}] \Rightarrow P^{-1} = \begin{bmatrix} \frac{1}{4} & -\frac{1}{4} & -\frac{1}{4} \\ \frac{1}{2} & -\frac{1}{2} & \frac{1}{2} \\ \frac{1}{2} & \frac{3}{2} & \frac{1}{2} \end{bmatrix}$$

(b) $[B \quad \vdots \quad B'] = \begin{bmatrix} 1 & 1 & 0 & \vdots & 2 & 0 & 1 \\ 1 & -1 & 0 & \vdots & 2 & 1 & 0 \\ 1 & 1 & 1 & \vdots & 0 & 1 & 1 \end{bmatrix} \Rightarrow \begin{bmatrix} 1 & 0 & 0 & \vdots & 2 & \frac{1}{2} & \frac{1}{2} \\ 0 & 1 & 0 & \vdots & 0 & -\frac{1}{2} & \frac{1}{2} \\ 0 & 0 & 1 & \vdots & -2 & 1 & 0 \end{bmatrix} =$

$$[I \quad \vdots \quad P] \Rightarrow P = \begin{bmatrix} 2 & \frac{1}{2} & \frac{1}{2} \\ 0 & -\frac{1}{2} & \frac{1}{2} \\ -2 & 1 & 0 \end{bmatrix}.$$

(c) $PP^{-1} = \begin{bmatrix} 2 & \frac{1}{2} & \frac{1}{2} \\ 0 & -\frac{1}{2} & \frac{1}{2} \\ -2 & 1 & 0 \end{bmatrix} \begin{bmatrix} \frac{1}{4} & -\frac{1}{4} & -\frac{1}{4} \\ \frac{1}{2} & -\frac{1}{2} & \frac{1}{2} \\ \frac{1}{2} & \frac{3}{2} & \frac{1}{2} \end{bmatrix} = \begin{bmatrix} 1 & 0 & 0 \\ 0 & 1 & 0 \\ 0 & 0 & 1 \end{bmatrix}$

(d) $[\mathbf{x}]_B = P[\mathbf{x}]_{B'} = \begin{bmatrix} 2 & \frac{1}{2} & \frac{1}{2} \\ 0 & -\frac{1}{2} & \frac{1}{2} \\ -2 & 1 & 0 \end{bmatrix} \begin{bmatrix} 2 \\ 3 \\ 1 \end{bmatrix} = \begin{bmatrix} 6 \\ -1 \\ -1 \end{bmatrix}$

28. (a) $[B' \quad \vdots \quad B] = \begin{bmatrix} 1 & 4 & -2 & \vdots & 1 & 2 & -4 \\ 2 & 1 & 5 & \vdots & 3 & -5 & 2 \\ -2 & -4 & 8 & \vdots & 4 & 2 & -6 \end{bmatrix}$

$$[I \quad \vdots \quad P^{-1}] = \begin{bmatrix} 1 & 0 & 0 & \vdots & -\frac{11}{16} & -\frac{55}{16} & \frac{73}{16} \\ 0 & 1 & 0 & \vdots & \frac{25}{32} & \frac{45}{32} & -\frac{83}{32} \\ 0 & 0 & 1 & \vdots & \frac{23}{32} & \frac{3}{32} & -\frac{29}{32} \end{bmatrix}$$

So, $P^{-1} = \begin{bmatrix} -\frac{11}{16} & -\frac{55}{16} & \frac{73}{16} \\ \frac{25}{32} & \frac{45}{32} & -\frac{83}{32} \\ \frac{23}{32} & \frac{3}{32} & -\frac{29}{32} \end{bmatrix}.$

(b) $[B \quad \vdots \quad B'] = \begin{bmatrix} 1 & 2 & -4 & \vdots & 1 & 4 & -2 \\ 3 & -5 & 2 & \vdots & 2 & 1 & 5 \\ 4 & 2 & -6 & \vdots & -2 & -4 & 8 \end{bmatrix}$

$$[I \quad \vdots \quad P] = \begin{bmatrix} 1 & 0 & 0 & \vdots & -\frac{33}{13} & -\frac{86}{13} & \frac{80}{13} \\ 0 & 1 & 0 & \vdots & -\frac{37}{13} & -\frac{85}{13} & \frac{57}{13} \\ 0 & 0 & 1 & \vdots & -\frac{30}{13} & -\frac{77}{13} & \frac{55}{13} \end{bmatrix}$$

So, $P = \begin{bmatrix} -\frac{33}{13} & -\frac{86}{13} & \frac{80}{13} \\ -\frac{37}{13} & -\frac{85}{13} & \frac{57}{13} \\ -\frac{30}{13} & -\frac{77}{13} & \frac{55}{13} \end{bmatrix}.$

—CONTINUED—

28. —CONTINUED—

(c) Using a graphing calculator, we have $PP^{-1} = I$.

(d) $[\mathbf{x}]_B = P[\mathbf{x}]_{B'} = P\begin{bmatrix} -1 \\ 0 \\ 2 \end{bmatrix} = \begin{bmatrix} \frac{193}{13} \\ \frac{151}{13} \\ \frac{140}{13} \end{bmatrix}.$

30. The standard basis in P_2 is $S = \{1, x, x^2\}$ and since

$$\mathbf{p} = 13(1) + 114(x) + 3(x^2),$$

it follows that

$$[\mathbf{p}]_S = \begin{bmatrix} 13 \\ 114 \\ 3 \end{bmatrix}.$$

32. The standard basis in $M_{3,1}$ is

$$S = \left\{ \begin{bmatrix} 1 \\ 0 \\ 0 \end{bmatrix}, \begin{bmatrix} 0 \\ 1 \\ 0 \end{bmatrix}, \begin{bmatrix} 0 \\ 0 \\ 1 \end{bmatrix} \right\}$$

and since

$$X = 2\begin{bmatrix} 1 \\ 0 \\ 0 \end{bmatrix} - 1\begin{bmatrix} 0 \\ 1 \\ 0 \end{bmatrix} + 4\begin{bmatrix} 0 \\ 0 \\ 1 \end{bmatrix},$$

it follows that

$$[X]_S = \begin{bmatrix} 2 \\ -1 \\ 4 \end{bmatrix}.$$

34. (a) *True.* If P is the transition matrix from B to B', then $P[\mathbf{x}]_B = [\mathbf{x}]_{B'}$. Multiplying both sides by P^{-1} we see that $[\mathbf{x}]_B = P^{-1}[\mathbf{x}]_{B'}$, *i.e.*, P^{-1} is the transition matrix from B' to B.

(b) *False.* The transition matrix is B' not B.

36. Let P be the transition matrix from B'' to B' and let Q be the transition matrix from B' to B. Then for any vector $\mathbf{x}$ the coordinate matrices with respect to these bases are related as follows.

$$[\mathbf{x}]_{B'} = P[\mathbf{x}]_{B''} \quad and \quad [\mathbf{x}]_B = Q[\mathbf{x}]_{B'}.$$

Then the transition matrix from B'' to B is QP because

$$[\mathbf{x}]_B = Q[\mathbf{x}]_{B'} = QP[\mathbf{x}]_{B''}.$$

Hence the transition matrix from B to B'' which is the inverse of the transition matrix from B'' to B, is equal to $(QP)^{-1} = P^{-1}Q^{-1}$.

38. Yes, if the bases are the same, $B = B'$.

Section 4.8   Applications of Vector Spaces

2. (a) If $y = x$, then $y' = 1$, $y'' = 0$, and $y''' = 0$. Thus, $y''' + 3y'' + 3y' + y = 3 + x \neq 0$, and x is not a solution.

   (b) If $y = e^x$, then $y' = y'' = y''' = e^x$. Thus, $y''' + 3y'' + 3y' + y = e^x + 3e^x + 3e^x + e^x \neq 0$, and e^x is not a solution.

   (c) If $y = e^{-x}$, then $y' = -e^{-x}$, $y'' = e^{-x}$ and $y''' = -e^{-x}$. Thus, $y''' + 3y'' + 3y' + y = -e^{-x} + 3e^{-x} - 3e^{-x} + e^{-x} = 0$, and e^{-x} is a solution.

   (d) If $y = xe^{-x}$, then $y' = (1 - x)e^{-x}$, $y'' = (x - 2)e^{-x}$ and $y''' = (3 - x)e^{-x}$. Thus, $y''' + 3y'' + 3y' + y = (3 - x)e^{-x} + 3(x - 2)e^{-x} + 3(1 - x)e^{-x} + xe^{-x} = 0$, and xe^{-x} is a solution.

4. (a) If $y = 1$, then $y' = y'' = y''' = y'''' = 0$. Thus, $y'''' - 2y''' + y'' = 0$, and 1 is a solution.

   (b) If $y = x$, then $y' = 1$, $y'' = y''' = y'''' = 0$. Thus, $y'''' - 2y''' + y'' = 0$, and x is a solution.

   (c) If $y = x^2$, then $y' = 2x$, $y'' = 2$ and $y''' = y'''' = 0$. Thus, $y'''' - 2y''' + y'' = 2 \neq 0$, and x^2 is not a solution.

   (d) If $y = e^x$, then $y' = y'' = y''' = y'''' = e^x$. Thus, $y'''' - 2y''' + y'' = 0$, and e^x is a solution.

6. $W(x, \sin x, \cos x) = \begin{vmatrix} x & \sin x & \cos x \\ 1 & \cos x & -\sin x \\ 0 & -\sin x & -\cos x \end{vmatrix} = x(-\cos^2 x - \sin^2 x) - 1(0) = -x$

8. $W(1, e^x, e^{2x}) = \begin{vmatrix} 1 & e^x & e^{2x} \\ 0 & e^x & 2e^{2x} \\ 0 & e^x & 4e^{2x} \end{vmatrix} = 4e^{3x} - 2e^{3x} = 2e^{3x}$

10. Since

$$W(e^{-2x}, xe^{-2x}) = \begin{vmatrix} e^{-2x} & xe^{-2x} \\ -2e^{-2x} & (1 - 2x)e^{-2x} \end{vmatrix} = e^{-4x} \neq 0,$$

the set is linearly independent.

12. Since

$$W(1, \sin x, \cos x) = \begin{vmatrix} 1 & \sin x & \cos x \\ 0 & \cos x & -\sin x \\ 0 & -\sin x & -\cos x \end{vmatrix} = -\cos^2 x - \sin^2 x = -1 \neq 0,$$

the set is linearly independent.

14. Since

$$W(e^{-x}, xe^{-x}, x^2e^{-x}) = \begin{vmatrix} e^{-x} & xe^{-x} & x^2e^{-x} \\ -e^{-x} & (1-x)e^{-x} & (2x-x^2)e^{-x} \\ e^{-x} & (x-2)e^{-x} & (x^2-4x+2)e^{-x} \end{vmatrix}$$

$$= e^{-3x}\begin{vmatrix} 1 & x & x^2 \\ -1 & 1-x & 2x-x^2 \\ 1 & x-2 & x^2-4x+2 \end{vmatrix}$$

$$= e^{-3x}\begin{vmatrix} 1 & x & x^2 \\ 0 & 1 & 2x \\ 0 & -2 & -4x+2 \end{vmatrix}$$

$$= 2e^{-3x} \neq 0,$$

the set is linearly independent.

16. Since

$$W(1, x, e^x, xe^x) = \begin{vmatrix} 1 & x & e^x & xe^x \\ 0 & 1 & e^x & (x+1)e^x \\ 0 & 0 & e^x & (x+2)e^x \\ 0 & 0 & e^x & (x+3)e^x \end{vmatrix}$$

$$= \begin{vmatrix} e^x & (x+2)e^x \\ e^x & (x+3)e^x \end{vmatrix}$$

$$= e^{2x}(x+3) - e^{2x}(x+2)$$

$$= e^{2x} \neq 0,$$

the set is linearly independent.

18. From Exercise 10 we have a set of two linearly independent solutions. Since $y'' + 4y' + 4y = 0$ is second order, it has a general solution of the form $C_1e^{-2x} + C_2xe^{-2x}$.

20. From Exercise 16 we have a set of four linearly independent solutions. Since $y'''' - 2y''' + y'' = 0$ is fourth order, it has a general solution of the form $C_1 + C_2x + C_3e^x + C_4xe^x$.

22. We first calculate the Wronskian of the two functions

$$W(e^{ax}, e^{bx}) = \begin{vmatrix} e^{ax} & e^{bx} \\ ae^{ax} & be^{bx} \end{vmatrix} = (b-a)e^{(a+b)x}.$$

If $a \neq b$, then $W(e^{ax}, e^{bx}) \neq 0$. Since e^{ax} and e^{bx} are solutions to $y'' - (a+b)y' + aby = 0$, the functions are linearly independent. On the other hand, if $a = b$, then $e^{ax} = e^{bx}$, and the functions are linearly dependent.

24. We first calculate the Wronskian.

$$W(e^{ax} \cos bx, e^{ax} \sin bx) = \begin{vmatrix} e^{ax} \cos bx & e^{ax} \sin bx \\ e^{ax}(a \cos bx - b \sin bx) & e^{ax}(a \sin bx + b \cos bx) \end{vmatrix}$$

$$= be^{2ax} \neq 0, \quad \text{since } b \neq 0.$$

Since these functions satisfy the differential equation
$y'' - 2ay' + (a^2 + b^2)y = 0$, they are linearly independent.

26. No, this is not true. For instance, consider the nonhomogeneous differential
equation $y'' = 1$. Clearly, $y = x^2/2$ is a solution, whereas the scalar multiple
$2(x^2/2)$ is not.

28. By rewriting the equation as

$$\frac{x^2}{3} + \frac{y^2}{5} = 1$$

we see that this is the equation of an ellipse centered
at the origin with major axis falling along the y-axis.

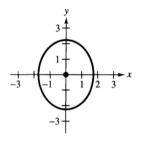

30. First we complete the square to find the standard form.

$$(x - 1)^2 = 4(-2)(y + 2)$$

We see that this is the equation of a parabola with vertex
at $(1, -2)$ and opening downward.

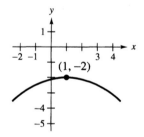

32. First we complete the square to find the standard form.

$$\frac{(x + 3)^2}{\left(\frac{1}{3}\right)^2} - \frac{(y - 5)^2}{1} = 1$$

We see that this is the equation of a hyperbola centered at $(-3, 5)$ with transverse
axis parallel to the x-axis.

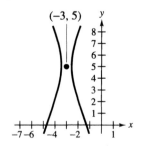

34. First we complete the square to find the standard form.

$$\frac{(y-5)^2}{1} - \frac{(x+1)^2}{\frac{1}{2}} = 1$$

We see that this is the equation of a hyperbola centered at $(-1, 5)$ with transverse axis parallel to the y-axis.

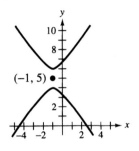

36. First we complete the square to find the standard form.

$$(y+3)^2 = 4(-2)(x+2)$$

We see that this is the equation of a parabola with vertex at $(-2, -3)$ and opening to the left.

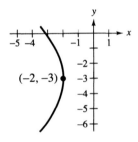

38. We begin by finding the rotation angle, θ, where

$$\cot 2\theta = \frac{a-c}{b} = \frac{4-4}{2} = 0 \implies \theta = \frac{\pi}{4}.$$

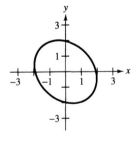

Thus, $\sin \theta = \dfrac{1}{\sqrt{2}}$ and $\cos \theta = \dfrac{1}{\sqrt{2}}$. By substituting

$$x = x'\cos\theta - y'\sin\theta = \frac{1}{\sqrt{2}}(x'-y')$$

and

$$y = x'\sin\theta + y'\cos\theta = \frac{1}{\sqrt{2}}(x'+y')$$

into $4x^2 + 2xy + 4y^2 - 15 = 0$ and simplifying, we obtain

$$\frac{(x')^2}{3} + \frac{(y')^2}{5} = 1,$$ which is an ellipse.

40. We begin by finding the rotation angle, θ, where

$$\cot 2\theta = \frac{a-c}{b} = \frac{1-1}{2} = 0 \implies \theta = \frac{\pi}{4}.$$

Thus, $\sin \theta = \dfrac{1}{\sqrt{2}}$ and $\cos \theta = \dfrac{1}{\sqrt{2}}$. By substituting

$$x = x' \cos \theta - y' \sin \theta = \frac{1}{\sqrt{2}} (x' - y')$$

and

$$y = x' \sin \theta + y' \cos \theta = \frac{1}{\sqrt{2}} (x' + y')$$

into

$$x^2 + 2xy + y^2 - 8x + 8y = 0 \text{ and simplifying, we obtain}$$

$$(x')^2 = -4\sqrt{2}y' \text{ or } y' = \frac{-1}{4\sqrt{2}} (x')^2, \text{which is a parabola.}$$

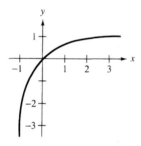

42. We begin by finding the rotation angle, θ, where

$$\cot 2\theta = \frac{a-c}{b} = \frac{3-1}{-2\sqrt{3}} = \frac{-1}{\sqrt{3}} \implies 2\theta = \frac{2\pi}{3} \implies \theta = \frac{\pi}{3}.$$

Thus, $\sin \theta = \dfrac{\sqrt{3}}{2}$ and $\cos \theta = \dfrac{1}{2}$. By substituting

$$x = x' \cos \theta - y' \sin \theta = \frac{1}{2} x' - \frac{\sqrt{3}}{2} y'$$

and

$$y = x' \sin \theta + y' \cos \theta = \frac{\sqrt{3}}{2} x' + \frac{1}{2} y'$$

into $3x^2 - 2\sqrt{3}xy + y^2 + 2x + 2\sqrt{3}y = 0$ and simplifying, we obtain

$$x' = -(y')^2, \text{ which is a parabola.}$$

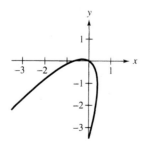

44. We begin by finding the rotation angle, θ, where

$$\cot 2\theta = \frac{a-c}{b} = \frac{7-5}{-2\sqrt{3}} = \frac{-1}{\sqrt{3}} \implies 2\theta = \frac{2\pi}{3} \implies \theta = \frac{\pi}{3}.$$

Thus, $\sin \theta = \dfrac{\sqrt{3}}{2}$ and $\cos \theta = \dfrac{1}{2}$. By substituting

$$x = x' \cos \theta - y' \sin \theta = \frac{1}{2}x' - \frac{\sqrt{3}}{2}y'$$

and

$$y = x' \sin \theta + y' \cos \theta = \frac{\sqrt{3}}{2}x' + \frac{1}{2}y'$$

into $7x^2 - 2\sqrt{3}xy + 5y^2 = 16$ and simplifying, we obtain

$$\frac{(x')^2}{4} + \frac{(y')^2}{2} = 1, \text{ which is an ellipse.}$$

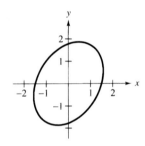

46. We begin by finding the rotation angle, θ, where

$$\cot 2\theta = \frac{a-c}{b} = \frac{5-5}{-2} = 0 \implies \theta = \frac{\pi}{4}.$$

Thus, $\sin \theta = \dfrac{1}{\sqrt{2}}$ and $\cos \theta = \dfrac{1}{\sqrt{2}}$. By substituting

$$x = x' \cos \theta - y' \sin \theta = \frac{1}{\sqrt{2}}(x' - y')$$

and

$$y = x' \sin \theta + y' \cos \theta = \frac{1}{\sqrt{2}}(x' + y')$$

into $5x^2 - 2xy + 5y^2 = 0$ and simplifying, we obtain

$$4(x')^2 + 6(y')^2 = 0, \text{ which is a single point, } (0, 0).$$

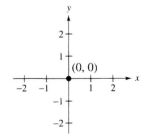

48. Let θ satisfy $\cot 2\theta = (a - c)/b$. We substitute $x = x' \cos\theta - y' \sin\theta$ and $y = x' \sin\theta + y' \cos\theta$ into the equation $ax^2 + bxy + cy^2 + dx + ey + f = 0$. To show that the xy-term will be eliminated, we analyze the first three terms under this substitution.

$$ax^2 + bxy + cy^2$$
$$= a(x' \cos\theta - y' \sin\theta)^2 + b(x' \cos\theta - y' \sin\theta)(x' \sin\theta + y' \cos\theta) +$$
$$c(x' \sin\theta + y' \cos\theta)^2$$
$$= a(x')^2 \cos^2\theta + a(y')^2 \sin^2\theta - 2ax'y' \cos\theta \sin\theta$$
$$+ b(x')^2 \cos\theta \sin\theta + bx'y' \cos^2\theta - bx'y' \sin^2\theta - b(y')^2 \cos\theta \sin\theta$$
$$+ c(x')^2 \sin^2\theta + c(y')^2 \cos^2\theta + 2cx'y' \sin\theta \cos\theta.$$

Hence, the new xy-terms are

$$-2ax'y' \cos\theta \sin\theta + bx'y'(\cos^2\theta - \sin^2\theta) + 2cx'y' \sin\theta \cos\theta$$
$$= x'y'[-a \sin 2\theta + b \cos 2\theta + c \sin 2\theta]$$
$$= -x'y'[(a - c) \sin 2\theta - b \cos 2\theta]$$

But, $\cot 2\theta = \dfrac{\cos 2\theta}{\sin 2\theta} = \dfrac{a - c}{b} \implies b \cos 2\theta = (a - c) \sin 2\theta$ which shows that the coefficient is zero.

50. If $|A| = \begin{vmatrix} a & b/2 \\ b/2 & c \end{vmatrix} = 0$, then $b^2 = 4ac$, and we have

$$ax^2 + bxy + cy^2 = acx^2 + bcxy + c^2y^2 = 0$$
$$\implies b^2x^2 + 4bcxy + 4c^2y^2 = 0$$
$$\implies (bx + 2cy)^2 = 0$$
$$\implies bx + 2cy = 0, \text{ which is the equation of a line.}$$

Chapter 4 ❑ Review Exercises

2. (a) $\mathbf{u} + \mathbf{v} = (-1, 2, 1) + (0, 1, 1) = (-1, 3, 2)$
   (b) $2\mathbf{v} = 2(0, 1, 1) = (0, 2, 2)$
   (c) $\mathbf{u} - \mathbf{v} = (-1, 2, 1) - (0, 1, 1) = (-1, 1, 0)$
   (d) $3\mathbf{u} - 2\mathbf{v} = 3(-1, 2, 1) - 2(0, 1, 1) = (-3, 6, 3) - (0, 2, 2) = (-3, 4, 1)$

4. (a) $\mathbf{u} + \mathbf{v} = (0, 1, -1, 2) + (1, 0, 0, 2) = (1, 1, -1, 4)$
   (b) $2\mathbf{v} = 2(1, 0, 0, 2) = (2, 0, 0, 4)$
   (c) $\mathbf{u} - \mathbf{v} = (0, 1, -1, 2) - (1, 0, 0, 2) = (-1, 1, -1, 0)$
   (d) $3\mathbf{u} - 2\mathbf{v} = 3(0, 1, -1, 2) - 2(1, 0, 0, 2)$
   $$= (0, 3, -3, 6) - (2, 0, 0, 4) = (-2, 3, -3, 2)$$

6. $\mathbf{x} = \frac{1}{3}[-2\mathbf{u} + \mathbf{v} - 2\mathbf{w}]$

$= \frac{1}{3}[-2(1, -1, 2) + (0, 2, 3) - 2(0, 1, 1)]$

$= \frac{1}{3}[(-2, 2, -4) + (0, 0, 1)]$

$= \frac{1}{3}(-2, 2, -3)$

$= \left(-\frac{2}{3}, \frac{2}{3}, -1\right)$

8. To write $\mathbf{v}$ as a linear combination of $\mathbf{u}_1$, $\mathbf{u}_2$, and $\mathbf{u}_3$, we solve the equation

$$c_1\mathbf{u}_1 + c_2\mathbf{u}_2 + c_3\mathbf{u}_3 = \mathbf{v}$$

for c_1, c_2 and c_3. This vector equation corresponds to the system

$$\begin{aligned} c_1 - 2c_2 + c_3 &= 4 \\ 2c_1 &= 4 \\ 3c_1 + c_2 &= 5. \end{aligned}$$

The solution of this system is $c_1 = 2$, $c_2 = -1$ and $c_3 = 0$. Thus, $\mathbf{v} = 2\mathbf{u}_1 - \mathbf{u}_2$.

10. The zero vector is the zero polynomial $p(x) = 0$. The additive inverse of a vector in P_8 is

$$-(a_0 + a_1x + a_2x^2 + \cdots + a_8x^8) = -a_0 - a_1x - a_2x^2 - \cdots - a_8x^8.$$

12. W is not a subspace of R^2. For instance, $(2, 1) \in W$ and $(3, 2) \in W$, but their sum $(5, 3) \notin W$. Hence, W is not closed under addition (nor scalar multiplication).

14. W is not a subspace of R^3, since it is not closed under scalar multiplication. For instance $(1, 1, 1) \in W$ and $-2 \in R$, but $-2(1, 1, 1) = (-2, -2, -2) \notin W$.

16. Since W is a nonempty subset of $C[-1, 1]$, we need only check that W is closed under addition and scalar multiplication. If f and g are in W, then $f(-1) = g(-1) = 0$, and $(f + g)(-1) = f(-1) + g(-1) = 0$, which implies that $f + g \in W$. Similarly, if c is a scalar, then $cf(-1) = c0 = 0$, which implies that $cf \in W$. Hence, W is a subspace of $C[-1, 1]$.

18. (a) W is a subspace of R^3, since W is nonempty $((0, 0, 0) \in W)$ and W is closed under addition and scalar multiplication.

For if (x_1, x_2, x_3) and (y_1, y_2, y_3) are in W, then $x_1 + x_2 + x_3 = 0$ and $y_1 + y_2 + y_3 = 0$. Since $(x_1, x_2, x_3) + (y_1, y_2, y_3) = (x_1 + y_1, x_2 + y_2, x_3 + y_3)$ satisfies $(x_1 + y_1) + (x_2 + y_2) + (x_3 + y_3) = 0$, W is closed under addition. Similarly, $c(x_1, x_2, x_3) = (cx_1, cx_2, cx_3)$ satisfies $cx_1 + cx_2 + cx_3 = 0$, showing that W is closed under scalar multiplication.

(b) W is not closed under addition or scalar multiplication, so it is not a subspace of R^3. For example, $(1, 0, 0) \in W$, and yet $2(1, 0, 0) = (2, 0, 0) \notin W$.

20. (a) To find out whether S spans R^3, we form the vector equation

$$c_1(4, 0, 1) + c_2(0, -3, 2) + c_3(5, 10, 0) = (u_1, u_2. u_3).$$

This yields the system of equations

$$\begin{aligned}
4c_1 \quad\quad\; + 5c_3 &= u_1 \\
-3c_2 + 10c_3 &= u_2 \\
c_1 + 2c_2 \quad\quad &= u_3.
\end{aligned}$$

This system has a unique solution for every (u_1, u_2, u_3) since the determinant of the coefficient matrix is not zero. Thus S spans R^3.

(b) Solving the same system in (a) with $(u_1, u_2, u_3) = (0, 0, 0)$ yields the trivial solution. Thus, S is linearly independent.

(c) Because S is linearly independent and spans R^3, it is a basis for R^3.

22. (a) S spans R^3 because the first three vectors in the set form the standard basis of R^3.

(b) S is linearly dependent because the fourth vector is a linear combination of the first three $(-1, 2, -3) = -1(1, 0, 0) + 2(0, 1, 0) - 3(0, 0, 1)$.

(c) S is not a basis because it is not linearly independent.

24. S has four vectors, so we need only check that S is linearly independent. We form the vector equation.

$$c_1\begin{bmatrix} 1 & 0 \\ 2 & 3 \end{bmatrix} + c_2\begin{bmatrix} -2 & 1 \\ -1 & 0 \end{bmatrix} + c_3\begin{bmatrix} 3 & 4 \\ 2 & 3 \end{bmatrix} + c_4\begin{bmatrix} -3 & -3 \\ 1 & 3 \end{bmatrix} = \begin{bmatrix} 0 & 0 \\ 0 & 0 \end{bmatrix},$$

which yields the homogeneous system of linear equations

$$\begin{aligned}
c_1 - 2c_2 + 3c_3 - 3c_4 &= 0 \\
c_2 + 4c_3 - 3c_4 &= 0 \\
2c_1 - c_2 + 2c_3 + c_4 &= 0 \\
3c_1 \quad\quad + 3c_3 + 3c_4 &= 0.
\end{aligned}$$

Since this system has nontrivial solutions, S is not a basis. For example, one solution is $c_1 = 2, c_2 = 1, c_3 = -1, c_4 = -1$.

$$2\begin{bmatrix} 1 & 0 \\ 2 & 3 \end{bmatrix} + \begin{bmatrix} -2 & 1 \\ -1 & 0 \end{bmatrix} - \begin{bmatrix} 3 & 4 \\ 2 & 3 \end{bmatrix} - \begin{bmatrix} -3 & -3 \\ 1 & 3 \end{bmatrix} = \begin{bmatrix} 0 & 0 \\ 0 & 0 \end{bmatrix}$$

26. (a) This system has solutions of the form $\left(3t, -\tfrac{1}{2}t, -4t, t\right)$, where t is any real number. A basis for the solution space is $\left\{\left(3, -\tfrac{1}{2}, -4, 1\right)\right\}$.

(b) The dimension of the solution space is 1, the number of vectors in the basis.

28. (a) This system has solutions of the form $\left(0, -\tfrac{3}{2}t, -t, t\right)$, where t is any real number. A basis for the solution space is $\left\{\left(0, -\tfrac{3}{2}, -1, 1\right)\right\}$.

(b) The dimension of the solution space is 1, the number of vectors in a basis.

30. The system given by $A\mathbf{x} = \mathbf{0}$ has only the trivial solution $(0, 0)$. Thus, the solution space is $\{(0, 0)\}$, which does not have a basis. The rank of A is 2 (the number of nonzero row vectors in the reduced row-echelon matrix) and the nullity is 0. Note that $\text{rank}(A) + \text{nullity}(A) = 2 + 0 = 2 = n$.

32. The system given by $A\mathbf{x} = \mathbf{0}$ has solutions of the form $(4t, -2t, t)$, where t is any real number. Thus, a basis for the solution space is $\{(4, -2, 1)\}$. The rank of A is 2 (the number of nonzero row vectors in the reduced row-echelon matrix) and the nullity is 1. Note that $\text{rank}(A) + \text{nullity}(A) = 2 + 1 = 3 = n$.

34. (a) Using Gauss-Jordan elimination, the matrix reduces to

$$\begin{bmatrix} 1 & 0 & \frac{26}{11} \\ 0 & 1 & \frac{8}{11} \\ 0 & 0 & 0 \end{bmatrix}.$$

Thus, the rank is 2.

(b) A basis for the row space is $\left\{\left(1, 0, \frac{26}{11}\right), \left(0, 1, \frac{8}{11}\right)\right\}$.

36. (a) Since the matrix is already row-reduced, its rank is 1.

(b) A basis for the row space is $\{(1, -4, 0, 4)\}$.

38. Because $[\mathbf{x}]_B = \begin{bmatrix} 1 \\ 1 \end{bmatrix}$, we can write $\mathbf{x}$ as $\mathbf{x} = 1(2, 0) + 1(3, 3) = (5, 3)$.

Since $(5, 3) = 5(1, 0) + 3(0, 1)$, the coordinate vector of $\mathbf{x}$ relative to the standard basis is

$$[\mathbf{x}]_S = \begin{bmatrix} 5 \\ 3 \end{bmatrix}.$$

40. Because $[\mathbf{x}]_B = \begin{bmatrix} \frac{1}{2} \\ \frac{1}{2} \end{bmatrix}$, we can write $\mathbf{x}$ as

$$\mathbf{x} = \tfrac{1}{2}\left(\tfrac{1}{2}, \tfrac{1}{2}\right) + \tfrac{1}{2}(1, 0) = \left(\tfrac{3}{4}, \tfrac{1}{4}\right).$$

Since $\left(\tfrac{3}{4}, \tfrac{1}{4}\right) = \tfrac{3}{4}(1, 0) + \tfrac{1}{4}(0, 1)$, the coordinate vector of $\mathbf{x}$ relative to the standard basis is

$$[\mathbf{x}]_S = \begin{bmatrix} \frac{3}{4} \\ \frac{1}{4} \end{bmatrix}.$$

42. To find $[\mathbf{x}]_{B'} = \begin{bmatrix} c_1 \\ c_2 \\ c_3 \end{bmatrix}$ we solve the equation

$$c_1(1, 2, 3) + c_2(1, 2, 0) + c_3(0, -6, 2) = (3, -3, 0).$$

The resulting system of linear equations is

$$\begin{aligned} c_1 + c_2 \qquad\quad &= \quad 3 \\ 2c_1 + 2c_2 - 6c_3 &= -3 \\ 3c_1 \qquad\quad + 2c_3 &= \quad 0. \end{aligned}$$

The solution to this system is $c_1 = -1, c_2 = 4, c_3 = \frac{3}{2}$, and we have

$$[\mathbf{x}]_{B'} = \begin{bmatrix} -1 \\ 4 \\ \frac{3}{2} \end{bmatrix}.$$

44. To find $[\mathbf{x}]_{B'} = \begin{bmatrix} c_1 \\ c_2 \\ c_3 \end{bmatrix}$ we solve the equation

$$c_1(1, 0, 0) + c_2(0, 1, 0) + c_3(1, 1, 1) = (4, -2, 9).$$

Forming the corresponding linear system, we find its solution to be $c_1 = -5$, $c_2 = -11, c_3 = 9$. Thus,

$$[\mathbf{x}]_{B'} = \begin{bmatrix} -5 \\ -11 \\ 9 \end{bmatrix}.$$

46. We begin by finding $\mathbf{x}$ relative to the standard basis

$$\mathbf{x} = -1(1, 0, 0) + 2(1, 1, 0) - 3(1, 1, 1) = (-2, -1, -3).$$

Then we solve for $[\mathbf{x}]_{B'} = \begin{bmatrix} c_1 \\ c_2 \\ c_3 \end{bmatrix}$ by forming the equation

$$c_1(0, 0, 1) + c_2(0, 1, 1) + c_3(1, 1, 1) = (-2, -1, -3).$$

Forming the corresponding linear system, we find its solution to be $c_1 = -2$, $c_2 = 1, c_3 = -2$. Thus,

$$[\mathbf{x}]_{B'} = \begin{bmatrix} -2 \\ 1 \\ -2 \end{bmatrix}.$$

48. We begin by forming

$$[B' \; \vdots \; B] = \begin{bmatrix} 0 & 0 & 1 & \vdots & 1 & 0 & 0 \\ 0 & 1 & 0 & \vdots & 0 & 1 & 0 \\ 1 & 0 & 0 & \vdots & 0 & 0 & 1 \end{bmatrix}.$$

We then use Gauss-Jordan elimination to obtain

$$[I_3 \; \vdots \; P^{-1}] = \begin{bmatrix} 1 & 0 & 0 & \vdots & 0 & 0 & 1 \\ 0 & 1 & 0 & \vdots & 0 & 1 & 0 \\ 0 & 0 & 1 & \vdots & 1 & 0 & 0 \end{bmatrix}.$$

Thus, we have

$$P^{-1} = \begin{bmatrix} 0 & 0 & 1 \\ 0 & 1 & 0 \\ 1 & 0 & 0 \end{bmatrix}.$$

50. We begin by forming

$$[B' \; \vdots \; B] = \begin{bmatrix} 1 & 0 & 1 & \vdots & 1 & 1 & 1 \\ 2 & 1 & 0 & \vdots & 1 & 1 & 0 \\ 3 & 0 & 1 & \vdots & 1 & 0 & 0 \end{bmatrix}.$$

We then use Gauss-Jordan elimination to obtain

$$[I_3 \; \vdots \; P^{-1}] = \begin{bmatrix} 1 & 0 & 0 & \vdots & 0 & -\frac{1}{2} & -\frac{1}{2} \\ 0 & 1 & 0 & \vdots & 1 & 2 & 1 \\ 0 & 0 & 1 & \vdots & 1 & \frac{3}{2} & \frac{3}{2} \end{bmatrix}.$$

Thus, we have

$$P^{-1} = \begin{bmatrix} 0 & -\frac{1}{2} & -\frac{1}{2} \\ 1 & 2 & 1 \\ 1 & \frac{3}{2} & \frac{3}{2} \end{bmatrix}.$$

52. (a) Since W is a nonempty subset of V, we need to only check that W is closed under addition and scalar multiplication. If $f, g \in W$, then $f' = 3f$ and $g' = 3g$. Thus, $(f + g)' = f' + g' = 3f + 3g = 3(f + g)$, which shows that $f + g \in W$. Finally, if c is a scalar, then $(cf)' = c(f') = c(3f) = 3(cf)$, which implies that $cf \in W$.

(b) V is not closed under addition nor scalar multiplication. For instance, let $f = e^x - 1 \in U$. Note that $2f = 2e^x - 2 \notin U$ since $(2f)' = 2e^x \neq (2f) + 1 = 2e^x - 1$.

54. Suppose, on the contrary, that A and B are linearly dependent. Then $B = cA$ for some scalar c. Thus, $(cA)^T = B^T = -B$, which implies that $cA = -B$. Hence, $B = O$, a contradiction.

56. To see if the given set is linearly independent, we solve the equation

$$c_1(\mathbf{v}_1 - \mathbf{v}_2) + c_2(\mathbf{v}_2 - \mathbf{v}_3) + c_3(\mathbf{v}_3 - \mathbf{v}_1) = 0\mathbf{v}_1 + 0\mathbf{v}_2 + 0\mathbf{v}_3$$

which yields the homogeneous system of linear equations

$$
\begin{aligned}
c_1 \quad\quad - c_3 &= 0 \\
-c_1 + c_2 \quad\quad &= 0 \\
-c_2 + c_3 &= 0.
\end{aligned}
$$

This system has infinitely many solutions, so $\{\mathbf{v}_1 - \mathbf{v}_2, \mathbf{v}_2 - \mathbf{v}_3, \mathbf{v}_3 - \mathbf{v}_1\}$ is linearly dependent.

58. S is a nonempty subset of R^n, and hence we need to only show closure under addition and scalar multiplication. Let $\mathbf{x}, \mathbf{y} \in S$. Then $A\mathbf{x} = \lambda\mathbf{x}$ and $A\mathbf{y} = \lambda\mathbf{y}$. Hence, $A(\mathbf{x} + \mathbf{y}) = A\mathbf{x} + A\mathbf{y} = \lambda\mathbf{x} + \lambda\mathbf{y} = \lambda(\mathbf{x} + \mathbf{y})$, which implies that $\mathbf{x} + \mathbf{y} \in S$. Finally, for any scalar c, $A(c\mathbf{x}) = c(A\mathbf{x}) = c(\lambda\mathbf{x}) = \lambda(c\mathbf{x})$ which implies that $c\mathbf{x} \in S$.

If $\lambda = 3$, then we solve for $\mathbf{x}$ in the equation $A\mathbf{x} = \lambda\mathbf{x} = 3\mathbf{x}$, or $A\mathbf{x} - 3\mathbf{x} = \mathbf{0}$, or $(A - 3I_3)\mathbf{x} = \mathbf{0}$

$$
\left(\begin{bmatrix} 3 & 1 & 0 \\ 0 & 3 & 0 \\ 0 & 0 & 1 \end{bmatrix} - 3\begin{bmatrix} 1 & 0 & 0 \\ 0 & 1 & 0 \\ 0 & 0 & 1 \end{bmatrix}\right)\begin{bmatrix} x_1 \\ x_2 \\ x_3 \end{bmatrix} = \begin{bmatrix} 0 \\ 0 \\ 0 \end{bmatrix}
$$

$$
\begin{bmatrix} 0 & 1 & 0 \\ 0 & 0 & 0 \\ 0 & 0 & -2 \end{bmatrix}\begin{bmatrix} x_1 \\ x_2 \\ x_3 \end{bmatrix} = \begin{bmatrix} 0 \\ 0 \\ 0 \end{bmatrix}.
$$

The solution to this homogeneous system is $x_1 = t$, $x_2 = 0$ and $x_3 = 0$, where t is any real number. Thus, a basis for S is $\{(1, 0, 0)\}$, and the dimension of S is 1.

60. From Exercise 57, we see that a set of functions $\{f_1, \ldots, f_n\}$ can be linearly independent in $C[a, b]$ and linearly dependent in $C[c, d]$, where $[a, b]$ and $[c, d]$ are different domains.

62. (a) *False.* This set is not closed under addition or scalar multiplication: $(0, 1, 1) \in W$, but $2(0, 1, 1) = (0, 2, 2)$ is not in W.

    (b) *True.* See definition of basis on page 215.

    (c) *False.* For example, let $A = I_3$ be 3×3 identity matrix. It is invertible and the rows of A form the standard basis for R^3 and, in particular, the rows of A are linearly independent.

64. (a) *True.* It is a nonempty subset of R^2, and it closed under addition and scalar multiplication.

    (b) *True.* See definition of linear independence on page 207.

    (c) *False.* These operations only preserve the linear relations among the columns.

66. (a) Since $y' = y'' = y''' = y'''' = e^x$, we have

$$y'''' - y = e^x - e^x = 0.$$

Therefore, e^x is a solution.

(b) Since $y' = -e^{-x}$, $y'' = e^{-x}$, $y''' = -e^{-x}$ and $y'''' = e^{-x}$, we have

$$y'''' - y = e^{-x} - e^{-x} = 0.$$

Therefore, e^{-x} is a solution.

(c) Since $y' = -\sin x$, $y'' = -\cos x$, $y''' = \sin x$, $y'''' = \cos x$, we have

$$y'''' - y = \cos x - \cos x = 0.$$

Therefore, $\cos x$ is a solution.

(d) Since $y' = \cos x$, $y'' = -\sin x$, $y''' = -\cos x$, $y'''' = \sin x$, we have

$$y'''' - y = \sin x - \sin x = 0.$$

Therefore, $\sin x$ is a solution.

68. $W(1, x, 2 + x) = \begin{vmatrix} 1 & x & (2 + x) \\ 0 & 1 & 1 \\ 0 & 0 & 0 \end{vmatrix} = 0$

70. The Wronskian of this set is

$$W(e^{-3x}, 3e^{-3x}) = \begin{vmatrix} e^{-3x} & 3e^{-3x} \\ -3x^{-3x} & -9e^{-3x} \end{vmatrix} = -9e^{-6x} + 9e^{-6x} = 0 = 0.$$

Since $W(e^{-3x}, 3e^{-3x}) = 0$, the set is linearly dependent.

72. The Wronskian of this set is

$$W(\sin 2x, \cos 2x) = \begin{vmatrix} \sin 2x & \cos 2x \\ 2\cos 2x & -2\sin 2x \end{vmatrix} = -2\sin^2 2x - 2\cos^2 2x = -2.$$

Since $W(\sin 2x, \cos 2x) \neq 0$ the set is linearly independent.

74. We begin by completing the square.

$$x^2 - y^2 + 2x - 3 = 0$$
$$(x^2 + 2x + 1) - y^2 = 3 + 1$$
$$(x + 1)^2 - y^2 = 4$$
$$\frac{(x + 1)^2}{2^2} - \frac{y^2}{2^2} = 1$$

This is the equation of a hyperbola with center $(-1, 0)$.

76. We begin by completing the square.

$$4x^2 + y^2 + 32x + 4y + 63 = 0$$
$$4(x^2 + 8x + 16) + (y^2 + 4y + 4) = -63 + 64 + 4$$
$$4(x + 4)^2 + (y + 2)^2 = 5$$

This is the equation of an ellipse with center $(-4, -2)$.

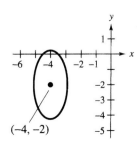

78. From the equation

$$\cot 2\theta = \frac{a - c}{b} = \frac{9 - 9}{4} = 0,$$

we find that the angle of rotation is $\theta = \frac{\pi}{4}$. Therefore, $\sin \theta = \frac{1}{\sqrt{2}}$ and $\cos \theta = \frac{1}{\sqrt{2}}$.

By substituting

$$x = x'\cos\theta - y'\sin\theta = \frac{1}{\sqrt{2}}(x' - y')$$

and

$$y = x'\sin\theta + y'\cos\theta = \frac{1}{\sqrt{2}}(x' + y')$$

into $9x^2 + 4xy + 9y^2 - 20 = 0$, we obtain $11(x')^2 + 7(y')^2 = 20$.

In standard form

$$\frac{(x')^2}{\left(\frac{20}{11}\right)} + \frac{(y')^2}{\frac{20}{7}} = 1$$

which is the equation of an ellipse.

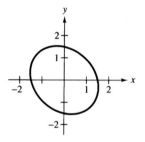

Chapter 4 ❑ Project Solutions

1 Solutions to Linear Systems

1. Since $(-2, -1, 1, 1)$ is a solution to $A\mathbf{x} = \mathbf{0}$, so is any multiple
    $-2(-2, -1, 1, 1) = (4, 2, -2, -2)$ because the solution space is a subspace.

2. The solutions to $A\mathbf{x} = \mathbf{0}$ form a subspace, so any linear combination
    $2\mathbf{x}_1 - 3\mathbf{x}_2$ of solutions $\mathbf{x}_1$ and $\mathbf{x}_2$ is again a solution.

3. Let the first system be $A\mathbf{x} = \mathbf{b}_1$. Since it is consistent, $\mathbf{b}_1$ is in the column
    space of A. The second system is $A\mathbf{x} = \mathbf{b}_2$, and $\mathbf{b}_2$ is a multiple of $\mathbf{b}_1$, so it
    is in the column space of A as well. Hence, the second system is consistent.

4. $2\mathbf{x}_1 - 3\mathbf{x}_2$ is *not* a solution (unless $\mathbf{b} = \mathbf{0}$). The set of solutions to a
    nonhomogeneous system is not a subspace. If $A\mathbf{x}_1 = \mathbf{b}$ and $A\mathbf{x}_2 = \mathbf{b}$, then
    $A(2\mathbf{x}_1 - 3\mathbf{x}_2) = 2A\mathbf{x}_1 - 3A\mathbf{x}_2 = 2\mathbf{b} - 3\mathbf{b} = -\mathbf{b} \neq \mathbf{b}$.

5. Yes, $\mathbf{b}_1$ and $\mathbf{b}_2$ are in the column space of A, and hence so is $\mathbf{b}_1 + \mathbf{b}_2$.

6. If rank A = rank$[A : \mathbf{b}]$, then b is in the column space of A and the system
    is consistent. If rank A < rank$[A : \mathbf{b}]$, then $\mathbf{b}$ is not in the column space and
    the system is inconsistent.

2 Direct Sum

1. $U + W$ is nonempty since $\mathbf{0} = \mathbf{0} + \mathbf{0} \in U + W$. Let $\mathbf{u}_1 + \mathbf{w}_1$ and $\mathbf{u}_2 + \mathbf{w}_2$ be in $U + W$. Then $(\mathbf{u}_1 + \mathbf{w}_1) + (\mathbf{u}_2 + \mathbf{w}_2) = (\mathbf{u}_1 + \mathbf{u}_2) + (\mathbf{w}_1 + \mathbf{w}_2) \in U + W$ and $c(\mathbf{u}_1 + \mathbf{w}_1) = (c\mathbf{u}_1) + (c\mathbf{w}_1) \in U + W$.

2. Basis for $U = \{(1, 0, 1), (0, 1, -1)\}$

    Basis for $W = \{(1, 0, 1)\}$

    Basis for $Z = \{(1, 1, 1)\}$

    $U + W = U$ since $W \subseteq U$

    $U + Z = R^3$ since $\{(1, 0, 1), (0, 1, -1), (1, 1, 1)\}$ is a basis for R^3.

    $\begin{aligned} W + Z &= \operatorname{span}\{(1, 0, 1), (1, 1, 1)\} \\ &= \operatorname{span}\{(1, 0, 1), (0, 1, 0)\} \end{aligned}$

3. Suppose $\mathbf{u}_1 + \mathbf{w}_1 = \mathbf{u}_2 + \mathbf{w}_2$, which implies

    $$\mathbf{u}_1 - \mathbf{u}_2 = \mathbf{w}_2 - \mathbf{w}_1.$$

    Since $\mathbf{u}_1 - \mathbf{u}_2 \in U \cap W$ and $\mathbf{w}_2 - \mathbf{w}_1 \in U \cap W$, and $U \cap W = \{\mathbf{0}\}$, $\mathbf{u}_1 = \mathbf{u}_2$ and $\mathbf{w}_1 = \mathbf{w}_2$.

    $U \oplus Z$ and $W \oplus Z$ are direct sums.

4. Let $\mathbf{v} \in V$, then $\mathbf{v} = \mathbf{u} + \mathbf{w}, \mathbf{u} \in U, \mathbf{w} \in W$. Then $\mathbf{v} = (c_1\mathbf{u}_1 + \cdots + c_k\mathbf{u}_k) + (d_1\mathbf{w}_1 + \cdots + d_m\mathbf{w}_m)$, and $\mathbf{v}$ is in the span of $\{\mathbf{u}_1, \ldots, \mathbf{u}_k, \mathbf{w}_1, \ldots, \mathbf{w}_m\}$. To show that this set is linearly independent, suppose

    $$c_1\mathbf{u}_1 + \cdots + c_k\mathbf{u}_k + d_1\mathbf{w}_1 + \cdots + d_m\mathbf{w}_m = \mathbf{0}$$

    $$\Rightarrow c_1\mathbf{u}_1 + \cdots + c_k\mathbf{u}_k = -(d_1\mathbf{w}_1 + \cdots + d_m\mathbf{w}_m)$$

    But $U \cap W \neq \{\mathbf{0}\} \Rightarrow c_1\mathbf{u}_1 + \cdots + c_k\mathbf{u}_k = \mathbf{0}$ and $d_1\mathbf{w}_1 + \cdots + d_m\mathbf{w}_m = \mathbf{0}$.

    Since $\{\mathbf{u}_1, \ldots, \mathbf{u}_k\}$ and $\{\mathbf{w}_1, \ldots, \mathbf{w}_m\}$ are linearly independent, $c_1 = \cdots = c_k = 0$ and $d_1 = \cdots = d_m = 0$.

5. Basis for U: $\{(1, 0, 0), (0, 0, 1)\}$

    Basis for W: $\{(0, 1, 0), (0, 0, 1)\}$

    $U + W$ is spanned by $\{(1, 0, 0), (0, 0, 1), (0, 1, 0)\} \Rightarrow U + W = R^3$. This is not a direct sum since $(0, 0, 1) \in U \cap W$.

    $\dim U = 2$, $\dim W = 2$, $\dim(U \cap W) = 1$

    $\dim U + \dim W = \dim(U + W) + \dim(U \cap W)$.

    $\qquad 2 \ + \ 2 \quad = \quad\ \ 3 \quad\ + \quad 1$

    In general, $\dim U + \dim W = \dim(U + W) + \dim(U \cap W)$

6. No, $\dim U + \dim W = 2 + 2 = 4$, then $\dim(U + W) + \dim(U \cap W) = \dim(U + W) = 4$, which is impossible in R^3.

CHAPTER 5
Inner Product Spaces

Section 5.1   Length and Dot Product in R^n

2. $\|\mathbf{v}\| = \sqrt{0^2 + 1^2} = \sqrt{1} = 1$

4. $\|\mathbf{v}\| = \sqrt{2^2 + 0^2 + 6^2} = \sqrt{40} = 2\sqrt{10}$

6. $\|\mathbf{v}\| = \sqrt{2^2 + (-4)^2 + 5^2 + (-1)^2 + 1^2} = \sqrt{47}$

8. (a) $\|\mathbf{u}\| = \sqrt{1^2 + \left(\frac{1}{2}\right)^2} = \sqrt{\frac{5}{4}} = \frac{1}{2}\sqrt{5}$

   (b) $\|\mathbf{v}\| = \sqrt{2^2 + \left(-\frac{1}{2}\right)^2} = \sqrt{\frac{17}{4}} = \frac{1}{2}\sqrt{17}$

   (c) $\|\mathbf{u} + \mathbf{v}\| = \|(3, 0)\| = \sqrt{3^2 + 0^2} = \sqrt{9} = 3$

10. (a) $\|\mathbf{u}\| = \sqrt{1^2 + 0^2 + 0^2 + 0^2} = \sqrt{1} = 1$

   (b) $\|\mathbf{v}\| = \sqrt{0^2 + 1^2 + 0^2 + 0^2} = \sqrt{1} = 1$

   (c) $\|\mathbf{u} + \mathbf{v}\| = \|(1, 1, 0, 0)\| = \sqrt{1^2 + 1^2 + 0^2 + 0^2} = \sqrt{2}$

12. (a) A unit vector $\mathbf{v}$ in the direction of $\mathbf{u}$ is given by

$$\mathbf{v} = \frac{\mathbf{u}}{\|\mathbf{u}\|} = \frac{1}{\sqrt{1^2 + (-1)^2}}(1, -1)$$
$$= \frac{1}{\sqrt{2}}(1, -1) = \left(\frac{1}{\sqrt{2}}, -\frac{1}{\sqrt{2}}\right).$$

   (b) A unit vector in the direction opposite that of $\mathbf{u}$ is given by

$$-\mathbf{v} = -\left(\frac{1}{\sqrt{2}}, -\frac{1}{\sqrt{2}}\right) = \left(-\frac{1}{\sqrt{2}}, \frac{1}{\sqrt{2}}\right).$$

14. (a) A unit vector $\mathbf{v}$ in the direction of $\mathbf{u}$ is given by

$$\mathbf{v} = \frac{\mathbf{u}}{\|\mathbf{u}\|} = \frac{1}{\sqrt{1^2 + 0^2 + 2^2 + 2^2}}(1, 0, 2, 2)$$
$$= \frac{1}{3}(1, 0, 2, 2) = \left(\frac{1}{3}, 0, \frac{2}{3}, \frac{2}{3}\right).$$

   (b) A unit vector in the direction opposite that of $\mathbf{u}$ is given by

$$-\mathbf{v} = -\left(\frac{1}{3}, 0, \frac{2}{3}, \frac{2}{3}\right) = \left(-\frac{1}{3}, 0, -\frac{2}{3}, -\frac{2}{3}\right).$$

16. We solve the equation for c as follows.

$$\|c(2, 2, -1)\| = 3$$
$$|c|\,\|(2, 2, -1)\| = 3$$
$$|c|\sqrt{2^2 + 2^2 + (-1)^2} = 3$$
$$|c|3 = 3 \quad \Rightarrow \quad c = \pm 1.$$

18. First we find a unit vector in the direction of **u**.

$$\frac{\mathbf{u}}{\|\mathbf{u}\|} = \frac{1}{\sqrt{(-1)^2 + 1^2}}(-1, 1) = \frac{1}{\sqrt{2}}(-1, 1) = \left(-\frac{1}{\sqrt{2}}, \frac{1}{\sqrt{2}}\right)$$

Then **v** is four times this vector.

$$\mathbf{v} = 4\frac{\mathbf{u}}{\|\mathbf{u}\|} = 4\left(-\frac{1}{\sqrt{2}}, \frac{1}{\sqrt{2}}\right) = \left(-\frac{4}{\sqrt{2}}, \frac{4}{\sqrt{2}}\right) = \left(-2\sqrt{2}, 2\sqrt{2}\right)$$

20. First we find a unit vector in the direction of **u**.

$$\frac{\mathbf{u}}{\|\mathbf{u}\|} = \frac{1}{\sqrt{0 + 4 + 1 + 1}}(0, 2, 1, -1) = \frac{1}{\sqrt{6}}(0, 2, 1, -1)$$

Then **v** is three times this vector.

$$\mathbf{v} = 3\frac{1}{\sqrt{6}}(0, 2, 1, -1) = \left(0, \frac{6}{\sqrt{6}}, \frac{3}{\sqrt{6}}, -\frac{3}{\sqrt{6}}\right)$$

22. (a) Since $\dfrac{\mathbf{v}}{\|\mathbf{v}\|}$ is a unit vector in the direction of **v**, we have

$$\mathbf{u} = \frac{\|\mathbf{v}\|}{2}\frac{\mathbf{v}}{\|\mathbf{v}\|} = \frac{1}{2}\mathbf{v} = \frac{1}{2}\left(-1, 3, 0, 4\right) = \left(-\frac{1}{2}, \frac{3}{2}, 0, 2\right).$$

(b) Since $-\dfrac{\mathbf{v}}{\|\mathbf{v}\|}$ is a unit vector with direction opposite that of **v**, we have

$$\mathbf{u} = \frac{\|\mathbf{v}\|}{4}\left(-\frac{\mathbf{v}}{\|\mathbf{v}\|}\right) = -\frac{1}{4}\mathbf{v} = -\frac{1}{4}\left(-1, 3, 0, 4\right) = \left(\frac{1}{4}, -\frac{3}{4}, 0, -1\right).$$

24. $d(\mathbf{u}, \mathbf{v}) = \|\mathbf{u} - \mathbf{v}\| = \|(-4, 3)\|$
$$= \sqrt{16 + 9} = 5$$

26. $d(\mathbf{u}, \mathbf{v}) = \|\mathbf{u} - \mathbf{v}\| = \|(-1, 1, -2, 4)\|$
$$= \sqrt{1 + 1 + 4 + 16} = \sqrt{22}$$

28. (a) $\mathbf{u} \cdot \mathbf{v} = (-1)(1) + 1(-3) + (-2)(-2) = 0$

(b) $\mathbf{u} \cdot \mathbf{u} = (-1)(-1) + 1(1) + (-2)(-2) = 6$

(c) $\|\mathbf{u}\|^2 = \mathbf{u} \cdot \mathbf{u} = 6$

(d) $(\mathbf{u} \cdot \mathbf{v})\mathbf{v} = 0(1, -3, -2) = (0, 0, 0) = \mathbf{0}$

(e) $\mathbf{u} \cdot (5\mathbf{v}) = 5(\mathbf{u} \cdot \mathbf{v}) = 5 \cdot 0 = 0$

30. (a) $\mathbf{u} \cdot \mathbf{v} = 0(6) + 4(8) + 3(-3) + 4(3) + 4(-5) = 15$

(b) $\mathbf{u} \cdot \mathbf{u} = 0(0) + 4(4) + 3(3) + 4(4) + 4(4) = 57$

(c) $\|\mathbf{u}\|^2 = \mathbf{u} \cdot \mathbf{u} = 57$

(d) $(\mathbf{u} \cdot \mathbf{v})\mathbf{v} = 15(6, 8, -3, 3, -5) = (90, 120, -45, 45, -75)$

(e) $\mathbf{u} \cdot (5\mathbf{v}) = 5(\mathbf{u} \cdot \mathbf{v}) = 5 \cdot 15 = 75$

32. $(3\mathbf{u} - \mathbf{v}) \cdot (\mathbf{u} - 3\mathbf{v}) = 3\mathbf{u} \cdot (\mathbf{u} - 3\mathbf{v}) - \mathbf{v} \cdot (\mathbf{u} - 3\mathbf{v})$
$$= 3\mathbf{u} \cdot \mathbf{u} - 9\mathbf{u} \cdot \mathbf{v} - \mathbf{v} \cdot \mathbf{u} + 3\mathbf{v} \cdot \mathbf{v}$$
$$= 3\mathbf{u} \cdot \mathbf{u} - 10\mathbf{u} \cdot \mathbf{v} + 3\mathbf{v} \cdot \mathbf{v}$$
$$= 3(8) - 10(7) + 3(6)$$
$$= -28$$

34. $\mathbf{u} = (3, -4)$ and $\mathbf{v} = (5, 12)$

(a) $\|\mathbf{u}\| = \sqrt{9 + 16} = 5$ and $\|\mathbf{v}\| = \sqrt{25 + 144} = 13$.

(b) Unit vector in the direction of $\mathbf{v}$ is
$$\frac{1}{\|\mathbf{v}\|}\mathbf{v} = \left(\frac{5}{13}, \frac{12}{13}\right).$$

(c) Unit vector in the opposite direction of $\mathbf{u}$ is
$$-\frac{1}{\|\mathbf{u}\|}\mathbf{u} = \left(-\frac{3}{5}, \frac{4}{5}\right).$$

(d) $\mathbf{u} \cdot \mathbf{v} = 3 \cdot 5 - 4 \cdot 12 = 15 - 48 = -33$

(e) $\mathbf{u} \cdot \mathbf{u} = \|\mathbf{u}\|^2 = 25$

(f) $\mathbf{v} \cdot \mathbf{v} = \|\mathbf{v}\|^2 = 25 + 144 = 169$

36. $\mathbf{u} = (3, -4)$ and $\mathbf{v} = (4, 3)$

(a) $\|\mathbf{u}\| = \sqrt{9 + 16} = 5$ and $\|\mathbf{v}\| = \sqrt{16 + 9} = 5$.

(b) Unit vector in the direction of $\mathbf{v}$ is
$$\frac{1}{\|\mathbf{v}\|}\mathbf{v} = \left(\frac{4}{5}, \frac{3}{5}\right).$$

(c) Unit vector in the opposite direction of $\mathbf{u}$ is
$$-\frac{1}{\|\mathbf{u}\|}\mathbf{u} = \left(-\frac{3}{5}, \frac{4}{5}\right).$$

(d) $\mathbf{u} \cdot \mathbf{v} = 0$.

(e) $\mathbf{u} \cdot \mathbf{u} = \|\mathbf{u}\|^2 = 25$

(f) $\mathbf{v} \cdot \mathbf{v} = \|\mathbf{v}\|^2 = 25$.

38. $\mathbf{u} = (9, 12)$ and $\mathbf{v} = (-7, 24)$

(a) $\|\mathbf{u}\| = \sqrt{81 + 144} = 15$ and $\|\mathbf{v}\| = \sqrt{49 + 576} = \sqrt{625} = 25$.

(b) Unit vector in the direction of $\mathbf{v}$ is
$$\frac{1}{\|\mathbf{v}\|}\mathbf{v} = \left(-\frac{7}{25}, \frac{24}{25}\right).$$

—CONTINUED—

38. **—CONTINUED—**

(c) Unit vector in the opposite direction of **u** is

$$-\frac{1}{\|\mathbf{u}\|}\mathbf{u} = \left(-\frac{3}{5}, -\frac{4}{5}\right).$$

(d) $\mathbf{u} \cdot \mathbf{v} = -63 + 288 = 225.$

(e) $\mathbf{u} \cdot \mathbf{u} = \|\mathbf{u}\|^2 = 225$

(f) $\mathbf{v} \cdot \mathbf{v} = \|\mathbf{v}\|^2 = 625.$

40. $\mathbf{u} = (3, 0, -4)$ and $\mathbf{v} = (-3, -4, 0)$

(a) $\|\mathbf{u}\| = \sqrt{9 + 16} = 5$ and $\|\mathbf{v}\| = \sqrt{9 + 16} = 5.$

(b) Unit vector in the direction of **v** is

$$\frac{1}{\|\mathbf{v}\|}\mathbf{v} = \left(-\frac{3}{5}, -\frac{4}{5}, 0\right)$$

(c) Unit vector in the opposite direction of **u** is

$$-\frac{1}{\|\mathbf{u}\|}\mathbf{u} = \left(-\frac{3}{5}, 0, \frac{4}{5}\right)$$

(d) $\mathbf{u} \cdot \mathbf{v} = -9.$

(e) $\mathbf{u} \cdot \mathbf{u} = \|\mathbf{u}\|^2 = 25$

(f) $\mathbf{v} \cdot \mathbf{v} = \|\mathbf{v}\|^2 = 9 + 16 = 25.$

42. $\mathbf{u} = (1, 2, 3, -2, -1, -3)$ and $\mathbf{v} = (-1, 0, 2, 1, 2, -3)$

Using a graphing calculator (TI-86), we have

(a) $\|\mathbf{u}\| = 5.2915$ and $\|\mathbf{v}\| = 4.3589$

(b) $\frac{1}{\|\mathbf{v}\|}\mathbf{v} = (-0.2294, 0, 0.4588, 0.2294, 0.4588, -0.6882)$

(c) $-\frac{1}{\|\mathbf{u}\|}\mathbf{u} = (-0.1890, -0.3780, -0.5669, 0.3780, 0.1890, 0.5669)$

(d) $\mathbf{u} \cdot \mathbf{v} = 0$

(e) $\mathbf{u} \cdot \mathbf{u} = \|\mathbf{u}\|^2 = 28$

(f) $\mathbf{v} \cdot \mathbf{v} = \|\mathbf{v}\|^2 = 19$

44. $\mathbf{u} = (3, -1, 2, 1, 0, 1, 2, -1)$ and $\mathbf{v} = (1, 2, 0, -1, 2, -2, 1, 0)$

Using a graphing calculator (TI-86), we have

(a) $\|\mathbf{u}\| = 4.5826$ and $\|\mathbf{v}\| = 3.8730$

(b) $\dfrac{1}{\|\mathbf{v}\|}\mathbf{v} = (0.2582, 0.5164, 0, -0.2582, 0.5164, -0.5164, 0.2582, 0)$

(c) $-\dfrac{1}{\|\mathbf{u}\|}\mathbf{u} = (-0.6547, 0.2182, -0.4364, -0.2182, 0, -0.2182, -0.4364, 0.2182)$

(d) $\mathbf{u} \cdot \mathbf{v} = 0$

(e) $\mathbf{u} \cdot \mathbf{u} = \|\mathbf{u}\|^2 = 21$

(f) $\mathbf{v} \cdot \mathbf{v} = \|\mathbf{v}\|^2 = 15$

46. We have

$$\mathbf{u} \cdot \mathbf{v} = (1) + 1(-3) + (-2)(-2) = 2,$$
$$\|\mathbf{u}\| = \sqrt{1^2 + 1^2 + (-2)^2} = \sqrt{6}, \text{ and}$$
$$\|\mathbf{v}\| = \sqrt{1^2 + (-3)^2 + (-2)^2} = \sqrt{14}. \text{ Thus,}$$
$$|\mathbf{u} \cdot \mathbf{v}| \le \|\mathbf{u}\|\,\|\mathbf{v}\|$$
$$2 \le \sqrt{6}\sqrt{14} \approx 9.17.$$

48. The cosine of the angle θ between $\mathbf{u}$ and $\mathbf{v}$ is given by

$$\cos\theta = \frac{\mathbf{u}\cdot\mathbf{v}}{\|\mathbf{u}\|\,\|\mathbf{v}\|} = \frac{\left(\sqrt{3}/2, \sqrt{1}/2\right)\cdot\left(-\sqrt{2}/2, \sqrt{2}/2\right)}{(1)(1)}$$
$$= -\frac{\sqrt{6}}{4} + \frac{\sqrt{2}}{4} = \frac{\sqrt{2}-\sqrt{6}}{4}.$$

Thus, $\theta = \cos^{-1}\left(\dfrac{\sqrt{2}-\sqrt{6}}{4}\right) = \dfrac{7\pi}{12} \approx 1.833$ radians (105°).

50. The cosine of the angle θ between $\mathbf{u}$ and $\mathbf{v}$ is given by

$$\cos\theta = \frac{\mathbf{u}\cdot\mathbf{v}}{\|\mathbf{u}\|\|\mathbf{v}\|} = \frac{2(-3) + 3(2) + 1(0)}{\|\mathbf{u}\|\,\|\mathbf{v}\|} = 0$$

Thus, $\theta = \dfrac{\pi}{2}$ radians (90°).

52. The cosine of the angle θ between $\mathbf{u}$ and $\mathbf{v}$ is given by

$$\cos\theta = \frac{\mathbf{u}\cdot\mathbf{v}}{\|\mathbf{u}\|\|\mathbf{v}\|}$$
$$= \frac{1(-1) + 3(4) + (-1)(5) + 2(-3) + 0(2)}{\sqrt{1^2 + 3^2 + (-1)^2 + 2^2 + 0^2}\sqrt{(-1)^2 + 4^2 + 5^2 + (-3)^2 + 2^2}}$$
$$= \frac{0}{\sqrt{15}\sqrt{55}} = 0.$$

Thus, $\theta = \dfrac{\pi}{2}$.

54.
$$\mathbf{u} \cdot \mathbf{v} = 0$$
$$(2, 7) \cdot (v_1, v_2) = 0$$
$$2v_1 + 7v_2 = 0$$

Thus, $\mathbf{v} = (-7t, 2t)$, where t is any real number.

56.
$$\mathbf{u} \cdot \mathbf{v} = 0$$
$$(0, 0) \cdot (v_1, v_2) = 0$$
$$0v_1 + 0v_2 = 0$$

Thus, $\mathbf{v} = (v_1, v_2)$ can be any vector in R^2.

58.
$$\mathbf{u} \cdot \mathbf{v} = 0$$
$$(0, 1, 0, 0, 0) \cdot (v_1, v_2, v_3, v_4, v_5) = 0$$
$$v_2 = 0$$

Thus, $\mathbf{v} = (r, 0, s, t, w)$, where r, s, t and w are any real numbers.

60. Since

$$\mathbf{u} \cdot \mathbf{v} = (4, 3) \cdot \left(\frac{1}{2}, -\frac{2}{3} \right) = 2 - 2 = 0$$

the vectors $\mathbf{u}$ and $\mathbf{v}$ are orthogonal.

62. Since $\mathbf{u} \cdot \mathbf{v} = (0, 1, 6) \cdot (1, -2, -1) = -2 - 6 = -8 \neq 0$ the vectors $\mathbf{u}$ and $\mathbf{v}$ are not orhogonal. Moreover, because one is not a scalar multiple of the other, they are not parallel either.

64. Since

$$\frac{\mathbf{u} \cdot \mathbf{v}}{\|\mathbf{u}\| \|\mathbf{v}\|} = \frac{4(-2) + \frac{3}{2}\left(-\frac{3}{4}\right) + (-1)\left(\frac{1}{2}\right) + \frac{1}{2}\left(-\frac{1}{4}\right)}{\sqrt{4^2 + \left(\frac{3}{2}\right)^2 + (-1)^2 + \left(\frac{1}{2}\right)^2} \sqrt{(-2)^2 + \left(-\frac{3}{4}\right)^2 + \left(\frac{1}{2}\right)^2 + \left(-\frac{1}{4}\right)^2}}$$

$$= \frac{-\frac{39}{4}}{\sqrt{\frac{39}{2}} \sqrt{\frac{39}{8}}} = -1$$

the angle between $\mathbf{u}$ and $\mathbf{v}$ is π. Consequently, $\mathbf{u}$ and $\mathbf{v}$ are parallel.

66. $\mathbf{u} = \left(-\frac{21}{2}, \frac{43}{2}, -12, \frac{3}{2} \right)$ and $\mathbf{v} = \left(0, 6, \frac{21}{2}, -\frac{9}{2} \right)$

Using a graphing calculator, we have $\mathbf{u} \cdot \mathbf{v} = -3.75 \neq 0$. Since $\mathbf{u} \cdot \mathbf{v} \neq 0$, the vectors are not orthogonal. Because one is not a scalar multiple of the other, they are not parallel.

68. $\mathbf{u} = \left(-\frac{4}{3}, \frac{8}{3}, -4, -\frac{32}{3} \right)$ and $\mathbf{v} = \left(-\frac{16}{3}, -2, \frac{4}{3}, -\frac{2}{3} \right)$

Using a graphing calculator, we have $\mathbf{u} \cdot \mathbf{v} = \frac{32}{9} \neq 0$. Since $\mathbf{u} \cdot \mathbf{v} \neq 0$, the vectors are not orthogonal. Because one is not a scalar multiple of the other, they are not parallel.

70. (a) *False.* The unit vector in the direction of $\mathbf{v}$ is given by $\dfrac{\mathbf{v}}{\|\mathbf{v}\|}$.

(b) *False.* If $\mathbf{u} \cdot \mathbf{v} < 0$ then the angle between them lies between $\dfrac{\pi}{2}$ and π, because

$$\cos \theta < 0 \implies \frac{\pi}{2} < \theta < \pi.$$

72. (a) $(\mathbf{u} \cdot \mathbf{v}) \cdot \mathbf{u}$ is meaningless because $\mathbf{u} \cdot \mathbf{v}$ is a scalar.

    (b) $c \cdot (\mathbf{u} \cdot \mathbf{v})$ is meaningless because c is a scalar, as well as $\mathbf{u} \cdot \mathbf{v}$.

74. Since $\mathbf{u} + \mathbf{v} = (1, 1, 1) + (0, -1, 2) = (1, 0, 3)$, we have

$$\|\mathbf{u} + \mathbf{v}\| \le \|\mathbf{u}\| + \|\mathbf{v}\|$$
$$\|(1, 0, 3)\| \le \|(1, 1, 1)\| + \|(0, -1, 2)\|$$
$$\sqrt{10} \le \sqrt{3} + \sqrt{5}$$

$$(3.162278 \le 1.732051 + 2.236068 = 3.968119)$$

76. First note that $\mathbf{u}$ and $\mathbf{v}$ are orthogonal, since $\mathbf{u} \cdot \mathbf{v} = (3, 4, -2) \cdot (4, -3, 0) = 0$. On the other hand,

$$\|\mathbf{u} + \mathbf{v}\|^2 = \|\mathbf{u}\|^2 + \|\mathbf{v}\|^2$$
$$\|(7, 1, -2)\|^2 = \|(3, 4, -2)\|^2 + \|(4, -3, 0)\|^2$$
$$54 = 29 + 25.$$

78. $(v_1, v_2) \cdot (v_2, -v_1) = v_1 v_2 - v_2 v_1 = 0.$

    $(5, -12)$ and $(-5, 12)$ are orthogonal to $(12, 5)$.

80. Let $\mathbf{v} = (t, t, t)$ be the diagonal of the cube, and $\mathbf{u} = (t, t, 0)$ the diagonal of one of its sides. Then,

$$\cos \theta = \frac{\mathbf{u} \cdot \mathbf{v}}{\|\mathbf{u}\|\|\mathbf{v}\|} = \frac{2t^2}{(\sqrt{2}\,t)(\sqrt{3}\,t)} = \frac{2}{\sqrt{6}} = \frac{\sqrt{6}}{3}$$

and $\theta = \cos^{-1}\left(\dfrac{\sqrt{6}}{3}\right) \approx 35.26°.$

82. We are given that $\mathbf{u} \cdot \mathbf{v} = 0$ and $\mathbf{u} \cdot \mathbf{w} = 0$. Hence,

$$\begin{aligned}
\mathbf{u} \cdot (c\mathbf{v} + d\mathbf{w}) &= \mathbf{u} \cdot (c\mathbf{v}) + \mathbf{u} \cdot (d\mathbf{w}) \\
&= c(\mathbf{u} \cdot \mathbf{v}) + d(\mathbf{u} \cdot \mathbf{w}) \\
&= c(0) + d(0) \\
&= 0.
\end{aligned}$$

Hence, $\mathbf{u}$ is orthogonal to $c\mathbf{v} + d\mathbf{w}$.

84. $$\begin{aligned}
\|\mathbf{u} + \mathbf{v}\|^2 + \|\mathbf{u} - \mathbf{v}\|^2 &= (\mathbf{u} + \mathbf{v}) \cdot (\mathbf{u} + \mathbf{v}) + (\mathbf{u} - \mathbf{v}) \cdot (\mathbf{u} - \mathbf{v}) \\
&= (\mathbf{u} \cdot \mathbf{u} + \mathbf{v} \cdot \mathbf{v} + 2\mathbf{u} \cdot \mathbf{v}) + (\mathbf{u} \cdot \mathbf{u} + \mathbf{v} \cdot \mathbf{v} - 2\mathbf{u} \cdot \mathbf{v}) \\
&= 2\|\mathbf{u}\|^2 + 2\|\mathbf{v}\|^2
\end{aligned}$$

86. If **u** and **v** have the same direction, then $\mathbf{u} = c\mathbf{v}, c > 0$, and

$$\|\mathbf{u} + \mathbf{v}\| = \|c\mathbf{v} + \mathbf{v}\| = (c+1)\|\mathbf{v}\|$$
$$= c\|\mathbf{v}\| + \|\mathbf{v}\| = \|c\mathbf{v}\| + \|\mathbf{v}\|$$
$$= \|\mathbf{u}\| + \|\mathbf{v}\|.$$

On the other hand, if

$$\|\mathbf{u} + \mathbf{v}\| = \|\mathbf{u}\| + \|\mathbf{v}\|, \quad \text{then}$$
$$\|\mathbf{u} + \mathbf{v}\|^2 = (\|\mathbf{u}\| + \|\mathbf{v}\|)^2$$
$$(\mathbf{u} + \mathbf{v}) \cdot (\mathbf{u} + \mathbf{v}) = \|\mathbf{u}\|^2 + \|\mathbf{v}\|^2 + 2\|\mathbf{u}\|\,\|\mathbf{v}\|$$
$$\|\mathbf{u}\|^2 + \|\mathbf{v}\|^2 + 2\mathbf{u} \cdot \mathbf{v} = \|\mathbf{u}\|^2 + \|\mathbf{v}\|^2 + 2\|\mathbf{u}\|\|\mathbf{v}\|$$
$$2\mathbf{u} \cdot \mathbf{v} = 2\|\mathbf{u}\|\|\mathbf{v}\|$$
$$\Rightarrow \cos\theta = \frac{\mathbf{u} \cdot \mathbf{v}}{\|\mathbf{u}\|\,\|\mathbf{v}\|} = 1 \quad \Rightarrow \quad \theta = 0 \quad \Rightarrow \quad \mathbf{u} \text{ and } \mathbf{v} \text{ have the same direction.}$$

88. $A\mathbf{x} = \mathbf{0}$ means that the dot product of each row of A with the column vector $\mathbf{x}$ is zero. Thus, $\mathbf{x}$ is orthogonal to the row vectors of A.

Section 5.2   Inner Product Spaces

2. (a) $\langle \mathbf{u}, \mathbf{v} \rangle = \mathbf{u} \cdot \mathbf{v} = 1(7) + 1(9) = 16$

   (b) $\|\mathbf{u}\| = \sqrt{\langle \mathbf{u}, \mathbf{u} \rangle} = \sqrt{\mathbf{u} \cdot \mathbf{u}} = \sqrt{1^2 + 1^2} = \sqrt{2}$

   (c) $\|\mathbf{v}\| = \sqrt{\langle \mathbf{v}, \mathbf{v} \rangle} = \sqrt{\mathbf{v} \cdot \mathbf{v}} = \sqrt{7^2 + 9^2} = \sqrt{130}$

   (d) $d(\mathbf{u}, \mathbf{v}) = \|\mathbf{u} - \mathbf{v}\| = \|(-6, -8)\| = \sqrt{(-6)^2 + (-8)^2} = \sqrt{100} = 10$

4. (a) $\langle \mathbf{u}, \mathbf{v} \rangle = 0(-1) + 2(-6)(1) = -12$

   (b) $\|\mathbf{u}\| = \sqrt{\langle \mathbf{u}, \mathbf{u} \rangle} = \sqrt{0(0) + 2(-6)(-6)} = 6\sqrt{2}$

   (c) $\|\mathbf{v}\| = \sqrt{\langle \mathbf{v}, \mathbf{v} \rangle} = \sqrt{(-1)(-1) + 2(1)(1)} = \sqrt{3}$

   (d) $d(\mathbf{u}, \mathbf{v}) = \|\mathbf{u} - \mathbf{v}\| = \|(1, -7)\| = \sqrt{1(1) + 2(-7)(-7)} = \sqrt{99} = 3\sqrt{11}$

6. $\mathbf{u} = (8, 0, -8)$ and $\mathbf{v} = (8, 3, 16)$

   (a) $\langle \mathbf{u}, \mathbf{v} \rangle = 2u_1v_1 + 3u_2v_2 + u_3v_3 = 2 \cdot 8 \cdot 8 + 3 \cdot 0 \cdot 3 + (-8) \cdot 16 = 0.$

   (b) $\|\mathbf{u}\| = \sqrt{2 \cdot 8 \cdot 8 + 3 \cdot 0 \cdot 0 + (-8)^2} = 8\sqrt{3}.$

   (c) $\|\mathbf{v}\| = \sqrt{\langle \mathbf{v}, \mathbf{v} \rangle} = \sqrt{2 \cdot 8^2 + 3 \cdot 3^2 + 16^2} = \sqrt{411}$

   (d) $d(\mathbf{u}, \mathbf{v}) = \|\mathbf{u} - \mathbf{v}\| = \|(0, -3, -24)\| = 3\sqrt{67}.$

8. (a) $\langle \mathbf{u}, \mathbf{v} \rangle = \mathbf{u} \cdot \mathbf{v} = 2(2) + 0(2) + 1(0) + (-1)(1) = 3$

   (b) $\|\mathbf{u}\| = \sqrt{\langle \mathbf{u}, \mathbf{u} \rangle} = \sqrt{\mathbf{u} \cdot \mathbf{u}} = \sqrt{2^2 + 0^2 + 1^2 + (-1)^2} = \sqrt{6}$

   (c) $\|\mathbf{v}\| = \sqrt{\langle \mathbf{v}, \mathbf{v} \rangle} = \sqrt{\mathbf{v} \cdot \mathbf{v}} = \sqrt{2^2 + 2^2 + 0^2 + 1^2} = 3$

   (d) $d(\mathbf{u}, \mathbf{v}) = \|\mathbf{u} - \mathbf{v}\| = (0, -2, 1, -2) = \sqrt{0^2 + (-2)^2 + 1^2 + (-2)^2} = 3$

10. (a) $\langle f, g \rangle = \int_{-1}^{1} f(x)g(x)\,dx = \int_{-1}^{1} (-x)(x^2 - x + 2)\,dx = \int_{-1}^{1} (-x^3 + x^2 - 2x)\,dx$

$$= -\frac{x^4}{4} + \frac{x^3}{3} - x^2 \Big]_{-1}^{1} = \left(-\frac{1}{4} + \frac{1}{3} - 1\right) - \left(-\frac{1}{4} - \frac{1}{3} - 1\right) = \frac{2}{3}$$

(b) $\|f\|^2 = \langle f, f \rangle = \int_{-1}^{1} (-x)(-x)\,dx = \frac{x^3}{3}\Big]_{-1}^{1} = \frac{2}{3} \implies \|f\| = \sqrt{\frac{2}{3}}$

(c) $\|g\|^2 = \langle g, g \rangle = \int_{-1}^{1} (x^2 - x + 2)^2\,dx$

$$= \int_{-1}^{1} (x^4 - 2x^3 + 5x^2 - 4x + 4)\,dx$$

$$= \frac{x^5}{5} - \frac{x^4}{2} + \frac{5x^3}{3} - 2x^2 + 4x \Big]_{-1}^{1} = \frac{176}{15}$$

So, $\|g\| = \sqrt{176/15}$.

(d) We use the fact that $d(f, g) = \|f - g\|$. Since $f - g = -x - (x^2 - x + 2) = -x^2 - 2$, we have

$$\langle f - g, f - g \rangle = \langle -x^2 - 2, -x^2 - 2 \rangle = \int_{-1}^{1} (x^4 + 4x^2 + 4)\,dx = \frac{x^5}{5} + \frac{4x^3}{3} + 4x \Big]_{-1}^{1}$$

$$= \left(\frac{1}{5} + \frac{4}{3} + 4\right) - \left(-\frac{1}{5} - \frac{4}{3} - 4\right) = \frac{166}{15}.$$

Hence, $d(f, g) = \sqrt{\langle f - g, f - g \rangle} = \sqrt{166/15}$.

12. (a) $\langle f, g \rangle = \int_{-1}^{1} 1(3x^2 - 1)\,dx = x^3 - x \Big]_{-1}^{1} = (1 - 1) - (-1 + 1) = 0$

(b) $\|f\|^2 = \langle f, f \rangle = \int_{-1}^{1} 1\,dx = x \Big]_{-1}^{1} = 2 \implies \|f\| = \sqrt{2}$

(c) $\|g\|^2 = \langle g, g \rangle = \int_{-1}^{1} (3x^2 - 1)^2\,dx$

$$= \int_{-1}^{1} (9x^4 - 6x^2 + 1)\,dx$$

$$= \frac{9x^5}{5} - 2x^3 + x \Big]_{-1}^{1}$$

$$= \left(\frac{9}{5} - 2 + 1\right) - \left(-\frac{9}{5} + 2 - 1\right) = \frac{8}{5}$$

So, $\|g\| = \sqrt{8/5}$.

—CONTINUED—

12. —CONTINUED—

(d) We use the fact that $d(f, g) = \|f - g\|$. Since $f - g = 1 - (3x^2 - 1) = 2 - 3x^2$, we have

$$\langle f - g, f - g \rangle = \int_{-1}^{1} (2 - 3x^2)\, dx = \int_{-1}^{1} (9x^4 - 12x^2 + 4)\, dx$$

$$= \frac{9x^5}{5} - 4x^3 + 4x \bigg]_{-1}^{1} = \left(\frac{9}{5} - 4 + 4 \right) - \left(-\frac{9}{5} + 4 - 4 \right) = \frac{18}{5}.$$

Hence, $d(f, g) = \sqrt{\langle f - g, f - g \rangle} = \sqrt{18/5}$.

14. (a) $\langle A, B \rangle = 2(1)(0) + (0)(1) + (0)(1) + 2(1)(0) = 0$

(b) $\langle A, A \rangle = 2(1)^2 + 0^2 + 0^2 + 2(1)^2 = 4 \implies \|A\| = \sqrt{\langle A, A \rangle} = 2$

(c) $\langle B, B \rangle = 2 \cdot 0^2 + 1^2 + 1^2 + 2 \cdot 0^2 = 2 \implies \|B\| = \sqrt{\langle B, B \rangle} = \sqrt{2}$

(d) We use the fact that $d(A, B) = \|A - B\|$. Since

$$A - B = \begin{bmatrix} 1 & -1 \\ -1 & 1 \end{bmatrix}, \text{ we have}$$

$$\langle A - B, A - B \rangle = 2(1)^2 + (-1)^2 + (-1)^2 + 2(1)^2 = 6.$$

Hence, $d(A, B) = \sqrt{\langle A - B, A - B \rangle} = \sqrt{6}$.

16. (a) $\langle \mathbf{p}, \mathbf{q} \rangle = \langle 1 + x^2, 1 - x^2 \rangle = 1(1) + 0(0) + 1(-1) = 0$

(b) $\langle \mathbf{p}, \mathbf{p} \rangle = \langle 1 + x^2, 1 + x^2 \rangle = 1(1) + 0(0) + 1(1) = 2 \implies \|\mathbf{p}\| = \sqrt{\langle \mathbf{p}, \mathbf{p} \rangle} = \sqrt{2}$

(c) $\langle \mathbf{q}, \mathbf{q} \rangle = \langle 1 - x^2, 1 - x^2 \rangle = 1(1) + 0(0) - 1(-1) = 2$

So, $\|\mathbf{q}\| = \sqrt{\langle \mathbf{q}, \mathbf{q} \rangle} = \sqrt{2}$.

(d) $d\langle \mathbf{p}, \mathbf{q} \rangle = \|\mathbf{p} - \mathbf{q}\| = \sqrt{\langle \mathbf{p} - \mathbf{q}, \mathbf{p} - \mathbf{q} \rangle} = \sqrt{4} = 2$

18. We verify that the function $\langle \mathbf{u}, \mathbf{v} \rangle = 2u_1 v_1 + 3u_2 v_2 + u_3 v_3$ satisfies the four parts of the definition.

1. $\langle \mathbf{u}, \mathbf{v} \rangle = 2u_1 v_1 + 3u_2 v_2 + u_3 v_3 = 2v_1 u_1 + 3v_2 u_2 + v_3 u_3 = \langle \mathbf{v}, \mathbf{u} \rangle$

2. $\langle \mathbf{u}, \mathbf{v} + \mathbf{w} \rangle = 2u_1(v_1 + w_1) + 3u_2(v_2 + w_2) + u_3(v_3 + w_3)$

   $= 2u_1 v_1 + 3u_2 v_2 + u_3 v_3 + 2u_1 w_1 + 3u_2 w_2 + u_3 w_3$

   $= \langle \mathbf{u}, \mathbf{v} \rangle + \langle \mathbf{u}, \mathbf{w} \rangle$

3. $c\langle \mathbf{u}, \mathbf{v} \rangle = c(2u_1 v_1 + 3u_2 v_2 + u_3 v_3)$

   $= 2(cu_1)v_1 + 3(cu_2)v_2 + (cu_3)v_3$

   $= \langle c\mathbf{u}, \mathbf{v} \rangle$

4. $\langle \mathbf{v}, \mathbf{v} \rangle = 2v_1^2 + 3v_2^2 + v_3^2 \geq 0$, and

   $\langle \mathbf{v}, \mathbf{v} \rangle = 0$ if and only if $\mathbf{v} = (0, 0, 0)$.

20. We verify that the function $\langle \mathbf{p}, \mathbf{q} \rangle = p_0 q_0 + p_1 q_1 + p_2 q_2$ satisfies the four parts of the definition. Here, $\mathbf{p}(x) = p_0 + p_1 x + p_2 x^2$ is a polynomial in P_2.

1. $\langle \mathbf{p}, \mathbf{q} \rangle = p_0 q_0 + p_1 q_1 + p_2 q_2 = q_0 p_0 + q_1 p_1 + q_2 p_2 = \langle \mathbf{q}, \mathbf{p} \rangle$

2. $\langle \mathbf{p}, \mathbf{q} + \mathbf{r} \rangle = p_0 (q_0 + r_0) + p_1 (q_1 + r_1) + p_2 (q_2 + r_2)$
$$= p_0 q_0 + p_1 q_1 + p_2 q_2 + p_0 r_0 + p_1 r_1 + p_2 r_2$$
$$= \langle \mathbf{p}, \mathbf{q} \rangle + \langle \mathbf{p}, \mathbf{r} \rangle.$$

3. $c\langle \mathbf{p}, \mathbf{q} \rangle = c(p_0 q_0 + p_1 q_1 + p_2 q_2)$
$$= (cp_0) q_0 + (cp_1) q_1 + (cp_2) q_2)$$
$$= \langle c\mathbf{p}, \mathbf{q} \rangle.$$

4. $\langle \mathbf{p}, \mathbf{p} \rangle = p_0^2 + p_1^2 + p_2^2 \geq 0$, and $\langle \mathbf{p}, \mathbf{p} \rangle = 0$ if and only if $\mathbf{p} = 0$.

22. The product $\langle \mathbf{u}, \mathbf{v} \rangle$ is not an inner product because nonzero vectors can have a norm of zero. For example, if $\mathbf{v} = (1, 1)$, then $\langle (1, 1), (1, 1) \rangle = 0$.

24. The product $\langle \mathbf{u}, \mathbf{v} \rangle$ is not an inner product because it is not commutative. For example, if $\mathbf{u} = (1, 2)$, and $\mathbf{v} = (2, 3)$, then $\langle \mathbf{u}, \mathbf{v} \rangle = 3(1)(3) - 2(2) = 5$ while $\langle \mathbf{v}, \mathbf{u} \rangle = 3(2)(2) - 3(1) = 9$.

26. Since

$$\frac{\langle \mathbf{u}, \mathbf{v} \rangle}{\|\mathbf{u}\| \, \|\mathbf{v}\|} = \frac{3(-4)(0) + (3)(5)}{\sqrt{3(-4)^2 + 3^2} \sqrt{3(0)^2 + 5^2}} = \frac{15}{\sqrt{57} \cdot 5} = \frac{3}{\sqrt{57}},$$

the angle between $\mathbf{u}$ and $\mathbf{v}$ is $\cos^{-1}\left(\frac{3}{\sqrt{57}} \right) \approx 1.16$ radians ($66.59°$).

28. Since

$$\frac{\langle \mathbf{p}, \mathbf{q} \rangle}{\|\mathbf{p}\| \|\mathbf{q}\|} = \frac{1 - 1 + 1}{\sqrt{3} \sqrt{3}} = \frac{1}{3},$$

the angle between $\mathbf{p}$ and $\mathbf{q}$ is $\cos^{-1}\left(\frac{1}{3} \right) \approx 1.23$ radians ($70.53°$).

30. We first compute

$$\langle f, g \rangle = \langle 1, x^2 \rangle = \int_{-1}^{1} x^2 \, dx = \frac{x^3}{3} \bigg]_{-1}^{1} = \frac{2}{3}$$

$$\|\mathbf{f}\|^2 = \langle 1, 1 \rangle = \int_{-1}^{1} 1 \, dx = x \bigg]_{-1}^{1} = 2 \quad \Rightarrow \quad \|\mathbf{f}\| = \sqrt{2}$$

$$\|\mathbf{g}\|^2 = \langle x^2, x^2 \rangle = \int_{-1}^{1} x^4 \, dx = \frac{x^5}{5} \bigg]_{-1}^{1} = \frac{2}{5} \quad \Rightarrow \quad \|\mathbf{g}\| = \sqrt{\frac{2}{5}}.$$

Hence,

$$\frac{\langle \mathbf{f}, \mathbf{g} \rangle}{\|\mathbf{f}\| \|\mathbf{g}\|} = \frac{2/3}{\sqrt{2} \sqrt{2/5}} = \frac{\sqrt{5}}{3}$$

and the angle between $\mathbf{f}$ and $\mathbf{g}$ is $\cos^{-1}\left(\frac{\sqrt{5}}{3} \right) \approx 0.73$ radians ($41.81°$).

32. (a) To verify the Cauchy-Schwarz Inequality, we observe

$$|\langle \mathbf{u}, \mathbf{v} \rangle| \leq \|\mathbf{u}\| \|\mathbf{v}\|$$

$$|(1, 0, 4) \cdot (-5, 4, 1)| \leq \sqrt{17}\sqrt{42}$$

$$1 \leq \sqrt{714}.$$

(b) To verify the Triangle Inequality, we observe

$$\|\mathbf{u} + \mathbf{v}\| \leq \|\mathbf{u}\| + \|\mathbf{v}\|$$

$$\|(-4, 4, 5)\| \leq \sqrt{17} + \sqrt{42}$$

$$\sqrt{57} \leq \sqrt{17} + \sqrt{42}$$

$$7.5498 \leq 10.6038.$$

34. (a) To verify the Cauchy-Schwarz Inequality, we observe

$$|\langle A, B \rangle| \leq \|A\| \|B\|$$

$$|0(-3) + 3(1) + 2(4) + 1(3)| \leq \sqrt{14}\sqrt{35}$$

$$14 \leq \sqrt{14}\sqrt{35}.$$

(b) To verify the Triangle Inequality, we observe

$$\|A + B\| \leq \|A\| + \|B\|$$

$$\left\| \begin{bmatrix} -3 & 4 \\ 6 & 4 \end{bmatrix} \right\| \leq \sqrt{14} + \sqrt{35}$$

$$\sqrt{77} \leq \sqrt{14} + \sqrt{35}$$

$$8.775 \leq 9.658.$$

36. (a) To verify the Cauchy-Schwarz Inequality, we compute

$$\langle \mathbf{f}, \mathbf{g} \rangle = \langle 1, \cos \pi x \rangle = \int_0^2 \cos \pi x \, dx = \frac{\sin \pi x}{\pi} \Big]_0^2 = 0$$

$$\|\mathbf{f}\|^2 = \langle 1, 1 \rangle = \int_0^2 1 \, dx = x \Big]_0^2 = 2 \quad \Rightarrow \quad \|\mathbf{f}\| = \sqrt{2}$$

$$\|\mathbf{g}\|^2 = \langle \cos \pi x, \cos \pi x \rangle = \int_0^2 \cos^2 \pi x \, dx = \int_0^2 \frac{1 + \cos 2\pi x}{2} dx$$

$$= \frac{1}{2}x + \frac{\sin 2\pi x}{4\pi} \Big]_0^2 = 1 \quad \Rightarrow \quad \|\mathbf{g}\| = 1$$

and observe that

$$|\langle \mathbf{f}, \mathbf{g} \rangle| \leq \|\mathbf{f}\| \|\mathbf{g}\|$$

$$0 \leq \sqrt{2} \, (1).$$

(b) To verify the Triangle Inequality, we compute

$$\|\mathbf{f} + \mathbf{g}\|^2 = \|1 + \cos \pi x\|^2 = \int_0^2 (1 + \cos \pi x)^2 dx = \int_0^2 dx + \int_0^2 \cos^2 \pi x \, dx + \int_0^2 2 \cos \pi x \, dx$$

$$= 2 + 1 + 0 = 3 \quad \Rightarrow \quad \|\mathbf{f} + \mathbf{g}\| = \sqrt{3}.$$

Hence, we see that $\|\mathbf{f} + \mathbf{g}\| \leq \|\mathbf{f}\| + \|\mathbf{g}\|$

$$\sqrt{3} \leq \sqrt{2} + 1.$$

38. The functions $\mathbf{f}(x) = x$ and $\mathbf{g}(x) = \frac{1}{2}(3x^2 - 1)$ are orthogonal since $\langle \mathbf{f}, \mathbf{g} \rangle =$

$$\int_{-1}^{1} x\frac{1}{2}(3x^2 - 1)\,dx = \frac{1}{2}\int_{-1}^{1}(3x^3 - x)\,dx = \frac{1}{2}\left(\frac{3x^4}{4} - \frac{x^2}{2}\right)\Big]_{-1}^{1} = 0.$$

40. The functions $\mathbf{f}(x) = 1$ and $\mathbf{g}(x) = \cos(2nx)$ are orthogonal since

$$\langle \mathbf{f}, \mathbf{g} \rangle = \int_{0}^{\pi} \cos(2nx)\,dx = \frac{1}{2n}\sin(2nx)\Big]_{0}^{\pi} = 0.$$

42. (a) $\operatorname{proj}_{\mathbf{v}}\mathbf{u} = \dfrac{\langle \mathbf{u}, \mathbf{v} \rangle}{\langle \mathbf{v}, \mathbf{v} \rangle}\mathbf{v} = \dfrac{(-1)(4) + 3(4)}{4(4) + 4(4)}(4, 4)$

$\qquad\qquad = \dfrac{1}{4}(4, 4) = (1, 1)$

(b) $\operatorname{proj}_{\mathbf{u}}\mathbf{v} = \dfrac{\langle \mathbf{v}, \mathbf{u} \rangle}{\langle \mathbf{u}, \mathbf{u} \rangle}\mathbf{u} = \dfrac{4(-1) + 4(3)}{(-1)(-1) + 3(3)}(-1, 3)$

$\qquad\qquad = \dfrac{4}{5}(-1, 3) = \left(-\dfrac{4}{5}, \dfrac{12}{5}\right)$

(c)

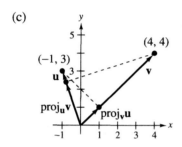

44. (a) $\operatorname{proj}_{\mathbf{v}}\mathbf{u} = \dfrac{\langle \mathbf{u}, \mathbf{v} \rangle}{\langle \mathbf{v}, \mathbf{v} \rangle}\mathbf{v} = \dfrac{0(-1) + 1(1) + 3(2) + (-6)(2)}{(-1)(-1) + 1(1) + 2(2) + 2(2)}\mathbf{v}$

$\qquad\qquad = -\dfrac{5}{10}(-1, 1, 2, 2)$

$\qquad\qquad = \left(\dfrac{1}{2}, -\dfrac{1}{2}, -1, -1\right)$

(b) $\operatorname{proj}_{\mathbf{u}}\mathbf{v} = \dfrac{\langle \mathbf{v}, \mathbf{u} \rangle}{\langle \mathbf{u}, \mathbf{u} \rangle}\mathbf{u} = \dfrac{(-1)(0) + 1(1) + 2(3) + 2(-6)}{0 + 1(1) + 3(3) + (-6)(-6)}\mathbf{u}$

$\qquad\qquad = -\dfrac{5}{46}(0, 1, 3, -6)$

46. The inner products $\langle \mathbf{f}, \mathbf{g} \rangle$ and $\langle \mathbf{g}, \mathbf{g} \rangle$ are as follows.

$$\langle \mathbf{f}, \mathbf{g} \rangle = \int_{-1}^{1} (x^3 - x)(2x - 1)\, dx = \int_{-1}^{1} (2x^4 - x^3 - 2x^2 + x)dx$$

$$= \frac{2x^5}{5} - \frac{x^4}{4} - \frac{2x^3}{3} + \frac{x^2}{2} \Bigg]_{-1}^{1} = -\frac{8}{15}$$

$$\langle \mathbf{g}, \mathbf{g} \rangle = \int_{-1}^{1} (2x - 1)^2 dx = \int_{-1}^{1} (4x^2 - 4x + 1)dx$$

$$= \frac{4x^3}{3} - 2x^2 + x \Bigg]_{-1}^{1} = \frac{14}{3}$$

Thus, the projection of $\mathbf{f}$ onto $\mathbf{g}$ is

$$\text{proj}_{\mathbf{g}}\mathbf{f} = \frac{\langle \mathbf{f}, \mathbf{g} \rangle}{\langle \mathbf{g}, \mathbf{g} \rangle}\mathbf{g} = \frac{-8/15}{14/3}(2x - 1) = -\frac{4}{35}(2x - 1).$$

48. The inner product $\langle \mathbf{f}, \mathbf{g} \rangle$ is

$$\langle \mathbf{f}, \mathbf{g} \rangle = \int_{-\pi}^{\pi} \sin x \cos x \, dx = \frac{\sin^2 x}{2} \Bigg]_{-\pi}^{\pi} = 0$$

which implies that $\text{proj}_{\mathbf{g}}\mathbf{f} = 0$.

50. The inner product $\langle \mathbf{f}, \mathbf{g} \rangle$ is

$$\langle \mathbf{f}, \mathbf{g} \rangle = \int_{-\pi}^{\pi} \sin 2x \sin 3x \, dx = \int_{-\pi}^{\pi} \frac{1}{2}\left[\cos x - \cos 5x\right] dx$$

$$= \frac{1}{2}\left(\sin x - \frac{\sin 5x}{5}\right)\Bigg]_{-\pi}^{\pi} = 0$$

which implies that $\text{proj}_{\mathbf{g}}\mathbf{f} = 0$.

52. (a) *False.* The norm of a vector $\mathbf{u}$ is defined as a square root of $\langle \mathbf{u}, \mathbf{u} \rangle$.

(b) *False.* The angle between $a\mathbf{v}$ and $\mathbf{v}$ is zero if $a > 0$ and it is π if $a < 0$.

54. $\|\mathbf{u} + \mathbf{v}\|^2 + \|\mathbf{u} - \mathbf{v}\|^2 = \langle \mathbf{u} + \mathbf{v}, \mathbf{u} + \mathbf{v} \rangle + \langle \mathbf{u} - \mathbf{v}, \mathbf{u} - \mathbf{v} \rangle$

$$= (\langle \mathbf{u}, \mathbf{u} \rangle + 2\langle \mathbf{u}, \mathbf{v} \rangle + \langle \mathbf{v}, \mathbf{v} \rangle) + (\langle \mathbf{u}, \mathbf{u} \rangle - 2\langle \mathbf{u}, \mathbf{v} \rangle + \langle \mathbf{v}, \mathbf{v} \rangle)$$

$$= 2\|\mathbf{u}\|^2 + 2\|\mathbf{v}\|^2$$

56. To prove that $\mathbf{u} - \text{proj}_{\mathbf{v}}\mathbf{u}$ is orthogonal to $\mathbf{v}$, we calculate their inner product as follows $\langle \mathbf{u} - \text{proj}_{\mathbf{v}}\mathbf{u}, \mathbf{v} \rangle = \langle \mathbf{u}, \mathbf{v} \rangle - \langle \text{proj}_{\mathbf{v}}\mathbf{u}, \mathbf{v} \rangle$

$$= \langle \mathbf{u}, \mathbf{v} \rangle - \left\langle \frac{\langle \mathbf{u}, \mathbf{v} \rangle}{\langle \mathbf{v}, \mathbf{v} \rangle}\mathbf{v}, \mathbf{v} \right\rangle$$

$$= \langle \mathbf{u}, \mathbf{v} \rangle - \frac{\langle \mathbf{u}, \mathbf{v} \rangle}{\langle \mathbf{v}, \mathbf{v} \rangle}\langle \mathbf{v}, \mathbf{v} \rangle = \langle \mathbf{u}, \mathbf{v} \rangle - \langle \mathbf{u}, \mathbf{v} \rangle = 0$$

58. We have from the definition of inner product

$$\langle \mathbf{u}, c\mathbf{v} \rangle = \langle c\mathbf{v}, \mathbf{u} \rangle$$
$$= c\langle \mathbf{v}, \mathbf{u} \rangle$$
$$= c\langle \mathbf{u}, \mathbf{v} \rangle.$$

60. Let $W = \{(c, 2c, 3c) | c \in R\}$. Then

$$W^{\perp} = \{\mathbf{v} \in R^3 | \mathbf{v} \cdot (c, 2c, 3c) = 0\} = \{(x, y, z) \in R^3 | (x, y, z) \cdot (1, 2, 3) = 0\}.$$

Thus we need to solve $x + 2y + 3z = 0$. Choosing y and z as free variables, we obtain the solution $x = -2t - 3s, y = t, z = s$ for any real numbers t and s. Therefore,

$$W^{\perp} = \{t(-2, 1, 0) + s(-3, 0, 1) | t, s \in R\} = \text{span}\{(-2, 1, 0), (-3, 0, 1)\}.$$

62. From example 10, we have $\text{proj}_v \mathbf{u} = (2, 4, 0)$. So,

$$d(\mathbf{u}, \text{proj}_v \mathbf{u}) = \|\mathbf{u} - \text{proj}_v \mathbf{u}\| = \|(4, -2, 4)\| = \sqrt{36} = 6.$$

Let x be any real number different from $2 = \dfrac{\langle \mathbf{u}, \mathbf{v} \rangle}{\langle \mathbf{v}, \mathbf{v} \rangle}$, so that $x\mathbf{v} \neq \text{proj}_v \mathbf{u}$. We want to show that

$$d(\mathbf{u}, x\mathbf{v}) > d(\mathbf{u}, \text{proj}_v \mathbf{u}).$$

$$d(\mathbf{u}, x\mathbf{v}) = \sqrt{(6 - x)^2 + 4(1 - x)^2 + 16} = \sqrt{36 + 5x^2 - 20x + 20}$$

$$= \sqrt{36 + 5(x - 2)^2} > \sqrt{36} = d(\mathbf{u}, \text{proj}_v \mathbf{u}),$$

if

$$x \neq 2 = \frac{\langle \mathbf{u}, \mathbf{v} \rangle}{\langle \mathbf{v}, \mathbf{v} \rangle}.$$

Section 5.3   Orthonormal Bases: Gram-Schmidt Process

2. The set is *not* orthogonal because

$$(11, 4) \cdot (8, -3) = 88 - 12 = 76 \neq 0.$$

4. The set is orthogonal because

$$(1, 2) \cdot \left(-\tfrac{2}{5}, \tfrac{1}{5}\right) = -\tfrac{2}{5} + \tfrac{2}{5} = 0.$$

However, the set is *not* orthonormal because

$$\|(1, 2)\| = \sqrt{1^2 + 2^2} = \sqrt{5} \neq 1.$$

6. The set is orthogonal because

$$\left(\frac{\sqrt{2}}{2}, 0, \frac{\sqrt{2}}{2}\right) \cdot \left(-\frac{\sqrt{6}}{6}, \frac{\sqrt{6}}{3}, \frac{\sqrt{6}}{6}\right) = 0$$

$$\left(\frac{\sqrt{2}}{2}, 0, \frac{\sqrt{2}}{2}\right) \cdot \left(\frac{\sqrt{3}}{3}, \frac{\sqrt{3}}{3}, -\frac{\sqrt{3}}{3}\right) = 0$$

$$\left(-\frac{\sqrt{6}}{6}, \frac{\sqrt{6}}{3}, \frac{\sqrt{6}}{6}\right) \cdot \left(\frac{\sqrt{3}}{3}, \frac{\sqrt{3}}{3}, -\frac{\sqrt{3}}{3}\right) = 0.$$

Furthermore, the set is orthonormal because

$$\left\|\left(\frac{\sqrt{2}}{2}, 0, \frac{\sqrt{2}}{2}\right)\right\| = \sqrt{\frac{1}{2} + 0 + \frac{1}{2}} = 1$$

$$\left\|\left(-\frac{\sqrt{6}}{6}, \frac{\sqrt{6}}{3}, \frac{\sqrt{6}}{6}\right)\right\| = \sqrt{\frac{1}{6} + \frac{2}{3} + \frac{1}{6}} = 1$$

$$\left\|\left(\frac{\sqrt{3}}{3}, \frac{\sqrt{3}}{3}, -\frac{\sqrt{3}}{3}\right)\right\| = \sqrt{\frac{1}{3} + \frac{1}{3} + \frac{1}{3}} = 1.$$

8. The set is orthogonal because

$$(-6, 3, 2, 1) \cdot (2, 0, 6, 0) = -12 + 12 = 0.$$

However, the set is *not* orthonormal because

$$\|(-6, 3, 2, 1)\| = \sqrt{36 + 9 + 4 + 1} = \sqrt{50} \neq 1.$$

10. The set is orthogonal because

$$\left(\frac{\sqrt{10}}{10}, 0, 0, \frac{3\sqrt{10}}{10}\right) \cdot (0, 0, 1, 0) = 0$$

$$\left(\frac{\sqrt{10}}{10}, 0, 0, \frac{3\sqrt{10}}{10}\right) \cdot (0, 1, 0, 0) = 0$$

$$\left(\frac{\sqrt{10}}{10}, 0, 0, \frac{3\sqrt{10}}{10}\right) \cdot \left(-\frac{3\sqrt{10}}{10}, 0, 0, \frac{\sqrt{10}}{10}\right) = -\frac{3}{10} + \frac{3}{10} = 0$$

$$(0, 0, 1, 0) \cdot (0, 1, 0, 0) = 0$$

$$(0, 0, 1, 0) \cdot \left(-\frac{3\sqrt{10}}{10}, 0, 0, \frac{\sqrt{10}}{10}\right) = 0$$

$$(0, 1, 0, 0) \cdot \left(-\frac{3\sqrt{10}}{10}, 0, 0, \frac{\sqrt{10}}{10}\right) = 0.$$

Furthermore, the set is orthonormal because

$$\left\|\left(\frac{\sqrt{10}}{10}, 0, 0, \frac{3\sqrt{10}}{10}\right)\right\| = \frac{1}{10} + \frac{9}{10} = 1$$

$$\|(0, 0, 1, 0)\| = 1$$

$$\|(0, 1, 0, 0)\| = 1$$

$$\left\|\left(-\frac{3\sqrt{10}}{10}, 0, 0, \frac{\sqrt{10}}{10}\right)\right\| = \frac{9}{10} + \frac{1}{10} = 1.$$

12. The set $\{(\sin\theta, \cos\theta), (\cos\theta, -\sin\theta)\}$ is orthogonal because

$$(\sin\theta, \cos\theta) \cdot (\cos\theta, -\sin\theta) = \sin\theta\cos\theta - \cos\theta\sin\theta = 0.$$

Furthermore, the set is orthonormal because

$$\|(\sin\theta, \cos\theta)\| = \sin^2\theta + \cos^2\theta = 1$$

$$\|(\cos\theta, -\sin\theta)\| = \cos^2\theta + (-\sin\theta)^2 = 1.$$

Hence, the set forms an orthonormal basis for R^2.

14. We use Theorem 5.11 to find the coordinates of $\mathbf{x} = (-3, 4)$ relative to B.

$$(-3, 4) \cdot \left(\frac{\sqrt{5}}{5}, \frac{2\sqrt{5}}{5}\right) = -\frac{3\sqrt{5}}{5} + \frac{8\sqrt{5}}{5} = \sqrt{5}$$

$$(-3, 4) \cdot \left(-\frac{2\sqrt{5}}{5}, \frac{\sqrt{5}}{5}\right) = \frac{6\sqrt{5}}{5} + \frac{4\sqrt{5}}{5} = 2\sqrt{5}$$

Thus, $[\mathbf{x}]_B = [(\sqrt{5}, 2\sqrt{5})]^T$.

16. We use Theorem 5.11 to find the coordinates of $\mathbf{x} = (3, -5, 11)$ relative to B.

$$(3, -5, 11) \cdot (1, 0, 0) = 3$$
$$(3, -5, 11) \cdot (0, 1, 0) = -5$$
$$(3, -5, 11) \cdot (0, 0, 1) = 11$$

Thus, $[\mathbf{x}]_B = [(3, -5, 11)]^T$.

18. We use Theorem 5.11 to find the coordinates of $\mathbf{x} = (2, -1, 4, 3)$ relative to B.

$$(2, -1, 4, 3) \cdot (\tfrac{5}{13}, 0, \tfrac{12}{13}, 0) = \tfrac{10}{13} + \tfrac{48}{13} = \tfrac{58}{13}$$
$$(2, -1, 4, 3) \cdot (0, 1, 0, 0) = -1$$
$$(2, -1, 4, 3) \cdot (-\tfrac{12}{13}, 0, \tfrac{5}{13}, 0) = -\tfrac{24}{13} + \tfrac{20}{13} = -\tfrac{4}{13}$$
$$(2, -1, 4, 3) \cdot (0, 0, 0, 1) = 3$$

Thus, $[\mathbf{x}]_B = \left[\left(\tfrac{58}{13}, -1, -\tfrac{4}{13}, 3\right)\right]^T$.

20. First we orthogonalize each vector in B.

$$\mathbf{w}_1 = \mathbf{v}_1 = (0, 1)$$

$$\mathbf{w}_2 = \mathbf{v}_2 - \frac{\langle \mathbf{v}_2, \mathbf{w}_1 \rangle}{\langle \mathbf{w}_1, \mathbf{w}_1 \rangle}\mathbf{w}_1 = (2, 5) - \frac{2(0) + 5(1)}{0^2 + 1^2}(0, 1)$$

$$= (2, 5) - 5(0, 1) = (2, 0)$$

Then we normalize the vectors.

$$\mathbf{u}_1 = \frac{\mathbf{w}_1}{\|\mathbf{w}_1\|} = \mathbf{w}_1 = (0, 1)$$

$$\mathbf{u}_2 = \frac{\mathbf{w}_2}{\|\mathbf{w}_2\|} = \tfrac{1}{2}(2, 0) = (1, 0)$$

Thus, the orthonormal basis is $\{(0, 1), (1, 0)\}$.

22. First we orthogonalize each vector in B.

$$\mathbf{w}_1 = \mathbf{v}_1 = (1, 0, 0)$$

$$\mathbf{w}_2 = \mathbf{v}_2 - \frac{\langle \mathbf{v}_2, \mathbf{w}_1 \rangle}{\langle \mathbf{w}_1, \mathbf{w}_1 \rangle}\mathbf{w}_1 = (1, 1, 1) - \tfrac{1}{1}(1, 0, 0) = (0, 1, 1)$$

$$\mathbf{w}_3 = \mathbf{v}_3 - \frac{\langle \mathbf{v}_3, \mathbf{w}_1 \rangle}{\langle \mathbf{w}_1, \mathbf{w}_1 \rangle}\mathbf{w}_1 - \frac{\langle \mathbf{v}_3, \mathbf{w}_2 \rangle}{\langle \mathbf{w}_2, \mathbf{w}_2 \rangle}\mathbf{w}_2$$

$$= (1, 1, -1) - \tfrac{1}{1}(1, 0, 0) - \tfrac{0}{2}(0, 1, 1) = (0, 1, -1)$$

Then we normalize the vectors.

$$\mathbf{u}_1 = \frac{\mathbf{w}_1}{\|\mathbf{w}_1\|} = (1, 0, 0)$$

$$\mathbf{u}_2 = \frac{\mathbf{w}_2}{\|\mathbf{w}_2\|} = \frac{1}{\sqrt{2}}(0, 1, 1) = \left(0, \frac{1}{\sqrt{2}}, \frac{1}{\sqrt{2}}\right)$$

$$\mathbf{u}_3 = \frac{\mathbf{w}_3}{\|\mathbf{w}_3\|} = \frac{1}{\sqrt{2}}(0, 1, -1) = \left(0, \frac{1}{\sqrt{2}}, -\frac{1}{\sqrt{2}}\right)$$

Thus, the orthonormal basis is

$$\left\{(1, 0, 0), \left(0, \frac{1}{\sqrt{2}}, \frac{1}{\sqrt{2}}\right), \left(0, \frac{1}{\sqrt{2}}, -\frac{1}{\sqrt{2}}\right)\right\}.$$

24. First we orthogonalize each vector in B.

$$\mathbf{w}_1 = \mathbf{v}_1 = (0, 1, 2)$$

$$\mathbf{w}_2 = \mathbf{v}_2 - \frac{\langle \mathbf{v}_2, \mathbf{w}_1 \rangle}{\langle \mathbf{w}_1, \mathbf{w}_1 \rangle}\mathbf{w}_1 = (2, 0, 0) - 0(0, 1, 2) = (2, 0, 0)$$

$$\mathbf{w}_3 = \mathbf{v}_3 - \frac{\langle \mathbf{v}_3, \mathbf{w}_1 \rangle}{\langle \mathbf{w}_1, \mathbf{w}_1 \rangle}\mathbf{w}_1 - \frac{\langle \mathbf{v}_3, \mathbf{w}_2 \rangle}{\langle \mathbf{w}_2, \mathbf{w}_2 \rangle}\mathbf{w}_2$$

$$= (1, 1, 1) - \tfrac{3}{5}(0, 1, 2) - \tfrac{2}{4}(2, 0, 0) = (0, \tfrac{2}{5}, -\tfrac{1}{5})$$

Then we normalize the vectors.

$$\mathbf{u}_1 = \frac{\mathbf{w}_1}{\|\mathbf{w}_1\|} = \frac{1}{\sqrt{5}}(0, 1, 2) = \left(0, \frac{1}{\sqrt{5}}, \frac{2}{\sqrt{5}}\right)$$

$$\mathbf{u}_2 = \frac{\mathbf{w}_2}{\|\mathbf{w}_2\|} = \tfrac{1}{2}(2, 0, 0) = (1, 0, 0)$$

$$\mathbf{u}_3 = \frac{\mathbf{w}_3}{\|\mathbf{w}_3\|} = \sqrt{5}(0, \tfrac{2}{5}, -\tfrac{1}{5}) = \left(0, \frac{2}{\sqrt{5}}, -\frac{1}{\sqrt{5}}\right)$$

Thus, the orthonormal basis is

$$\left\{\left(0, \frac{1}{\sqrt{5}}, \frac{2}{\sqrt{5}}\right), (1, 0, 0), \left(0, \frac{2}{\sqrt{5}}, -\frac{1}{\sqrt{5}}\right)\right\}.$$

26. First we orthogonalize each vector in *B*.

$$\mathbf{w}_1 = \mathbf{v}_1 = (3, 4, 0, 0)$$

$$\mathbf{w}_2 = \mathbf{v}_2 - \frac{\langle \mathbf{v}_2, \mathbf{w}_1 \rangle}{\langle \mathbf{w}_1, \mathbf{w}_1 \rangle} \mathbf{w}_1 = (-1, 1, 0, 0) - \frac{1}{25}(3, 4, 0, 0) = (-\tfrac{28}{25}, \tfrac{21}{25}, 0, 0)$$

$$\mathbf{w}_3 = \mathbf{v}_3 - \frac{\langle \mathbf{v}_3, \mathbf{w}_1 \rangle}{\langle \mathbf{w}_1, \mathbf{w}_1 \rangle} \mathbf{w}_1 - \frac{\langle \mathbf{v}_3, \mathbf{w}_2 \rangle}{\langle \mathbf{w}_2, \mathbf{w}_2 \rangle} \mathbf{w}_2$$

$$= (2, 1, 0, -1) - \frac{10}{25}(3, 4, 0, 0) - \frac{-\frac{7}{5}}{\frac{49}{25}}(-\tfrac{28}{25}, \tfrac{21}{25}, 0, 0)$$

$$= (2, 1, 0, -1) - (\tfrac{6}{5}, \tfrac{8}{5}, 0, 0) + (-\tfrac{4}{5}, \tfrac{3}{5}, 0, 0) = (0, 0, 0, -1)$$

$$\mathbf{w}_4 = \mathbf{v}_4 - \frac{\langle \mathbf{v}_4, \mathbf{w}_1 \rangle}{\langle \mathbf{w}_1, \mathbf{w}_1 \rangle} \mathbf{w}_1 - \frac{\langle \mathbf{v}_4, \mathbf{w}_2 \rangle}{\langle \mathbf{w}_2, \mathbf{w}_2 \rangle} \mathbf{w}_2 - \frac{\langle \mathbf{v}_4, \mathbf{w}_3 \rangle}{\langle \mathbf{w}_3, \mathbf{w}_3 \rangle} \mathbf{w}_3$$

$$= (0, 1, 1, 0) - \frac{4}{25}(3, 4, 0, 0) - \frac{\frac{21}{25}}{\frac{49}{25}}(-\tfrac{28}{25}, \tfrac{21}{25}, 0, 0) - 0(0, 0, 0, -1)$$

$$= (0, 1, 1, 0) - (\tfrac{12}{25}, \tfrac{16}{25}, 0, 0) - (-\tfrac{12}{25}, \tfrac{9}{25}, 0, 0) = (0, 0, 1, 0)$$

Then we normalize the vectors.

$$\mathbf{u}_1 = \frac{\mathbf{w}_1}{\|\mathbf{w}_1\|} = \tfrac{1}{5}(3, 4, 0, 0) = (\tfrac{3}{5}, \tfrac{4}{5}, 0, 0)$$

$$\mathbf{u}_2 = \frac{\mathbf{w}_2}{\|\mathbf{w}_2\|} = \tfrac{5}{7}(-\tfrac{28}{25}, \tfrac{21}{25}, 0, 0) = (-\tfrac{4}{5}, \tfrac{3}{5}, 0, 0)$$

$$\mathbf{u}_3 = \frac{\mathbf{w}_3}{\|\mathbf{w}_3\|} = (0, 0, 0, -1)$$

$$\mathbf{u}_4 = \mathbf{w}_4 = (0, 0, 1, 0)$$

Thus, the orthonormal basis is

$$\{(\tfrac{3}{5}, \tfrac{4}{5}, 0, 0), (-\tfrac{4}{5}, \tfrac{3}{5}, 0, 0), (0, 0, 0, -1), (0, 0, 1, 0)\}.$$

28. Since there is just one vector, we simply need to normalize it.

$$\mathbf{u}_1 = \frac{1}{\sqrt{4^2 + (-7) + 6^2}}(4, -7, 6) = \frac{1}{\sqrt{101}}(4, -7, 6) = \left(\frac{4}{\sqrt{101}}, -\frac{7}{\sqrt{101}}, \frac{6}{\sqrt{101}}\right)$$

30. First we orthogonalize each vector in *B*.

$$\mathbf{w}_1 = \mathbf{v}_1 = (1, 2, 0)$$

$$\mathbf{w}_2 = \mathbf{v}_2 - \frac{\langle \mathbf{v}_2, \mathbf{w}_1 \rangle}{\langle \mathbf{w}_1, \mathbf{w}_1 \rangle} \mathbf{w}_1 = (2, 0, -2) - \tfrac{2}{5}(1, 2, 0) = (\tfrac{8}{5}, -\tfrac{4}{5}, -2)$$

Then we normalize the vectors.

$$\mathbf{u}_1 = \frac{\mathbf{w}_1}{\|\mathbf{w}_1\|} = \frac{1}{\sqrt{5}}(1, 2, 0) = \left(\frac{1}{\sqrt{5}}, \frac{2}{\sqrt{5}}, 0 \right)$$

$$\mathbf{u}_2 = \frac{\mathbf{w}_2}{\|\mathbf{w}_2\|} = \frac{1}{6/\sqrt{5}} (\tfrac{8}{5}, -\tfrac{4}{5}, -2) = \left(\frac{4}{3\sqrt{5}}, -\frac{2}{3\sqrt{5}}, -\frac{5}{3\sqrt{5}} \right)$$

Thus, the orthonormal basis is

$$\left\{ \left(\frac{1}{\sqrt{5}}, \frac{2}{\sqrt{5}}, 0 \right), \left(\frac{4}{3\sqrt{5}}, -\frac{2}{3\sqrt{5}}, -\frac{5}{3\sqrt{5}} \right) \right\}.$$

32. First we normalize each vector in *B*.

$$\mathbf{w}_1 = \mathbf{v}_1 = (7, 24, 0, 0)$$

$$\mathbf{w}_2 = \mathbf{v}_2 - \frac{\langle \mathbf{v}_2, \mathbf{w}_1 \rangle}{\langle \mathbf{w}_1, \mathbf{w}_1 \rangle} \mathbf{w}_1 = (0, 0, 1, 1) - 0(7, 24, 0, 0) = (0, 0, 1, 1)$$

$$\mathbf{w}_3 = \mathbf{v}_3 - \frac{\langle \mathbf{v}_3, \mathbf{w}_1 \rangle}{\langle \mathbf{w}_1, \mathbf{w}_1 \rangle} \mathbf{w}_1 - \frac{\langle \mathbf{v}_3, \mathbf{w}_2 \rangle}{\langle \mathbf{w}_2, \mathbf{w}_2 \rangle} \mathbf{w}_2$$

$$= (0, 0, 1, -2) - 0(7, 24, 0, 0) - \tfrac{-1}{2}(0, 0, 1, 1) = (0, 0, \tfrac{3}{2}, -\tfrac{3}{2})$$

Then we normalize the vectors.

$$\mathbf{u}_1 = \frac{\mathbf{w}_1}{\|\mathbf{w}_1\|} = \tfrac{1}{25}(7, 24, 0, 0) = (\tfrac{7}{25}, \tfrac{24}{25}, 0, 0)$$

$$\mathbf{u}_2 = \frac{\mathbf{w}_2}{\|\mathbf{w}_2\|} = \frac{1}{\sqrt{2}}(0, 0, 1, 1) = \left(0, 0, \frac{1}{\sqrt{2}}, \frac{1}{\sqrt{2}} \right)$$

$$\mathbf{u}_3 = \frac{\mathbf{w}_3}{\|\mathbf{w}_3\|} = \frac{1}{3/\sqrt{2}}(0, 0, \tfrac{3}{2}, -\tfrac{3}{2}) = \left(0, 0, \frac{1}{\sqrt{2}}, -\frac{1}{\sqrt{2}} \right)$$

Thus, the orthonormal basis is

$$\left\{ (\tfrac{7}{25}, \tfrac{24}{25}, 0, 0), \left(0, 0, \frac{1}{\sqrt{2}}, \frac{1}{\sqrt{2}} \right), \left(0, 0, \frac{1}{\sqrt{2}}, -\frac{1}{\sqrt{2}} \right) \right\}.$$

34. $\langle 1, 1 \rangle = \displaystyle\int_{-1}^{1} 1 \, dx = x \Big]_{-1}^{1} = 1 - (-1) = 2$

36. $\langle x^2, x \rangle = \displaystyle\int_{-1}^{1} x^2 x \, dx = \int_{-1}^{1} x^3 \, dx = \frac{x^4}{4} \Big]_{-1}^{1} = \tfrac{1}{4} - (\tfrac{1}{4}) = 0$

38. (a) *True.* See definition on page 298.

(b) *True.* See Theorem 5.10 on page 301.

(c) *True.* See page 303.

40. The solutions of the homogeneous system are of the form $(s + t, 2s + t, s, t)$ where s and t are any real numbers. Thus, a basis for the solution space is

$$\{(1, 2, 1, 0), (1, 1, 0, 1)\}.$$

We orthogonalize this basis as follows

$$\mathbf{w}_1 = \mathbf{v}_1 = (1, 2, 1, 0)$$

$$\mathbf{w}_2 = \mathbf{v}_2 - \frac{\langle \mathbf{v}_2, \mathbf{w}_1 \rangle}{\langle \mathbf{w}_1, \mathbf{w}_1 \rangle} \mathbf{w}_1 = (1, 1, 0, 1) - \tfrac{3}{6}(1, 2, 1, 0) = (\tfrac{1}{2}, 0, -\tfrac{1}{2}, 1)$$

Then we normalize these vectors.

$$\mathbf{u}_1 = \frac{\mathbf{w}_1}{\|\mathbf{w}_1\|} = \frac{1}{\sqrt{6}}(1, 2, 1, 0) = \left(\frac{1}{\sqrt{6}}, \frac{2}{\sqrt{6}}, \frac{1}{\sqrt{6}}, 0\right)$$

$$\mathbf{u}_2 = \frac{\mathbf{w}_2}{\|\mathbf{w}_2\|} = \frac{1}{\sqrt{6}/2}(\tfrac{1}{2}, 0, -\tfrac{1}{2}, 1) = \left(\frac{1}{\sqrt{6}}, 0, -\frac{1}{\sqrt{6}}, \frac{2}{\sqrt{6}}\right)$$

Thus, the orthonormal basis for the solution set is

$$\left\{\left(\frac{1}{\sqrt{6}}, \frac{2}{\sqrt{6}}, \frac{1}{\sqrt{6}}, 0\right), \left(\frac{1}{\sqrt{6}}, 0, -\frac{1}{\sqrt{6}}, \frac{2}{\sqrt{6}}\right)\right\}.$$

42. The solutions of the homogeneous system are of the form $(-3s + 3t, s, t)$ where s and t are any real numbers. Thus, a basis for the solution space is

$$\{(-3, 1, 0), (3, 0, 1)\}.$$

We orthogonalize this basis as follows

$$\mathbf{w}_1 = \mathbf{v}_1 = (-3, 1, 0)$$

$$\mathbf{w}_2 = \mathbf{v}_2 - \frac{\langle \mathbf{v}_2, \mathbf{w}_1 \rangle}{\langle \mathbf{w}_1, \mathbf{w}_1 \rangle} \mathbf{w}_1 = (3, 0, 1) - \tfrac{-9}{10}(-3, 1, 0)$$

$$= (\tfrac{3}{10}, \tfrac{9}{10}, 1)$$

Then we normalize these vectors.

$$\mathbf{u}_1 = \frac{\mathbf{w}_1}{\|\mathbf{w}_1\|} = \frac{1}{\sqrt{10}}(-3, 1, 0) = \left(-\frac{3}{\sqrt{10}}, \frac{1}{\sqrt{10}}, 0\right)$$

$$\mathbf{u}_2 = \frac{\mathbf{w}_2}{\|\mathbf{w}_2\|} = \frac{1}{\sqrt{190}/10}(\tfrac{3}{10}, \tfrac{9}{10}, 1) = \left(\frac{3}{\sqrt{190}}, \frac{9}{\sqrt{190}}, \frac{10}{\sqrt{190}}\right)$$

Thus, the orthonormal basis for the solution set is

$$\left\{\left(-\frac{3}{\sqrt{10}}, \frac{1}{\sqrt{10}}, 0\right), \left(\frac{3}{\sqrt{190}}, \frac{9}{\sqrt{190}}, \frac{10}{\sqrt{190}}\right)\right\} \quad \text{(answer not unique)}.$$

44. Let $\mathbf{p}(x) = \sqrt{2}(x^2 - 1)$ and $\mathbf{q}(x) = \sqrt{2}(x^2 + x + 2)$. Then, since $\langle \mathbf{p}, \mathbf{q} \rangle = \sqrt{2}\sqrt{2} + 0(\sqrt{2}) + (-\sqrt{2})(2\sqrt{2}) = -2 \neq 0$, the set is not orthogonal. We orthogonalize the set as follows.

$$\mathbf{w}_1 = \mathbf{p} = \sqrt{2}(x^2 - 1)$$

$$\mathbf{w}_2 = \mathbf{q} - \frac{\langle \mathbf{q}, \mathbf{w}_1 \rangle}{\langle \mathbf{w}_1, \mathbf{w}_1 \rangle}\mathbf{w}_1 = \sqrt{2}(x^2 + x + 2) - \frac{-2}{4}(\sqrt{2}(x^2 - 1))$$

$$= (\sqrt{2}x^2 + \sqrt{2}x + 2\sqrt{2}) + \left(\frac{\sqrt{2}}{2}x^2 - \frac{\sqrt{2}}{2}\right) = \frac{3\sqrt{2}}{2}x^2 + \sqrt{2}x + \frac{3\sqrt{2}}{2}$$

Then we normalize the vectors.

$$\mathbf{u}_1 = \frac{\mathbf{w}_1}{\|\mathbf{w}_1\|} = \frac{1}{2}\sqrt{2}(x^2 - 1) = \frac{\sqrt{2}}{2}x^2 - \frac{\sqrt{2}}{2}$$

$$\mathbf{u}_2 = \frac{\mathbf{w}_2}{\|\mathbf{w}_2\|} = \frac{1}{\sqrt{11}}\left(\frac{3\sqrt{2}}{2}x^2 + \sqrt{2}x + \frac{3\sqrt{2}}{2}\right) = \frac{3}{\sqrt{22}}x^2 + \frac{2}{\sqrt{22}}x + \frac{3}{\sqrt{22}}$$

Thus, the orthonormal set is

$$\left\{\frac{\sqrt{2}}{2}x^2 - \frac{\sqrt{2}}{2}, \frac{3}{\sqrt{22}}x^2 + \frac{2}{\sqrt{22}}x + \frac{3}{\sqrt{22}}\right\}.$$

46. The set $\{1, x, x^2\}$ of polynomials is orthonormal. (see Example 2)

48. Let $\mathbf{p}_1(x) = \dfrac{3x^2 + 4x}{5}$, $\mathbf{p}_2(x) = \dfrac{-4x^2 + 3x}{5}$, $\mathbf{p}_3(x) = 1$. Then,

$$\langle \mathbf{p}_1, \mathbf{p}_2 \rangle = -\frac{12}{25} + \frac{12}{25} = 0, \langle \mathbf{p}_1, \mathbf{p}_3 \rangle = 0 \text{ and } \langle \mathbf{p}_2, \mathbf{p}_3 \rangle = 0$$

Furthermore,

$$\|\mathbf{p}_1\| = \sqrt{\frac{9 + 16}{25}} = 1, \|\mathbf{p}_2\| = \sqrt{\frac{16 + 9}{25}} = 1 \text{ and } \|\mathbf{p}_3\| = 1.$$

Thus, $\{\mathbf{p}_1, \mathbf{p}_2, \mathbf{p}_3\}$ is an orthonormal set.

50. The set $\left\{(\frac{2}{3}, -\frac{1}{3}), \left(\frac{\sqrt{2}}{6}, \frac{2\sqrt{2}}{3}\right)\right\}$ from Exercise 49 is not orthonormal using the Euclidean inner product because

$$\|(\tfrac{2}{3}, -\tfrac{1}{3})\| = \sqrt{\tfrac{4}{9} + \tfrac{1}{9}} = \frac{\sqrt{5}}{3} \neq 1.$$

52. Let $\mathbf{v} = c_1\mathbf{v}_1 + \cdots + c_n\mathbf{v}_n$ be an arbitrary linear combination of vectors in S. Then
$$\langle \mathbf{w}, \mathbf{v} \rangle = \langle \mathbf{w}, c_1\mathbf{v}_1 + \cdots + c_n\mathbf{v}_n \rangle =$$

$$= \langle \mathbf{w}, c_1\mathbf{v}_1 \rangle + \ldots + \langle \mathbf{w}, c_n\mathbf{v}_n \rangle =$$

$$= c_1\langle \mathbf{w}, \mathbf{v}_1 \rangle + \cdots + c_n\langle \mathbf{w}, \mathbf{v}_n \rangle = c_1 \cdot 0 + \cdots + c_n \cdot 0 = 0.$$

Since $c_1, \ldots, c_n$ are arbitrary real numbers, we conclude that $\mathbf{w}$ is orthogonal to *any* linear combination of vectors in S.

54. (a) We see that

$$P^{-1} = P^T = \begin{bmatrix} -1 & 0 & 0 \\ 0 & 0 & -1 \\ 0 & 1 & 0 \end{bmatrix}.$$

Furthermore, the rows (and columns) of P form an orthonormal basis for R^n.

(b) We see that

$$P^{-1} = P^T = \begin{bmatrix} \frac{1}{\sqrt{2}} & \frac{1}{\sqrt{2}} & 0 \\ \frac{1}{\sqrt{2}} & -\frac{1}{\sqrt{2}} & 0 \\ 0 & 0 & 1 \end{bmatrix}.$$

Furthermore, the rows (and columns) of A form an orthonormal basis for R^n.

56. Since $W^\perp$ is a nonempty subset of V, we only verify the closure axioms. Let $\mathbf{v}_1, \mathbf{v}_2 \in W^\perp$. Then $\mathbf{v}_1 \cdot \mathbf{w} = \mathbf{v}_2 \cdot \mathbf{w} = 0$, for all $\mathbf{w} \in W$. Hence, $(\mathbf{v}_1 + \mathbf{v}_2) \cdot \mathbf{w} = \mathbf{v}_1 \cdot \mathbf{w} + \mathbf{v}_1 \cdot \mathbf{w} = 0 + 0 = 0$, which implies that $\mathbf{v}_1 + \mathbf{v}_2 \in W^\perp$. Finally, if c is a scalar, then $(c\mathbf{v}_1) \cdot \mathbf{w} = c(\mathbf{v}_1 \cdot \mathbf{w}) = c0 = 0$, which implies that $c\mathbf{v}_1 \in W^\perp$.

Let $\mathbf{v} \in W \cap W^\perp$. Then $\mathbf{v} \cdot \mathbf{w} = 0$ for all $\mathbf{w}$ in W. In particular, since $\mathbf{v} \in W^\perp$, $\mathbf{v} \cdot \mathbf{v} = 0$, which implies that $\mathbf{v} = \mathbf{0}$.

58. $A = \begin{bmatrix} 0 & 1 & -1 \\ 0 & -2 & 2 \\ 0 & -1 & 1 \end{bmatrix} \Rightarrow \begin{bmatrix} 0 & 1 & -1 \\ 0 & 0 & 0 \\ 0 & 0 & 0 \end{bmatrix}$

$A^T = \begin{bmatrix} 0 & 0 & 0 \\ 1 & -2 & -1 \\ -1 & 2 & 1 \end{bmatrix} \Rightarrow \begin{bmatrix} 1 & -2 & -1 \\ 0 & 0 & 0 \\ 0 & 0 & 0 \end{bmatrix}$

$N(A)$ — basis: $\left\{ \begin{bmatrix} 1 \\ 0 \\ 0 \end{bmatrix}, \begin{bmatrix} 0 \\ 1 \\ 1 \end{bmatrix} \right\}$

$N(A^T)$ — basis: $\left\{ \begin{bmatrix} 2 \\ 1 \\ 0 \end{bmatrix}, \begin{bmatrix} 1 \\ 0 \\ 1 \end{bmatrix} \right\}$

$R(A)$ — basis: $\left\{ \begin{bmatrix} 1 \\ -2 \\ -1 \end{bmatrix} \right\}$

$R(A^T)$ — basis: $\left\{ \begin{bmatrix} 0 \\ 1 \\ -1 \end{bmatrix} \right\}$

$N(A) = R(A^T)^\perp$ and $N(A^T) = R(A)^\perp$

60. $A = \begin{bmatrix} 0 & 0 & 1 & 2 & 0 \\ 1 & -2 & 0 & 2 & 0 \\ -1 & 2 & 1 & 0 & 0 \\ 0 & 0 & 1 & 2 & 1 \end{bmatrix} \Rightarrow \begin{bmatrix} 1 & -2 & 0 & 2 & 0 \\ 0 & 0 & 1 & 2 & 0 \\ 0 & 0 & 0 & 0 & 1 \\ 0 & 0 & 0 & 0 & 0 \end{bmatrix}$

$A^T = \begin{bmatrix} 0 & 1 & -1 & 0 \\ 0 & -2 & 2 & 0 \\ 1 & 0 & 1 & 1 \\ 2 & 2 & 0 & 2 \\ 0 & 0 & 0 & 1 \end{bmatrix} \Rightarrow \begin{bmatrix} 1 & 0 & 1 & 0 \\ 0 & 1 & -1 & 0 \\ 0 & 0 & 0 & 1 \\ 0 & 0 & 0 & 0 \\ 0 & 0 & 0 & 0 \end{bmatrix}$

$N(A)$ — basis: $\left\{ \begin{bmatrix} 2 \\ 1 \\ 0 \\ 0 \\ 0 \end{bmatrix}, \begin{bmatrix} -2 \\ 0 \\ -2 \\ 1 \\ 0 \end{bmatrix} \right\}$

$N(A^T)$ — basis: $\left\{ \begin{bmatrix} 1 \\ -1 \\ -1 \\ 0 \end{bmatrix} \right\}$

$R(A)$ — basis: $\left\{ \begin{bmatrix} 0 \\ 1 \\ -1 \\ 0 \end{bmatrix}, \begin{bmatrix} 1 \\ 0 \\ 1 \\ 1 \end{bmatrix}, \begin{bmatrix} 0 \\ 0 \\ 0 \\ 1 \end{bmatrix} \right\}$

$R(A^T)$ — basis: $\left\{ \begin{bmatrix} 0 \\ 0 \\ 1 \\ 2 \\ 0 \end{bmatrix}, \begin{bmatrix} 1 \\ -2 \\ 0 \\ 2 \\ 0 \end{bmatrix}, \begin{bmatrix} 0 \\ 0 \\ 1 \\ 2 \\ 1 \end{bmatrix} \right\}$

$N(A) = R(A^T)^\perp$ and $N(A^T) = R(A)^\perp$

Section 5.4   Mathematical Models and Least Squares Analysis

2. Orthogonal: $\begin{bmatrix} -3 \\ 0 \\ 1 \end{bmatrix} \cdot \begin{bmatrix} 2 \\ 1 \\ 6 \end{bmatrix} = \begin{bmatrix} -3 \\ 0 \\ 1 \end{bmatrix} \cdot \begin{bmatrix} 0 \\ 1 \\ 0 \end{bmatrix} = 0$

4. Not Orthogonal: $\begin{bmatrix} 0 \\ 0 \\ 1 \\ -2 \end{bmatrix} \cdot \begin{bmatrix} 0 \\ 1 \\ -2 \\ 2 \end{bmatrix} = -6 \neq 0$

6. Since $S = \{[x, y, 0, 0, z]^T\}$, $S^\perp = \text{span}\left\{\begin{bmatrix} 0 \\ 0 \\ 1 \\ 0 \\ 0 \end{bmatrix}, \begin{bmatrix} 0 \\ 0 \\ 0 \\ 1 \\ 0 \end{bmatrix}\right\}$.

8. $A^T = [0 \quad 1 \quad -1 \quad 1] \implies S^\perp - \text{basis is} \left\{\begin{bmatrix} 1 \\ 0 \\ 0 \\ 0 \end{bmatrix}, \begin{bmatrix} 0 \\ 1 \\ 1 \\ 0 \end{bmatrix}, \begin{bmatrix} 0 \\ 1 \\ 0 \\ -1 \end{bmatrix}\right\}$

10. The orthogonal complement of $S^\perp = \text{span}\left\{\begin{bmatrix} 1 \\ 0 \\ 0 \\ 0 \end{bmatrix}, \begin{bmatrix} 0 \\ 1 \\ 1 \\ 0 \end{bmatrix}, \begin{bmatrix} 0 \\ 1 \\ 0 \\ -1 \end{bmatrix}\right\}$ is

$$(S^\perp)^\perp = S = \text{span}\left\{\begin{bmatrix} 0 \\ 1 \\ -1 \\ 1 \end{bmatrix}\right\}$$

12. An orthonormal basis for S is $\left\{\begin{bmatrix} -\dfrac{1}{\sqrt{5}} \\ \dfrac{2}{\sqrt{5}} \\ 0 \\ 0 \end{bmatrix}, \begin{bmatrix} 0 \\ 0 \\ 1 \\ 0 \end{bmatrix}, \begin{bmatrix} 0 \\ 0 \\ 0 \\ 1 \end{bmatrix}\right\}$.

$$\text{proj}_s\mathbf{v} = (\mathbf{u}_1 \cdot \mathbf{v})\mathbf{u}_1 + (\mathbf{u}_2 \cdot \mathbf{v})\mathbf{u}_2 + (\mathbf{u}_3 \cdot \mathbf{v})\mathbf{u}_3$$

$$= \frac{1}{\sqrt{5}}\begin{bmatrix} -\dfrac{1}{\sqrt{5}} \\ \dfrac{2}{\sqrt{5}} \\ 0 \\ 0 \end{bmatrix} + 1\begin{bmatrix} 0 \\ 0 \\ 1 \\ 0 \end{bmatrix} + 1\begin{bmatrix} 0 \\ 0 \\ 0 \\ 1 \end{bmatrix} = \begin{bmatrix} -\dfrac{1}{5} \\ \dfrac{2}{5} \\ 1 \\ 1 \end{bmatrix}$$

14. Using the Gram-Schmidt process, we obtain an orthonormal basis for S:

$$\left\{ \begin{bmatrix} \frac{1}{2} \\ \frac{1}{2} \\ \frac{1}{2} \\ \frac{1}{2} \end{bmatrix}, \begin{bmatrix} 0 \\ \frac{1}{\sqrt{2}} \\ -\frac{1}{\sqrt{2}} \\ 0 \end{bmatrix}, \begin{bmatrix} -\frac{1}{2} \\ \frac{1}{2} \\ \frac{1}{2} \\ -\frac{1}{2} \end{bmatrix} \right\}.$$

$$\text{proj}_s\mathbf{v} = (\mathbf{u}_1 \cdot \mathbf{v})\mathbf{u}_1 + (\mathbf{u}_2 \cdot \mathbf{v})\mathbf{u}_2 + (\mathbf{u}_3 \cdot \mathbf{v})\mathbf{u}_3$$

$$= 5\begin{bmatrix} \frac{1}{2} \\ \frac{1}{2} \\ \frac{1}{2} \\ \frac{1}{2} \end{bmatrix} + \frac{-1}{\sqrt{2}}\begin{bmatrix} 0 \\ \frac{1}{\sqrt{2}} \\ -\frac{1}{\sqrt{2}} \\ 0 \end{bmatrix} + 0\begin{bmatrix} -\frac{1}{2} \\ \frac{1}{2} \\ \frac{1}{2} \\ -\frac{1}{2} \end{bmatrix} = \begin{bmatrix} \frac{5}{2} \\ 2 \\ 3 \\ \frac{5}{2} \end{bmatrix}$$

16. An orthonormal basis for the column space is

$$\left\{ \begin{bmatrix} 0 \\ \frac{1}{\sqrt{2}} \\ \frac{1}{\sqrt{2}} \end{bmatrix}, \begin{bmatrix} \frac{2}{\sqrt{6}} \\ -\frac{1}{\sqrt{6}} \\ \frac{1}{\sqrt{6}} \end{bmatrix} \right\}$$

$$\text{proj}_s\mathbf{b} = (\mathbf{u}_1 \cdot \mathbf{b})\mathbf{u}_1 + (\mathbf{u}_2 \cdot \mathbf{b})\mathbf{u}_2$$

$$= \frac{-1}{\sqrt{2}}\begin{bmatrix} 0 \\ \frac{1}{\sqrt{2}} \\ \frac{1}{\sqrt{2}} \end{bmatrix} + \frac{7}{\sqrt{6}}\begin{bmatrix} \frac{2}{\sqrt{6}} \\ -\frac{1}{\sqrt{6}} \\ \frac{1}{\sqrt{6}} \end{bmatrix} = \begin{bmatrix} \frac{7}{3} \\ -\frac{5}{3} \\ \frac{2}{3} \end{bmatrix}$$

18. $A = \begin{bmatrix} 0 & -1 & 1 \\ 1 & 2 & 0 \\ 1 & 1 & 1 \end{bmatrix} \Rightarrow \begin{bmatrix} 1 & 0 & 2 \\ 0 & 1 & -1 \\ 0 & 0 & 0 \end{bmatrix}$

$A^T = \begin{bmatrix} 0 & 1 & 1 \\ -1 & 2 & 1 \\ 1 & 0 & 1 \end{bmatrix} \Rightarrow \begin{bmatrix} 1 & 0 & 1 \\ 0 & 1 & 1 \\ 0 & 0 & 0 \end{bmatrix}$

$N(A) - \text{basis:} \left\{ \begin{bmatrix} -2 \\ 1 \\ 1 \end{bmatrix} \right\}$

$N(A^T) - \text{basis:} \left\{ \begin{bmatrix} -1 \\ -1 \\ 1 \end{bmatrix} \right\}$

$R(A) - \text{basis:} \left\{ \begin{bmatrix} 0 \\ 1 \\ 1 \end{bmatrix}, \begin{bmatrix} -1 \\ 2 \\ 1 \end{bmatrix} \right\}$

$R(A^T) - \text{basis:} \left\{ \begin{bmatrix} 0 \\ -1 \\ 1 \end{bmatrix}, \begin{bmatrix} 1 \\ 2 \\ 0 \end{bmatrix} \right\}$

20. $A = \begin{bmatrix} 1 & 0 & -1 \\ 0 & -1 & 1 \\ 1 & 1 & 0 \\ 1 & 0 & 1 \end{bmatrix} \Rightarrow \begin{bmatrix} 1 & 0 & 0 \\ 0 & 1 & 0 \\ 0 & 0 & 1 \\ 0 & 0 & 0 \end{bmatrix}$

$A^T = \begin{bmatrix} 1 & 0 & 1 & 1 \\ 0 & -1 & 1 & 0 \\ -1 & 1 & 0 & 1 \end{bmatrix} \Rightarrow \begin{bmatrix} 1 & 0 & 0 & 0 \\ 0 & 1 & 0 & 1 \\ 0 & 0 & 1 & 1 \end{bmatrix}$

$N(A) = \left\{ \begin{bmatrix} 0 \\ 0 \\ 0 \end{bmatrix} \right\}$

$N(A^T) - \text{basis:} \left\{ \begin{bmatrix} 0 \\ -1 \\ -1 \\ 1 \end{bmatrix} \right\}$

$R(A) - \text{basis:} \left\{ \begin{bmatrix} 1 \\ 0 \\ 1 \\ 1 \end{bmatrix}, \begin{bmatrix} 0 \\ -1 \\ 1 \\ 0 \end{bmatrix}, \begin{bmatrix} -1 \\ 1 \\ 0 \\ 1 \end{bmatrix} \right\}$

$R(A^T) - \text{basis:} \left\{ \begin{bmatrix} 1 \\ 0 \\ -1 \end{bmatrix}, \begin{bmatrix} 0 \\ -1 \\ 1 \end{bmatrix}, \begin{bmatrix} 1 \\ 1 \\ 0 \end{bmatrix} \right\} \quad (R(A^T) = R^3)$

22. $A^T A = \begin{bmatrix} 0 & 1 & 1 \\ 1 & 0 & 2 \end{bmatrix} \begin{bmatrix} 0 & 1 \\ 1 & 0 \\ 1 & 2 \end{bmatrix} = \begin{bmatrix} 2 & 2 \\ 2 & 5 \end{bmatrix}$

$A^T \mathbf{b} = \begin{bmatrix} 0 & 1 & 1 \\ 1 & 0 & 2 \end{bmatrix} \begin{bmatrix} -1 \\ -1 \\ 3 \end{bmatrix} = \begin{bmatrix} 2 \\ 5 \end{bmatrix}$

$\begin{bmatrix} 2 & 2 & 2 \\ 2 & 5 & 5 \end{bmatrix} \Rightarrow \begin{bmatrix} 1 & 0 & 0 \\ 0 & 1 & 1 \end{bmatrix} \Rightarrow \mathbf{x} = \begin{bmatrix} 0 \\ 1 \end{bmatrix}$

24. $A^T A = \begin{bmatrix} 3 & 2 & 0 \\ 2 & 6 & 1 \\ 0 & 1 & 3 \end{bmatrix}, A^T \mathbf{b} = \begin{bmatrix} 1 \\ 1 \\ 1 \end{bmatrix}$

$\begin{bmatrix} 3 & 2 & 0 & 1 \\ 2 & 6 & 1 & 1 \\ 0 & 1 & 3 & 1 \end{bmatrix} \Rightarrow \begin{bmatrix} 1 & 0 & 0 & \frac{1}{3} \\ 0 & 1 & 0 & 0 \\ 0 & 0 & 1 & \frac{1}{3} \end{bmatrix} \Rightarrow \mathbf{x} = \begin{bmatrix} \frac{1}{3} \\ 0 \\ \frac{1}{3} \end{bmatrix}$

26. $A^TA = \begin{bmatrix} 1 & 1 & 1 & 1 \\ -2 & -1 & 1 & 2 \end{bmatrix} \begin{bmatrix} 1 & -2 \\ 1 & -1 \\ 1 & 1 \\ 1 & 2 \end{bmatrix} = \begin{bmatrix} 4 & 0 \\ 0 & 10 \end{bmatrix}$

$A^T\mathbf{b} = \begin{bmatrix} 1 & 1 & 1 & 1 \\ -2 & -1 & 1 & 2 \end{bmatrix} \begin{bmatrix} -1 \\ 0 \\ 0 \\ 2 \end{bmatrix} = \begin{bmatrix} 1 \\ 6 \end{bmatrix}$

$\begin{bmatrix} 4 & 0 & 1 \\ 0 & 10 & 6 \end{bmatrix} \Rightarrow \begin{bmatrix} 1 & 0 & \frac{1}{4} \\ 0 & 1 & \frac{3}{5} \end{bmatrix} \Rightarrow y = \frac{1}{4} + \frac{3}{5}x$

28. $A^TA = \begin{bmatrix} 1 & 1 & 1 & 1 & 1 \\ -2 & -1 & 0 & 1 & 2 \end{bmatrix} \begin{bmatrix} 1 & -2 \\ 1 & -1 \\ 1 & 0 \\ 1 & 1 \\ 1 & 2 \end{bmatrix} = \begin{bmatrix} 5 & 0 \\ 0 & 10 \end{bmatrix}$

$A^T\mathbf{b} = \begin{bmatrix} 1 & 1 & 1 & 1 & 1 \\ -2 & -1 & 0 & 1 & 2 \end{bmatrix} \begin{bmatrix} 1 \\ 2 \\ 1 \\ 2 \\ 1 \end{bmatrix} = \begin{bmatrix} 7 \\ 0 \end{bmatrix}$

$\begin{bmatrix} 5 & 0 & 7 \\ 0 & 10 & 0 \end{bmatrix} \Rightarrow \begin{bmatrix} \frac{7}{5} \\ 0 \end{bmatrix} \Rightarrow y = \frac{7}{5}$

30. $A^TA = \begin{bmatrix} 1 & 1 & 1 & 1 \\ 0 & 2 & 3 & 4 \\ 0 & 4 & 9 & 16 \end{bmatrix} \begin{bmatrix} 1 & 0 & 0 \\ 1 & 2 & 4 \\ 1 & 3 & 9 \\ 1 & 4 & 16 \end{bmatrix} = \begin{bmatrix} 4 & 9 & 29 \\ 9 & 29 & 99 \\ 29 & 99 & 353 \end{bmatrix}$

$A^T\mathbf{b} = \begin{bmatrix} 1 & 1 & 1 & 1 \\ 0 & 2 & 3 & 4 \\ 0 & 4 & 9 & 16 \end{bmatrix} \begin{bmatrix} 0 \\ 2 \\ 6 \\ 12 \end{bmatrix} = \begin{bmatrix} 20 \\ 70 \\ 254 \end{bmatrix}$

$\begin{bmatrix} 4 & 9 & 29 & 20 \\ 9 & 29 & 99 & 70 \\ 29 & 99 & 353 & 254 \end{bmatrix} \Rightarrow \begin{bmatrix} 1 & 0 & 0 & 0 \\ 0 & 1 & 0 & -1 \\ 0 & 0 & 1 & 1 \end{bmatrix} \Rightarrow y = x^2 - x$

32. One model can be the least squares regression line.

$$A = \begin{bmatrix} 1 & 8{,}463 \\ 1 & 9{,}404 \\ 1 & 9{,}484 \\ 1 & 9{,}637 \\ 1 & 10{,}467 \\ 1 & 10{,}461 \\ 1 & 9{,}788 \\ 1 & 9{,}565 \\ 1 & 9{,}845 \\ 1 & 9{,}194 \\ 1 & 9{,}339 \end{bmatrix} \quad \text{and} \quad b = \begin{bmatrix} 6{,}204 \\ 7{,}041 \\ 7{,}031 \\ 7{,}618 \\ 8{,}214 \\ 7{,}936 \\ 7{,}667 \\ 7{,}476 \\ 7{,}248 \\ 7{,}174 \\ 6{,}832 \end{bmatrix}$$

Then

$$A^T A = \begin{bmatrix} 11 & 105{,}647 \\ 105{,}647 & 1{,}017{,}830{,}971 \end{bmatrix}$$

$$A^T b = \begin{bmatrix} 80{,}441 \\ 775{,}480{,}020 \end{bmatrix}.$$

Using Gauss-Jordan elimination to solve $A^T A x = A^T b$, we obtain

$$\begin{bmatrix} 11 & 105{,}647 & 80{,}441 \\ 105{,}647 & 1{,}017{,}830{,}971 & 775{,}480{,}020 \end{bmatrix} \Rightarrow \begin{bmatrix} 1 & 0 & -1486.18236331 \\ 0 & 1 & 0.916154798493 \end{bmatrix}.$$

Thus, the least squares regression line is

$$y = 0.916154798493x - 1486.18236331.$$

34. (a) *False.* They are orthogonal subspace of R^m not R^n.

(b) *True.* See the defintion of orthogonal complement on page 313.

(c) *True.* See page 313 for the definition of the least squares problem.

36. Let S be a subspace of R^n and $S^\perp$ its orthogonal complement. $S^\perp$ contains the zero vector. If $v_1, v_2 \in S^\perp$, then for all $w \in S$,

$$(v_1 + v_2) \cdot w = v_1 \cdot w + v_2 \cdot w = 0 + 0 = 0 \implies v_1 + v_2 \in S^\perp$$

and for any scalar c,

$$(cv_1) \cdot w = c(v_1 \cdot w) = c0 = 0 \implies cv_1 \in S^\perp$$

38. Let $x \in S_1 \cap S_2$, where $R^n = S_1 \oplus S_2$. Then $x = v_1 + v_2, v_1 \in S_1$ and $v_2 \in S_2$. But, $x \in S_1 \implies x = x + 0, x \in S_1, 0 \in S_2$, and $x \in S_2 \implies x = 0 + x$, $0 \in S_1, x \in S_2$. Thus, $x = 0$ by the uniqueness of direct sum representation.

Section 5.5   Applications of Inner Product Spaces

2. The cross product is

$$\mathbf{u} \times \mathbf{v} = \begin{vmatrix} \mathbf{i} & \mathbf{j} & \mathbf{k} \\ 0 & 1 & 0 \\ 1 & 0 & 0 \end{vmatrix} = -\mathbf{k} = (0, 0, -1).$$

Furthermore, $\mathbf{u} \times \mathbf{v} = (0, 0, -1)$ is orthogonal to both $(0, 1, 0)$ and $(1, 0, 0)$ because $(0, 0, -1) \cdot (0, 1, 0) = 0$ and $(0, 0, -1) \cdot (1, 0, 0) = 0.$

4. The cross product is

$$\mathbf{u} \times \mathbf{v} = \begin{vmatrix} \mathbf{i} & \mathbf{j} & \mathbf{k} \\ 0 & 0 & 1 \\ 0 & 1 & 0 \end{vmatrix} = -\mathbf{i} = (-1, 0, 0).$$

Furthermore, $\mathbf{u} \times \mathbf{v} = (-1, 0, 0)$ is orthogonal to both $(0, 0, 1)$ and $(0, 1, 0)$ because $(-1, 0, 0) \cdot (0, 0, 1) = 0$ and $(-1, 0, 0) \cdot (0, 1, 0) = 0.$

6. The cross product is

$$\mathbf{u} \times \mathbf{v} = \begin{vmatrix} \mathbf{i} & \mathbf{j} & \mathbf{k} \\ 1 & -2 & 1 \\ -1 & 3 & -2 \end{vmatrix} = \mathbf{i} + \mathbf{j} + \mathbf{k} = (1, 1, 1).$$

Furthermore, $\mathbf{u} \times \mathbf{v} = (1, 1, 1)$ is orthogonal to both $(1, -2, 1)$ and $(-1, 3, -2)$ because $(1, 1, 1) \cdot (1, -2, 1) = 0$ and $(1, 1, 1) \cdot (-1, 3, -2) = 0.$

8. The cross product is

$$\mathbf{u} \times \mathbf{v} = \begin{vmatrix} \mathbf{i} & \mathbf{j} & \mathbf{k} \\ 4 & 1 & 0 \\ 3 & 2 & -2 \end{vmatrix} = -2\mathbf{i} + 8\mathbf{j} + 5\mathbf{k} = (-2, 8, 5).$$

Furthermore, $\mathbf{u} \times \mathbf{v} = (-2, 8, 5)$ is orthogonal to both $(4, 1, 0)$ and $(3, 2, -2)$ because $(-2, 8, 5) \cdot (4, 1, 0) = 0$ and $(-2, 8, 5) \cdot (3, 2, -2) = 0.$

10. Using computer software Maple V we find

$$\mathbf{w} = \mathbf{u} \times \mathbf{v} = (2, -1, -1).$$

We check if $\mathbf{w}$ is orthogonal to both $\mathbf{u}$ and $\mathbf{v}$:

$$\mathbf{w} \cdot \mathbf{u} = (2, -1, -1) \cdot (0, 1, -1) = -1 + 1 = 0,$$
$$\mathbf{w} \cdot \mathbf{v} = (2, -1, -1) \cdot (1, 2, 0) = 2 - 2 = 0.$$

12. Using computer software Maple V we find

$$\mathbf{w} = \mathbf{u} \times \mathbf{v} = (1, -5, -3).$$

We check if $\mathbf{w}$ is orthogonal to both $\mathbf{u}$ and $\mathbf{v}$:

$$\mathbf{w} \cdot \mathbf{u} = (1, -5, -3) \cdot (2, 1, -1) = 2 - 5 + 3 = 0,$$
$$\mathbf{w} \cdot \mathbf{v} = (1, -5, -3) \cdot (1, -1, 2) = 1 + 5 - 6 = 0.$$

14. Since

$$\mathbf{u} \times \mathbf{v} = \begin{vmatrix} \mathbf{i} & \mathbf{j} & \mathbf{k} \\ 1 & 1 & 1 \\ 0 & 1 & 1 \end{vmatrix} = -\mathbf{j} + \mathbf{k} = (0, -1, 1),$$

the area of the parallelogram is

$$\|\mathbf{u} \times \mathbf{v}\| = \|(0, -1, 1)\| = \sqrt{2}.$$

16. Since

$$\mathbf{u} \times \mathbf{v} = \begin{vmatrix} \mathbf{i} & \mathbf{j} & \mathbf{k} \\ 2 & -1 & 0 \\ -1 & 2 & 0 \end{vmatrix} = 3\mathbf{k} = (0, 0, 3),$$

the area of the parallelogram is

$$\|(0, 0, 3)\| = 3.$$

18. Since

$$\mathbf{v} \times \mathbf{w} = \begin{vmatrix} \mathbf{i} & \mathbf{j} & \mathbf{k} \\ 2 & 1 & 0 \\ 0 & 0 & 1 \end{vmatrix} = \mathbf{i} - 2\mathbf{j} = (1, -2, 0),$$

the triple scalar product is

$$\mathbf{u} \cdot (\mathbf{v} \times \mathbf{w}) = (1, 1, 1) \cdot (1, -2, 0) = -1.$$

20. The area of the base of the parallelogram is $\|\mathbf{v} \times \mathbf{w}\|$.

The height is $|\cos \theta| \, \|\mathbf{u}\|$, where

$$|\cos \theta| = \frac{|\mathbf{u} \cdot (\mathbf{v} \times \mathbf{w})|}{\|\mathbf{u}\| \, \|\mathbf{v} \times \mathbf{w}\|}.$$

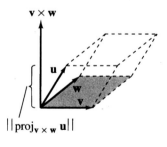

Hence,

$$\text{volume} = \text{base} \times \text{height} = \|\mathbf{v} \times \mathbf{w}\| \frac{|\mathbf{u} \cdot (\mathbf{v} \times \mathbf{w})|}{\|\mathbf{u}\| \, \|\mathbf{v} \times \mathbf{w}\|} \|\mathbf{u}\|$$

$$= |\mathbf{u} \cdot (\mathbf{v} \times \mathbf{w})|.$$

22. Since

$$\mathbf{v} \times \mathbf{w} = \begin{vmatrix} \mathbf{i} & \mathbf{j} & \mathbf{k} \\ 0 & 1 & 1 \\ 1 & 0 & 1 \end{vmatrix} = \mathbf{i} + \mathbf{j} - \mathbf{k} = (1, 1, -1),$$

the volume is given by

$$|\mathbf{u} \cdot (\mathbf{v} \times \mathbf{w})| = |(1, 1, 0) \cdot (1, 1, -1)| = 2.$$

24. $\mathbf{u} \times (\mathbf{v} + \mathbf{w})$

$$= \begin{vmatrix} \mathbf{i} & \mathbf{j} & \mathbf{k} \\ u_1 & u_2 & u_3 \\ v_1 + w_1 & v_2 + w_2 & v_3 + w_3 \end{vmatrix}$$

$$= [u_2(v_3 + w_3) - u_3(v_2 + w_2)]\mathbf{i} - [u_1(v_3 + w_3) - u_3(v_1 + w_1)]\mathbf{j} + [u_1(v_2 + w_2) - u_2(v_1 + w_1)]\mathbf{k}$$

$$= (u_2 v_3 - v_2 u_3)\mathbf{i} - (u_1 v_3 - u_3 v_1)\mathbf{j} + (u_1 v_2 - u_2 v_1)\mathbf{k}$$
$$\quad + (u_2 w_3 - u_3 w_2)\mathbf{i} - (u_1 w_3 - u_3 w_1)\mathbf{j} + (u_1 w_2 - u_2 w_1)\mathbf{k}$$

$$= \begin{vmatrix} \mathbf{i} & \mathbf{j} & \mathbf{k} \\ u_1 & u_2 & u_3 \\ v_1 & v_2 & v_3 \end{vmatrix} + \begin{vmatrix} \mathbf{i} & \mathbf{j} & \mathbf{k} \\ u_1 & u_2 & u_3 \\ w_1 & w_2 & w_3 \end{vmatrix}$$

$$= (\mathbf{u} \times \mathbf{v}) + (\mathbf{u} \times \mathbf{w})$$

26. $\mathbf{u} \times \mathbf{u} = \begin{vmatrix} \mathbf{i} & \mathbf{j} & \mathbf{k} \\ u_1 & u_2 & u_3 \\ u_1 & u_2 & u_3 \end{vmatrix} = \mathbf{0}$, since two rows are the same.

28. Since

$$\mathbf{u} \times \mathbf{v} = (u_2 v_3 - v_2 u_3)\mathbf{i} - (u_1 v_3 - u_3 v_1)\mathbf{j} + (u_1 v_2 - v_1 u_2)\mathbf{k}$$

we see that

$$\mathbf{u} \cdot (\mathbf{u} \times \mathbf{v}) = (u_1, u_2, u_3) \cdot (u_2 v_3 - v_2 u_3, -u_1 v_3 + u_3 v_1, u_1 v_2 - v_1 u_2)$$
$$= (u_1 u_2 v_3 - u_1 v_2 u_3 - u_2 u_1 v_3 + u_2 u_3 v_1 + u_3 u_1 v_2 - u_3 v_1 u_2)$$
$$= 0,$$

which shows that $\mathbf{u}$ is orthogonal to $\mathbf{u} \times \mathbf{v}$. A similar computation shows that $\mathbf{v} \cdot (\mathbf{u} \times \mathbf{v}) = 0$. [Note that $\mathbf{v} \cdot (\mathbf{u} \times \mathbf{v}) = -\mathbf{v} \cdot (\mathbf{v} \times \mathbf{u}) = 0$ by the above with the roles of $\mathbf{u}$ and $\mathbf{v}$ reversed.]

30. We have the following equivalences.

$$\mathbf{u} \times \mathbf{v} = \mathbf{0} \iff \|\mathbf{u} \times \mathbf{v}\| = 0$$
$$\iff \|\mathbf{u}\| \, \|\mathbf{v}\| \sin \theta = 0 \quad \text{(Theorem 5.18 (2))}$$
$$\iff \sin \theta = 0$$
$$\iff \theta = 0$$
$$\iff \mathbf{u} \text{ and } \mathbf{v} \text{ are parallel.}$$

32. (a) $\mathbf{u} \times (\mathbf{v} \times \mathbf{w})$

$$= \mathbf{u} \times \begin{vmatrix} \mathbf{i} & \mathbf{j} & \mathbf{k} \\ v_1 & v_2 & v_3 \\ w_1 & w_2 & w_3 \end{vmatrix}$$

$$= \mathbf{u} \times [(v_2w_3 - w_2v_3)\mathbf{i} - (v_1w_3 - w_1v_3)\mathbf{j} + (v_1w_2 - v_2w_1)\mathbf{k}]$$

$$= \begin{vmatrix} \mathbf{i} & \mathbf{j} & \mathbf{k} \\ u_1 & u_2 & u_3 \\ (v_2w_3 - w_2v_3) & (w_1v_3 - v_1w_3) & (v_1w_2 - v_2w_1) \end{vmatrix}$$

$$= [(u_2(v_1w_2 - v_2w_1)) - u_3(w_1v_3 - v_1w_3)]\mathbf{i} - [u_1(v_1w_2 - v_2w_1) - u_3(v_2w_3 - w_2v_3)]\mathbf{j}$$
$$+ [u_1(w_1v_3 - v_1w_3) - u_2(v_2w_3 - w_2v_3)]\mathbf{k}$$

$$= (u_2w_2v_1 + u_3w_3v_1 - u_2v_2w_1 - u_3v_3w_1, u_1w_1v_2 + u_3w_3v_2 - u_1v_1w_2 - u_3v_3w_2,$$
$$u_1w_1v_3 + u_2w_2v_3 - u_1v_1w_3 - u_2v_2w_3)$$

$$= (u_1w_1 + u_2w_2 + u_3w_3)(v_1, v_2, v_3) - (u_1v_1 + u_2v_2 + u_3v_3)(w_1, w_2, w_3)$$

$$= (\mathbf{u} \cdot \mathbf{w})\mathbf{v} - (\mathbf{u} \cdot \mathbf{v})\mathbf{w}$$

(b) Let

$$\mathbf{u} = (1, 0, 0), \mathbf{v} = (0, 1, 0) \text{ and } \mathbf{w} = (1, 1, 1)$$

Then

$$\mathbf{v} \times \mathbf{w} = (1, 0, -1) \text{ and } \mathbf{u} \times \mathbf{v} = (0, 0, 1).$$

Hence

$$\mathbf{u} \times (\mathbf{v} \times \mathbf{w}) = (1, 0, 0) \times (1, 0, -1) = (0, 1, 0),$$

while

$$(\mathbf{u} \times \mathbf{v}) \times \mathbf{w} = (0, 0, 1) \times (1, 1, 1) = (-1, 1, 0),$$

which are not equal.

34. (a) The standard basis for P_1 is $\{1, x\}$. Applying the Gram-Schmidt orthonormalization process produces the orthonormal basis

$$B = \{\mathbf{w}_1, \mathbf{w}_2\} = \left\{\frac{1}{\sqrt{3}}, \frac{1}{3}(2x - 5)\right\}.$$

The least squares approximating function is given by

$$g(x) = \langle f, \mathbf{w}_1 \rangle \mathbf{w}_1 + \langle f, \mathbf{w}_2 \rangle \mathbf{w}_2.$$

Thus, we find the inner products

$$\langle f, \mathbf{w}_1 \rangle = \int_1^4 \sqrt{x}\, \frac{1}{\sqrt{3}}\, dx = \frac{1}{\sqrt{3}}\frac{2}{3} x^{3/2} \Big]_1^4 = \frac{2}{3\sqrt{3}}(8 - 1) = \frac{14}{3\sqrt{3}}$$

$$\langle f, \mathbf{w}_2 \rangle = \int_1^4 \sqrt{x}\,\frac{1}{3}(2x - 5)\, dx = \frac{4}{15}x^{5/2} - \frac{10}{9} x^{3/2} \Big]_1^4$$

$$= \left(\frac{4}{15}32 - \frac{10}{9}8\right) - \left(\frac{4}{15} - \frac{10}{9}\right) = \frac{124}{15} - \frac{70}{9} = \frac{22}{45}$$

—CONTINUED—

34. **—CONTINUED—**

and conclude that

$$g(x) = \langle f, \mathbf{w}_1 \rangle \mathbf{w}_1 + \langle f, \mathbf{w}_2 \rangle \mathbf{w}_2$$

$$= \frac{14}{3\sqrt{3}} \frac{1}{\sqrt{3}} + \frac{22}{45} \frac{1}{3} (2x - 5)$$

$$= \tfrac{44}{135}x + \tfrac{20}{27} = \tfrac{4}{135}(25 + 11x).$$

(b)

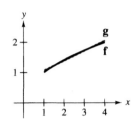

36. (a) The standard basis for P_1 is $\{1, x\}$. Applying the Gram-Schmidt orthonormalization process produces the orthonormal basis.

$$B = \{\mathbf{w}_1, \mathbf{w}_2\} = \left\{ \frac{1}{\sqrt{\pi}}, \frac{\sqrt{3}}{\pi^{3/2}}(2x - \pi) \right\}$$

The least squares approximating function is given by

$$g(x) = \langle f, \mathbf{w}_1 \rangle \mathbf{w}_1 + \langle f, \mathbf{w}_2 \rangle \mathbf{w}_2.$$

Thus, we find the inner products

$$\langle f, \mathbf{w}_1 \rangle = \int_0^{\pi} \cos x \, \frac{1}{\sqrt{\pi}} \, dx = \frac{1}{\sqrt{\pi}} \sin x \bigg]_0^{\pi} = 0$$

$$\langle f, \mathbf{w}_2 \rangle = \int_0^{\pi} \cos x \, \frac{\sqrt{3}}{\pi^{3/2}}(2x - \pi) \, dx = \frac{\sqrt{3}}{\pi^{3/2}} \bigg[(2x - \pi) \sin x + 2 \cos x \bigg]_0^{\pi}$$

$$= \frac{\sqrt{3}}{\pi^{3/2}}[-2 - 2] = -\frac{4\sqrt{3}}{\pi^{3/2}}$$

and we conclude that

$$g(x) = \langle f, \mathbf{w}_1 \rangle \mathbf{w}_1 + \langle f, \mathbf{w}_2 \rangle \mathbf{w}_2$$

$$= 0 + \frac{-4\sqrt{3}}{\pi^{3/2}} \left(\frac{\sqrt{3}}{\pi^{3/2}} \right) (2x - \pi)$$

$$= \frac{12}{\pi^3}(\pi - 2x).$$

—CONTINUED—

36. **—CONTINUED—**

(b)

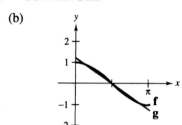

38. (a) The standard basis for P_1 is $\{1, x\}$. Applying the Gram-Schmidt orthonormalization process produces the orthonormal basis

$$B = \{\mathbf{w}_1, \mathbf{w}_2\} = \left\{ \frac{1}{\sqrt{\pi}}, \frac{2\sqrt{3}}{\pi^{3/2}}x \right\}.$$

The least squares approximating function is then given by

$$g(x) = \langle f, \mathbf{w}_1 \rangle \mathbf{w}_1 + \langle f, \mathbf{w}_2 \rangle \mathbf{w}_2.$$

Thus, we find the inner products

$$\langle f, \mathbf{w}_1 \rangle = \int_{-\pi/2}^{\pi/2} \sin x \frac{1}{\sqrt{\pi}}\, dx = \frac{\cos x}{\sqrt{\pi}} \bigg]_{-\pi/2}^{\pi/2} = 0$$

$$\langle f, \mathbf{w}_2 \rangle = \int_{-\pi/2}^{\pi/2} \sin x \frac{2\sqrt{3}}{\pi^{3/2}}\, dx = \frac{2\sqrt{3}}{\pi^{3/2}} [-x \cos x + \sin x] \bigg]_{-\pi/2}^{\pi/2}$$

$$= \frac{2\sqrt{3}}{\pi^{3/2}}[1 + 1] = \frac{4\sqrt{3}}{\pi^{3/2}}$$

and we conclude that

$$g(x) = \langle f, \mathbf{w}_1 \rangle \mathbf{w}_1 + \langle f, \mathbf{w}_2 \rangle \mathbf{w}_2$$

$$= 0 + \frac{4\sqrt{3}}{\pi^{3/2}} \frac{2\sqrt{3}}{\pi^{3/2}}x = \frac{24}{\pi^3}x.$$

(b)

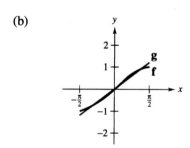

40. (a) The standard basis for P_2 is $\{1, x, x^2\}$. Applying the Gram-Schmidt orthonormalization process produces the orthonormal basis

$$B = \{\mathbf{w}_1, \mathbf{w}_2, \mathbf{w}_3\} = \left\{ \frac{1}{\sqrt{3}}, \frac{1}{3}(2x - 5), \frac{2\sqrt{5}}{3\sqrt{3}}\left(x^2 - 5x + \frac{11}{2}\right) \right\}.$$

The least squares approximating function is then given by

$$g(x) = \langle f, \mathbf{w}_1 \rangle \mathbf{w}_1 + \langle f, \mathbf{w}_2 \rangle \mathbf{w}_2 + \langle f, \mathbf{w}_3 \rangle \mathbf{w}_3.$$

Thus, we find the inner products

$$\langle f, \mathbf{w}_1 \rangle = \int_1^4 \sqrt{x}\, \frac{1}{\sqrt{3}}\, dx = \frac{14}{3\sqrt{3}} \quad \text{(see Exercise 34)}$$

$$\langle f, \mathbf{w}_2 \rangle = \int_1^4 \sqrt{x}\, \frac{1}{3}(2x - 5)\, dx = \frac{22}{45} \quad \text{(see Exercise 34)}$$

$$\langle f, \mathbf{w}_3 \rangle = \int_1^4 \sqrt{x}\, \frac{2\sqrt{5}}{3\sqrt{3}}\left(x^2 - 5x + \frac{11}{2}\right) dx$$

$$= \frac{2\sqrt{5}}{3\sqrt{3}} \int_1^4 \left(x^{5/2} - 5x^{3/2} + \frac{11}{2}x^{1/2}\right) dx$$

$$= \frac{2\sqrt{5}}{3\sqrt{3}} \left[\frac{2}{7}x^{7/2} - 2x^{5/2} + \frac{11}{3}x^{3/2}\right]_1^4$$

$$= \frac{2\sqrt{5}}{3\sqrt{3}} \left[\left(\frac{2}{7}128 - 64 + \frac{11}{3}8\right) - \left(\frac{2}{7} - 2 + \frac{11}{3}\right)\right]$$

$$= \frac{2\sqrt{5}}{3\sqrt{3}}\left(\frac{254}{7} - 62 + \frac{77}{3}\right) = \frac{2\sqrt{5}}{3\sqrt{3}}\left(\frac{-1}{21}\right) = \frac{-2\sqrt{5}}{63\sqrt{3}}$$

and conclude that g is given by

$$g(x) = \frac{14}{3\sqrt{3}}\left(\frac{1}{\sqrt{3}}\right) + \frac{22}{45}\left(\frac{1}{3}(2x - 5)\right) - \frac{2\sqrt{5}}{63\sqrt{3}} \cdot \frac{2\sqrt{5}}{3\sqrt{3}}\left(x^2 - 5x + \frac{11}{2}\right)$$

$$= \frac{14}{9} + \frac{44x}{135} - \frac{22}{27} - \frac{20}{567}x^2 + \frac{100}{567}x - \frac{110}{567}$$

$$= -\frac{20}{567}x^2 + \frac{1424}{2835}x + \frac{310}{567}.$$

(b)

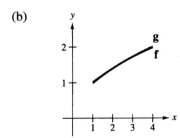

42. (a) The standard basis for P_2 is $\{1, x, x^2\}$. Applying the Gram-Schmidt orthonormalization process produces the orthonormal basis

$$B = \{\mathbf{w}_1, \mathbf{w}_2, \mathbf{w}_3\} = \left\{ \frac{1}{\sqrt{\pi}}, \frac{2\sqrt{3}}{\pi^{3/2}}x, \frac{6\sqrt{5}}{\pi^{5/2}}\left(x^2 - \frac{\pi^2}{12}\right) \right\}.$$

The least squares approximating function is given by

$$g(x) = \langle f, \mathbf{w}_1 \rangle \mathbf{w}_1 + \langle f, \mathbf{w}_2 \rangle \mathbf{w}_2 + \langle f, \mathbf{w}_3 \rangle \mathbf{w}_3.$$

Thus, we find the inner products

$$\langle f, \mathbf{w}_1 \rangle = \int_{-\pi/2}^{\pi/2} \sin x \frac{1}{\sqrt{\pi}}\, dx = 0 \quad \text{(see Exercise 36)}$$

$$\langle f, \mathbf{w}_2 \rangle = \int_{-\pi/2}^{\pi/2} \sin x \frac{2\sqrt{3}}{\pi^{3/2}} x\, dx = \frac{4\sqrt{3}}{\pi^{3/2}} \quad \text{(see Exercise 36)}$$

$$\langle f, \mathbf{w}_3 \rangle = \int_{-\pi/2}^{\pi/2} \sin x \frac{6\sqrt{5}}{\pi^{5/2}}\left(x^2 - \frac{x^2}{12}\right) dx$$

$$= \frac{6\sqrt{5}}{\pi^{3/2}}\left[2\cos x - x^2\cos x + 2x\sin x + \frac{\pi^2}{12}\cos x \right]_{-\pi/2}^{\pi/2}$$

$$= \frac{6\sqrt{5}}{\pi^{3/2}}[0] = 0$$

and conclude that

$$g(x) = 0 + \frac{4\sqrt{3}}{\pi^{3/2}}\left(\frac{2\sqrt{3}}{\pi^{3/2}}x\right) + 0 = \frac{24}{\pi^3}x.$$

(b)

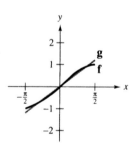

44. The fourth order Fourier approximation of $f(x) = \pi - x$ is of the form

$$g(x) = \frac{a_0}{2} + a_1\cos x + b_1\sin x + a_2\cos 2x + b_2\sin 2x + a_3\cos 3x + b_3\sin 3x$$
$$+ a_4\cos 4x + b_4\sin 4x.$$

In Exercise 43, we determined a_0 and the general form of the coefficients a_j and b_j.

$$a_0 = 0$$
$$a_j = 0, \quad j = 1, 2, 3, \ldots$$
$$b_j = \frac{2}{j}, \quad j = 1, 2, 3, \ldots$$

Thus, the approximation is

$$g(x) = 2\sin x + \sin 2x + \frac{2}{3}\sin 3x + \frac{1}{2}\sin 4x.$$

46. The fourth order Fourier approximation of $f(x) = (x - \pi)^2$ is of the form

$$g(x) = \frac{a_0}{2} + a_1 \cos x + b_1 \sin x + a_2 \cos 2x + b_2 \sin 2x + a_3 \cos 3x + b_3 \sin 3x$$
$$+ a_4 \cos 4x + b_4 \sin 4x.$$

In Exercise 45, we determined a_0 and the general form of the coefficients a_j and b_j.

$$a_0 = \frac{2\pi^2}{3}$$

$$a_j = \frac{4}{j^2}, \quad j = 1, 2, \ldots$$

$$b_j = 0, \quad j = 1, 2, \ldots$$

Thus, the approximation is

$$g(x) = \frac{\pi^2}{3} + 4 \cos x + \cos 2x + \frac{4}{9} \cos 3x + \frac{1}{4} \cos 4x.$$

48. The second order Fourier approximation of $f(x) = e^{-x}$ is of the form

$$g(x) = \frac{a_0}{2} + a_1 \cos x + b_1 \sin x + a_2 \cos 2x + b_2 \sin 2x.$$

In Exercise 47, we found that

$$a_0 = (1 - e^{-2\pi})/\pi$$
$$a_1 = (1 - e^{-2\pi})/2\pi$$
$$b_1 = (1 - e^{-2\pi})/2\pi.$$

Hence, we need to determine a_2 and b_2.

$$a_2 = \frac{1}{\pi} \int_0^{2\pi} f(x) \cos 2x \, dx = \frac{1}{\pi} \int_0^{2\pi} e^{-x} \cos 2x \, dx$$

$$= \frac{1}{\pi} \left[\frac{1}{5} (-e^{-x} \cos 2x + 2e^{-x} \sin 2x) \right]_0^{2\pi} = \frac{1}{5\pi} (1 - e^{-2\pi})$$

$$b_2 = \frac{1}{\pi} \int_0^{2\pi} f(x) \sin 2x \, dx = \frac{1}{\pi} \int_0^{2\pi} e^{-x} \sin 2x \, dx$$

$$= \frac{1}{\pi} \left[\frac{1}{5} (-e^{-x} \sin 2x - 2e^{-x} \cos 2x) \right]_0^{2\pi} = \frac{2}{5\pi} (1 - e^{-2\pi})$$

Thus, the approximation is

$$g(x) = \frac{1 - e^{-2\pi}}{2\pi} + \frac{1 - e^{-2\pi}}{2\pi} \cos x + \frac{1 - e^{-2\pi}}{2\pi} \sin x + \frac{1 - e^{-2\pi}}{5\pi} \cos 2x + \frac{1 - e^{-2\pi}}{5\pi} 2 \sin 2x$$

$$= \frac{1}{10\pi} (1 - e^{-2\pi})[5 + 5 \cos x + 5 \sin x + 2 \cos 2x + 4 \sin 2x].$$

50. The fourth order Fourier approximation of $f(x) = 1 + x$ is of the form

$$g(x) = \frac{a_0}{2} + a_1 \cos x + b_1 \sin x + a_2 \cos 2x + b_2 \sin 2x + a_3 \cos 3x + b_3 \sin 3x$$
$$+ a_4 \cos 4x + b_4 \sin 4x.$$

In Exercise 47, we found that

$$a_0 = 2 + 2\pi$$
$$a_j = 0, \quad j = 1, 2, \ldots$$
$$b_j = \frac{-2}{j}, \quad j = 1, 2, \ldots$$

Hence, the approximation is

$$g(x) = (1 + \pi) - 2 \sin x - \sin 2x - \tfrac{2}{3} \sin 3x - \tfrac{1}{2} \sin 4x.$$

52. Since $f(x) = \sin^2 x = \tfrac{1}{2} - \tfrac{1}{2} \cos 2x$, we see that the fourth order Fourier approximation is simply

$$g(x) = \tfrac{1}{2} - \tfrac{1}{2} \cos 2x.$$

54. Since

$$a_0 = 2\pi^2/3, \, a_j = 4/j^2 (j = 1, 2, \ldots), \, b_j = 0 (j = 1, 2, \ldots),$$

the nth order Fourier approximation is

$$g(x) = \tfrac{\pi^2}{3} + 4 \cos x + \cos 2x + \tfrac{4}{9} \cos 3x + \tfrac{4}{16} \cos 4x + \cdots + \tfrac{4}{n^2} \cos nx.$$

Chapter 5 ❑ Review Exercises

2. $\mathbf{u} = (1, -1, 2)$ and $\mathbf{v} = (2, 3, 1)$

$$\|\mathbf{u}\| = \sqrt{1 + 1 + 4} = \sqrt{6}$$
$$\|\mathbf{v}\| = \sqrt{4 + 9 + 1} = \sqrt{14}$$
$$\mathbf{u} \cdot \mathbf{v} = 2 - 3 + 2 = 1$$
$$d(\mathbf{u}, \mathbf{v}) = \|\mathbf{u} - \mathbf{v}\| = \|(-1, -4, 1)\| = \sqrt{1 + 16 + 1} = \sqrt{18}$$

4. (a) $\|\mathbf{u}\| = \sqrt{1^2 + (-1)^2 + 0^2 + 1^2 + 1^2} = \sqrt{4} = 2$

(b) $\|\mathbf{v}\| = \sqrt{0^2 + 1^2 + (-2)^2 + 2^2 + 1^2} = \sqrt{10}$

(c) $\mathbf{u} \cdot \mathbf{v} = 1(0) + (-1)(1) + 0(-2) + 1(2) + 1(1) = 2$

(d) $d(\mathbf{u}, \mathbf{v}) = \|\mathbf{u} - \mathbf{v}\| = \|(1, -2, 2, -1, 0\| = \sqrt{1^2 + (-2)^2 + 2^2 + (-1)^2} = \sqrt{10}$

6. The norm of **v** is

$$\|\mathbf{v}\| = \sqrt{1^2 + (-2)^2 + 1^2} = \sqrt{6}.$$

Thus, a unit vector in the direction of **v** is

$$\mathbf{u} = \frac{1}{\|\mathbf{v}\|}\mathbf{v} = \frac{1}{\sqrt{6}}(1, -2, 1) = \left(\frac{1}{\sqrt{6}}, \frac{-2}{\sqrt{6}}, \frac{1}{\sqrt{6}}\right).$$

8. The cosine of the angle θ between **u** and **v** is given by

$$\cos\theta = \frac{\mathbf{u}\cdot\mathbf{v}}{\|\mathbf{u}\|\|\mathbf{v}\|} = \frac{\cos\frac{3\pi}{4}\cos\frac{2\pi}{3} + \sin\frac{3\pi}{4}\sin\frac{2\pi}{3}}{\sqrt{\cos^2\frac{3\pi}{4} + \sin^2\frac{3\pi}{4}} + \sqrt{\cos^2\frac{2\pi}{3} + \sin^2\frac{2\pi}{3}}}$$

$$= \frac{\cos\left(\frac{3\pi}{4} - \frac{2\pi}{3}\right)}{1\cdot 1} = \cos\frac{\pi}{12}$$

which implies that $\theta = \frac{\pi}{12}$ radians (15°).

10. The cosine of the angle θ between **u** and **v** is given by

$$\cos\theta = \frac{\mathbf{u}\cdot\mathbf{v}}{\|\mathbf{u}\|\|\mathbf{v}\|} = \frac{2-3}{\sqrt{10}\sqrt{10}} = -\frac{1}{10}.$$

Thus, $\theta = \cos^{-1}\left(\frac{-1}{10}\right) \approx 1.67$ radians (95.7°).

12. The projection of **u** onto **v** is given by

$$\text{proj}_\mathbf{v}\mathbf{u} = \frac{\mathbf{u}\cdot\mathbf{v}}{\mathbf{v}\cdot\mathbf{v}}\mathbf{v} = \frac{12}{16}(0, 4) = (0, 3).$$

14. The projection of **u** onto **v** is given by

$$\text{proj}_\mathbf{v}\mathbf{u} = \frac{\mathbf{u}\cdot\mathbf{v}}{\mathbf{v}\cdot\mathbf{v}}\mathbf{v} = \frac{4-3}{4+9}(0, 2, 3) = \left(0, \frac{2}{13}, \frac{3}{13}\right).$$

16. (a) $\langle\mathbf{u}, \mathbf{v}\rangle = 2(0)(\frac{4}{3}) + (3)(1) + 2(\frac{1}{3})(-3) = 1$

(b) $d(\mathbf{u},\mathbf{v}) = \|\mathbf{u} - \mathbf{v}\| = \sqrt{\langle\mathbf{u} - \mathbf{v}, \mathbf{u} - \mathbf{v}\rangle}$

$$= \sqrt{2\left(-\frac{4}{3}\right)^2 + 2^2 + 2\left(\frac{10}{3}\right)^2}$$

$$= \frac{\sqrt{268}}{3} = \frac{2}{3}\sqrt{67}$$

18. We verify the Triangle Inequality as follows.

$$\|\mathbf{u} + \mathbf{v}\| \leq \|\mathbf{u}\| + \|\mathbf{v}\|$$

$$\|(\tfrac{4}{3}, 4, -\tfrac{8}{3})\| \leq \sqrt{9 + 2(\tfrac{1}{9})} + \sqrt{2(\tfrac{16}{9}) + 1 + 18}$$

$$\sqrt{2(\tfrac{4}{3})^2 + 4^2 + 2(-\tfrac{8}{3})^2} \leq 3.037 + 4.749$$

$$5.812 \leq 7.786$$

We verify the Cauchy-Schwarz Inequality as follows.

$$|\langle \mathbf{u}, \mathbf{v}\rangle| \leq \|\mathbf{u}\|\,\|\mathbf{v}\|$$

$$1 \leq (3.037)(4.749|$$

$$1 \leq 14.423$$

20. A vector $\mathbf{v} = (v_1, v_2, v_3, v_4)$ that is orthogonal to $\mathbf{u} = (1, -2, 2, 1)$ must satisfy the equation

$$\mathbf{u} \cdot \mathbf{v} = (1, -2, 2, 1) \cdot (v_1, v_2, v_3, v_4) = v_1 - 2v_2 + 2v_3 + v_4 = 0.$$

This equation has solutions of the form $(2r - 2s - t, r, s, t)$, where r, s, and t are any real numbers.

22. First we orthogonalize the vectors in B.

$$\mathbf{w}_1 = (3, 4)$$

$$\mathbf{w}_2 = (1, 2) - \tfrac{11}{25}(3, 4) = \left(-\tfrac{8}{25}, \tfrac{6}{25}\right)$$

Then we normalize each vector.

$$\mathbf{u}_1 = \frac{1}{\|\mathbf{w}_1\|}\mathbf{w}_1 = \frac{1}{5}(3, 4) = \left(\frac{3}{5}, \frac{4}{5}\right)$$

$$\mathbf{u}_2 = \frac{1}{\|\mathbf{w}_2\|}\mathbf{w}_2 = \frac{1}{2/5}\left(-\frac{8}{25}, \frac{6}{25}\right) = \left(-\frac{4}{5}, \frac{3}{5}\right)$$

Thus, an orthonormal basis for R^2 is $\left\{\left(\tfrac{3}{5}, \tfrac{4}{5}\right), \left(-\tfrac{4}{5}, \tfrac{3}{5}\right)\right\}$.

24. First we orthogonalize the vectors in B.

$$\mathbf{w}_1 = (0, 0, 2)$$

$$\mathbf{w}_2 = (0, 1, 1) - \tfrac{2}{4}(0, 0, 2) = (0, 1, 0)$$

$$\mathbf{w}_3 = (1, 1, 1) - \tfrac{2}{4}(0, 0, 2) - \tfrac{1}{1}(0, 1, 0) = (1, 0, 0)$$

Then we normalize each vector to obtain the orthonormal basis for R^3.

$$\{(0, 0, 1), (0, 1, 0), (1, 0, 0)\}.$$

26. (a) To find $\mathbf{x} = (-3, 4, 4)$ as a linear combination of the vectors in

$B = \{(-1, 2, 2), (1, 0, 0)\}$ we solve the vector equation

$$c_1(-1, 2, 2) + c_2(1, 0, 0) = (-3, 4, 4).$$

The solution to the corresponding system of equations is $c_1 = 2$ and $c_2 = -1$.
Thus, $[\mathbf{x}]_B = (2, -1)$, and we can write

$$(-3, 4, 4) = 2(-1, 2, 2) - (1, 0, 0).$$

(b) To apply the Gram-Schmidt orthonormalization process, we first orthogonalize
each vector in B.

$$\mathbf{w}_1 = (-1, 2, 2)$$

$$\mathbf{w}_2 = (1, 0, 0) - \frac{-1}{9}(-1, 2, 2) = \left(\frac{8}{9}, \frac{2}{9}, \frac{2}{9}\right)$$

Then we normalize $\mathbf{w}_1$ and $\mathbf{w}_2$ as follows

$$\mathbf{u}_1 = \frac{1}{\|\mathbf{w}_1\|}\mathbf{w}_1 = \frac{1}{3}(-1, 2, 2) = \left(-\frac{1}{3}, \frac{2}{3}, \frac{2}{3}\right)$$

$$\mathbf{u}_2 = \frac{1}{\|\mathbf{w}_2\|}\mathbf{w}_2 = \frac{1}{2\sqrt{2}/3}\left(\frac{8}{9}, \frac{2}{9}, \frac{2}{9}\right) = \left(\frac{4}{3\sqrt{2}}, \frac{1}{3\sqrt{2}}, \frac{1}{3\sqrt{2}}\right)$$

Thus, $B' = \left\{\left(-\frac{1}{3}, \frac{2}{3}, \frac{2}{3}\right), \left(\frac{4}{3\sqrt{2}}, \frac{1}{3\sqrt{2}}, \frac{1}{3\sqrt{2}}\right)\right\}$.

(c) The coordinates of $\mathbf{x}$ relative to B' are found by calculating

$$\langle \mathbf{x}, \mathbf{u}_1 \rangle = (-3, 4, 4) \cdot \left(-\frac{1}{3}, \frac{2}{3}, \frac{2}{3}\right) = \frac{19}{3}$$

$$\langle \mathbf{x}, \mathbf{u}_2 \rangle = (-3, 4, 4) \cdot \left(\frac{4}{3\sqrt{2}}, \frac{1}{3\sqrt{2}}, \frac{1}{3\sqrt{2}}\right) = \frac{-4}{3\sqrt{2}}$$

Thus,

$$(-3, 4, 4) = \frac{19}{3}\left(-\frac{1}{3}, \frac{2}{3}, \frac{2}{3}\right) - \frac{4}{3\sqrt{2}}\left(\frac{4}{3\sqrt{2}}, \frac{1}{3\sqrt{2}}, \frac{1}{3\sqrt{2}}\right).$$

28. (a) $\langle f, g \rangle = \int_0^1 f(x)g(x)\, dx = \int_0^1 (x + 2)(15x - 8)\, dx$

$$= \int_0^1 (15x^2 + 22x - 16)dx = 5x^3 + 11x^2 - 16x \Big]_0^1 = 0$$

(b) $\langle -4f, g \rangle = -4\langle f, g \rangle = -4(0) = 0$

(c) Since

$$\langle f, f \rangle = \int_0^1 (x + 2)^2 dx = \int_0^1 (x^2 + 4x + 4)dx$$

$$= \frac{x^3}{3} + 2x^2 + 4x \Big]_0^1 = \frac{19}{3}$$

$$\| f \| = \sqrt{\langle f, f \rangle} = \sqrt{\frac{19}{3}}.$$

(d) Since f and g are already orthogonal, we only need to normalize them. We know $\| f \| = \sqrt{\frac{19}{3}}$ and so we compute $\| g \|$

$$\langle g, g \rangle = \int_0^1 (15x - 8)^2 dx = \int_0^1 (225x^2 - 240x + 64)dx$$

$$\langle g, g \rangle = 75x^3 - 120x^2 + 64x \Big]_0^1 = 19 \quad \Rightarrow \quad \| g \| = \sqrt{19}.$$

Hence,

$$\mathbf{u}_1 = \frac{1}{\| f \|}f = \frac{1}{\sqrt{\frac{19}{3}}}(x + 2) = \sqrt{\frac{3}{19}}(x + 2)$$

$$\mathbf{u}_2 = \frac{1}{\| g \|}g = \frac{1}{\sqrt{19}}(15x - 8).$$

The orthonormal set is $B' = \left\{ \left(\sqrt{\frac{3}{19}}x + 2\sqrt{\frac{3}{19}} \right), \left(\frac{15}{\sqrt{19}}x - \frac{8}{\sqrt{19}} \right) \right\}.$

30. The set is already orthogonal, as shown in Example 3, Section 5.3. Hence, we need to normalize each vector, and we obtain the orthonormal set

$$\left\{ \frac{1}{\sqrt{2\pi}}, \frac{1}{\sqrt{\pi}}\cos x, \frac{1}{\sqrt{\pi}}\sin x, \dots, \frac{1}{\sqrt{\pi}}\cos nx, \frac{1}{\sqrt{\pi}}\sin nx \right\}.$$

32. The solution space of the homogeneous system consists of vectors of the form $(-t, s, s, t)$, where s and t are any real numbers. Hence, a basis for the solution space is $B = \{(-1, 0, 0, 1), (0, 1, 1, 0)\}$. Since these vectors are orthogonal, and their length is $\sqrt{2}$, we normalize them to obtain the orthonormal basis

$$\left\{ \left(-\frac{\sqrt{2}}{2}, 0, 0, \frac{\sqrt{2}}{2} \right), \left(0, \frac{\sqrt{2}}{2}, \frac{\sqrt{2}}{2}, 0 \right) \right\}.$$

34. (a) $\langle f, g \rangle = \int_0^1 x \, 4x^2 \, dx = x^4 \Big]_0^1 = 1$

(b) The vectors are not orthogonal.

(c) Since $\|f\| = \sqrt{\dfrac{1}{3}}$ and $\|g\| = \dfrac{4}{\sqrt{5}}$,

we verify the Cauchy-Schwarz Inequality as follows

$$|\langle f, g \rangle| \le \|f\| \, \|g\|$$

$$1 \le \sqrt{\frac{1}{3}} \frac{4}{\sqrt{5}} \approx 1.0328.$$

36. We use the Triangle Inequality

$$\|\mathbf{u} + \mathbf{w}\| \le \|\mathbf{u}\| + \|\mathbf{w}\| \text{ with } \mathbf{w} = \mathbf{v} - \mathbf{u}$$

$$\|\mathbf{u} + \mathbf{w}\| = \|\mathbf{u} + (\mathbf{v} - \mathbf{u})\| = \|\mathbf{v}\| \le \|\mathbf{u}\| + \|\mathbf{v} - \mathbf{u}\|$$

and hence, $\|\mathbf{v}\| - \|\mathbf{u}\| \le \|\mathbf{v} - \mathbf{u}\|$. By symmetry, we also have

$$\|\mathbf{u}\| - \|\mathbf{v}\| \le \|\mathbf{u} - \mathbf{v}\| = \|\mathbf{v} - \mathbf{u}\|.$$

Hence,

$$\Big| \|\mathbf{u}\| - \|\mathbf{v}\| \Big| \le \|\mathbf{u} - \mathbf{v}\|.$$

To complete the proof, we first observe that the Triangle Inequality implies that

$$\|\mathbf{u} - \mathbf{w}\| \le \|\mathbf{u}\| + \|-\mathbf{w}\| = \|\mathbf{u}\| + \|\mathbf{w}\|.$$

Letting $\mathbf{w} = \mathbf{u} + \mathbf{v}$, we have

$$\|\mathbf{u} - \mathbf{w}\| = \|\mathbf{u} - (\mathbf{u} + \mathbf{v})\| = \|-\mathbf{v}\| = \|\mathbf{v}\| \le \|\mathbf{u}\| + \|\mathbf{u} + \mathbf{v}\|$$

and hence $\|\mathbf{v}\| - \|\mathbf{u}\| \le \|\mathbf{u} + \mathbf{v}\|$.

Similarly,

$$\|\mathbf{u}\| - \|\mathbf{v}\| \le \|\mathbf{u} + \mathbf{v}\|, \quad \text{and} \quad \Big| \|\mathbf{u}\| - \|\mathbf{v}\| \Big| \le \|\mathbf{u} + \mathbf{v}\|.$$

In conclusion, $\Big| \|\mathbf{u}\| - \|\mathbf{v}\| \Big| \le \|\mathbf{u} \pm \mathbf{v}\|$.

38. We extend the V-basis $\{(0, 1, 0, 1), (0, 2, 0, 0)\}$ to a basis of R^4.

$$B = \{(0, 1, 0, 1), (0, 2, 0, 0), (1, 0, 0, 0), (0, 0, 1, 0)\}$$

Now, $(1, 1, 1, 1) = (0, 1, 0, 1) + (1, 0, 1, 0)$

$$= \mathbf{v} + \mathbf{w}$$

where $\mathbf{v} \in V$ and $\mathbf{w}$ is orthogonal to every vector in V.

40. $(x_1 + x_2 + \cdots + x_n)^2 = (x_1 + x_2 + \cdots + x_n)(x_1 + x_2 + \cdots + x_n)$

$$= (x_1, \ldots, x_n) \cdot (x_1, \ldots, x_n) + (x_2, \ldots, x_n, x_1) \cdot (x_1, \ldots x_n)$$

$$+ \cdots + (x_n, x_1, \ldots, x_{n-1}) \cdot (x_1, \ldots, x_n)$$

$$\leq (x_1^2 + \cdots + x_n^2)^{\frac{1}{2}}(x_1^2 + \cdots + x_n^2)^{\frac{1}{2}}$$

$$+ (x_2^2 + \cdots + x_n^2 + x_1^2)^{\frac{1}{2}}(x_1^2 + \cdots + x_n^2)^{\frac{1}{2}} + \cdots$$

$$+ (x_n^2 + x_1^2 + \cdots + x_{n-1}^2)^{\frac{1}{2}}(x_1^2 + \cdots + x_n^2)^{\frac{1}{2}}$$

$$= n(x_1^2 + \cdots + x_n^2)$$

42. Let $\{\mathbf{u}_1, \mathbf{u}_2, \ldots, \mathbf{u}_n\}$ be a dependent set of vectors, and assume $\mathbf{u}_k$ is a linear combination of $\mathbf{u}_1, \mathbf{u}_2, \ldots, \mathbf{u}_{k-1}$, which are linearly independent. The Gram-Schmidt process will orthonormalize $\mathbf{u}_1, \ldots, \mathbf{u}_{k-1}$, but then $\mathbf{u}_k$ will be a linear combination of $\mathbf{u}_1, \ldots, \mathbf{u}_{k-1}$.

44. An orthonormal basis for S is

$$\left\{ \begin{bmatrix} 0 \\ \frac{-1}{\sqrt{2}} \\ \frac{1}{\sqrt{2}} \end{bmatrix}, \begin{bmatrix} 0 \\ \frac{1}{\sqrt{2}} \\ \frac{1}{\sqrt{2}} \end{bmatrix} \right\}$$

$$\text{proj}_s\mathbf{v} = (\mathbf{v} \cdot \mathbf{u}_1)\mathbf{u}_1 + (\mathbf{v} \cdot \mathbf{u}_2)\mathbf{u}_2$$

$$= \left(\frac{-2}{\sqrt{2}}\right)\begin{bmatrix} 0 \\ \frac{-1}{\sqrt{2}} \\ \frac{1}{\sqrt{2}} \end{bmatrix} + \left(-\frac{2}{\sqrt{2}}\right)\begin{bmatrix} 0 \\ \frac{1}{\sqrt{2}} \\ \frac{1}{\sqrt{2}} \end{bmatrix} = \begin{bmatrix} 0 \\ 0 \\ -2 \end{bmatrix}.$$

46. $A = \begin{bmatrix} 1 & -2 \\ 1 & -1 \\ 1 & 0 \\ 1 & 1 \end{bmatrix} \Rightarrow \mathbf{b} = \begin{bmatrix} 2 \\ 1 \\ 1 \\ 3 \end{bmatrix}$

$$A^TA = \begin{bmatrix} 4 & -2 \\ -2 & 6 \end{bmatrix}$$

$$A^T\mathbf{b} = \begin{bmatrix} 7 \\ -2 \end{bmatrix}$$

$$A^TA\mathbf{x} = A^T\mathbf{b} \Rightarrow \mathbf{x} = \begin{bmatrix} 1.9 \\ 0.3 \end{bmatrix} \Rightarrow y = 0.3x + 1.9$$

48. One model can be the least squares regression line. Let $x = 0$ correspond to 1990. We have:

$$A = \begin{bmatrix} 1 & 0 \\ 1 & 1 \\ 1 & 2 \\ 1 & 3 \\ 1 & 4 \\ 1 & 5 \\ 1 & 6 \\ 1 & 7 \\ 1 & 8 \\ 1 & 9 \end{bmatrix} \quad \text{and} \quad \mathbf{b} = \begin{bmatrix} 0.60 \\ 0.85 \\ 1.03 \\ 1.08 \\ 1.17 \\ 1.11 \\ 1.12 \\ 1.34 \\ 1.40 \\ 1.61 \end{bmatrix}.$$

Then

$$A^T A = \begin{bmatrix} 10 & 45 \\ 45 & 285 \end{bmatrix} \quad \text{and} \quad A^T \mathbf{b} = \begin{bmatrix} 11.31 \\ 58.17 \end{bmatrix}.$$

Using Gauss-Jordan elimination to solve $A^T A x = A^T \mathbf{b}$, we obtain

$$\begin{bmatrix} 10 & 45 & 11.31 \\ 45 & 285 & 58.17 \end{bmatrix} \implies \begin{bmatrix} 1 & 0 & 0.734181818 \\ 0 & 1 & 0.088181818 \end{bmatrix}.$$

Thus, the least squares regression line is $y \approx 0.734181818 + 0.088181818x$ where y is in millions of dollars and $x = 0$ corresponds to the year 1990.

50. The cross product is

$$\mathbf{u} \times \mathbf{v} = \begin{vmatrix} \mathbf{i} & \mathbf{j} & \mathbf{k} \\ 0 & 1 & 6 \\ 1 & -2 & 1 \end{vmatrix} = 13\mathbf{i} + 6\mathbf{j} - \mathbf{k} = (13, 6, -1).$$

Furthermore, $\mathbf{u} \times \mathbf{v}$ is orthogonal to both $\mathbf{u}$ and $\mathbf{v}$ because

$$\mathbf{u} \cdot (\mathbf{u} \times \mathbf{v}) = (0, 1, 6) \cdot (13, 6, -1) = 6 - 6 = 0$$

and

$$\mathbf{v} \cdot (\mathbf{u} \times \mathbf{v}) = (1, -2, 1) \cdot (13, 6, -1) = 13 - 12 - 1 = 0.$$

52. Since $\|\mathbf{u} \times \mathbf{v}\| = \|\mathbf{u}\| \|\mathbf{v}\| \sin \theta$, we see that $\mathbf{u}$ and $\mathbf{v}$ are orthogonal if and only if $\sin \theta = 1$, which means $\|\mathbf{u} \times \mathbf{v}\| = \|\mathbf{u}\| \|\mathbf{v}\|$.

54. Since

$$\mathbf{v} \times \mathbf{w} = \begin{vmatrix} \mathbf{i} & \mathbf{j} & \mathbf{k} \\ -1 & -1 & 0 \\ 3 & 4 & -1 \end{vmatrix} = \mathbf{i} - \mathbf{j} - \mathbf{k} = (1, -1, -1),$$

the volume is

$$\left| \mathbf{u} \cdot (\mathbf{v} \times \mathbf{w}) \right| = \left| (1, 2, 1) \cdot (1, -1, -1) \right| = \left| -2 \right| = 2.$$

56. The standard basis for P_1 is $\{1, x\}$. In $C[0, 2]$, the Gram-Schmidt orthonormalization process yields the orthonormal basis $\left\{\dfrac{1}{\sqrt{2}}, \dfrac{\sqrt{3}}{\sqrt{2}}(x - 1)\right\}$.

Since

$$\langle f, \mathbf{w}_1 \rangle = \int_0^2 x^3 \frac{1}{\sqrt{2}}\, dx = \frac{4}{\sqrt{2}}$$

$$\langle f, \mathbf{w}_2 \rangle = \int_0^2 x^3 \frac{\sqrt{3}}{\sqrt{2}}(x - 1)\, dx = \frac{\sqrt{3}}{\sqrt{2}} \int_0^2 (x^4 - x^3)\, dx$$

$$= \frac{\sqrt{3}}{\sqrt{2}}\left(\frac{x^5}{5} - \frac{x^4}{4}\right)\Bigg]_0^2$$

$$= \frac{\sqrt{3}}{\sqrt{2}}\left(\frac{32}{5} - 4\right) = \frac{\sqrt{3}}{\sqrt{2}}\left(\frac{12}{5}\right).$$

g is given by

$$g(x) = \langle f, \mathbf{w}_1 \rangle + \langle f, \mathbf{w}_2 \rangle \mathbf{w}_2$$

$$= \frac{4}{\sqrt{2}}\left(\frac{1}{\sqrt{2}}\right) + \frac{\sqrt{3}}{\sqrt{2}}\left(\frac{12}{5}\right)\frac{\sqrt{3}}{\sqrt{2}}(x - 1) = \frac{18}{5}x - \frac{8}{5}.$$

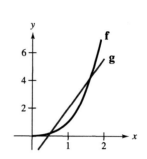

58. The standard basis for P_1 is $\{1, x\}$. In $C[0, \pi]$, the Gram-Schmidt orthonormalization process yields the orthonormal basis

$$\left\{\frac{1}{\sqrt{\pi}}, \frac{\sqrt{3}}{\pi^{3/2}}(2x - \pi)\right\}.$$

Since

$$\langle f, \mathbf{w}_1 \rangle = \int_0^\pi \sin x \cos x \, \frac{1}{\sqrt{\pi}}\, dx = 0$$

$$\langle f, \mathbf{w}_2 \rangle = \int_0^\pi \sin x \cos x \left(\frac{\sqrt{3}}{\pi^{3/2}}\right)(2x - \pi)\, dx = -\frac{\sqrt{3}}{2\pi^{1/2}}$$

g is given by

$$g(x) = \langle f, \mathbf{w}_1 \rangle \mathbf{w}_1 + \langle f, \mathbf{w}_2 \rangle \mathbf{w}_2$$

$$= 0\left(\frac{1}{\sqrt{\pi}}\right) + \left(-\frac{\sqrt{3}}{2\pi^{1/2}}\right)\left(\frac{\sqrt{3}}{\pi^{3/2}}(2x - \pi)\right)$$

$$= -\frac{3x}{\pi^2} + \frac{3}{2\pi}$$

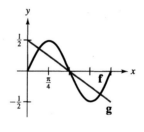

60. The standard basis for P_2 is $\{1, x, x^2\}$. In $C[1, 2]$, the Gram-Schmidt orthonormalization process yields the orthonormal basis

$$\left\{1, 2\sqrt{3}\left(x - \frac{3}{2}\right), \frac{30}{\sqrt{5}}\left(x^2 - 3x + \frac{13}{6}\right)\right\}.$$

—CONTINUED—

60. —CONTINUED—

Since

$$\langle f, \mathbf{w}_1 \rangle = \int_1^2 \frac{1}{x} \, dx = \ln 2$$

$$\langle f, \mathbf{w}_2 \rangle = \int_1^2 \frac{1}{x} 2\sqrt{3} \left(x - \frac{3}{2} \right) dx = 2\sqrt{3} \int_1^2 \left(1 - \frac{3}{2x} \right) dx$$

$$= 2\sqrt{3} \left(1 - \frac{3}{2} \ln 2 \right)$$

$$\langle f, \mathbf{w}_3 \rangle = \int_1^2 \frac{1}{x} \frac{30}{\sqrt{5}} \left(x^2 - 3x + \frac{13}{6} \right) dx = \frac{30}{\sqrt{5}} \int_1^2 \left(x - 3 + \frac{13}{6x} \right) dx$$

$$= \frac{30}{\sqrt{5}} \left(\frac{13}{6} \ln 2 - \frac{3}{2} \right),$$

g is given by $g(x)$

$$= \langle f, \mathbf{w}_1 \rangle \mathbf{w}_1 + \langle f, \mathbf{w}_2 \rangle \mathbf{w}_2 + \langle f, \mathbf{w}_3 \rangle \mathbf{w}_3$$

$$= (\ln 2) + 2\sqrt{3} \left(1 - \frac{3}{2} \ln 2 \right) 2\sqrt{3} \left(x - \frac{3}{2} \right) + \frac{30}{\sqrt{5}} \left(\frac{13}{6} \ln 2 - \frac{3}{2} \right) \frac{30}{\sqrt{5}} \left(x^2 - 3x + \frac{13}{6} \right)$$

$$= \ln 2 + 12 \left(1 - \frac{3}{2} \ln 2 \right) \left(x - \frac{3}{2} \right) + 180 \left(\frac{13}{6} \ln 2 - \frac{3}{2} \right) \left(x^2 - 3x + \frac{13}{6} \right)$$

$$= .3274x^2 - 1.459x + 2.1175.$$

62. We find the coefficients as follows

$$a_0 = \frac{1}{\pi} \int_{-\pi}^{\pi} f(x) \, dx = \frac{1}{\pi} \int_{-\pi}^{\pi} x \, dx = 0$$

$$a_j = \frac{1}{\pi} \int_{-\pi}^{\pi} x \cos(jx) \, dx = \frac{1}{\pi} \left[\frac{1}{j^2} \cos(jx) + \frac{x}{j} \sin(jx) \right]_{-\pi}^{\pi}$$

$$= 0, \quad j = 1, 2 \ldots$$

$$b_j = \frac{1}{\pi} \int_{-\pi}^{\pi} x \sin(jx) = \frac{1}{\pi} \left[\frac{1}{j^2} \sin(jx) - \frac{x}{j} \cos(jx) \right]_{-\pi}^{\pi}$$

$$= -\frac{2}{j} \cos(\pi j) \quad j = 1, 2, \ldots$$

Thus, the approximation is

$$g(x) = \frac{a_0}{2} + a_1 \cos x + a_2 \cos 2x + b_1 \sin x + b_2 \sin 2x$$

$$= 2 \sin x - \sin 2x.$$

64. (a) *True.* See note following Theorem 5.17, page 329.

    (b) *True.* See Theorem 5.18, part 3, page 330.

    (c) *True.* See discussion starting on page 337.

Chapter 5 ❏ Project Solutions

1 The *QR*-factorization

1. $A = QR$

2. (a) $A = \begin{bmatrix} 1 & 1 \\ 0 & 1 \\ 1 & 0 \end{bmatrix} = \begin{bmatrix} .7071 & .4082 \\ 0 & .8165 \\ .7071 & -.4082 \end{bmatrix} \begin{bmatrix} 1.4142 & 0.7071 \\ 0 & 1.2247 \end{bmatrix} = QR$

    (b) $A = \begin{bmatrix} 1 & 0 \\ 0 & 0 \\ 1 & 1 \\ 1 & 2 \end{bmatrix} = \begin{bmatrix} .5774 & -.7071 \\ 0 & 0 \\ .5774 & 0 \\ .5774 & .7071 \end{bmatrix} \begin{bmatrix} 1.7321 & 1.7321 \\ 0 & 1.4142 \end{bmatrix} = QR$

    (c) $A = \begin{bmatrix} 1 & 0 & 0 \\ 1 & 1 & 0 \\ 1 & 1 & 1 \end{bmatrix} = \begin{bmatrix} .5774 & -.8165 & 0 \\ .5774 & .4082 & -.7071 \\ .5774 & .4082 & .7071 \end{bmatrix} \begin{bmatrix} 1.7321 & 1.1547 & .5774 \\ 0 & .8165 & .4082 \\ 0 & 0 & .7071 \end{bmatrix} = QR$

    (d) $A = \begin{bmatrix} 1 & 0 & -1 \\ 1 & 2 & 0 \\ 1 & 2 & 0 \\ 1 & 0 & 0 \end{bmatrix} = \begin{bmatrix} .5 & -.5 & -.7071 \\ .5 & .5 & 0 \\ .5 & .5 & 0 \\ .5 & -.5 & .7071 \end{bmatrix} \begin{bmatrix} 2 & 2 & -.5 \\ 0 & 2 & .5 \\ 0 & 0.7071 \end{bmatrix} = QR$

3. The normal equations simplify using $A = QR$ as follows

$$A^T A \mathbf{x} = A^T \mathbf{b}$$
$$(QR)^T QR \mathbf{x} = (QR)^T \mathbf{b}$$
$$R^T Q^T QR \mathbf{x} = R^T Q^T \mathbf{b}$$
$$R^T R \mathbf{x} = R^T Q^T \mathbf{b} \quad (Q^T Q = I)$$
$$R \mathbf{x} = Q^T \mathbf{b}.$$

Since R is upper triangular, only back-substitution is needed.

4. $A = \begin{bmatrix} 1 & 1 \\ 0 & 1 \\ 1 & 0 \end{bmatrix} = \begin{bmatrix} .7071 & .4082 \\ 0 & .8165 \\ .7071 & -.4082 \end{bmatrix} \begin{bmatrix} 1.4142 & 0.7071 \\ 0 & 1.2247 \end{bmatrix} = QR.$

$R\mathbf{x} = Q^T\mathbf{b}$

$\begin{bmatrix} 1.4142 & 0.7071 \\ 0 & 1.2247 \end{bmatrix} \begin{bmatrix} x_1 \\ x_2 \end{bmatrix} = \begin{bmatrix} .7071 & 0 & .7071 \\ .4082 & .8165 & -.4082 \end{bmatrix} \begin{bmatrix} -1 \\ 1 \\ -1 \end{bmatrix} = \begin{bmatrix} -1.4142 \\ 0.8165 \end{bmatrix}$

$\Rightarrow \quad \begin{bmatrix} x_1 \\ x_2 \end{bmatrix} = \begin{bmatrix} -1.3333 \\ 0.6667 \end{bmatrix}$

2 Orthogonal Matrices and Change of Basis

1. $P^{-1} = \begin{bmatrix} -1 & 2 \\ -2 & 3 \end{bmatrix} \neq P^T$

2. $\begin{bmatrix} \cos\theta & -\sin\theta \\ \sin\theta & \cos\theta \end{bmatrix}^{-1} = \begin{bmatrix} \cos\theta & \sin\theta \\ -\sin\theta & \cos\theta \end{bmatrix} = \begin{bmatrix} \cos\theta & -\sin\theta \\ \sin\theta & \cos\theta \end{bmatrix}^T$

3. If $P^{-1} = P^T$, then $P^TP = I \implies$ columns of P are pairwise orthogonal.

4. If P is orthogonal, then $P^{-1} = P^T$ by definition of orthogonal matrix. Then $(P^{-1})^{-1} = (P^T)^{-1} = (P^{-1})^T$. The last equality holds because $(A^T)^{-1} = (A^{-1})^T$ for any invertible matrix A. Thus, P^{-1} is orthogonal.

5. No. For example, $\begin{bmatrix} 1 & 0 \\ 0 & 1 \end{bmatrix} + \begin{bmatrix} 1 & 0 \\ 0 & 1 \end{bmatrix} = \begin{bmatrix} 2 & 0 \\ 0 & 2 \end{bmatrix}$ is not orthogonal.

   The product of orthogonal matrices is orthogonal. If $P^{-1} = P^T$ and $Q^{-1} = Q^T$, then $(PQ)^{-1} = Q^{-1}P^{-1} = Q^TP^T = (PQ)^T$.

6. $\det P = \pm 1$ because $1 = \det I = \det P^TP = (\det P)^2$.

7. $\|P\mathbf{x}\| = (P\mathbf{x})^TP\mathbf{x} = \mathbf{x}^TP^TP\mathbf{x} = \mathbf{x}^T\mathbf{x} = \|\mathbf{x}\|$

8. Let

   $$P = \begin{bmatrix} -\dfrac{2}{\sqrt{5}} & \dfrac{1}{\sqrt{5}} \\ \dfrac{1}{\sqrt{5}} & \dfrac{2}{\sqrt{5}} \end{bmatrix}$$

   be the change of basis matrix from B' to B. Since P is orthogonal, lengths are preserved.

CHAPTER 6
Linear Transformations

Section 6.1   Introduction to Linear Transformations

2. (a) The image of **v** is

$$T(0, 6) = (2(6) - 0, 0, 6) = (12, 0, 6).$$

(b) If $T(v_1, v_2) = (2v_2 - v_1, v_1, v_2) = (3, 1, 2)$, then

$$2v_2 - v_1 = 3$$
$$v_1 = 1$$
$$v_2 = 2$$

which implies that the preimage of **w** is $(v_1, v_2) = (1, 2)$.

4. (a) The image of **v** is

$$T(-4, 5, 1) = (2(-4) + 5, 2(5) - 3(-4), -4 - 1) = (-3, 22, -5).$$

(b) If $T(v_1, v_2, v_3) = (2v_1, +v_2, 2v_2 - 3v_1, v_1 - v_3) = (4, 1, -1)$, then

$$2v_1 + v_2 \quad = \quad 4$$
$$-3v_1 + 2v_2 \quad = \quad 1$$
$$v_1 \quad - v_3 = -1$$

which implies that $v_1 = 1$, $v_2 = 2$ and $v_3 = 2$. Thus, the preimage of **w** is $(1, 2, 2)$.

6. (a) The image of **v** is

$$T(1, 1) = \left(\frac{\sqrt{2}}{2}(1) - \frac{\sqrt{2}}{2}(1), 1 + 1, 2(1) - 1\right) = (0, 2, 1).$$

(b) If $T(v_1, v_2) = \left(\frac{\sqrt{2}}{2}v_1 - \frac{\sqrt{2}}{2}v_2, v_1 + v_2, 2v_1 - v_2\right) = (-5\sqrt{2}, -2, -16)$,

then

$$\frac{\sqrt{2}}{2}v_1 - \frac{\sqrt{2}}{2}v_2 = -5\sqrt{2}$$

$$v_1 + \quad v_2 = -2$$

$$2v_1 - \quad v_2 = -16$$

which implies that $v_1 = -6$ and $v_2 = 4$. Thus, the preimage of **w** is $(-6, 4)$.

8. *T* preserves addition.

$$T(x_1, y_1, z_1) + T(x_2, y_2, z_2) = (x_1 + y_1, x_1 - y_1, z_1) + (x_2 + y_2, x_2 - y_2, z_2)$$
$$= (x_1 + y_1 + x_2 + y_2, x_1 - y_1 + x_2 - y_2, z_1 + z_2)$$
$$= ((x_1 + x_2) + (y_1 + y_2), (x_1 + x_2) - (y_1 + y_2), z_1 + z_2)$$
$$= T(x_1 + x_2, y_1 + y_2, z_1 + z_2)$$

T preserves scalar multiplication.

$$T(c(x, y, z)) = T(cx, cy, cz)$$
$$= (cx + cy, cx - cy, cz)$$
$$= c(x + y, x - y, z)$$
$$= cT(x, y, z)$$

Therefore, *T is* a linear transformation.

10. *T* is *not* a linear transformation because it does not preserve addition nor scalar multiplication. For example, $T(I_2) = 1$ but $T(2I_2) = 4 \neq 2T(I_2)$.

12. *T* preserves addition.

$$T(A_1 + A_2) = (A_1 + A_2)^T = A_1^T + A_2^T = T(A_1) + T(A_2)$$

T preserves scalar multiplication.

$$T(cA) = (cA)^T = c(A^T) = cT(A).$$

Therefore, *T is* a linear transformation.

14. *T* preserves addition.

$$T(a_0 + a_1x + a_2x^2) + T(b_0 + b_1x + b_2x^2) = (a_1 + 2a_2x) + (b_1 + 2b_2x)$$
$$= (a_1 + b_1) + 2(a_2 + b_2)x$$
$$= T((a_0 + b_0) + (a_1 + b_1)x + (a_2 + b_2)x^2)$$

T preserves scalar multiplication.

$$T(c(a_0 + a_1x + a_2x^2)) = T(ca_0 + ca_1x + ca_2x^2)$$
$$= ca_1 + 2ca_2x$$
$$= c(a_1 + 2a_2x)$$
$$= cT(a_0 + a_1x + a_2x^2)$$

Therefore, *T is* a linear transformation.

16. Because $(2, -1, 0)$ can be written as

$$(2, -1, 0) = 2(1, 0, 0) - 1(0, 1, 0) + 0(0, 0, 1),$$

we can use Property 4 of Theorem 6.1 to write

$$T(2, -1, 0) = 2T(1, 0, 0) - T(0, 1, 0) + 0T(0, 0, 1)$$
$$= 2(2, 4, -1) - (1, 3, -2) + (0, 0, 0)$$
$$= (3, 5, 0).$$

18. Because $(-2, 4, -1)$ can be written as

$$(-2, 4, -1) = -2(1, 0, 0) + 4(0, 1, 0) - 1(0, 0, 1),$$

we can use Property 4 of Theorem 6.1 to write

$$\begin{aligned} T(-2, 4, -1) &= -2T(1, 0, 0) + 4T(0, 1, 0) - T(0, 0, 1) \\ &= -2(2, 4, -1) + 4(1, 3, -2) - (0, -2, 2) \\ &= (0, 6, -8). \end{aligned}$$

20. Since the matrix has 2 columns, the dimension of R^n is 2. Since the matrix has 3 rows, the dimension of R^m is 3. Thus $T: R^2 \rightarrow R^3$.

22. Since the matrix has 4 columns and 4 rows it defines a linear transformation from R^4 to R^4.

24. The linear transformation is defined by

$$A = \begin{bmatrix} 0 & 1 & -2 & 1 \\ -1 & 4 & 5 & 0 \\ 0 & 1 & 3 & 1 \end{bmatrix},$$

i.e., $T(\mathbf{v}) = A\mathbf{v}$ for any $\mathbf{v}$ in R^4.

(a) $T(1, 0, 2, 3) = A \cdot \begin{bmatrix} 1 \\ 0 \\ 2 \\ 3 \end{bmatrix} = \begin{bmatrix} -1 \\ 9 \\ 9 \end{bmatrix}.$

(b) We need to solve $T(x, y, z, w) = (0, 0, 0)$. Using Gauss-Jordan elimination we find that solution of resulting system is $t(-4, -1, 0, 1)$ for any real number t.

26. (a) $T(1, 0, -1, 3, 0) = \begin{bmatrix} -1 & 2 & 1 & 3 & 4 \\ 0 & 0 & 2 & -1 & 0 \end{bmatrix} \begin{bmatrix} 1 \\ 0 \\ -1 \\ 3 \\ 0 \end{bmatrix} = \begin{bmatrix} 7 \\ -5 \end{bmatrix} = (7, -5).$

(b) The preimage of $(-1, 8)$ is determined by solving the equation

$$T(v_1, v_2, v_3, v_4, v_5) = \begin{bmatrix} -1 & 2 & 1 & 3 & 4 \\ 0 & 0 & 2 & -1 & 0 \end{bmatrix} \begin{bmatrix} v_1 \\ v_2 \\ v_3 \\ v_4 \\ v_5 \end{bmatrix} = \begin{bmatrix} -1 \\ 8 \end{bmatrix}$$

for $(v_1, v_2, v_3, v_4, v_5)$. The equivalent system of linear equations has the solution $v_1 = 5 + 2r + \frac{7}{2}s + 4t$, $v_2 = r$, $v_3 = 4 + \frac{1}{2}s$, $v_4 = s$, and $v_5 = t$, where r, s, and t are any real numbers. Thus, the preimage is given by the set of vectors

$$\left\{ \left(5 + 2r + \tfrac{7}{2}s + 4t, r, 4 + \tfrac{1}{2}s, s, t\right) \middle| r, s, t \text{ are real numbers} \right\}.$$

28. (a) $T(1, 1) = \begin{bmatrix} 0 & -1 \\ -1 & 0 \end{bmatrix} \begin{bmatrix} 1 \\ 1 \end{bmatrix} = \begin{bmatrix} -1 \\ -1 \end{bmatrix} = (-1, -1).$

(b) The preimage of $(1, 1)$ is determined by solving the equation

$$T(v_1, v_2) = \begin{bmatrix} 0 & -1 \\ -1 & 0 \end{bmatrix} \begin{bmatrix} v_1 \\ v_2 \end{bmatrix} = \begin{bmatrix} 1 \\ 1 \end{bmatrix}$$

for (v_1, v_2). The equivalent system of linear equations has the solution $v_1 = -1$ and $v_2 = -1$. Thus, the preimage is $(-1, -1)$.

(c) The preimage of $(0, 0)$ is determined by solving the equation

$$T(v_1, v_2) = \begin{bmatrix} 0 & -1 \\ -1 & 0 \end{bmatrix} \begin{bmatrix} v_1 \\ v_2 \end{bmatrix} = \begin{bmatrix} 0 \\ 0 \end{bmatrix}$$

for (v_1, v_2). The equivalent system of linear equations has the solution $v_1 = 0$ and $v_2 = 0$. Thus, the preimage is $(0, 0)$.

30. If $\theta = 45°$, then T is given by

$$T(x, y) = (x \cos \theta - y \sin \theta, x \sin \theta + y \cos \theta) = \left(\frac{\sqrt{2}}{2}x - \frac{\sqrt{2}}{2}y, \frac{\sqrt{2}}{2}x + \frac{\sqrt{2}}{2}y \right).$$

Solving $T(x, y) = \mathbf{v} = (1, 1)$, we have

$$\frac{\sqrt{2}}{2}x - \frac{\sqrt{2}}{2}y = 1 \quad \text{and} \quad \frac{\sqrt{2}}{2}x + \frac{\sqrt{2}}{2}y = 1.$$

Hence, $x = \sqrt{2}$ and $y = 0$, and the preimage of $\mathbf{v}$ is $\left(\sqrt{2}, 0 \right)$.

32. (a) If $D_x(g(x)) = 2x + 1,$ then $g(x) = x^2 + x + C.$

(b) If $D_x(g(x)) = e^x,$ then $g(x) = e^x + C.$

(c) If $D_x(g(x)) = \sin x,$ then $g(x) = -\cos x + C.$

34. We solve the equation $\int_0^1 p(x)dx = 1$ for $p(x)$ in P_2.

$$\int_0^1 (a_0 + a_1 x + a_2 x^2)dx = 1 \implies \left[a_0 x + a_1 \frac{x^2}{2} + a_2 \frac{x^3}{3} \right]_0^1 = 1$$

$$\implies a_0 + \frac{1}{2}a_1 + \frac{1}{3}a_2 = 1.$$

Letting $a_2 = -3b$ and $a_1 = -2a$ be free variables,
$a_0 = 1 + a + b,$ and $p(x) = (1 + a + b) - 2ax - 3bx^2.$

36. Since $(1, 4) = 1(1, 0) + 4(0, 1)$, we have

$$\begin{aligned} T(1, 4) &= T[(1, 0) + 4(0, 1)] \\ &= T(1, 0) + 4T(0, 1) \\ &= (1, 1) + 4(-1, 1) = (-3, 5). \end{aligned}$$

Similarly, $(-2, 1) = -2(1, 0) + 1(0, 1)$, which gives

$$\begin{aligned} T(-2, 1) &= T[-2(1, 0) + (0, 1)] \\ &= -2T(1, 0) + T(0, 1) \\ &= -2(1, 1) + (-1, 1) \\ &= (-3, -1). \end{aligned}$$

38. $T\left(\begin{bmatrix} 1 & 3 \\ -1 & 4 \end{bmatrix}\right) = T\begin{bmatrix} 1 & 0 \\ 0 & 0 \end{bmatrix} + 3T\begin{bmatrix} 0 & 1 \\ 0 & 0 \end{bmatrix} - T\begin{bmatrix} 0 & 0 \\ 1 & 0 \end{bmatrix} + 4T\begin{bmatrix} 0 & 0 \\ 0 & 1 \end{bmatrix}$

$$= \begin{bmatrix} 1 & -1 \\ 0 & 2 \end{bmatrix} + 3\begin{bmatrix} 0 & 2 \\ 1 & 1 \end{bmatrix} - \begin{bmatrix} 1 & 2 \\ 0 & 1 \end{bmatrix} + 4\begin{bmatrix} 3 & -1 \\ 1 & 0 \end{bmatrix} = \begin{bmatrix} 12 & -1 \\ 7 & 4 \end{bmatrix}$$

40. (a) *False.* A linear transformation is *always* operation preserving.

(b) *False.* This function does not preserve addition nor scalar multiplication. For example, $f(3x) = 27x^3 \neq 3f(x)$.

(c) *False.* If $f: R \to R$ is given by $f(x) = ax + b$ for some $a, b \in R$, then it preserves addition and scalar multiplication if and only if $b = 0$.

42. (a) $T(x, y) = T[x(1, 0) + y(0, 1)] = xT(1, 0) + yT(0, 1) = x(0, 1) + y(1, 0) = (y, x)$

(b) T is a reflection about the line $y = x$.

44. From the result of Exercise 43, where $(x, y) = (5, 0)$,

$$T(x, y) = \left(\frac{x + y}{2}, \frac{x + y}{2}\right) = \left(\frac{5}{2}, \frac{5}{2}\right).$$

46. From the result of Exercise 43,

$$T(c\mathbf{u}) = T[c(x, y)] = T(cx, cy) = \left(\frac{cx + cy}{2}, \frac{cx + cy}{2}\right)$$

$$= c\left(\frac{x + y}{2}, \frac{x + y}{2}\right) = cT(x, y) = cT(\mathbf{u}).$$

48. We observe that

$$A\mathbf{u} = \begin{bmatrix} \frac{1}{2} & \frac{1}{2} \\ \frac{1}{2} & \frac{1}{2} \end{bmatrix}\begin{bmatrix} x \\ y \end{bmatrix} = \begin{bmatrix} \frac{1}{2}x + \frac{1}{2}y \\ \frac{1}{2}x + \frac{1}{2}y \end{bmatrix} = T(\mathbf{u}).$$

50. Let F be the set of fixed points of $T: V \to V$. F is nonempty since $\mathbf{0} \in F$. Furthermore, if $\mathbf{u}, \mathbf{v} \in F$, then $T(\mathbf{u} + \mathbf{v}) = T(\mathbf{u}) + T(\mathbf{v}) = \mathbf{u} + \mathbf{v}$ and $T(c\mathbf{u}) = cT(\mathbf{u}) = c\mathbf{u}$, which shows that F is closed under addition and scalar multiplication.

52. A vector $\mathbf{u}$ is a fixed point if $T(\mathbf{u}) = \mathbf{u}$. Since $T(x, y) = (y, x)$ has solutions $x = y$, the set of fixed points of T is $\{(x, x) \,|\, x \text{ is any real number}\}$.

54. $T(0, \quad 0) = (0 - 2, \quad 0 + 1) = (-2, 1)$
$T(2, -1) = (2 - 2, -1 + 1) = (\quad 0, 0)$
$T(5, \quad 4) = (5 - 2, \quad 4 + 1) = (\quad 3, 5)$

56. Since $\{\mathbf{v}_1, \ldots, \mathbf{v}_n\}$ are linearly dependent, there exist constants $c_1, \ldots, c_n$, not all zero, such that $c_1\mathbf{v}_1 + \cdots + c_n\mathbf{v}_n = \mathbf{0}$. Hence,

$$T(c_1\mathbf{v}_1 + \cdots + c_n\mathbf{v}_n) = c_1T(\mathbf{v}_1) + \cdots + c_nT(\mathbf{v}_n) = \mathbf{0},$$

which shows that the set $\{T(\mathbf{v}_1), \ldots, T(\mathbf{v}_n)\}$ is linearly dependent.

58. Let $T(\mathbf{v}) = \mathbf{0}$ be the zero transformation. Since $T(\mathbf{u} + \mathbf{v}) = \mathbf{0} = T(\mathbf{u}) + T(\mathbf{v})$ and $T(c\mathbf{u}) = \mathbf{0} = cT(\mathbf{u})$, T is a linear transformation.

60. Let T be defined by $T(\mathbf{v}) = \langle \mathbf{v}, \mathbf{v}_0 \rangle$. Then since

$$T(\mathbf{v} + \mathbf{w}) = \langle \mathbf{v} + \mathbf{w}, \mathbf{v}_0 \rangle = \langle \mathbf{v}, \mathbf{v}_0 \rangle + \langle \mathbf{w}, \mathbf{v}_0 \rangle = T(\mathbf{v}) + T(\mathbf{w})$$

and $T(c\mathbf{v}) = \langle c\mathbf{v}, \mathbf{v}_0 \rangle = c\langle \mathbf{v}, \mathbf{v}_0 \rangle = cT(\mathbf{v})$, T is a linear transformation.

62. Since

$$
\begin{aligned}
T(\mathbf{u} + \mathbf{v}) &= \langle \mathbf{u} + \mathbf{v}, \mathbf{w}_1 \rangle \mathbf{w}_1 + \cdots + \langle \mathbf{u} + \mathbf{v}, \mathbf{w}_n \rangle \mathbf{w}_n \\
&= (\langle \mathbf{u}, \mathbf{w}_1 \rangle \mathbf{w}_1 + \langle \mathbf{v}, \mathbf{w}_1 \rangle \mathbf{w}_1) + \cdots + (\langle \mathbf{u}, \mathbf{w}_n \rangle \mathbf{w}_n + \langle \mathbf{v}, \mathbf{w}_n \rangle \mathbf{w}_n) \\
&= (\langle \mathbf{u}, \mathbf{w}_1 \rangle \mathbf{w}_1 + \cdots + \langle \mathbf{u}, \mathbf{w}_n \rangle \mathbf{w}_n) + \langle \mathbf{v}, \mathbf{w}_1 \rangle \mathbf{w}_1 + \cdots + \langle \mathbf{v}, \mathbf{w}_n \rangle \mathbf{w}_n \\
&= T(\mathbf{u}) + T(\mathbf{v})
\end{aligned}
$$

and

$$
\begin{aligned}
T(c\mathbf{u}) &= \langle c\mathbf{u}, \mathbf{w}_1 \rangle \mathbf{w}_1 + \cdots + \langle c\mathbf{u}, \mathbf{w}_n \rangle \mathbf{w}_n \\
&= c\langle \mathbf{u}, \mathbf{w}_1 \rangle \mathbf{w}_1 + \cdots + c\langle \mathbf{u}, \mathbf{w}_n \rangle \mathbf{w}_n \\
&= c[\langle \mathbf{u}, \mathbf{w}_1 \rangle \mathbf{w}_1 + \cdots + \langle \mathbf{u}, \mathbf{w}_n \rangle \mathbf{w}_n] \\
&= cT(\mathbf{u})
\end{aligned}
$$

T is a linear transformation.

64. Suppose first that T is a linear transformation. Then

$$
\begin{aligned}
T(a\mathbf{u} + b\mathbf{v}) &= T(a\mathbf{u}) + T(b\mathbf{v}) \\
&= aT(\mathbf{u}) + bT(\mathbf{v}).
\end{aligned}
$$

Second, suppose $T(a\mathbf{u} + b\mathbf{v}) = aT(\mathbf{u}) + bT(\mathbf{v})$. Then

$$
\begin{aligned}
T(\mathbf{u} + \mathbf{v}) &= T(1\mathbf{u} + 1\mathbf{v}) \\
&= T(\mathbf{u}) + T(\mathbf{v})
\end{aligned}
$$

and

$$
\begin{aligned}
T(c\mathbf{u}) &= T(c\mathbf{u} + \mathbf{0}) \\
&= cT(\mathbf{u}) + T(\mathbf{0}) \\
&= cT(\mathbf{u}).
\end{aligned}
$$

Section 6.2   The Kernel and Range of a Linear Transformation

2. Solving the equation $T(x, y, z, w) = (y, x, w, z) = (0, 0, 0, 0)$ yields that trivial solution $x = y = z = w = 0$. Thus, $\ker(T) = \{(0, 0, 0, 0)\}$.

4. Solving the equation $T(a_0 + a_1x + a_2x^2) = a_1 + 2a_2x = 0$ yields solutions of the form $a_1 = a_2 = 0$, and a_0 any real number. Thus, $\ker(T) = \{a_0 | a_0 \in R\}$.

6. Solving the equation $T(x, y) = (x - y, y - x) = (0, 0)$ yields solutions of the form $x = y$. Thus, $\ker(T) = \{(x, x) | x \in R\}$.

8. (a) Since

$$T(\mathbf{v}) = \begin{bmatrix} 1 & 2 \\ -2 & -4 \end{bmatrix} \begin{bmatrix} v_1 \\ v_2 \end{bmatrix} = \begin{bmatrix} 0 \\ 0 \end{bmatrix}$$

has solutions of the form $(-2t, t)$ where t is any real number, a basis for $\ker(T)$ is $\{(-2, 1)\}$.

(b) We transpose A and find the equivalent reduced row-echelon form

$$A^T = \begin{bmatrix} 1 & -2 \\ 2 & -4 \end{bmatrix} \implies \begin{bmatrix} 1 & -2 \\ 0 & 0 \end{bmatrix}.$$

Thus, a basis for range (T) is $\{(1, -2)\}$.

10. (a) Since

$$T(\mathbf{v}) = \begin{bmatrix} 1 & 2 \\ -1 & -2 \\ 1 & 1 \end{bmatrix} \begin{bmatrix} v_1 \\ v_2 \end{bmatrix} = \begin{bmatrix} 0 \\ 0 \\ 0 \end{bmatrix}$$

has only the trivial solution $v_1 = v_2 = 0$, the kernel is $\{(0, 0)\}$.

(b) We transpose A and find the equivalent reduced row-echelon form.

$$A^T = \begin{bmatrix} 1 & -1 & 1 \\ 2 & -2 & 1 \end{bmatrix} \implies \begin{bmatrix} 1 & -1 & 0 \\ 0 & 0 & 1 \end{bmatrix}$$

Thus, a basis for range (T) is $\{(1, -1, 0), (0, 0, 1)\}$.

12. (a) Since

$$T(\mathbf{v}) = \begin{bmatrix} -1 & 3 & 2 & 1 & 4 \\ 2 & 3 & 5 & 0 & 0 \\ 2 & 1 & 2 & 1 & 0 \end{bmatrix} \begin{bmatrix} v_1 \\ v_2 \\ v_3 \\ v_4 \\ v_5 \end{bmatrix} = \begin{bmatrix} 0 \\ 0 \\ 0 \end{bmatrix}$$

has solutions of the form $(-10s - 4t, -15s - 24t, 13s + 16t, 9s, 9t)$, a basis for $\ker(T)$ is $\{(-10, -15, 13, 9, 0), (-4, -24, 16, 0, 9)\}$.

—CONTINUED—

12. —CONTINUED—

(b) We transpose A and find the equivalent reduced row-echelon form.

$$A^T = \begin{bmatrix} -1 & 2 & 2 \\ 3 & 3 & 1 \\ 2 & 5 & 2 \\ 1 & 0 & 1 \\ 4 & 0 & 0 \end{bmatrix} \Rightarrow \begin{bmatrix} 1 & 0 & 0 \\ 0 & 1 & 0 \\ 0 & 0 & 1 \\ 0 & 0 & 0 \\ 0 & 0 & 0 \end{bmatrix}$$

Thus, a basis for range (T) is $\{(1, 0, 0), (0, 1, 0), (0, 0, 1)\}$, and the range of T is all of R^3.

14. (a) The kernel of T is given by the solution to the equation $T(\mathbf{x}) = 0$. Thus, $\ker(T) = \{(2t, -3t) \,|\, t \text{ is any real number}\}$.

(b) $\text{nullity}(T) = \dim(\ker(T)) = 1$.

(c) We transpose T and find the equivalent reduced row-echelon form.

$$A^T = \begin{bmatrix} 3 & -9 \\ 2 & -6 \end{bmatrix} \Rightarrow \begin{bmatrix} 1 & -3 \\ 0 & 0 \end{bmatrix}$$

Thus, $\text{range}(T) = \{(t, -3t) \,|\, t \text{ is any real number}\}$.

(d) $\text{rank}(T) = \dim(\text{range}(T)) = 1$.

16. (a) Since $T(\mathbf{x}) = \mathbf{0}$ has only the trivial solution $\mathbf{x} = (0, 0)$, the kernel of T is $\{(0, 0)\}$.

(b) $\text{nullity}(T) = \dim(\ker(T)) = 0$.

(c) We transpose A and find the equivalent row-echelon form.

$$A^T = \begin{bmatrix} 4 & 0 & 2 \\ 1 & 0 & -3 \end{bmatrix} \Rightarrow \begin{bmatrix} 1 & 0 & 0 \\ 0 & 0 & 1 \end{bmatrix}$$

Thus, $\text{range}(T) = \{(t, 0, s) \,|\, s, t \in R\}$.

(d) $\text{rank}(T) = \dim(\text{range}(T)) = 2$.

18. (a) The kernel of T is given by the solution to the equation $T(\mathbf{x}) = \mathbf{0}$. Thus, $\ker(T) = \{(t, -t, s, -s) \,|\, s, t \in R\}$.

(b) $\text{nullity}(T) = \dim(\ker(T)) = 2$

(c) We transpose A and find its equivalent row-echelon form.

$$A^T = \begin{bmatrix} 1 & 0 \\ 1 & 0 \\ 0 & 1 \\ 0 & 1 \end{bmatrix} \Rightarrow \begin{bmatrix} 1 & 0 \\ 0 & 1 \\ 0 & 0 \\ 0 & 0 \end{bmatrix}$$

Thus, $\text{range}(T) = R^2$.

(d) $\text{rank}(T) = \dim(\text{range}(T)) = 2$.

20. (a) The kernel of T is given by the solution to the equation $T(\mathbf{x}) = \mathbf{0}$. Thus,
$\ker(T) = \{(5t, t) \mid t \in R\}$.

   (b) $\text{nullity}(T) = \dim(\ker(T)) = 1$

   (c) We transpose A and find its equivalent row-echelon form.

$$A^T = \begin{bmatrix} \frac{1}{26} & -\frac{5}{26} \\ -\frac{5}{26} & \frac{25}{26} \end{bmatrix} \implies \begin{bmatrix} 1 & -5 \\ 0 & 0 \end{bmatrix}$$

Thus, $\text{range}(T) = \{(t, -5t) \mid t \in R\}$.

   (d) $\text{rank}(T) = \dim(\text{range}(T)) = 1$.

22. (a) The kernel of T is given by the solution to the equation $T(\mathbf{x}) = \mathbf{0}$. Thus,
$\ker(T) = \{(-t - s - 2r, 6t - 2s, r, s, t) \mid r, s, t \in R\}$.

   (b) $\text{nullity}(T) = \dim(\ker(T)) = 3$

   (c) We transpose A and find its equivalent row-echelon form.

$$A^T = \begin{bmatrix} 3 & 4 & 2 \\ -2 & 3 & -3 \\ 6 & 8 & 4 \\ -1 & 10 & -4 \\ 15 & -14 & 20 \end{bmatrix} \implies \begin{bmatrix} 17 & 0 & 18 \\ 0 & 17 & -5 \\ 0 & 0 & 0 \\ 0 & 0 & 0 \\ 0 & 0 & 0 \end{bmatrix}$$

Thus, $\text{range}(T) = \{(17s, 17t, 18s - 5t) \mid s, t \in R\}$.

   (d) $\text{rank}(T) = \dim(\text{range}(T)) = 2$.

24. (a) The kernel of T is given by the solution to the equation $T(\mathbf{x}) = \mathbf{0}$. Thus,
$\ker(T) = \{(0, t, 0) \mid t \in R\}$.

   (b) $\text{nullity}(T) = \dim(\ker(T)) = 1$

   (c) We transpose A and find its equivalent row-echelon form.

$$A^T = \begin{bmatrix} 1 & 0 & 0 \\ 0 & 0 & 0 \\ 0 & 0 & 1 \end{bmatrix} \implies \begin{bmatrix} 1 & 0 & 0 \\ 0 & 0 & 1 \\ 0 & 0 & 0 \end{bmatrix}$$

Thus, $\text{range}(T) = \{(t, 0, s) \mid s, t \in R\}$.

   (d) $\text{rank}(T) = \dim(\text{range}(T)) = 2$.

26. Since $\text{rank}(T) + \text{nullity}(T) = 3$, and we are given $\text{rank}(T) = 1$, then
$\text{nullity}(T) = 2$. Hence, the kernel of T is a plane, and the range is a line.

28. Since $\text{rank}(T) + \text{nullity}(T) = 3$, and we are given $\text{rank}(T) = 3$, then
$\text{nullity}(T) = 0$. Hence, the kernel of T is the single point $\{(0, 0, 0)\}$, and the range
is all of R^3.

30. The kernel of T is determined by solving $T(x, y, z) = (-x, y, z) = (0, 0, 0)$,
which implies that the kernel is the single point $\{(0, 0, 0)\}$. From the equation
$\text{rank}(T) + \text{nullity}(T) = 3$, we see that the rank of T is 3. Thus, the range of T is
all of R^3.

32. The kernel of T is determined by solving $T(x, y, z) = (x, y, 0) = (0, 0, 0)$, which implies that $x = y = 0$. Hence, the nullity of T is 1, and the kernel is a line (the z-axis). The range of T is found by observing that $\text{rank}(T) + \text{nullity}(T) = 3$. That is, the range of T is 2-dimensional, the xy-plane in R^3.

34. $\text{rank}(T) + \text{nullity}(T) = \dim R^5 \implies \text{nullity}(T) = 5 - 2 = 3$

36. $\text{rank}(T) + \text{nullity}(T) = \dim P_3 \implies \text{nullity}(T) = 4 - 2 = 2$

38. The vector spaces isomorphic to R^6 are those whose dimension is six. That is,
(a) $M_{2,3}$ (d) $M_{6,1}$ (e) P_5 and (f) $\{(x_1, x_2, x_3, 0, x_5, x_6, x_7) : x_i \in R\}$ are isomorphic to R^6.

40. We solve the equation

$$T(p) = \int_0^1 p(x)\, dx = \int_0^1 (a_0 + a_1 x + a_2 x^2)\, dx = 0 \text{ yielding}$$

$a_0 + a_1/2 + a_2/3 = 0$.

Letting $a_2 = -3b$, $a_1 = -2a$, we have

$a_0 = -a_1/2 - a_2/3 = a + b$, and

$\ker(T) = \{(a + b) - 2ax - 3bx^2 \,|\, a, b \in R\}$.

42. We first compute $T(\mathbf{u}) = \text{proj}_v\mathbf{u}$, for $\mathbf{u} = (x, y, z)$.

$$T(\mathbf{u}) = \text{proj}_v\mathbf{u} = \frac{(x, y, z) \cdot (3, 0, 4)}{(3, 0, 4) \cdot (3, 0, 4)}(3, 0, 4) = \frac{3x + 4z}{25}(3, 0, 4).$$

(a) Setting $T(\mathbf{u}) = \mathbf{0}$, we have $3x + 4z = 0$, and hence $\text{nullity}(T) = 2$. Thus, $\text{rank}(T) = 3 - 2 = 1$.

(b) A basis for the kernel of T is obtained by solving $3x + 4z = 0$. Letting $t = z$ and $s = y$, we have $x = \frac{1}{3}(-4z) = -\frac{4}{3}t$. Thus, a basis for the kernel of T is $\left\{(0, 1, 0), \left(-\frac{4}{3}, 0, 1\right)\right\}$.

44. Since $|A| = -1 \neq 0$, the homogeneous equation $A\mathbf{x} = \mathbf{0}$ has only the trivial solution. Thus, $\ker(T) = \{(0, 0)\}$ and T is one-to-one (by Theorem 6.6). Furthermore, since

$\text{rank}(T) = \dim(R^2) - \text{nullity}(T) = 2 - 0 = 2 = \dim(R^2)$

T is onto (by Theorem 6.7).

46. Since $|A| = -24 \neq 0$, the homogeneous equation $A\mathbf{x} = \mathbf{0}$ has only the trivial solution. Thus, $\ker(T) = \{(0, 0, 0)\}$ and T is one-to-one (by Theorem 6.6). Furthermore, since

$\text{rank}(T) = \dim R^3 - \text{nullity}(T) = 3 - 0 = 3 = \dim(R^3)$

T is onto (by Theorem 6.7).

48. (a) *True.* This is a nonempty subset of V since $\mathbf{0}$ is in it. Moreover, if $c \in R$ and $\mathbf{u}$ and $\mathbf{v}$ are such that $T(\mathbf{u}) = \mathbf{0}$ and $T(\mathbf{v}) = \mathbf{0}$, then

$$T(\mathbf{u} + \mathbf{v}) = T(\mathbf{u}) + T(\mathbf{v}) = \mathbf{0} \text{ and } T(c\mathbf{u}) = cT(\mathbf{u}) = \mathbf{0}.$$

This proves that $\ker(T)$ is a subspace of V.

(b) *False.* A concept of a dimension of a linear transformation does not exist.

(c) *True.* See discussion on page 372 before Theorem 6.6.

(d) *True.* Since $\dim(P_1) = \dim(R^2) = 2$ and any two vector spaces of equal finite dimension are isomorphic (Theorem 6.9 on page 375), the statement is true.

50. The kernel of T is given by $T(A) = \mathbf{0}$. Hence,

$$T(A) = A - A^T = \mathbf{0} \implies A = A^T$$

and

$$\ker(T) = \{A : A = A^T\}, \text{ the set of } n \times n \text{ symmetric matrices.}$$

52. Since T is a linear transformation of vector spaces with same dimension, we only need to show that T is one-to-one. It is sufficient to show that $\ker(T) = \{\mathbf{0}\}$. Let $A \in \ker(T)$. Then $T(A) = AB = \mathbf{0}$. We use the fact that B is invertible to obtain

$$AB = \mathbf{0} \implies AB(B^{-1}) = \mathbf{0} \implies A = \mathbf{0}.$$

Thus, $\ker(T) = \{\mathbf{0}\}$ and T is one-to-one.

54. $T^{-1}(U)$ is nonempty since $T(\mathbf{0}) = \mathbf{0} \in U \implies \mathbf{0} \in T^{-1}(U)$.

Let $\mathbf{v}_1, \mathbf{v}_2 \in T^{-1}(U) \implies T(\mathbf{v}_1) \in U$ and $T(\mathbf{v}_2) \in U$. Since U is a subspace of W, $T(\mathbf{v}_1) + T(\mathbf{v}_2) = T(\mathbf{v}_1 + \mathbf{v}_2) \in U \implies \mathbf{v}_1 + \mathbf{v}_2 \in T^{-1}(U)$

Let $\mathbf{v} \in T^{-1}(U)$ and $c \in R \implies T(\mathbf{v}) \in U$. Since U is a subspace of W, $cT(\mathbf{v}) = T(c\mathbf{v}) \in U \implies c\mathbf{v} \in T^{-1}(U)$.

If $U = \{\mathbf{0}\}$, then $T^{-1}(U)$ is the kernel of T.

56. If T is onto, then $m \geq n$.

If T is one-to-one, then $m \leq n$.

Section 6.3 Matrices for Linear Transformations

2. Since

$$T\left(\begin{bmatrix}1\\0\end{bmatrix}\right) = \begin{bmatrix}3\\-1\end{bmatrix} \text{ and } T\left(\begin{bmatrix}0\\1\end{bmatrix}\right) = \begin{bmatrix}2\\2\end{bmatrix}$$

the standard matrix for T is

$$\begin{bmatrix}3 & 2\\-1 & 2\end{bmatrix}.$$

4. Since

$$T\left(\begin{bmatrix} 1 \\ 0 \end{bmatrix}\right) = \begin{bmatrix} 4 \\ 0 \\ 2 \end{bmatrix} \quad \text{and} \quad T\left(\begin{bmatrix} 0 \\ 1 \end{bmatrix}\right) = \begin{bmatrix} 1 \\ 0 \\ -3 \end{bmatrix}$$

the standard matrix for T is

$$\begin{bmatrix} 4 & 1 \\ 0 & 0 \\ 2 & -3 \end{bmatrix}.$$

6. Since

$$T\left(\begin{bmatrix} 1 \\ 0 \\ 0 \end{bmatrix}\right) = \begin{bmatrix} 5 \\ 0 \\ 5 \end{bmatrix}, \; T\left(\begin{bmatrix} 0 \\ 1 \\ 0 \end{bmatrix}\right) = \begin{bmatrix} -3 \\ 4 \\ 3 \end{bmatrix}, \quad \text{and} \quad T\left(\begin{bmatrix} 0 \\ 0 \\ 1 \end{bmatrix}\right) = \begin{bmatrix} 1 \\ 2 \\ 0 \end{bmatrix}$$

the standard matrix for T is

$$\begin{bmatrix} 5 & -3 & 1 \\ 0 & 4 & 2 \\ 5 & 3 & 0 \end{bmatrix}.$$

8. Since

$$T\left(\begin{bmatrix} 1 \\ 0 \\ 0 \\ 0 \end{bmatrix}\right) = \begin{bmatrix} 0 \\ 0 \\ 0 \\ 0 \end{bmatrix}, \; T\left(\begin{bmatrix} 0 \\ 1 \\ 0 \\ 0 \end{bmatrix}\right) = \begin{bmatrix} 0 \\ 0 \\ 0 \\ 0 \end{bmatrix}, \; T\left(\begin{bmatrix} 0 \\ 0 \\ 1 \\ 0 \end{bmatrix}\right) = \begin{bmatrix} 0 \\ 0 \\ 0 \\ 0 \end{bmatrix}, \text{and } T\left(\begin{bmatrix} 0 \\ 0 \\ 0 \\ 1 \end{bmatrix}\right) = \begin{bmatrix} 0 \\ 0 \\ 0 \\ 0 \end{bmatrix}$$

the standard matrix for T is

$$\begin{bmatrix} 0 & 0 & 0 & 0 \\ 0 & 0 & 0 & 0 \\ 0 & 0 & 0 & 0 \\ 0 & 0 & 0 & 0 \end{bmatrix}.$$

10. Since

$$T\left(\begin{bmatrix} 1 \\ 0 \end{bmatrix}\right) = \begin{bmatrix} 1 \\ 1 \\ 2 \\ 0 \end{bmatrix} \quad \text{and} \quad T\left(\begin{bmatrix} 0 \\ 1 \end{bmatrix}\right) = \begin{bmatrix} 1 \\ -1 \\ 0 \\ 2 \end{bmatrix}$$

the standard matrix for T is

$$A = \begin{bmatrix} 1 & 1 \\ 1 & -1 \\ 2 & 0 \\ 0 & 2 \end{bmatrix}.$$

Hence, $T(\mathbf{v}) = \begin{bmatrix} 1 & 1 \\ 1 & -1 \\ 2 & 0 \\ 0 & 2 \end{bmatrix} \begin{bmatrix} 3 \\ -3 \end{bmatrix} = \begin{bmatrix} 0 \\ 6 \\ 6 \\ -6 \end{bmatrix}$ and $T(3, -3) = (0, 6, 6, -6)$.

12. Since

$$
T\left(\begin{bmatrix} 1 \\ 0 \\ 0 \\ 0 \end{bmatrix}\right) = \begin{bmatrix} 2 \\ 0 \\ -1 \\ 0 \end{bmatrix}, \quad T\left(\begin{bmatrix} 0 \\ 1 \\ 0 \\ 0 \end{bmatrix}\right) = \begin{bmatrix} 0 \\ 3 \\ 0 \\ 1 \end{bmatrix}, \quad T\left(\begin{bmatrix} 0 \\ 0 \\ 1 \\ 0 \end{bmatrix}\right) = \begin{bmatrix} -1 \\ 0 \\ 4 \\ 0 \end{bmatrix}, \text{ and } T\left(\begin{bmatrix} 0 \\ 0 \\ 0 \\ 1 \end{bmatrix}\right) = \begin{bmatrix} 0 \\ -4 \\ 0 \\ 1 \end{bmatrix}
$$

the standard matrix for T is

$$
\begin{bmatrix} 2 & 0 & -1 & 0 \\ 0 & 3 & 0 & -4 \\ -1 & 0 & 4 & 0 \\ 0 & 1 & 0 & 1 \end{bmatrix}.
$$

Hence, $T(\mathbf{v}) = \begin{bmatrix} 2 & 0 & -1 & 0 \\ 0 & 3 & 0 & -4 \\ -1 & 0 & 4 & 0 \\ 0 & 1 & 0 & 1 \end{bmatrix} \begin{bmatrix} 1 \\ 2 \\ 3 \\ -2 \end{bmatrix} = \begin{bmatrix} -1 \\ 14 \\ 11 \\ 0 \end{bmatrix}$ and $T(1, 2, 3, -2) = (-1, 14, 11, 0)$.

14. (a) The matrix of a reflection in the line $y = x$, $T(x, y) = (y, x)$, is given by

$$
A = [T(1, 0) \quad \vdots \quad T(0, 1)] = \begin{bmatrix} 0 & 1 \\ 1 & 0 \end{bmatrix}.
$$

(b) The image of $\mathbf{v} = (3, 4)$ is given by

$$
A\mathbf{v} = \begin{bmatrix} 0 & 1 \\ 1 & 0 \end{bmatrix} \begin{bmatrix} 3 \\ 4 \end{bmatrix} = \begin{bmatrix} 4 \\ 3 \end{bmatrix}.
$$

Thus, $T(3, 4) = (4, 3)$.

(c)

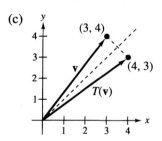

16. (a) The clockwise rotation of $60°$ is given by

$$T(x, y) = (\cos(-60)x - \sin(-60)y, \sin(-60)x + \cos(-60)y)$$

$$= \left(\frac{1}{2}x + \frac{\sqrt{3}}{2}y, -\frac{\sqrt{3}}{2}x + \frac{1}{2}y\right).$$

Thus, the matrix is

$$A = [T(1, 0) \quad \vdots \quad T(0, 1)] = \begin{bmatrix} \dfrac{1}{2} & \dfrac{\sqrt{3}}{2} \\ -\dfrac{\sqrt{3}}{2} & \dfrac{1}{2} \end{bmatrix}.$$

(b) The image of $\mathbf{v} = (1, 2)$ is given by

$$A\mathbf{v} = \begin{bmatrix} \dfrac{1}{2} & \dfrac{\sqrt{3}}{2} \\ -\dfrac{\sqrt{3}}{2} & \dfrac{1}{2} \end{bmatrix} \begin{bmatrix} 1 \\ 2 \end{bmatrix} = \begin{bmatrix} \dfrac{1}{2} + \sqrt{3} \\ 1 - \dfrac{\sqrt{3}}{2} \end{bmatrix}$$

Thus, $T(1, 2) = \left(\dfrac{1}{2} + \sqrt{3}, 1 - \dfrac{\sqrt{3}}{2}\right).$

(c)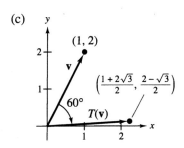

18. (a) The standard matrix for T is

$$A = [T(1, 0, 0) \quad \vdots \quad T(0, 1, 0) \quad \vdots \quad T(0, 0, 1)] = \begin{bmatrix} -1 & 0 & 0 \\ 0 & 1 & 0 \\ 0 & 0 & 1 \end{bmatrix}.$$

(b) The image of $\mathbf{v} = (2, 3, 4)$ is given by

$$A\mathbf{v} = \begin{bmatrix} -1 & 0 & 0 \\ 0 & 1 & 0 \\ 0 & 0 & 1 \end{bmatrix} \begin{bmatrix} 2 \\ 3 \\ 4 \end{bmatrix} = \begin{bmatrix} -2 \\ 3 \\ 4 \end{bmatrix}.$$

Thus, $T(2, 3, 4) = (-2, 3, 4)$.

(c)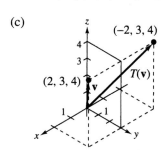

20. (a) The counterclockwise rotation of 45° is given by

$$T(x, y) = (\cos(45)x - \sin(45)y, \sin(45)x + \cos(45)y)$$

$$= \left(\frac{\sqrt{2}}{2}x - \frac{\sqrt{2}}{2}y, \frac{\sqrt{2}}{2}x + \frac{\sqrt{2}}{2}y\right).$$

Thus, the matrix is

$$A = [T(1, 0) \quad \vdots \quad T(0, 1)] = \begin{bmatrix} \dfrac{\sqrt{2}}{2} & -\dfrac{\sqrt{2}}{2} \\ \dfrac{\sqrt{2}}{2} & \dfrac{\sqrt{2}}{2} \end{bmatrix}.$$

(b) The image of $\mathbf{v} = (2, 2)$ is given by

$$A\mathbf{v} = \begin{bmatrix} \dfrac{\sqrt{2}}{2} & -\dfrac{\sqrt{2}}{2} \\ \dfrac{\sqrt{2}}{2} & \dfrac{\sqrt{2}}{2} \end{bmatrix}\begin{bmatrix} 2 \\ 2 \end{bmatrix} = \begin{bmatrix} 0 \\ 2\sqrt{2} \end{bmatrix}.$$

Thus, $T(2, 2) = \left(0, 2\sqrt{2}\right).$

(c)

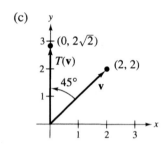

22. (a) The projection onto the vector $(-1, 5)$ is given by

$$T(\mathbf{v}) = \text{proj}_{\mathbf{w}}\mathbf{v} = \frac{-x + 5y}{26}(-1, 5) = \left(-\frac{1}{26}(-x + 5y), \frac{5}{26}(-x + 5y)\right).$$

Thus, the matrix is

$$A = [T(1, 0) \quad \vdots \quad T(0, 1)] = \begin{bmatrix} \dfrac{1}{26} & -\dfrac{5}{26} \\ -\dfrac{5}{26} & \dfrac{25}{26} \end{bmatrix}.$$

(b) The image of $\mathbf{v} = (2, -3)$ is given by

$$A\mathbf{v} = \begin{bmatrix} \dfrac{1}{26} & -\dfrac{5}{26} \\ -\dfrac{5}{26} & \dfrac{25}{26} \end{bmatrix}\begin{bmatrix} 2 \\ -3 \end{bmatrix} = \begin{bmatrix} \dfrac{17}{26} \\ -\dfrac{85}{26} \end{bmatrix}.$$

Thus, $T(2, -3) = \left(\dfrac{17}{26}, -\dfrac{85}{26}\right).$

—CONTINUED—

22. **—CONTINUED—**

(c)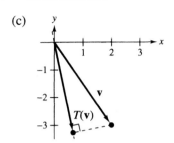

24. (a) The reflection of a vector **v** through **w** is given by

$$T(\mathbf{v}) = 2 \operatorname{proj}_{\mathbf{w}} \mathbf{v} - \mathbf{v}$$

$$= 2 \frac{4x - 2y}{20} (4, -2) - (x, y)$$

$$= \left(\frac{3}{5}x - \frac{4}{5}y, -\frac{4}{5}x - \frac{3}{5}y \right).$$

Thus, the matrix is

$$A = [T(1, 0) \quad \vdots \quad T(0, 1)] = \begin{bmatrix} \dfrac{3}{5} & -\dfrac{4}{5} \\[2mm] -\dfrac{4}{5} & -\dfrac{3}{5} \end{bmatrix}.$$

(b) The image of **v** = (5, 0) is

$$A\mathbf{v} = \begin{bmatrix} \dfrac{3}{5} & -\dfrac{4}{5} \\[2mm] -\dfrac{4}{5} & -\dfrac{3}{5} \end{bmatrix} \begin{bmatrix} 5 \\ 0 \end{bmatrix} = \begin{bmatrix} 3 \\ -4 \end{bmatrix}.$$

Thus, $T(5, 0) = (3, -4)$.

(c)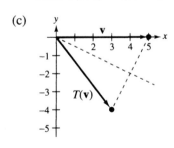

26. (a) The standard matrix for T is

$$A = \begin{bmatrix} 3 & -2 & 1 \\ 2 & -3 & 0 \\ 0 & 1 & -4 \end{bmatrix}.$$

(b) The image of $\mathbf{v} = (2, -1, -1)$ is

$$A\mathbf{v} = \begin{bmatrix} 3 & -2 & 1 \\ 2 & -3 & 0 \\ 0 & 1 & -4 \end{bmatrix} \begin{bmatrix} 2 \\ -1 \\ -1 \end{bmatrix} = \begin{bmatrix} 7 \\ 7 \\ 3 \end{bmatrix}.$$

Thus, $T(2, -1, -1)$ is $(7, 7, 3)$.

(c) Using a graphing calculator to perform the multiplication in part (b) gives the same result.

(d) Parts (b) and (c) verify that $T(2, -1, -1)$ is $(7, 7, 3)$.

28. (a) The standard matrix for T is

$$A = \begin{bmatrix} 1 & 2 & 0 & 0 \\ -1 & 1 & 0 & 0 \\ 0 & 0 & 2 & -1 \\ 1 & 0 & 0 & 0 \end{bmatrix}.$$

(b) The image of $\mathbf{v} = (0, 1, -1, 1)$ is

$$A\mathbf{v} = \begin{bmatrix} 1 & 2 & 0 & 0 \\ -1 & 1 & 0 & 0 \\ 0 & 0 & 2 & -1 \\ 1 & 0 & 0 & 0 \end{bmatrix} \begin{bmatrix} 0 \\ 1 \\ -1 \\ 1 \end{bmatrix} = \begin{bmatrix} 2 \\ 1 \\ -3 \\ 0 \end{bmatrix}.$$

Thus, $T(0, 1, -1, 1) = (2, 1, -3, 0)$.

(c) Using a graphing calculator to perform the multiplication in part (b) gives the same result.

(d) Parts (b) and (c) verify that $T(0, 1, -1, 1) = (2, 1, -3, 0)$.

30. The standard matrices for T_1 and T_2 are

$$A_1 = \begin{bmatrix} 1 & -2 \\ 2 & 3 \end{bmatrix} \quad \text{and} \quad A_2 = \begin{bmatrix} 0 & 1 \\ 0 & 0 \end{bmatrix}.$$

The standard matrix for $T = T_2 \circ T_1$ is

$$A_2 A_1 = \begin{bmatrix} 0 & 1 \\ 0 & 0 \end{bmatrix} \begin{bmatrix} 1 & -2 \\ 2 & 3 \end{bmatrix} = \begin{bmatrix} 2 & 3 \\ 0 & 0 \end{bmatrix}$$

and the standard matrix for $T' = T_1 \circ T_2$ is

$$A_1 A_2 = \begin{bmatrix} 1 & -2 \\ 2 & 3 \end{bmatrix} \begin{bmatrix} 0 & 1 \\ 0 & 0 \end{bmatrix} = \begin{bmatrix} 0 & 1 \\ 0 & 2 \end{bmatrix}.$$

32. The standard matrices for T_1 and T_2 are

$$A_1 = \begin{bmatrix} 1 & 2 & 0 \\ 0 & 1 & -1 \\ -2 & 1 & 2 \end{bmatrix} \quad \text{and} \quad A_2 = \begin{bmatrix} 0 & 1 & 1 \\ 1 & 0 & 1 \\ 0 & 2 & -2 \end{bmatrix}.$$

The standard matrix for $T = T_2 \circ T_1$ is

$$A_2 A_1 = \begin{bmatrix} 0 & 1 & 1 \\ 1 & 0 & 1 \\ 0 & 2 & -2 \end{bmatrix} \begin{bmatrix} 1 & 2 & 0 \\ 0 & 1 & -1 \\ -2 & 1 & 2 \end{bmatrix} = \begin{bmatrix} -2 & 2 & 1 \\ -1 & 3 & 2 \\ 4 & 0 & -6 \end{bmatrix}$$

and the standard matrix for $T' = T_1 \circ T_2$ is

$$A_1 A_2 = \begin{bmatrix} 1 & 2 & 0 \\ 0 & 1 & -1 \\ -2 & 1 & 2 \end{bmatrix} \begin{bmatrix} 0 & 1 & 1 \\ 1 & 0 & 1 \\ 0 & 2 & -2 \end{bmatrix} = \begin{bmatrix} 2 & 1 & 3 \\ 1 & -2 & 3 \\ 1 & 2 & -5 \end{bmatrix}.$$

34. The standard matrices for T_1 and T_2 are

$$A_1 = \begin{bmatrix} 1 & 0 \\ 0 & 1 \\ 0 & 1 \end{bmatrix} \quad \text{and} \quad A_2 = \begin{bmatrix} 0 & 1 & 0 \\ 0 & 0 & 1 \end{bmatrix}.$$

The standard matrix for $T = T_2 \circ T_1$ is

$$A_2 A_1 = \begin{bmatrix} 0 & 1 & 0 \\ 0 & 0 & 1 \end{bmatrix} \begin{bmatrix} 1 & 0 \\ 0 & 1 \\ 0 & 1 \end{bmatrix} = \begin{bmatrix} 0 & 1 \\ 0 & 1 \end{bmatrix}$$

and the standard matrix for $T' = T_1 \circ T_2$ is

$$A_1 A_2 = \begin{bmatrix} 1 & 0 \\ 0 & 1 \\ 0 & 1 \end{bmatrix} \begin{bmatrix} 0 & 1 & 0 \\ 0 & 0 & 1 \end{bmatrix} = \begin{bmatrix} 0 & 1 & 0 \\ 0 & 0 & 1 \\ 0 & 0 & 1 \end{bmatrix}.$$

36. The standard matrix for T is

$$A = \begin{bmatrix} 1 & 0 & 0 \\ 1 & 1 & 0 \\ 1 & 1 & 1 \end{bmatrix}$$

Since $|A| = 1 \neq 0$, A is invertible. We calculate A^{-1} by Gauss-Jordan elimination

$$A^{-1} = \begin{bmatrix} 1 & 0 & 0 \\ -1 & 1 & 0 \\ 0 & -1 & 1 \end{bmatrix}$$

and conclude that $T^{-1}(x_1, x_2, x_3) = (x_1, -x_1 + x_2, -x_2 + x_3)$.

38. The standard matrix for T is

$$A = \begin{bmatrix} 1 & 1 \\ 3 & 3 \end{bmatrix}.$$

Since $|A| = 0$, A is not invertible, and hence T is not invertible.

40. The standard matrix for T is

$$A = \begin{bmatrix} 1 & -2 & 0 & 0 \\ 0 & 1 & 0 & 0 \\ 0 & 0 & 1 & 1 \\ 0 & 0 & 1 & 0 \end{bmatrix}.$$

Since $|A| = -1 \neq 0$, A is invertible. We calculate A^{-1} by Gauss-Jordan elimination

$$A^{-1} = \begin{bmatrix} 1 & 2 & 0 & 0 \\ 0 & 1 & 0 & 0 \\ 0 & 0 & 0 & 1 \\ 0 & 0 & 1 & -1 \end{bmatrix}$$

and conclude that $T^{-1}(x_1, x_2, x_3, x_4) = (x_1 + 2x_2, x_2, x_4, x_3 - x_4)$.

42. (a) The standard matrix for T is

$$A' = \begin{bmatrix} 1 & -1 \\ 0 & 0 \\ 1 & 1 \end{bmatrix}$$

and the image of $\mathbf{v} = (-3, 2)$ under T is

$$A'\mathbf{v} = \begin{bmatrix} 1 & -1 \\ 0 & 0 \\ 1 & 1 \end{bmatrix} \begin{bmatrix} -3 \\ 2 \end{bmatrix} = \begin{bmatrix} -5 \\ 0 \\ -1 \end{bmatrix} \implies T(\mathbf{v}) = (-5, 0, -1).$$

(b) Since $T(1, 2) = (-1, 0, 3) = 2(1, 1, 1) - 3(1, 1, 0) + 1(0, 1, 1)$ and $T(1, 1) = (0, 0, 2) = 2(1, 1, 1) - 2(1, 1, 0)$ the matrix of T relative to B and B' is

$$A = \begin{bmatrix} 2 & 2 \\ -3 & -2 \\ 1 & 0 \end{bmatrix}.$$

Since $\mathbf{v} = (-3, 2) = 5(1, 2) - 8(1, 1)$ we have

$$[T(\mathbf{v})]_{B'} = A[\mathbf{v}]_B = \begin{bmatrix} 2 & 2 \\ -3 & -2 \\ 1 & 0 \end{bmatrix} \begin{bmatrix} 5 \\ -8 \end{bmatrix} = \begin{bmatrix} -6 \\ 1 \\ 5 \end{bmatrix}.$$

Thus, $T(\mathbf{v}) = -6(1, 1, 1) + 1(1, 1, 0) + 5(0, 1, 1) = (-5, 0, -1)$.

44. (a) The standard matrix for T is

$$A' = \begin{bmatrix} 2 & 0 & -1 \\ -2 & 1 & 0 \end{bmatrix}.$$

and the image of $\mathbf{v} = (0, -5, 7)$ under T is

$$A'\mathbf{v} = \begin{bmatrix} 2 & 0 & -1 \\ -2 & 1 & 0 \end{bmatrix} \begin{bmatrix} 0 \\ -5 \\ 7 \end{bmatrix} = \begin{bmatrix} -7 \\ -5 \end{bmatrix} \implies T(0, -5, 7) = (-7, -5).$$

—CONTINUED—

44. —CONTINUED—

(b) Since

$$T(2, 0, 1) = (3, -4) = -4(1, 1) + \tfrac{7}{2}(2, 0)$$

$$T(0, 2, 1) = (-1, 2) = 2(1, 1) - \tfrac{3}{2}(2, 0)$$

$$T(1, 2, 1) = (1, 0) = 0(1, 1) + \tfrac{1}{2}(2, 0),$$

the matrix for T relative to B and B' is

$$A = \begin{bmatrix} -4 & 2 & 0 \\ \tfrac{7}{2} & -\tfrac{3}{2} & \tfrac{1}{2} \end{bmatrix}.$$

Since $\mathbf{v} = (0, -5, 7) = \tfrac{19}{2}(2, 0, 1) + \tfrac{33}{2}(0, 2, 1) - 19(1, 2, 1)$ we have

$$[T(\mathbf{v})]_{B'} = A[\mathbf{v}]_B = \begin{bmatrix} -4 & 2 & 0 \\ \tfrac{7}{2} & -\tfrac{3}{2} & \tfrac{1}{2} \end{bmatrix} \begin{bmatrix} 19/2 \\ 33/2 \\ -19 \end{bmatrix} = \begin{bmatrix} -5 \\ -1 \end{bmatrix}.$$

Thus, $T(\mathbf{v}) = -5(1, 1) - 1(2, 0) = (-7, -5)$.

46. (a) The standard matrix for T is

$$A' = \begin{bmatrix} 1 & 1 & 1 & 1 \\ -1 & 0 & 0 & 1 \end{bmatrix}$$

and the image of $\mathbf{v} = (4, -3, 1, 1)$ under T is

$$A'\mathbf{v} = \begin{bmatrix} 1 & 1 & 1 & 1 \\ -1 & 0 & 0 & 1 \end{bmatrix} \begin{bmatrix} 4 \\ -3 \\ 1 \\ 1 \end{bmatrix} = \begin{bmatrix} 3 \\ -3 \end{bmatrix} \implies T(\mathbf{v}) = (3, -3).$$

(b) Since

$$T(1, 0, 0, 1) = (2, 0) = 0(1, 1) + (2, 0)$$

$$T(0, 1, 0, 1) = (2, 1) = (1, 1) + \tfrac{1}{2}(2, 0)$$

$$T(1, 0, 1, 0) = (2, -1) = -(1, 1) + \tfrac{3}{2}(2, 0)$$

$$T(1, 1, 0, 0) = (2, -1) = -(1, 1) + \tfrac{3}{2}(2, 0)$$

the matrix for T relative to B and B' is

$$A = \begin{bmatrix} 0 & 1 & -1 & -1 \\ 1 & \tfrac{1}{2} & \tfrac{3}{2} & \tfrac{3}{2} \end{bmatrix}.$$

Since $\mathbf{v} = (4, -3, 1, 1)$

$$= \tfrac{7}{2}(1, 0, 0, 1) - \tfrac{5}{2}(0, 1, 0, 1) + (1, 0, 1, 0) - \tfrac{1}{2}(1, 1, 0, 0),$$

$$[T(\mathbf{v})]_{B'} = A[\mathbf{v}]_B = \begin{bmatrix} 0 & 1 & -1 & -1 \\ 1 & \tfrac{1}{2} & \tfrac{3}{2} & \tfrac{3}{2} \end{bmatrix} \begin{bmatrix} 7/2 \\ -5/2 \\ 1 \\ -1/2 \end{bmatrix} = \begin{bmatrix} -3 \\ 3 \end{bmatrix}.$$

Thus, $T(\mathbf{v}) = -3(1, 1) + 3(2, 0) = (3, -3)$.

48. (a) The standard matrix for T is

$$A' = \begin{bmatrix} 2 & -12 \\ 1 & -5 \end{bmatrix}$$

and the image of $\mathbf{v} = (10, 5)$ under T is

$$A'\mathbf{v} = \begin{bmatrix} 2 & -12 \\ 1 & -5 \end{bmatrix}\begin{bmatrix} 10 \\ 5 \end{bmatrix} = \begin{bmatrix} -40 \\ -15 \end{bmatrix} \implies T(\mathbf{v}) = (-40, -15).$$

(b) Since

$$T(4, 1) = (-4, -1) = -(4, 1)$$
$$T(3, 1) = (-6, -2) = -2(3, 1)$$

the matrix for T relative to B and B' is

$$A = \begin{bmatrix} -1 & 0 \\ 0 & -2 \end{bmatrix}.$$

Since $\mathbf{v} = (10, 5) = -5(4, 1) + 10(3, 1)$, we have

$$[T(\mathbf{v})]_{B'} = A[\mathbf{v}]_B = \begin{bmatrix} -1 & 0 \\ 0 & -2 \end{bmatrix}\begin{bmatrix} -5 \\ 10 \end{bmatrix} = \begin{bmatrix} 5 \\ -20 \end{bmatrix}.$$

Thus, $T(\mathbf{v}) = 5(4, 1) - 20(3, 1) = (-40, -15)$.

50. The image of each vector in B is as follows

$$T(1) = x^2, \quad T(x) = x^3, \quad T(x^2) = x^4.$$

Thus, the matrix of T relative to B and B' is

$$A = \begin{bmatrix} 0 & 0 & 0 \\ 0 & 0 & 0 \\ 1 & 0 & 0 \\ 0 & 1 & 0 \\ 0 & 0 & 1 \end{bmatrix}.$$

52. The image of each vector in B is as follows.

$$D(e^{2x}) = 2e^{2x}$$
$$D(xe^{2x}) = e^{2x} + 2xe^{2x}$$
$$D(x^2e^{2x}) = 2xe^{2x} + 2x^2e^{2x}$$

Thus, the matrix of T relative to B is

$$A = \begin{bmatrix} 2 & 1 & 0 \\ 0 & 2 & 2 \\ 0 & 0 & 2 \end{bmatrix}.$$

54. Since $5e^{2x} - 3xe^{2x} + x^2e^{2x} = 5(e^{2x}) - 3(xe^{2x}) + 1(x^2e^{2x})$,

$$A[\mathbf{v}]_B = \begin{bmatrix} 2 & 1 & 0 \\ 0 & 2 & 2 \\ 0 & 0 & 2 \end{bmatrix} \begin{bmatrix} 5 \\ -3 \\ 1 \end{bmatrix} = \begin{bmatrix} 7 \\ -4 \\ 2 \end{bmatrix} \Rightarrow D_x(5e^{2x} - 3x^2 e + x^2e^{2x})$$

$$= 7e^{2x} - 4xe^{2x} + 2x^2e^{2x}.$$

56. (a) *True.* See Theorem 6.10 on page 379.

(b) *True.* See Theorem 6.11 on page 382.

(c) *False.* Let linear transformation $T: R^2 \to R^2$ be given by $T(x, y) = (x - y, -2x + 2y)$. Then the standard matrix for T is

$$\begin{bmatrix} 1 & -1 \\ -2 & 2 \end{bmatrix},$$

which is not invertible. Thus, by Theorem 6.12 on page 383, T is not invertible.

58. Since $T(\mathbf{v}) = k\mathbf{v}$ for all $\mathbf{v} \in R^n$, the standard matrix for T is the $n \times n$ diagonal matrix

$$\begin{bmatrix} k & 0 & \cdots & 0 \\ 0 & k & & \vdots \\ \vdots & & k & 0 \\ 0 & \cdots & 0 & k \end{bmatrix}.$$

60. Since $|T| \neq 0$, T is invertible and T is an isomorphism. The inverse of T is computed by Gauss-Jordan elimination, applied to A and $A^{-1} = A^T$, so the inverse of T exists and T^{-1} has the standard matrix A^T, and we find that $T^{-1} = T^T$, the transpose of T.

62. $(1 \Rightarrow 2)$: Let T be invertible. If $T(\mathbf{v}_1) = T(\mathbf{v}_2)$, then $T^{-1}(T(\mathbf{v}_1)) = T^{-1}(T(\mathbf{v}_2))$ and $\mathbf{v}_1 = \mathbf{v}_2$, so T is one-to-one. T is onto because for any $\mathbf{w} \in R^n$, $T^{-1}(\mathbf{w}) = \mathbf{v}$ satisfies $T(\mathbf{v}) = \mathbf{w}$.

$(2 \Rightarrow 1)$: Let T be an isomorphism. We define T^{-1} as follows: Since T is onto, for any $\mathbf{w} \in R^n$, there exists $\mathbf{v} \in R^n$ such that $T(\mathbf{v}) = \mathbf{w}$. Since T is one-to-one, this $\mathbf{v}$ is unique. Thus, we define the inverse of T by $T^{-1}(\mathbf{w}) = \mathbf{v}$ if and only if $T(\mathbf{v}) = \mathbf{w}$.

Finally, the corollaries to Theorems 6.3 and 6.4 show that 2 and 3 are equivalent.

If T is invertible, $T(\mathbf{x}) = A\mathbf{x}$ implies that $T^{-1}(T(\mathbf{x})) = \mathbf{x} = A^{-1}(A\mathbf{x})$ and the standard matrix of T^{-1} is A^{-1}.

64. $\mathbf{b}$ is in the range of the linear transformation $T: R^n \to R^m$ given by $T(\mathbf{x}) = A\mathbf{x}$ if and only if $\mathbf{b}$ is in the column space of A.

Section 6.4   Transition Matrices and Similarity

2. (a) The standard matrix for T is

$$A = \begin{bmatrix} 1 & 1 \\ 0 & 4 \end{bmatrix}.$$

Furthermore, the transition matrix P from B' to the standard basis B, and its inverse, are

$$P = \begin{bmatrix} -4 & 1 \\ 1 & -1 \end{bmatrix} \quad \text{and} \quad P^{-1} = \begin{bmatrix} -\frac{1}{3} & -\frac{1}{3} \\ -\frac{1}{3} & -\frac{4}{3} \end{bmatrix}.$$

Therefore, the matrix for T relative to B' is

$$A' = P^{-1}AP = \begin{bmatrix} -\frac{1}{3} & -\frac{1}{3} \\ -\frac{1}{3} & -\frac{4}{3} \end{bmatrix} \begin{bmatrix} 1 & 1 \\ 0 & 4 \end{bmatrix} \begin{bmatrix} -4 & 1 \\ 1 & -1 \end{bmatrix} = \begin{bmatrix} -\frac{1}{3} & \frac{4}{3} \\ -\frac{13}{3} & \frac{16}{3} \end{bmatrix}.$$

(b) Since $A' = P^{-1}AP$, it follows that A and A' are similar.

4. (a) The standard matrix for T is

$$A = \begin{bmatrix} 0 & 0 & 0 \\ 0 & 0 & 0 \\ 0 & 0 & 0 \end{bmatrix}.$$

Furthermore, the transition matrix P from B' to the standard basis B, and its inverse, are

$$P = \begin{bmatrix} 1 & 1 & 0 \\ 1 & 0 & 1 \\ 0 & 1 & 1 \end{bmatrix} \quad \text{and} \quad P^{-1} = \frac{1}{2}\begin{bmatrix} 1 & 1 & -1 \\ 1 & -1 & 1 \\ -1 & 1 & 1 \end{bmatrix}.$$

Therefore, the matrix for T relative to B' is

$$A' = P^{-1}AP = \begin{bmatrix} 0 & 0 & 0 \\ 0 & 0 & 0 \\ 0 & 0 & 0 \end{bmatrix}.$$

(b) Since $A' = P^{-1}AP$, it follows that A and A' are similar (in fact, equal!).

6. (a) The standard matrix for T is

$$A = \begin{bmatrix} 1 & 0 & 0 \\ 1 & 2 & 0 \\ 1 & 1 & 3 \end{bmatrix}.$$

Furthermore, the transition matrix P from B' to the standard basis B, and its inverse, are

$$P = \begin{bmatrix} 1 & 0 & 0 \\ -1 & 0 & 1 \\ 0 & 1 & -1 \end{bmatrix} \quad \text{and} \quad P^{-1} = \begin{bmatrix} 1 & 0 & 0 \\ 1 & 1 & 1 \\ 1 & 1 & 0 \end{bmatrix}.$$

Therefore, the matrix for T relative to B' is

$$A' = P^{-1}AP = \begin{bmatrix} 1 & 0 & 0 \\ 1 & 1 & 1 \\ 1 & 1 & 0 \end{bmatrix} \begin{bmatrix} 1 & 0 & 0 \\ 1 & 2 & 0 \\ 1 & 1 & 3 \end{bmatrix} \begin{bmatrix} 1 & 0 & 0 \\ -1 & 0 & 1 \\ 0 & 1 & -1 \end{bmatrix} = \begin{bmatrix} 1 & 0 & 0 \\ 0 & 3 & 0 \\ 0 & 0 & 2 \end{bmatrix}.$$

8. (a) The transition matrix P from B' to B is found by row-reducing $[B \vdots B']$ to $[I \vdots P]$.

$$[B \vdots B'] = \begin{bmatrix} 1 & -2 & \vdots & 1 & 0 \\ 1 & 3 & \vdots & -1 & 1 \end{bmatrix} \Rightarrow [I \vdots P] = \begin{bmatrix} 1 & 0 & \vdots & \frac{1}{5} & \frac{2}{5} \\ 0 & 1 & \vdots & -\frac{2}{5} & \frac{1}{5} \end{bmatrix}$$

Thus, $P = \begin{bmatrix} \frac{1}{5} & \frac{2}{5} \\ -\frac{2}{5} & \frac{1}{5} \end{bmatrix}$.

(b) The coordinate matrix for $\mathbf{v}$ relative to B is

$$[\mathbf{v}]_B = P[\mathbf{v}]_{B'} = \begin{bmatrix} \frac{1}{5} & \frac{2}{5} \\ -\frac{2}{5} & \frac{1}{5} \end{bmatrix} \begin{bmatrix} 1 \\ -3 \end{bmatrix} = \begin{bmatrix} -1 \\ -1 \end{bmatrix}.$$

Furthermore, the image of $\mathbf{v}$ under T relative to B is

$$[T(\mathbf{v})]_B = A[\mathbf{v}]_B = \begin{bmatrix} 3 & 2 \\ 0 & 4 \end{bmatrix} \begin{bmatrix} -1 \\ -1 \end{bmatrix} = \begin{bmatrix} -5 \\ -4 \end{bmatrix}.$$

(c) The matrix of T relative to B' is

$$A' = P^{-1}AP = \begin{bmatrix} 1 & -2 \\ 2 & 1 \end{bmatrix} \begin{bmatrix} 3 & 2 \\ 0 & 4 \end{bmatrix} \begin{bmatrix} \frac{1}{5} & \frac{2}{5} \\ -\frac{2}{5} & \frac{1}{5} \end{bmatrix} = \begin{bmatrix} 3 & 0 \\ -2 & 4 \end{bmatrix}.$$

(d) The image of $\mathbf{v}$ under T relative to B' is

$$P^{-1}[T(\mathbf{v})]_B = \begin{bmatrix} 1 & -2 \\ 2 & 1 \end{bmatrix} \begin{bmatrix} -5 \\ -4 \end{bmatrix} = \begin{bmatrix} 3 \\ -14 \end{bmatrix}.$$

We can also find the image of $\mathbf{v}$ under T relative to B' by

$$A'[\mathbf{v}]_{B'} = \begin{bmatrix} 3 & 0 \\ -2 & 4 \end{bmatrix} \begin{bmatrix} 1 \\ -3 \end{bmatrix} = \begin{bmatrix} 3 \\ -14 \end{bmatrix}.$$

10. (a) The transition matrix P from B' to B is found by row-reducing $[B \vdots B']$ to $[I \vdots P]$. Since B is the standard basis, we have $B' = P$.

$$P = \begin{bmatrix} 1 & 1 & -1 \\ 1 & -1 & 1 \\ -1 & 1 & 1 \end{bmatrix}$$

(b) The coordinate matrix for $\mathbf{v}$ relative to B is

$$[\mathbf{v}]_B = P[\mathbf{v}]_{B'} = \begin{bmatrix} 1 & 1 & -1 \\ 1 & -1 & 1 \\ -1 & 1 & 1 \end{bmatrix} \begin{bmatrix} 2 \\ 1 \\ 1 \end{bmatrix} = \begin{bmatrix} 2 \\ 2 \\ 0 \end{bmatrix}.$$

Furthermore, the image of $\mathbf{v}$ under T relative to B is

$$[T(\mathbf{v})]_B = A[\mathbf{v}]_B = \begin{bmatrix} \frac{3}{2} & -1 & -\frac{1}{2} \\ -\frac{1}{2} & 2 & \frac{1}{2} \\ \frac{1}{2} & 1 & \frac{5}{2} \end{bmatrix} \begin{bmatrix} 2 \\ 2 \\ 0 \end{bmatrix} = \begin{bmatrix} 1 \\ 3 \\ 3 \end{bmatrix}.$$

—CONTINUED—

10. **—CONTINUED—**

(c) The matrix of T relative to B' is

$$A' = P^{-1}AP = \begin{bmatrix} \frac{1}{2} & \frac{1}{2} & 0 \\ \frac{1}{2} & 0 & \frac{1}{2} \\ 0 & \frac{1}{2} & \frac{1}{2} \end{bmatrix} \begin{bmatrix} \frac{3}{2} & -1 & -\frac{1}{2} \\ -\frac{1}{2} & 2 & \frac{1}{2} \\ \frac{1}{2} & 1 & \frac{5}{2} \end{bmatrix} \begin{bmatrix} 1 & 1 & -1 \\ 1 & -1 & 1 \\ -1 & 1 & 1 \end{bmatrix} = \begin{bmatrix} 1 & 0 & 0 \\ 0 & 2 & 0 \\ 0 & 0 & 3 \end{bmatrix}.$$

(d) The image of **v** under T relative to B' is

$$P^{-1}[T(\mathbf{v})]_B = \begin{bmatrix} \frac{1}{2} & \frac{1}{2} & 0 \\ \frac{1}{2} & 0 & \frac{1}{2} \\ 0 & \frac{1}{2} & \frac{1}{2} \end{bmatrix} \begin{bmatrix} 1 \\ 3 \\ 3 \end{bmatrix} = \begin{bmatrix} 2 \\ 2 \\ 3 \end{bmatrix}.$$

We can also find the image of **v** under T relative to B' by

$$A'[\mathbf{v}]_{B'} = \begin{bmatrix} 1 & 0 & 0 \\ 0 & 2 & 0 \\ 0 & 0 & 3 \end{bmatrix} \begin{bmatrix} 2 \\ 1 \\ 1 \end{bmatrix} = \begin{bmatrix} 2 \\ 2 \\ 3 \end{bmatrix}.$$

12. First, we note that A and B are similar.

$$P^{-1}AP = \begin{bmatrix} -1 & -1 & 2 \\ 0 & -1 & 2 \\ 1 & 2 & -3 \end{bmatrix} \begin{bmatrix} 1 & 0 & 0 \\ 0 & -2 & 0 \\ 0 & 0 & 3 \end{bmatrix} \begin{bmatrix} -1 & 1 & 0 \\ 2 & 1 & 2 \\ 1 & 1 & 1 \end{bmatrix} = \begin{bmatrix} 11 & 7 & 10 \\ 10 & 8 & 10 \\ -18 & -12 & -17 \end{bmatrix}$$

Now,

$$|B| = \begin{bmatrix} 11 & 7 & 10 \\ 10 & 8 & 10 \\ -18 & -12 & -17 \end{bmatrix} = 11(-16) - 7(10) + 10(24) = -6 = |A|.$$

14. Since

$$B = P^{-1}AP, \text{ and } A^4 = \begin{bmatrix} 1 & 0 \\ 0 & 2 \end{bmatrix}^4 = \begin{bmatrix} 1 & 0 \\ 0 & 16 \end{bmatrix},$$

we have

$$B^4 = P^{-1}A^4P = \begin{bmatrix} 3 & -5 \\ -1 & 2 \end{bmatrix} \begin{bmatrix} 1 & 0 \\ 0 & 16 \end{bmatrix} \begin{bmatrix} 2 & 5 \\ 1 & 3 \end{bmatrix} = \begin{bmatrix} -74 & -225 \\ 30 & 91 \end{bmatrix}.$$

16. If $B = P^{-1}AP$ and A is idempotent, then

$$B^2 = (P^{-1}AP)^2 = (P^{-1}AP)(P^{-1}AP) = P^{-1}A^2P = P^{-1}AP = B,$$

which shows that B is idempotent.

18. If $A\mathbf{x} = \mathbf{x}$ and $B = P^{-1}AP$, then

$$PB = AP \text{ and } PBP^{-1} = A.$$

Hence, $PBP^{-1}\mathbf{x} = A\mathbf{x} = \mathbf{x}$.

20. Since A and B are similar, they represent the same linear transformation with respect to different bases. Hence, the range is the same, and thus so is the rank.

22. As in Exercise 21, if $B = P^{-1}AP$, then

$$B^k = (P^{-1}AP)^k = (P^{-1}AP)(P^{-1}AP) \cdots (P^{-1}AP) \quad (k \text{ times})$$
$$= P^{-1}A^kP$$

which shows that A^k is similar to B^k.

24. Since $B = P^{-1}AP$, we have $AP = PB$, as follows.

$$\begin{bmatrix} a_{11} & \cdots & a_{1n} \\ \vdots & & \vdots \\ a_{n1} & \cdots & a_{nn} \end{bmatrix} \begin{bmatrix} p_{11} & \cdots & p_{1n} \\ \vdots & & \vdots \\ p_{n1} & \cdots & p_{nn} \end{bmatrix} = \begin{bmatrix} p_{11} & \cdots & p_{1n} \\ \vdots & & \vdots \\ p_{n1} & \cdots & p_{nn} \end{bmatrix} \begin{bmatrix} b_{11} & \cdots & 0 \\ & & \vdots \\ 0 & \cdots & b_{nn} \end{bmatrix}$$

Hence,

$$\begin{bmatrix} a_{11} & \cdots & a_{1n} \\ \vdots & & \vdots \\ a_{n1} & \cdots & a_{nn} \end{bmatrix} \begin{bmatrix} p_{1i} \\ \vdots \\ p_{ni} \end{bmatrix} = b_{ii} \begin{bmatrix} p_{1i} \\ \vdots \\ p_{ni} \end{bmatrix}$$

for $i = 1, 2, \ldots, n$.

26. (a) *True.* See page 390.

   (b) *False.* If T is a linear transformation with matrices A and A' relative to bases B and B' respectively, then $A' = P^{-1}AP$, where P is the transition matrix from B' to B. Therefore, two matrices representing the *same* linear transformation must be similar.

Section 6.5   Applications of Linear Transformations

2. The standard matrix for T is

$$A = \begin{bmatrix} 0 & 1 \\ 1 & 0 \end{bmatrix}.$$

(a) $\begin{bmatrix} 0 & 1 \\ 1 & 0 \end{bmatrix} \begin{bmatrix} 0 \\ 1 \end{bmatrix} = \begin{bmatrix} 1 \\ 0 \end{bmatrix} \qquad \Longrightarrow \qquad T(0, 1) = (1, 0)$

(b) $\begin{bmatrix} 0 & 1 \\ 1 & 0 \end{bmatrix} \begin{bmatrix} -1 \\ 3 \end{bmatrix} = \begin{bmatrix} 3 \\ -1 \end{bmatrix} \qquad \Longrightarrow \qquad T(-1, 3) = (3, -1)$

(c) $\begin{bmatrix} 0 & 1 \\ 1 & 0 \end{bmatrix} \begin{bmatrix} a \\ 0 \end{bmatrix} = \begin{bmatrix} 0 \\ a \end{bmatrix} \qquad \Longrightarrow \qquad T(a, 0) = (0, a)$

(d) $\begin{bmatrix} 0 & 1 \\ 1 & 0 \end{bmatrix} \begin{bmatrix} 0 \\ b \end{bmatrix} = \begin{bmatrix} b \\ 0 \end{bmatrix} \qquad \Longrightarrow \qquad T(0, b) = (b, 0)$

(e) $\begin{bmatrix} 0 & 1 \\ 1 & 0 \end{bmatrix} \begin{bmatrix} -c \\ d \end{bmatrix} = \begin{bmatrix} d \\ -c \end{bmatrix} \qquad \Longrightarrow \qquad T(-c, d) = (b, -c)$

(f) $\begin{bmatrix} 0 & 1 \\ 1 & 0 \end{bmatrix} \begin{bmatrix} f \\ -g \end{bmatrix} = \begin{bmatrix} -g \\ f \end{bmatrix} \qquad \Longrightarrow \qquad T(f, -g) = (-g, f)$

4. (a) $T(x, y) = xT(1, 0) + yT(0, 1) = x(2, 0) + y(0, 1) = (2x, y)$.

   (b) T is a horizontal expansion.

6. (a) We can identify T as a horizontal expansion from its standard matrix

$$A = \begin{bmatrix} 4 & 0 \\ 0 & 1 \end{bmatrix}.$$

   (b)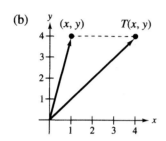

8. (a) We can identify T as a vertical shear from its matrix

$$A = \begin{bmatrix} 1 & 0 \\ 2 & 1 \end{bmatrix}.$$

   (b)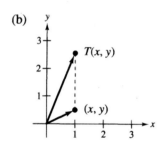

10. The reflection in the line $y = x$ is given by $T(x, y) = (y, x)$. If (x, y) is a fixed point, then $T(x, y) = (x, y) = (y, x)$ which implies that $x = y$. Hence, the set of fixed points is $\{(t, t) \mid t \in R\}$.

12. A horizontal shear has the form $T(x, y) = (x + ky, y)$. If (x, y) is a fixed point, then $T(x, y) = (x, y) = (x + ky, y)$ which implies that $y = 0$. Hence, the set of fixed points is $\{(t, 0) \mid t \in R\}$.

14. We find the image of each vertex under $T(x, y) = (y, x)$

$$T(0, 0) = (0, 0), \quad T(1, 0) = (0, 1),$$
$$T(1, 1) = (1, 1), \quad T(0, 1) = (1, 0).$$

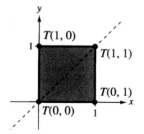

16. We find the image of each vertex under $T(x, y) = (x, 3y)$

$$T(0, 0) = (0, 0), \quad T(1, 0) = (1, 0),$$
$$T(1, 1) = (1, 3), \quad T(0, 1) = (0, 3).$$

The image of the unit square under T is shown in the following figure.

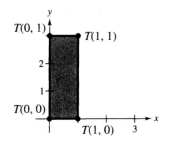

18. We find the image of each vertex under $T(x, y) = (x, y + 3x)$

$$T(0, 0) = (0, 0), \quad T(1, 0) = (1, 3),$$
$$T(1, 1) = (1, 4), \quad T(0, 1) = (0, 1).$$

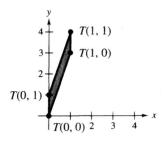

20. We find the image of each vertex under $T(x, y) = (y, x)$.

$$T(0, 0) = (0, 0), \quad T(0, 2) = (2, 0),$$
$$T(1, 2) = (2, 1), \quad T(1, 0) = (0, 1).$$

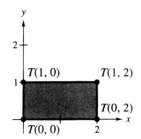

22. We find the image of each vertex under $T(x, y) = (2x, y)$.

$$T(0, 0) = (0, 0), \quad T(0, 2) = (0, 2),$$
$$T(1, 2) = (2, 2), \quad T(1, 0) = (2, 0).$$

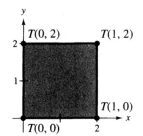

24. We find the image of each vertex under $T(x, y) = (x, y + 2x)$.

$$T(0, 0) = (0, 0), \quad T(0, 2) = (0, 2),$$
$$T(1, 2) = (1, 4), \quad T(1, 0) = (1, 2).$$

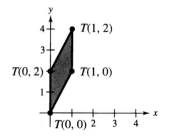

26. The images of the given vectors are as follows.

$$A\begin{bmatrix} 1 \\ 0 \end{bmatrix} = \begin{bmatrix} 3 & 0 \\ 0 & 3 \end{bmatrix}\begin{bmatrix} 1 \\ 0 \end{bmatrix} = \begin{bmatrix} 3 \\ 0 \end{bmatrix} \implies T(1, 0) = (3, 0)$$

$$A\begin{bmatrix} 0 \\ 1 \end{bmatrix} = \begin{bmatrix} 3 & 0 \\ 0 & 3 \end{bmatrix}\begin{bmatrix} 0 \\ 1 \end{bmatrix} = \begin{bmatrix} 0 \\ 3 \end{bmatrix} \implies T(0, 1) = (0, 3)$$

$$A\begin{bmatrix} 2 \\ 2 \end{bmatrix} = \begin{bmatrix} 3 & 0 \\ 0 & 3 \end{bmatrix}\begin{bmatrix} 2 \\ 2 \end{bmatrix} = \begin{bmatrix} 6 \\ 6 \end{bmatrix} \implies T(2, 2) = (6, 6)$$

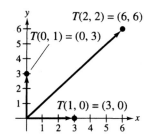

28. The linear transformation defined by A is a vertical shear.

30. The linear transformation defined by A is a horizontal shear.

32. The linear transformation defined by A is a reflection in the y-axis.

34. Since $\begin{bmatrix} 1 & 0 \\ 0 & 3 \end{bmatrix}$ represents a vertical expansion, and $\begin{bmatrix} 0 & 1 \\ 1 & 0 \end{bmatrix}$ represents a reflection in the line $x = y$, A is a vertical expansion *followed* by a reflection in the line $x = y$.

36. A rotation of 60° about the *x*-axis is given by the matrix

$$A = \begin{bmatrix} 1 & 0 & 0 \\ 0 & \cos 60° & -\sin 60° \\ 0 & \sin 60° & \cos 60° \end{bmatrix} = \begin{bmatrix} 1 & 0 & 0 \\ 0 & \dfrac{1}{2} & -\dfrac{\sqrt{3}}{2} \\ 0 & \dfrac{\sqrt{3}}{2} & \dfrac{1}{2} \end{bmatrix}.$$

38. A rotation of 120° about the *x*-axis is given by the matrix

$$A = \begin{bmatrix} 1 & -0 & 0 \\ 0 & \cos 120° & -\sin 120° \\ 0 & \sin 120° & \cos 120° \end{bmatrix} = \begin{bmatrix} 1 & 0 & 0 \\ 0 & -\dfrac{1}{2} & -\dfrac{\sqrt{3}}{2} \\ 0 & \dfrac{\sqrt{3}}{2} & -\dfrac{1}{2} \end{bmatrix}.$$

40. Using the matrix obtained in Exercise 36, we find

$$T(1, 1, 1) = \begin{bmatrix} 1 & 0 & 0 \\ 0 & \dfrac{1}{2} & -\dfrac{\sqrt{3}}{2} \\ 0 & \dfrac{\sqrt{3}}{2} & \dfrac{1}{2} \end{bmatrix} \begin{bmatrix} 1 \\ 1 \\ 1 \end{bmatrix} = \begin{bmatrix} 1 \\ (1 - \sqrt{3})/2 \\ (1 + \sqrt{3})/2 \end{bmatrix}.$$

42. Using the matrix obtained in Exercise 38, we find

$$T(1, 1, 1) = \begin{bmatrix} 1 & 0 & 0 \\ 0 & -\dfrac{1}{2} & -\dfrac{\sqrt{3}}{2} \\ 0 & \dfrac{\sqrt{3}}{2} & -\dfrac{1}{2} \end{bmatrix} \begin{bmatrix} 1 \\ 1 \\ 1 \end{bmatrix} = \begin{bmatrix} 1 \\ (-1 - \sqrt{3})/2 \\ (-1 + \sqrt{3})/2 \end{bmatrix}.$$

44. The indicated tetrahedron is produced by a −90° rotation about the *z*-axis.

46. The indicated tetrahedron is produced by a 180° rotation about the *z*-axis.

48. The indicated tetrahedron is produced by a 180° rotation about the *x*-axis.

50. A rotation of 45° about the *y*-axis is given by

$$A_1 = \begin{bmatrix} \cos 45° & 0 & \sin 45° \\ 0 & 1 & 0 \\ -\sin 45° & 0 & \cos 45° \end{bmatrix} = \begin{bmatrix} \frac{\sqrt{2}}{2} & 0 & \frac{\sqrt{2}}{2} \\ 0 & 1 & 0 \\ -\frac{\sqrt{2}}{2} & 0 & \frac{\sqrt{2}}{2} \end{bmatrix}$$

while a rotation of 90° about the *z*-axis is given by

$$A_2 = \begin{bmatrix} \cos 90° & -\sin 90° & 0 \\ \sin 90° & \cos 90° & 0 \\ 0 & 0 & 1 \end{bmatrix} = \begin{bmatrix} 0 & -1 & 0 \\ 1 & 0 & 0 \\ 0 & 0 & 1 \end{bmatrix}.$$

Thus, the desired matrix is

$$A = A_2 A_1 = \begin{bmatrix} 0 & -1 & 0 \\ 1 & 0 & 0 \\ 0 & 0 & 1 \end{bmatrix} \begin{bmatrix} \frac{\sqrt{2}}{2} & 0 & \frac{\sqrt{2}}{2} \\ 0 & 1 & 0 \\ -\frac{\sqrt{2}}{2} & 0 & \frac{\sqrt{2}}{2} \end{bmatrix} = \begin{bmatrix} 0 & -1 & 0 \\ \frac{\sqrt{2}}{2} & 0 & \frac{\sqrt{2}}{2} \\ -\frac{\sqrt{2}}{2} & 0 & \frac{\sqrt{2}}{2} \end{bmatrix}.$$

The image of the line segment from $(0, 0, 0)$ to $(1, 1, 1)$ is obtained by computing

$$\begin{bmatrix} 0 & -1 & 0 \\ \frac{\sqrt{2}}{2} & 0 & \frac{\sqrt{2}}{2} \\ -\frac{\sqrt{2}}{2} & 0 & \frac{\sqrt{2}}{2} \end{bmatrix} \begin{bmatrix} 0 \\ 0 \\ 0 \end{bmatrix} = \begin{bmatrix} 0 \\ 0 \\ 0 \end{bmatrix} \quad \text{and} \quad \begin{bmatrix} 0 & -1 & 0 \\ \frac{\sqrt{2}}{2} & 0 & \frac{\sqrt{2}}{2} \\ -\frac{\sqrt{2}}{2} & 0 & \frac{\sqrt{2}}{2} \end{bmatrix} \begin{bmatrix} 1 \\ 1 \\ 1 \end{bmatrix} = \begin{bmatrix} -1 \\ \sqrt{2} \\ 0 \end{bmatrix}.$$

Hence, the image is the line segment from $(0, 0, 0)$ to $(-1, \sqrt{2}, 0)$.

52. A rotation of 45° about the z-axis is given by

$$A_1 = \begin{bmatrix} \cos 45° & -\sin 45° & 0 \\ \sin 45° & \cos 45° & 0 \\ 0 & 0 & 1 \end{bmatrix} = \begin{bmatrix} \dfrac{\sqrt{2}}{2} & -\dfrac{\sqrt{2}}{2} & 0 \\ \dfrac{\sqrt{2}}{2} & \dfrac{\sqrt{2}}{2} & 0 \\ 0 & 0 & 1 \end{bmatrix}$$

while a rotation of 135° about the x-axis is given by

$$A_2 = \begin{bmatrix} 1 & 0 & 0 \\ 0 & \cos 135° & -\sin 135° \\ 0 & \sin 135° & \cos 135° \end{bmatrix} = \begin{bmatrix} 1 & 0 & 0 \\ 0 & -\dfrac{\sqrt{2}}{2} & -\dfrac{\sqrt{2}}{2} \\ 0 & \dfrac{\sqrt{2}}{2} & -\dfrac{\sqrt{2}}{2} \end{bmatrix}$$

Thus, the desired matrix is

$$A = A_2 A_1 = \begin{bmatrix} 1 & 0 & 0 \\ 0 & -\dfrac{\sqrt{2}}{2} & -\dfrac{\sqrt{2}}{2} \\ 0 & \dfrac{\sqrt{2}}{2} & -\dfrac{\sqrt{2}}{2} \end{bmatrix} \begin{bmatrix} \dfrac{\sqrt{2}}{2} & -\dfrac{\sqrt{2}}{2} & 0 \\ \dfrac{\sqrt{2}}{2} & \dfrac{\sqrt{2}}{2} & 0 \\ 0 & 0 & 1 \end{bmatrix} = \begin{bmatrix} \dfrac{\sqrt{2}}{2} & -\dfrac{\sqrt{2}}{2} & 0 \\ -\dfrac{1}{2} & -\dfrac{1}{2} & -\dfrac{\sqrt{2}}{2} \\ \dfrac{1}{2} & \dfrac{1}{2} & -\dfrac{\sqrt{2}}{2} \end{bmatrix}.$$

The image of the line segment from $(0, 0, 0)$ to $(1, 1, 1)$ is obtained by computing

$$\begin{bmatrix} \dfrac{\sqrt{2}}{2} & -\dfrac{\sqrt{2}}{2} & 0 \\ -\dfrac{1}{2} & -\dfrac{1}{2} & -\dfrac{\sqrt{2}}{2} \\ \dfrac{1}{2} & \dfrac{1}{2} & -\dfrac{\sqrt{2}}{2} \end{bmatrix} \begin{bmatrix} 0 \\ 0 \\ 0 \end{bmatrix} = \begin{bmatrix} 0 \\ 0 \\ 0 \end{bmatrix} \quad \text{and} \quad \begin{bmatrix} \dfrac{\sqrt{2}}{2} & -\dfrac{\sqrt{2}}{2} & 0 \\ -\dfrac{1}{2} & -\dfrac{1}{2} & -\dfrac{\sqrt{2}}{2} \\ \dfrac{1}{2} & \dfrac{1}{2} & -\dfrac{\sqrt{2}}{2} \end{bmatrix} \begin{bmatrix} 1 \\ 1 \\ 1 \end{bmatrix} = \begin{bmatrix} 0 \\ (-2 - \sqrt{2})/2 \\ (2 - \sqrt{2})/2 \end{bmatrix}.$$

Hence, the image is the line segment from $(0, 0, 0)$ to $\left(0, (-2 - \sqrt{2})/2, (2 - \sqrt{2})/2\right)$.

Chapter 6   ❑   Review Exercises

2. (a) $T(\mathbf{v}) = T(-3, 2, 5) = (0, -1, 7)$.

(b) The preimage of $\mathbf{w}$ is given by solving the equation

$$T(v_1, v_2, v_3) = (0, v_1 + v_2, v_2 + v_3) = (0, 2, 5).$$

The resulting system of linear equations has the solution of the form $v_1 = t - 3$, $v_2 = 5 - t$, $v_3 = t$, where t is any real number. Thus, the preimage of $\mathbf{w}$ is $\{(t - 3, 5 - t, t) \mid t \in R\}$.

4. T does not preserve addition or scalar multiplication, and hence, T is *not* a linear transformation. A counterexample is

$$T(1, 1) + T(1, 0) = (4, 1) + (4, 0) = (8, 1) \neq (5, 1) = T(2, 1).$$

6. *T* does not preserve addition or scalar multiplication, and hence, *T* is *not* a linear transformation. A counterexample is

$$-2T(3, -3) = -2(|3|, |-3|) = (-6, -6) \neq (6, 6)$$
$$= T(-6, 6) = T(-2(3), -2(-3)).$$

8. *T* preserves addition.

$$T(x_1, y_1, z_1) + T(x_2, y_2, z_2) = (z_1, y_1, x_1) + (z_2, y_2, x_2)$$
$$= (z_1 + z_2, y_1 + y_2, x_1 + x_2)$$
$$= T(x_1 + x_2, y_1 + y_2, z_1 + z_2)$$

T preserves scalar multiplication.

$$cT(x, y, z) = c(z, y, x) = (cz, cy, cx) = T(cx, cy, cz)$$

Thus, *T* is a linear transformation with standard matrix

$$\begin{bmatrix} 0 & 0 & 1 \\ 0 & 1 & 0 \\ 1 & 0 & 0 \end{bmatrix}.$$

10. Since $(0, 1, 1) = (1, 1, 1) - (1, 0, 0)$, we have

$$T(0, 1, 1) = T(1, 1, 1) - T(1, 0, 0)$$
$$= 1 - 3$$
$$= -2.$$

12. The standard matrix for *T* is

$$A = \begin{bmatrix} 1 & 0 & 0 \\ 0 & 1 & 0 \\ 0 & 0 & 0 \end{bmatrix}.$$

Therefore, we have

$$A^2 = \begin{bmatrix} 1 & 0 & 0 \\ 0 & 1 & 0 \\ 0 & 0 & 0 \end{bmatrix}\begin{bmatrix} 1 & 0 & 0 \\ 0 & 1 & 0 \\ 0 & 0 & 0 \end{bmatrix} = \begin{bmatrix} 1 & 0 & 0 \\ 0 & 1 & 0 \\ 0 & 0 & 0 \end{bmatrix} = A.$$

14. The standard matrix for *T*, relative to $B = \{1, x, x^2, x^3\}$, is

$$A = \begin{bmatrix} 0 & 1 & 0 & 0 \\ 0 & 0 & 2 & 0 \\ 0 & 0 & 0 & 3 \\ 0 & 0 & 0 & 0 \end{bmatrix}.$$

Therefore, we have

$$A^2 = \begin{bmatrix} 0 & 1 & 0 & 0 \\ 0 & 0 & 2 & 0 \\ 0 & 0 & 0 & 3 \\ 0 & 0 & 0 & 0 \end{bmatrix}\begin{bmatrix} 0 & 1 & 0 & 0 \\ 0 & 0 & 2 & 0 \\ 0 & 0 & 0 & 3 \\ 0 & 0 & 0 & 0 \end{bmatrix} = \begin{bmatrix} 0 & 0 & 2 & 0 \\ 0 & 0 & 0 & 6 \\ 0 & 0 & 0 & 0 \\ 0 & 0 & 0 & 0 \end{bmatrix}.$$

16. (a) Since A is a 1×2 matrix, it maps R^2 into $R^1 (n = 2, m = 1)$.

(b) Since $T(\mathbf{v}) = A\mathbf{v}$ and

$$A\mathbf{v} = \begin{bmatrix} 1 & 1 \end{bmatrix} \begin{bmatrix} 2 \\ 3 \end{bmatrix} = 5, \text{ it follows that } T(2, 3) = 5.$$

(c) The preimage of $\mathbf{w} = (4)$ is given by the solution to this equation

$$T(v_1, v_2) = \mathbf{w} = (4).$$

The equivalent system of linear equations is $v_1 + v_2 = 4$, which has the solution $\{(4 - t, t) \mid t \in R\}$.

18. (a) Since A is a 3×2 matrix, it maps R^2 into $R^3 (n = 2, m = 3)$.

(b) Since $T(\mathbf{v}) = A\mathbf{v}$ and

$$A\mathbf{v} = \begin{bmatrix} 4 & 0 \\ 0 & 5 \\ 1 & 1 \end{bmatrix} \begin{bmatrix} 2 \\ 2 \end{bmatrix} = \begin{bmatrix} 8 \\ 10 \\ 4 \end{bmatrix}$$

it follows that $T(2, 2) = (8, 10, 4)$.

(c) The preimage of $\mathbf{w} = (4, -5, 0)$ is given by the solution to the equation

$$T(v_1, v_2) = (4, -5, 0) = \mathbf{w}.$$

The equivalent system of linear equations has the solution $v_1 = 1$ and $v_2 = -1$. Thus, the preimage is $(1, -1)$.

20. (a) The standard matrix for T is

$$A = \begin{bmatrix} 1 & 2 & 0 \\ 0 & 1 & 2 \\ 2 & 0 & 1 \end{bmatrix}.$$

Solving $A\mathbf{v} = \mathbf{0}$ yields the solution $\mathbf{v} = \mathbf{0}$. Thus, $\ker(T)$ consists of the zero vector, $\ker(T) = \{(0, 0, 0)\}$.

(b) Since $\ker(T)$ is dimension 0, $\text{range}(T)$ must be all of R^3. Hence, a basis for the range is

$$\{(1, 0, 0), (0, 1, 0), (0, 0, 1)\}.$$

22. (a) To find the kernel of T, we row-reduce A,

$$A = \begin{bmatrix} 2 & 1 & 3 \\ 1 & 1 & 0 \\ 0 & 1 & -3 \end{bmatrix} \Rightarrow \begin{bmatrix} 1 & 0 & 3 \\ 0 & 1 & -3 \\ 0 & 0 & 0 \end{bmatrix}$$

which shows that kernel$(T) = \{(-3t, 3t, t) \mid t \in R\}$. Thus, a basis for kernel(T) is $\{(-3, 3, 1)\}$.

(b) The range of T can be found by row-reducing the transpose of A.

$$A^T = \begin{bmatrix} 2 & 1 & 0 \\ 1 & 1 & 1 \\ 3 & 0 & -3 \end{bmatrix} \Rightarrow \begin{bmatrix} 1 & 0 & -1 \\ 0 & 1 & 2 \\ 0 & 0 & 0 \end{bmatrix}$$

Thus, a basis for range(T) is $\{(1, 0, -1), (0, 1, 2)\}$.

(c) $\dim(\text{range}(T)) = \text{rank}(T) = 2$

(d) $\dim(\ker(T)) = \text{nullity } (T) = 1$

24. Rank$(T) = \dim P_5 - \text{nullity}(T) = 6 - 4 = 2$.

26. nullity$(T) = \dim(M_{2,2}) - \text{rank}(T) = 4 - 3 = 1$.

28. The standard matrix for T is

$$A = \begin{bmatrix} \cos \theta & -\sin \theta \\ \sin \theta & \cos \theta \end{bmatrix}.$$

Since A is invertible, T is invertible, and the standard matrix for T^{-1} is

$$A^{-1} = \begin{bmatrix} \cos \theta & \sin \theta \\ -\sin \theta & \cos \theta \end{bmatrix}.$$

30. The standard matrix for T is

$$A = \begin{bmatrix} 1 & 1 & 0 \\ 0 & 1 & -1 \end{bmatrix}.$$

Since A is *not* invertible, T has no inverse.

32. The standard matrices for T_1 and T_2 are

$$A_1 = \begin{bmatrix} 1 \\ 3 \end{bmatrix} \quad \text{and} \quad A_2 = [2 \quad 1].$$

The standard matrix for $T = T_1 \circ T_2$ is

$$A = A_1 A_2 = \begin{bmatrix} 1 \\ 3 \end{bmatrix} [2 \quad 1] = \begin{bmatrix} 2 & 1 \\ 6 & 3 \end{bmatrix}$$

and the standard matrix for $T' = T_2 \circ T_1$ is

$$A' = A_2 A_1 = [2 \quad 1] \begin{bmatrix} 1 \\ 3 \end{bmatrix} = [5].$$

34. If we translate the vertex $(5, 3)$ back to the origin $(0, 0)$, then the other vertices $(3, 5)$ and $(3, 0)$ are translated to $(-2, 2)$ and $(-2, -3)$, respectively. The rotation of $90°$ is given by the matrix in Exercise 33, and we have

$$\begin{bmatrix} 0 & -1 \\ 1 & 0 \end{bmatrix}\begin{bmatrix} -2 \\ 2 \end{bmatrix} = \begin{bmatrix} -2 \\ -2 \end{bmatrix} \qquad \begin{bmatrix} 0 & -1 \\ 1 & 0 \end{bmatrix}\begin{bmatrix} -2 \\ -3 \end{bmatrix} = \begin{bmatrix} 3 \\ -2 \end{bmatrix}.$$

Translating back to the original coordinate system, the new vertices are $(5, 3)$, $(3, 1)$ and $(8, 1)$.

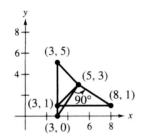

36. (a) Since $T: R^3 \rightarrow R^2$ and $\text{rank}(T) \leq 2$, $\text{nullity}(T) \geq 1$. Thus, T is not one-to-one.

(b) Since $\text{rank}(A) = 2$, T is onto.

(c) T is not invertible (A is not square!).

38. (a) Since $|A| = 40 \neq 0$, $\ker(T) = \{(0, 0, 0)\}$, and T is one-to-one.

(b) Since $\text{rank}(A) = 3$, T is onto.

(c) The transformation is one-to-one and onto, and is thus invertible.

40. (a) The standard matrix for T is

$$A = \begin{bmatrix} 0 & 2 \\ 0 & 0 \end{bmatrix}$$

so it follows that

$$Av = \begin{bmatrix} 0 & 2 \\ 0 & 0 \end{bmatrix}\begin{bmatrix} -1 \\ 3 \end{bmatrix} = \begin{bmatrix} 6 \\ 0 \end{bmatrix} \implies T(\mathbf{v}) = (6, 0).$$

(b) The image of each vector in B is as follows.

$$T(2, 1) = (2, 0) = -2(-1, 0) + 0(2, 2)$$
$$T(-1, 0) = (0, 0) = 0(-1, 0) + 0(2, 2)$$

Therefore, the matrix for T relative to B and B' is

$$A' = \begin{bmatrix} -2 & 0 \\ 0 & 0 \end{bmatrix}.$$

Since $\mathbf{v} = (-1, 3) = 3(2, 1) + 7(-1, 0)$,

$$[\mathbf{v}]_B = \begin{bmatrix} 3 \\ 7 \end{bmatrix} \quad \text{and} \quad A'[\mathbf{v}]_B = \begin{bmatrix} -2 & 0 \\ 0 & 0 \end{bmatrix}\begin{bmatrix} 3 \\ 7 \end{bmatrix} = \begin{bmatrix} -6 \\ 0 \end{bmatrix}.$$

Thus, $T(\mathbf{v}) = -6(-1, 0) + 0(2, 2) = (6, 0)$.

42. The standard matrix for T is

$$A = \begin{bmatrix} 1 & 3 & 0 \\ 3 & 1 & 0 \\ 0 & 0 & -2 \end{bmatrix}.$$

The transition matrix from B' to B, the standard matrix, is P

$$P = \begin{bmatrix} 1 & 1 & 0 \\ 1 & -1 & 0 \\ 0 & 0 & 1 \end{bmatrix} \quad P^{-1} = \begin{bmatrix} \frac{1}{2} & \frac{1}{2} & 0 \\ \frac{1}{2} & -\frac{1}{2} & 0 \\ 0 & 0 & 1 \end{bmatrix}.$$

The matrix A' for T relative to B' is

$$A' = P^{-1}AP = \begin{bmatrix} \frac{1}{2} & \frac{1}{2} & 0 \\ \frac{1}{2} & -\frac{1}{2} & 0 \\ 0 & 0 & 1 \end{bmatrix} \begin{bmatrix} 1 & 3 & 0 \\ 3 & 1 & 0 \\ 0 & 0 & -2 \end{bmatrix} \begin{bmatrix} 1 & 1 & 0 \\ 1 & -1 & 0 \\ 0 & 0 & 1 \end{bmatrix} = \begin{bmatrix} 4 & 0 & 0 \\ 0 & -2 & 0 \\ 0 & 0 & -2 \end{bmatrix}.$$

Since, $A' = P^{-1}AP$, it follows that A and A' are similar.

44. (a) Since $T(\mathbf{v}) = \text{proj}_\mathbf{u}\mathbf{v}$ where $\mathbf{u} = (4, 3)$, we have

$$T(\mathbf{v}) = \frac{4x + 3y}{25}(4, 3).$$

Thus,

$$T(1, 0) = \left(\frac{16}{25}, \frac{12}{25}\right) \quad \text{and} \quad T(0, 1) = \left(\frac{12}{25}, \frac{9}{25}\right)$$

and the standard matrix for T is

$$A = \frac{1}{25}\begin{bmatrix} 16 & 12 \\ 12 & 9 \end{bmatrix}.$$

(b) $(I - A)^2 = \left(\frac{1}{25}\begin{bmatrix} 9 & -12 \\ -12 & 16 \end{bmatrix}\right)^2 = \frac{1}{25}\begin{bmatrix} 9 & -12 \\ -12 & 16 \end{bmatrix} = I - A.$

(c) $\quad A\mathbf{v} = \frac{1}{25}\begin{bmatrix} 16 & 12 \\ 12 & 9 \end{bmatrix}\begin{bmatrix} 5 \\ 0 \end{bmatrix} = \begin{bmatrix} 16/5 \\ 12/5 \end{bmatrix}$

$(I - A)\mathbf{v} = \frac{1}{25}\begin{bmatrix} 9 & -12 \\ -12 & 16 \end{bmatrix}\begin{bmatrix} 5 \\ 0 \end{bmatrix} = \begin{bmatrix} 9/5 \\ -12/5 \end{bmatrix}$

(d)

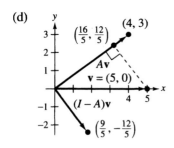

46. (a) Since $A = P^{-1}BP$ and A is invertible, we have

$$(PA^{-1}P^{-1})B = PA^{-1}(P^{-1}B) = PA^{-1}AP^{-1} = PP^{-1} = I$$

which shows that B is invertible.

(b) Since $A = P^{-1}BP$, $A^{-1} = (P^{-1}BP)^{-1} = P^{-1}B^{-1}P$, which shows that A^{-1} and B^{-1} are similar.

48. (a) Let $S = \begin{bmatrix} 1 & 0 \\ 0 & 0 \end{bmatrix}$ and $T = \begin{bmatrix} 0 & 0 \\ 0 & 1 \end{bmatrix}$.

Then $S + T = \begin{bmatrix} 1 & 0 \\ 0 & 1 \end{bmatrix}$ and $\text{rank}(S + T) = \text{rank}(S) + \text{rank}(T)$.

(b) Let $S = T = \begin{bmatrix} 1 & 0 \\ 0 & 0 \end{bmatrix}$.

Then $S + T = \begin{bmatrix} 2 & 0 \\ 0 & 0 \end{bmatrix}$ and $\text{rank}(S + T) = 1 < 2 = \text{rank}(S) + \text{rank}(T)$.

50. (a) Suppose that $(S \circ T)(\mathbf{v}_1) = (S \circ T)(\mathbf{v}_2)$. Since S is one-to-one, $T(\mathbf{v}_1) = T(\mathbf{v}_2)$. Since T is one-to-one, $\mathbf{v}_1 = \mathbf{v}_2$, and we have shown that $S \circ T$ is one-to-one.

(b) Let $\mathbf{v} \in \text{kernel}(T)$, which implies that $T(\mathbf{v}) = \mathbf{0}$. Clearly $(S \circ T)(\mathbf{v}) = \mathbf{0}$ as well, which shows that $\mathbf{v} \in \text{kernel}(S \circ T)$.

(c) Let $\mathbf{w} \in W$. Since $S \circ T$ is onto, there exists $\mathbf{v} \in V$ such that $(S \circ T)(\mathbf{v}) = \mathbf{w}$. Hence, $S(T(\mathbf{v})) = \mathbf{w}$, and S is onto.

52. We compute the images of the basis vectors under D_x.

$$D_x(1) = 0$$
$$D_x(x) = 1$$
$$D_x(\sin x) = \cos x$$
$$D_x(\cos x) = -\sin x$$

Thus, the matrix of D_x relative to this basis is

$$\begin{bmatrix} 0 & 1 & 0 & 0 \\ 0 & 0 & 0 & 0 \\ 0 & 0 & 0 & -1 \\ 0 & 0 & 1 & 0 \end{bmatrix}.$$

The range of D_x is spanned by $\{x, \sin x, \cos x\}$, whereas the kernel is spanned by $\{1\}$.

54. We first compute the effect of T on the basis $\{1, x, x^2, x^3\}$.

$$T(1) = 1$$
$$T(x) = 1 + x$$
$$T(x^2) = 2x + x^2$$
$$T(x^3) = 3x^2 + x^3$$

The standard matrix for T is thus

$$A = \begin{bmatrix} 1 & 1 & 0 & 0 \\ 0 & 1 & 2 & 0 \\ 0 & 0 & 1 & 3 \\ 0 & 0 & 0 & 1 \end{bmatrix}.$$

Since the rank$(A) = 4$, the rank$(T) = 4$ and nullity$(T) = 0$.

56. (a) T is a horizontal shear.

(b)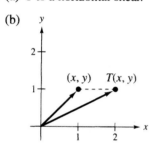

58. (a) T is a horizontal expansion.

(b)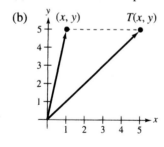

60. The image of each vertex is $T(0, 0) = (0, 0)$, $T(1, 0) = (2, 0)$, $T(0, 1) = (0, 1)$.
A sketch of the triangle and its image follows.

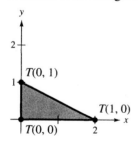

62. The image of each vertex is $T(0, 0) = (0, 0)$, $T(1, 0) = (1, 2)$, $T(0, 1) = (0, 1)$.

A sketch of the triangle and its image follows.

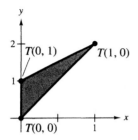

64. The transformation is a vertical shear

$$\begin{bmatrix} 1 & 0 \\ 3 & 1 \end{bmatrix}$$

followed by a vertical expansion $\begin{bmatrix} 1 & 0 \\ 0 & 2 \end{bmatrix}$.

66. A rotation of $90°$ about the x-axis is given by

$$A = \begin{bmatrix} 1 & 0 & 0 \\ 0 & \cos 90° & -\sin 90° \\ 0 & \sin 90° & \cos 90° \end{bmatrix} = \begin{bmatrix} 1 & 0 & 0 \\ 0 & 0 & -1 \\ 0 & 1 & 0 \end{bmatrix}.$$

Since

$$A\mathbf{v} = \begin{bmatrix} 1 & 0 & 0 \\ 0 & 0 & -1 \\ 0 & 1 & 0 \end{bmatrix}\begin{bmatrix} 1 \\ -1 \\ 1 \end{bmatrix} = \begin{bmatrix} 1 \\ -1 \\ -1 \end{bmatrix}$$

the image of $(1, -1, 1)$ is $(1, -1, -1)$.

68. A rotation of $120°$ about the y-axis is given by

$$A_1 = \begin{bmatrix} \cos 120° & 0 & \sin 120° \\ 0 & 1 & 0 \\ -\sin 120° & 0 & \cos 120° \end{bmatrix} = \begin{bmatrix} -\dfrac{1}{2} & 0 & \dfrac{\sqrt{3}}{2} \\ 0 & 1 & 0 \\ -\dfrac{\sqrt{3}}{2} & 0 & -\dfrac{1}{2} \end{bmatrix}$$

while a rotation of $45°$ about the z-axis is given by

$$A_2 = \begin{bmatrix} \cos 45° & -\sin 45° & 0 \\ \sin 45° & \cos 45° & 0 \\ 0 & 0 & 1 \end{bmatrix} = \begin{bmatrix} \dfrac{\sqrt{2}}{2} & -\dfrac{\sqrt{2}}{2} & 0 \\ \dfrac{\sqrt{2}}{2} & \dfrac{\sqrt{2}}{2} & 0 \\ 0 & 0 & 1 \end{bmatrix}.$$

—CONTINUED—

68. —**CONTINUED**—

Thus, the pair of rotations is given by

$$A_2 A_1 = \begin{bmatrix} \dfrac{\sqrt{2}}{2} & -\dfrac{\sqrt{2}}{2} & 0 \\ \dfrac{\sqrt{2}}{2} & \dfrac{\sqrt{2}}{2} & 0 \\ 0 & 0 & 1 \end{bmatrix} \begin{bmatrix} -\dfrac{1}{2} & 0 & \dfrac{\sqrt{3}}{2} \\ 0 & 1 & 0 \\ -\dfrac{\sqrt{3}}{2} & 0 & -\dfrac{1}{2} \end{bmatrix} = \begin{bmatrix} -\dfrac{\sqrt{2}}{4} & -\dfrac{\sqrt{2}}{2} & \dfrac{\sqrt{6}}{4} \\ -\dfrac{\sqrt{2}}{4} & \dfrac{\sqrt{2}}{2} & \dfrac{\sqrt{6}}{4} \\ -\dfrac{\sqrt{3}}{2} & 0 & -\dfrac{1}{2} \end{bmatrix}.$$

70. The standard matrix for T is

$$\begin{bmatrix} 1 & 0 & 0 \\ 0 & \cos 90° & -\sin 90° \\ 0 & \sin 90° & \cos 90° \end{bmatrix} = \begin{bmatrix} 1 & 0 & 0 \\ 0 & 0 & -1 \\ 0 & 1 & 0 \end{bmatrix}.$$

Therefore, T is given by $T(x, y, z) = (x, -z, y)$. The image of each vertex is as follows

$T(0, 0, 0) = (0, 0, 0)$

$T(1, 1, 0) = (1, 0, 1)$

$T(0, 0, 1) = (0, -1, 0)$

$T(1, 1, 1) = (1, -1, 1)$

$T(1, 0, 0) = (1, 0, 0)$

$T(0, 1, 0) = (0, 0, 1)$

$T(1, 0, 1) = (1, -1, 0)$

$T(0, 1, 1) = (0, -1, 1)$.

72. (a) *True.* The statement is true because if T is a reflection $T(x, y) = (x, -y)$, then the standard matrix is

$$\begin{bmatrix} 1 & 0 \\ 0 & -1 \end{bmatrix}.$$

(b) *True.* The statement is true because the linear transformation $T(x, y) = (x, ky)$ has the standard matrix.

$$\begin{bmatrix} 1 & 0 \\ 0 & k \end{bmatrix}.$$

(c) *True.* The statement is true because the matrix

$$\begin{bmatrix} \cos(\theta) & 0 & \sin(\theta) \\ 0 & 1 & 0 \\ -\sin(\theta) & 0 & \cos(\theta) \end{bmatrix}$$

will rotate a point θ degrees (page 401). If $\theta = 30$ degrees we obtain the matrix in the statement.

74. (a) *True.* D_x is a linear transformation because it preserves addition and scalar multiplication. Further, $D_x(P_n) = P_{n-1}$ because for all natural numbers $i \geq 1$ $D_x(x^i) = ix^{i-1}$.

(b) *False.* If T is a linear transformation $V \to W$, then kernel of T is defined to be a set of $\mathbf{v} \in V$, such that $T(\mathbf{v}) = \mathbf{0}_W$.

(c) *True.* If $T = T_2 \circ T_1$ and A_i is the standard matrix for T_i, $i = 1, 2$, then the standard matrix for T is equal $A_2 A_1$ by Theorem 6.11 on page 382.

Chapter 6 ❑ Project Solutions

Reflections in the Plane-I

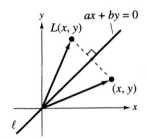

ax + by = 0

1.

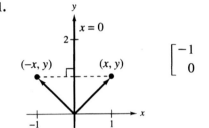

$$\begin{bmatrix} -1 & 0 \\ 0 & 1 \end{bmatrix}$$

2.

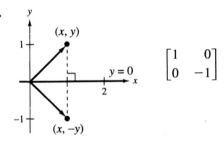

$$\begin{bmatrix} 1 & 0 \\ 0 & -1 \end{bmatrix}$$

3.

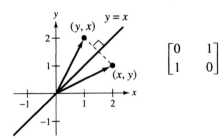

$$\begin{bmatrix} 0 & 1 \\ 1 & 0 \end{bmatrix}$$

4. $\mathbf{v} = (2, 1)$ $B = \{\mathbf{v}, \mathbf{w}\}$

 $\mathbf{w} = (-1, 2)$

 $L(\mathbf{v}) = \mathbf{v}$ $\begin{bmatrix} 1 & 0 \\ 0 & -1 \end{bmatrix} = A$

 $L(\mathbf{w}) = -\mathbf{w}$

 $B' = \{\mathbf{e}_1, \mathbf{e}_2\}$ standard basis

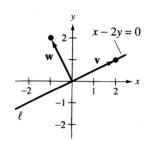

A is a matrix of L relative to basis B.

$A' = P^{-1}AP$ matrix of L relative to the standard basis B'.

$$[B' \vdots B] \rightarrow [I \vdots P^{-1}] \Rightarrow P^{-1} = \begin{bmatrix} 2 & -1 \\ 1 & 2 \end{bmatrix} \Rightarrow P = \tfrac{1}{5}\begin{bmatrix} 2 & 1 \\ -1 & 2 \end{bmatrix}$$

$$A' = P^{-1}AP = \tfrac{1}{5}\begin{bmatrix} 2 & -1 \\ 1 & 2 \end{bmatrix}\begin{bmatrix} 1 & 0 \\ 0 & -1 \end{bmatrix}\begin{bmatrix} 2 & 1 \\ -1 & 2 \end{bmatrix}$$

$$= \tfrac{1}{5}\begin{bmatrix} 2 & 1 \\ 1 & -2 \end{bmatrix}\begin{bmatrix} 2 & 1 \\ -1 & 2 \end{bmatrix} = \tfrac{1}{5}\begin{bmatrix} 3 & 4 \\ 4 & -3 \end{bmatrix} = \begin{bmatrix} \tfrac{3}{5} & \tfrac{4}{5} \\ \tfrac{4}{5} & -\tfrac{3}{5} \end{bmatrix}.$$

$$\begin{bmatrix} \tfrac{3}{5} & \tfrac{4}{5} \\ \tfrac{4}{5} & -\tfrac{3}{5} \end{bmatrix}\begin{bmatrix} 2 \\ 1 \end{bmatrix} = \begin{bmatrix} 2 \\ 1 \end{bmatrix}$$

$$\begin{bmatrix} \tfrac{3}{5} & \tfrac{4}{5} \\ \tfrac{4}{5} & -\tfrac{3}{5} \end{bmatrix}\begin{bmatrix} -1 \\ 2 \end{bmatrix} = \begin{bmatrix} 1 \\ -2 \end{bmatrix}$$

$$\begin{bmatrix} \tfrac{3}{5} & \tfrac{4}{5} \\ \tfrac{4}{5} & -\tfrac{3}{5} \end{bmatrix}\begin{bmatrix} 5 \\ 0 \end{bmatrix} = \begin{bmatrix} 3 \\ 4 \end{bmatrix}$$

5. $\mathbf{v} = (-b, a)$ $A = \begin{bmatrix} 1 & 0 \\ 0 & -1 \end{bmatrix}$

 $\mathbf{w} = (a, b)$

 $P^{-1} = \begin{bmatrix} -b & a \\ a & b \end{bmatrix}$

 $P = \dfrac{1}{a^2 + b^2}\begin{bmatrix} -b & +a \\ +a & +b \end{bmatrix}$

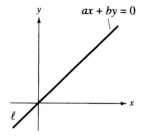

$$A' = P^{-1}AP = \begin{bmatrix} -b & a \\ a & b \end{bmatrix}\begin{bmatrix} 1 & 0 \\ 0 & -1 \end{bmatrix}P = \begin{bmatrix} -b & -a \\ a & -b \end{bmatrix}\begin{bmatrix} -b & a \\ a & b \end{bmatrix}\dfrac{1}{a^2 + b^2}$$

$$= \dfrac{1}{a^2 + b^2}\begin{bmatrix} b^2 - a^2 & -2ab \\ -2ab & a^2 - b^2 \end{bmatrix}$$

6. $3x + 4y = 0$ $A' = \dfrac{1}{3^2 + 4^2}\begin{bmatrix} 7 & -24 \\ -24 & -7 \end{bmatrix}$

$$\dfrac{1}{25}\begin{bmatrix} 7 & -24 \\ -24 & -7 \end{bmatrix}\begin{bmatrix} 3 \\ 4 \end{bmatrix} = \dfrac{1}{25}\begin{bmatrix} -75 \\ -100 \end{bmatrix} = \begin{bmatrix} -3 \\ -4 \end{bmatrix}$$

$$\dfrac{1}{25}\begin{bmatrix} 7 & -24 \\ -24 & -7 \end{bmatrix}\begin{bmatrix} -4 \\ 3 \end{bmatrix} = \dfrac{1}{25}\begin{bmatrix} -100 \\ 75 \end{bmatrix} = \begin{bmatrix} -4 \\ 3 \end{bmatrix}$$

$$\dfrac{1}{25}\begin{bmatrix} 7 & -24 \\ -24 & -7 \end{bmatrix}\begin{bmatrix} 0 \\ 5 \end{bmatrix} = \dfrac{1}{25}\begin{bmatrix} -24 \cdot 5 \\ -7 \cdot 5 \end{bmatrix} = \begin{bmatrix} -24/5 \\ -7/5 \end{bmatrix}$$

Reflections in the Plane-II

1. $\mathbf{v} = (0, 1)$ $\begin{bmatrix} 0 & 0 \\ 0 & 1 \end{bmatrix}$ **2.** $\mathbf{v} = (1, 0)$ $\begin{bmatrix} 1 & 0 \\ 0 & 0 \end{bmatrix}$

3. $\mathbf{v} = (2, 1)$ $B = \{\mathbf{v}, \mathbf{w}\}$
$\mathbf{w} = (-1, 2)$

$\left.\begin{array}{l} \text{proj}_{\mathbf{v}}\mathbf{v} = \mathbf{v} \\ \text{proj}_{\mathbf{v}}\mathbf{w} = \mathbf{0} \end{array}\right\}$ $A = \begin{bmatrix} 1 & 0 \\ 0 & 0 \end{bmatrix}$

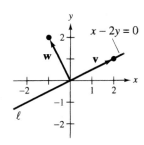

$P^{-1} = \begin{bmatrix} 2 & -1 \\ 1 & 2 \end{bmatrix}$, $P = \frac{1}{5}\begin{bmatrix} 2 & 1 \\ -1 & 2 \end{bmatrix}$

$A' = P^{-1}AP = $ matrix of L relative to standard basis.

$$= \begin{bmatrix} 2 & -1 \\ 1 & 2 \end{bmatrix}\begin{bmatrix} 1 & 0 \\ 0 & 0 \end{bmatrix}P = \begin{bmatrix} 2 & 0 \\ 1 & 0 \end{bmatrix}\begin{bmatrix} 2 & 1 \\ -1 & 2 \end{bmatrix}\frac{1}{5} = \begin{bmatrix} \frac{4}{5} & \frac{2}{5} \\ \frac{2}{5} & \frac{1}{5} \end{bmatrix}$$

$$\begin{bmatrix} \frac{4}{5} & \frac{2}{5} \\ \frac{2}{5} & \frac{1}{5} \end{bmatrix}\begin{bmatrix} 2 \\ 1 \end{bmatrix} = \begin{bmatrix} 2 \\ 1 \end{bmatrix}, \quad \begin{bmatrix} \frac{4}{5} & \frac{2}{5} \\ \frac{2}{5} & \frac{1}{5} \end{bmatrix}\begin{bmatrix} -1 \\ 2 \end{bmatrix} = \begin{bmatrix} 0 \\ 0 \end{bmatrix}$$

$$\begin{bmatrix} \frac{4}{5} & \frac{2}{5} \\ \frac{2}{5} & \frac{1}{5} \end{bmatrix}\begin{bmatrix} 5 \\ 0 \end{bmatrix} = \begin{bmatrix} 4 \\ 2 \end{bmatrix}$$

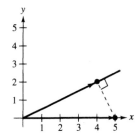

4. $\mathbf{v} = (-b, a)$ $A = \begin{bmatrix} 1 & 0 \\ 0 & 0 \end{bmatrix}$
$\mathbf{w} = (a, b)$

$P^{-1} = \begin{bmatrix} -b & a \\ a & b \end{bmatrix}$ $P = \frac{1}{a^2 + b^2}\begin{bmatrix} -b & a \\ a & b \end{bmatrix}$

$A' = P^{-1}AP = \dfrac{1}{a^2 + b^2}\begin{bmatrix} b^2 & -ab \\ -ab & a^2 \end{bmatrix}$

5. $\text{proj}_{\mathbf{v}}\mathbf{u} = \dfrac{1}{2}(\mathbf{u} + L(\mathbf{u})) \Rightarrow L(\mathbf{u}) = 2\text{proj}_{\mathbf{v}}\mathbf{u} - \mathbf{u}$

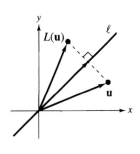

$L = 2\,\text{proj}_{\mathbf{v}} - I$

$$= 2\frac{1}{a^2 + b^2}\begin{bmatrix} b^2 & -ab \\ -ab & a^2 \end{bmatrix} - \begin{bmatrix} 1 & 0 \\ 0 & 1 \end{bmatrix}$$

$$= \frac{1}{a^2 + b^2}\left(\begin{bmatrix} 2b^2 & -2ab \\ -2ab & 2a^2 \end{bmatrix} - \begin{bmatrix} a^2 + b^2 & 0 \\ 0 & a^2 + b^2 \end{bmatrix}\right)$$

$$= \frac{1}{a^2 + b^2}\begin{bmatrix} b^2 - a^2 & -2ab \\ -2ab & a^2 - b^2 \end{bmatrix}$$

Section 7.1   Eigenvalues and Eigenvectors

2. $A\mathbf{x}_1 = \begin{bmatrix} 4 & -5 \\ 2 & -3 \end{bmatrix} \begin{bmatrix} 1 \\ 1 \end{bmatrix} = \begin{bmatrix} -1 \\ -1 \end{bmatrix} = -1 \begin{bmatrix} 1 \\ 1 \end{bmatrix} = \lambda_1 \mathbf{x}_1$

$A\mathbf{x}_2 = \begin{bmatrix} 4 & -5 \\ 2 & -3 \end{bmatrix} \begin{bmatrix} 5 \\ 2 \end{bmatrix} = \begin{bmatrix} 10 \\ 4 \end{bmatrix} = 2 \begin{bmatrix} 5 \\ 2 \end{bmatrix} = \lambda_2 \mathbf{x}_2$

4. $A\mathbf{x}_1 = \begin{bmatrix} 2 & 3 & 1 \\ 0 & -1 & 2 \\ 0 & 0 & 3 \end{bmatrix} \begin{bmatrix} 1 \\ 0 \\ 0 \end{bmatrix} = \begin{bmatrix} 2 \\ 0 \\ 0 \end{bmatrix} = 2 \begin{bmatrix} 1 \\ 0 \\ 0 \end{bmatrix} = \lambda_1 \mathbf{x}_1$

$A\mathbf{x}_2 = \begin{bmatrix} 2 & 3 & 1 \\ 0 & -1 & 2 \\ 0 & 0 & 3 \end{bmatrix} \begin{bmatrix} 1 \\ -1 \\ 0 \end{bmatrix} = \begin{bmatrix} -1 \\ 1 \\ 0 \end{bmatrix} = -1 \begin{bmatrix} 1 \\ -1 \\ 0 \end{bmatrix} = \lambda_2 \mathbf{x}_2$

$A\mathbf{x}_3 = \begin{bmatrix} 2 & 3 & 1 \\ 0 & -1 & 2 \\ 0 & 0 & 3 \end{bmatrix} \begin{bmatrix} 5 \\ 1 \\ 2 \end{bmatrix} = \begin{bmatrix} 15 \\ 3 \\ 6 \end{bmatrix} = 3 \begin{bmatrix} 5 \\ 1 \\ 2 \end{bmatrix} = \lambda_3 \mathbf{x}_3$

6. $A\mathbf{x}_1 = \begin{bmatrix} 0 & 1 & 0 \\ 0 & 0 & 1 \\ 1 & 0 & 0 \end{bmatrix} \begin{bmatrix} 1 \\ 1 \\ 1 \end{bmatrix} = \begin{bmatrix} 1 \\ 1 \\ 1 \end{bmatrix} = 1 \begin{bmatrix} 1 \\ 1 \\ 1 \end{bmatrix} = \lambda_1 \mathbf{x}_1$

8. (a) $A(c\mathbf{x}_1) = \begin{bmatrix} 2 & 3 & 1 \\ 0 & -1 & 2 \\ 0 & 0 & 3 \end{bmatrix} \begin{bmatrix} c \\ 0 \\ 0 \end{bmatrix} = \begin{bmatrix} 2c \\ 0 \\ 0 \end{bmatrix} = 2 \begin{bmatrix} c \\ 0 \\ 0 \end{bmatrix} = 2(c\mathbf{x}_1)$

(b) $A(c\mathbf{x}_2) = \begin{bmatrix} 2 & 3 & 1 \\ 0 & -1 & 2 \\ 0 & 0 & 3 \end{bmatrix} \begin{bmatrix} c \\ -c \\ 0 \end{bmatrix} = \begin{bmatrix} -c \\ c \\ 0 \end{bmatrix} = -1 \begin{bmatrix} c \\ -c \\ 0 \end{bmatrix} = -(c\mathbf{x}_2)$

(c) $A(c\mathbf{x}_3) = \begin{bmatrix} 2 & 3 & 1 \\ 0 & -1 & 2 \\ 0 & 0 & 3 \end{bmatrix} \begin{bmatrix} 5c \\ c \\ 2c \end{bmatrix} = \begin{bmatrix} 15c \\ 3c \\ 6c \end{bmatrix} = 3 \begin{bmatrix} 5c \\ c \\ 2c \end{bmatrix} = 3(c\mathbf{x}_3)$

10. (a) Since

$$A\mathbf{x} = \begin{bmatrix} -3 & 10 \\ 5 & 2 \end{bmatrix} \begin{bmatrix} 4 \\ 4 \end{bmatrix} = \begin{bmatrix} 28 \\ 28 \end{bmatrix} = 7 \begin{bmatrix} 4 \\ 4 \end{bmatrix}$$

$\mathbf{x}$ *is* an eigenvector of A (with corresponding eigenvalue 7).

(b) Since

$$A\mathbf{x} = \begin{bmatrix} -3 & 10 \\ 5 & 2 \end{bmatrix} \begin{bmatrix} -8 \\ 4 \end{bmatrix} = \begin{bmatrix} 64 \\ -32 \end{bmatrix} = -8 \begin{bmatrix} -8 \\ 4 \end{bmatrix}$$

$\mathbf{x}$ *is* an eigenvector of A (with corresponding eigenvalue -8).

(c) Since

$$A\mathbf{x} = \begin{bmatrix} -3 & 10 \\ 5 & 2 \end{bmatrix} \begin{bmatrix} -4 \\ 8 \end{bmatrix} = \begin{bmatrix} 92 \\ -4 \end{bmatrix} \neq \lambda \begin{bmatrix} -4 \\ 8 \end{bmatrix}$$

$\mathbf{x}$ is *not* an eigenvector of A.

(d) Since

$$A\mathbf{x} = \begin{bmatrix} -3 & 10 \\ 5 & 2 \end{bmatrix} \begin{bmatrix} 5 \\ -3 \end{bmatrix} = \begin{bmatrix} -45 \\ 19 \end{bmatrix} \neq \lambda \begin{bmatrix} 5 \\ -3 \end{bmatrix}$$

$\mathbf{x}$ is *not* an eigenvector of A

12. (a) Since

$$A\mathbf{x} = \begin{bmatrix} 1 & 0 & 5 \\ 0 & -2 & 4 \\ 1 & -2 & 9 \end{bmatrix} \begin{bmatrix} 1 \\ 1 \\ 0 \end{bmatrix} = \begin{bmatrix} 1 \\ -2 \\ -1 \end{bmatrix} \neq \lambda \begin{bmatrix} 1 \\ 1 \\ 0 \end{bmatrix}$$

$\mathbf{x}$ is *not* an eigenvector of A.

(b) Since

$$A\mathbf{x} = \begin{bmatrix} 1 & 0 & 5 \\ 0 & -2 & 4 \\ 1 & -2 & 9 \end{bmatrix} \begin{bmatrix} -5 \\ 2 \\ 1 \end{bmatrix} = \begin{bmatrix} 0 \\ 0 \\ 0 \end{bmatrix} = 0 \begin{bmatrix} -5 \\ 2 \\ 1 \end{bmatrix}$$

$\mathbf{x}$ *is* an eigenvector (with corresponding eigenvalue 0).

(c) The zero vector is never an eigenvector.

(d) Since

$$A\mathbf{x} = \begin{bmatrix} 1 & 0 & 5 \\ 0 & -2 & 4 \\ 1 & -2 & 9 \end{bmatrix} \begin{bmatrix} 2\sqrt{6} - 3 \\ -2\sqrt{6} + 6 \\ 3 \end{bmatrix} = \begin{bmatrix} 12 + 2\sqrt{6} \\ 4\sqrt{6} \\ 6\sqrt{6} + 12 \end{bmatrix} = (4 + 2\sqrt{6}) \begin{bmatrix} 2\sqrt{6} - 3 \\ -2\sqrt{6} + 6 \\ 3 \end{bmatrix}$$

$\mathbf{x}$ *is* an eigenvector of A $\left(\text{with corresponding eigenvalue } 4 + 2\sqrt{6}\right)$.

14. (a) The characteristic equation is

$$|\lambda I - A| = \begin{vmatrix} \lambda - 1 & 4 \\ 2 & \lambda - 8 \end{vmatrix} = \lambda^2 - 9\lambda = \lambda(\lambda - 9) = 0.$$

(b) The eigenvalues are $\lambda_1 = 0$ and $\lambda_2 = 9$. For $\lambda_1 = 0$, we have

$$\begin{bmatrix} \lambda_1 - 1 & 4 \\ 2 & \lambda_1 - 8 \end{bmatrix}\begin{bmatrix} x_1 \\ x_2 \end{bmatrix} = \begin{bmatrix} 0 \\ 0 \end{bmatrix} \implies \begin{bmatrix} 1 & -4 \\ 0 & 0 \end{bmatrix}\begin{bmatrix} x_1 \\ x_2 \end{bmatrix} = \begin{bmatrix} 0 \\ 0 \end{bmatrix}.$$

The solution is $\{(4t, t) : t \in R\}$. Thus, an eigenvector corresponding to $\lambda_1 = 0$ is $(4, 1)$. For $\lambda_2 = 9$, we have

$$\begin{bmatrix} \lambda_2 - 1 & 4 \\ 2 & \lambda_2 - 8 \end{bmatrix}\begin{bmatrix} x_1 \\ x_2 \end{bmatrix} = \begin{bmatrix} 0 \\ 0 \end{bmatrix} \implies \begin{bmatrix} 2 & 1 \\ 0 & 0 \end{bmatrix}\begin{bmatrix} x_1 \\ x_2 \end{bmatrix} = \begin{bmatrix} 0 \\ 0 \end{bmatrix}$$

The solution is $\{(-t, 2t) : t \in R\}$. Thus, an eigenvector corresponding to $\lambda_2 = 9$ is $(-1, 2)$.

16. (a) The characteristic equation is

$$|\lambda I - A| = \begin{vmatrix} \lambda - \frac{1}{4} & -\frac{1}{4} \\ -\frac{1}{2} & \lambda \end{vmatrix} = \lambda^2 - \frac{1}{4}\lambda - \frac{1}{8} = \left(\lambda - \frac{1}{2}\right)\left(\lambda + \frac{1}{4}\right) = 0.$$

(b) The eigenvalues are $\lambda_1 = \frac{1}{2}$ and $\lambda_2 = -\frac{1}{4}$. For $\lambda_1 = \frac{1}{2}$, we have

$$\begin{bmatrix} \lambda_1 - \frac{1}{4} & -\frac{1}{4} \\ -\frac{1}{2} & \lambda_1 \end{bmatrix}\begin{bmatrix} x_1 \\ x_2 \end{bmatrix} = \begin{bmatrix} 0 \\ 0 \end{bmatrix} \implies \begin{bmatrix} 1 & -1 \\ 0 & 0 \end{bmatrix}\begin{bmatrix} x_1 \\ x_2 \end{bmatrix} = \begin{bmatrix} 0 \\ 0 \end{bmatrix}.$$

The solution is $\{(t, t) : t \in R\}$. Thus, an eigenvector corresponding to $\lambda_1 = \frac{1}{2}$ is $(1, 1)$. For $\lambda_2 = -\frac{1}{4}$, we have

$$\begin{bmatrix} \lambda_2 - \frac{1}{4} & -\frac{1}{4} \\ -\frac{1}{2} & \lambda_2 \end{bmatrix}\begin{bmatrix} x_1 \\ x_2 \end{bmatrix} = \begin{bmatrix} 0 \\ 0 \end{bmatrix} \implies \begin{bmatrix} 1 & \frac{1}{2} \\ 0 & 0 \end{bmatrix}\begin{bmatrix} x_1 \\ x_2 \end{bmatrix} = \begin{bmatrix} 0 \\ 0 \end{bmatrix}.$$

The solution is $\{(t, -2t) : t \in R\}$. Thus, an eigenvector corresponding to $\lambda_2 = -\frac{1}{4}$ is $(1, -2)$.

18. (a) The characteristic equation is

$$|\lambda I - A| = \begin{vmatrix} \lambda + 5 & 0 & 0 \\ -3 & \lambda - 7 & 0 \\ -4 & 2 & \lambda - 3 \end{vmatrix} = (\lambda + 5)(\lambda - 7)(\lambda - 3) = 0.$$

(b) The eigenvalues are $\lambda_1 = -5$, $\lambda_2 = 7$ and $\lambda_3 = 3$. For $\lambda_1 = -5$, we have

$$\begin{bmatrix} \lambda_1 + 5 & 0 & 0 \\ -3 & \lambda_1 - 7 & 0 \\ -4 & 2 & \lambda_1 - 3 \end{bmatrix}\begin{bmatrix} x_1 \\ x_2 \\ x_3 \end{bmatrix} = \begin{bmatrix} 0 \\ 0 \\ 0 \end{bmatrix} \implies \begin{bmatrix} 9 & 0 & 16 \\ 0 & 9 & -4 \\ 0 & 0 & 0 \end{bmatrix}\begin{bmatrix} x_1 \\ x_2 \\ x_3 \end{bmatrix} = \begin{bmatrix} 0 \\ 0 \\ 0 \end{bmatrix}.$$

—CONTINUED—

18. —CONTINUED—

The solution is $\{(-16t, 4t, 9t) : t \in R\}$. Thus, an eigenvector corresponding to $\lambda_1 = -5$ is $(-16, 4, 9)$. For $\lambda_2 = 7$, we have

$$\begin{bmatrix} \lambda_2 + 5 & 0 & 0 \\ -3 & \lambda_2 - 7 & 0 \\ -4 & 2 & \lambda_2 - 3 \end{bmatrix}\begin{bmatrix} x_1 \\ x_2 \\ x_3 \end{bmatrix} = \begin{bmatrix} 0 \\ 0 \\ 0 \end{bmatrix} \implies \begin{bmatrix} 1 & 0 & 0 \\ 0 & 1 & 2 \\ 0 & 0 & 0 \end{bmatrix}\begin{bmatrix} x_1 \\ x_2 \\ x_3 \end{bmatrix} = \begin{bmatrix} 0 \\ 0 \\ 0 \end{bmatrix}.$$

The solution is $\{(0, -2t, t) : t \in R\}$. Thus, an eigenvector corresponding to $\lambda_2 = 7$ is $(0, -2, 1)$. For $\lambda_3 = 3$, we have

$$\begin{bmatrix} \lambda_3 + 5 & 0 & 0 \\ -3 & \lambda_3 - 7 & 0 \\ -4 & 2 & \lambda_3 - 3 \end{bmatrix}\begin{bmatrix} x_1 \\ x_2 \\ x_3 \end{bmatrix} = \begin{bmatrix} 0 \\ 0 \\ 0 \end{bmatrix} \implies \begin{bmatrix} 1 & 0 & 0 \\ 0 & 1 & 0 \\ 0 & 0 & 0 \end{bmatrix}\begin{bmatrix} x_1 \\ x_2 \\ x_3 \end{bmatrix} = \begin{bmatrix} 0 \\ 0 \\ 0 \end{bmatrix}.$$

The solution is $\{(0, 0, t) : t \in R\}$. Thus, an eigenvector corresponding to $\lambda_3 = 3$ is $(0, 0, 1)$.

20. (a) The characteristic equation is

$$|\lambda I - A| = \begin{vmatrix} \lambda - 3 & -2 & 3 \\ 3 & \lambda + 4 & -9 \\ 1 & 2 & \lambda - 5 \end{vmatrix} = \lambda^3 - 4\lambda^2 + 4\lambda = \lambda(\lambda - 2)^2 = 0.$$

(b) The eigenvalues are $\lambda_1 = 0, \lambda_2 = 2$ (repeated). For $\lambda_1 = 0$, we have

$$\begin{bmatrix} \lambda_1 - 3 & -2 & 3 \\ 3 & \lambda_1 + 4 & -9 \\ 1 & 2 & \lambda_1 - 5 \end{bmatrix}\begin{bmatrix} x_1 \\ x_2 \\ x_3 \end{bmatrix} = \begin{bmatrix} 0 \\ 0 \\ 0 \end{bmatrix} \implies \begin{bmatrix} 1 & 0 & 1 \\ 0 & 1 & -3 \\ 0 & 0 & 0 \end{bmatrix}\begin{bmatrix} x_1 \\ x_2 \\ x_3 \end{bmatrix} = \begin{bmatrix} 0 \\ 0 \\ 0 \end{bmatrix}.$$

The solution is $\{(-t, 3t, t) : t \in R\}$. Thus, an eigenvector corresponding to $\lambda_1 = 0$ is $(-1, 3, 1)$. For $\lambda_2 = 2$, we have

$$\begin{bmatrix} \lambda_2 - 3 & -2 & 3 \\ 3 & \lambda_2 + 4 & -9 \\ 1 & 2 & \lambda_2 - 5 \end{bmatrix}\begin{bmatrix} x_1 \\ x_2 \\ x_3 \end{bmatrix} = \begin{bmatrix} 0 \\ 0 \\ 0 \end{bmatrix} \implies \begin{bmatrix} 1 & 2 & -3 \\ 0 & 0 & 0 \\ 0 & 0 & 0 \end{bmatrix}\begin{bmatrix} x_1 \\ x_2 \\ x_3 \end{bmatrix} = \begin{bmatrix} 0 \\ 0 \\ 0 \end{bmatrix}.$$

The solution is $\{(-2s + 3t, s, t) : s, t \in R\}$. Thus, two independent eigenvectors corresponding to $\lambda_2 = 2$ are $(-2, 1, 0)$ and $(3, 0, 1)$.

22. (a) The characteristic equation is

$$|\lambda I - A| = \begin{vmatrix} \lambda - 1 & \frac{3}{2} & -\frac{5}{2} \\ 2 & \lambda - \frac{13}{2} & 10 \\ -\frac{3}{2} & \frac{9}{2} & \lambda - 8 \end{vmatrix} = \left(\lambda - \frac{29}{2}\right)\left(\lambda - \frac{1}{2}\right)^2 = 0.$$

(b) The eigenvalues are $\lambda_1 = \frac{29}{2}, \lambda_2 = \frac{1}{2}$ (repeated). For $\lambda_1 = \frac{29}{2}$, we have

$$\begin{bmatrix} \lambda_1 - 1 & \frac{3}{2} & -\frac{5}{2} \\ 2 & \lambda_1 - \frac{13}{2} & 10 \\ -\frac{3}{2} & \frac{9}{2} & \lambda_1 - 8 \end{bmatrix}\begin{bmatrix} x_1 \\ x_2 \\ x_3 \end{bmatrix} = \begin{bmatrix} 0 \\ 0 \\ 0 \end{bmatrix} \implies \begin{bmatrix} 3 & 0 & -1 \\ 0 & 3 & 4 \\ 0 & 0 & 0 \end{bmatrix}\begin{bmatrix} x_1 \\ x_2 \\ x_3 \end{bmatrix} = \begin{bmatrix} 0 \\ 0 \\ 0 \end{bmatrix}.$$

—CONTINUED—

22. —CONTINUED—

The solution is $\{(t, -4t, 3t) : t \in R\}$. Thus, an eigenvector corresponding to $\lambda_1 = \frac{29}{2}$ is $(1, -4, 3)$. For $\lambda_2 = \frac{1}{2}$, we have

$$\begin{bmatrix} \lambda_2 - 1 & \frac{3}{2} & -\frac{5}{2} \\ 2 & \lambda_2 - \frac{13}{2} & 10 \\ -\frac{3}{2} & \frac{9}{2} & \lambda_2 - 8 \end{bmatrix} \begin{bmatrix} x_1 \\ x_2 \\ x_3 \end{bmatrix} = \begin{bmatrix} 0 \\ 0 \\ 0 \end{bmatrix} \implies \begin{bmatrix} 1 & -3 & 5 \\ 0 & 0 & 0 \\ 0 & 0 & 0 \end{bmatrix} \begin{bmatrix} x_1 \\ x_2 \\ x_3 \end{bmatrix} = \begin{bmatrix} 0 \\ 0 \\ 0 \end{bmatrix}.$$

The solution is $\{(3s - 5t, s, t) : s, t \in R\}$. Thus, two eigenvectors corresponding to $\lambda_2 = \frac{1}{2}$ are $(3, 1, 0)$ and $(-5, 0, 1)$.

24. (a) The characteristic equation is

$$|\lambda I - A| = \begin{vmatrix} \lambda - 3 & 0 & 0 & 0 \\ -4 & \lambda - 1 & 0 & 0 \\ 0 & 0 & \lambda - 2 & -1 \\ 0 & 0 & 0 & \lambda - 2 \end{vmatrix} = (\lambda 3)^2 (\lambda - 1)(\lambda - 2)^2 = 0.$$

(b) The eigenvalues are $\lambda_1 = 3$, $\lambda_2 = 1$, $\lambda_3 = 2$ (repeated). For $\lambda_1 = 3$, we have

$$\begin{bmatrix} 0 & 0 & 0 & 0 \\ -4 & 2 & 0 & 0 \\ 0 & 0 & 1 & -1 \\ 0 & 0 & 0 & 1 \end{bmatrix} \begin{bmatrix} x_1 \\ x_2 \\ x_3 \\ x_4 \end{bmatrix} = \begin{bmatrix} 0 \\ 0 \\ 0 \\ 0 \end{bmatrix} \implies \begin{bmatrix} 1 & -\frac{1}{2} & 0 & 0 \\ 0 & 0 & 0 & 0 \\ 0 & 0 & 1 & 1 \\ 0 & 0 & 0 & 0 \end{bmatrix} \begin{bmatrix} x_1 \\ x_2 \\ x_3 \\ x_4 \end{bmatrix} = \begin{bmatrix} 0 \\ 0 \\ 0 \\ 0 \end{bmatrix}.$$

The solution is $\left\{ \left(\frac{1}{2}t, t, 0, 0 \right) : t \in R \right\}$. Thus, an eigenvector corresponding to $\lambda_1 = 3$ is $(1, 2, 0, 0)$. For $\lambda_2 = 1$, we have

$$\begin{bmatrix} -2 & 0 & 0 & 0 \\ -4 & 0 & 0 & 0 \\ 0 & 0 & -1 & -1 \\ 0 & 0 & 0 & -1 \end{bmatrix} \begin{bmatrix} x_1 \\ x_2 \\ x_3 \\ x_4 \end{bmatrix} = \begin{bmatrix} 0 \\ 0 \\ 0 \\ 0 \end{bmatrix} \implies \begin{bmatrix} 1 & 0 & 0 & 0 \\ 0 & 0 & 1 & 0 \\ 0 & 0 & 0 & 1 \\ 0 & 0 & 0 & 0 \end{bmatrix} \begin{bmatrix} x_1 \\ x_2 \\ x_3 \\ x_4 \end{bmatrix} = \begin{bmatrix} 0 \\ 0 \\ 0 \\ 0 \end{bmatrix}.$$

The solution is $\{(0, t, 0, 0) : t \in R\}$. Thus, an eigenvector corresponding to $\lambda_2 = 1$ is $(0, 1, 0, 0)$. For $\lambda_3 = 2$ we have

$$\begin{bmatrix} -1 & 0 & 0 & 0 \\ -4 & 1 & 0 & 0 \\ 0 & 0 & 0 & -1 \\ 0 & 0 & 0 & 0 \end{bmatrix} \begin{bmatrix} x_1 \\ x_2 \\ x_3 \\ x_4 \end{bmatrix} = \begin{bmatrix} 0 \\ 0 \\ 0 \\ 0 \end{bmatrix} \implies \begin{bmatrix} 1 & 0 & 0 & 0 \\ 0 & 1 & 0 & 0 \\ 0 & 0 & 0 & 1 \\ 0 & 0 & 0 & 0 \end{bmatrix} \begin{bmatrix} x_1 \\ x_2 \\ x_3 \\ x_4 \end{bmatrix} = \begin{bmatrix} 0 \\ 0 \\ 0 \\ 0 \end{bmatrix}.$$

The solution is $\{(0, 0, t, 0) : t \in R\}$. Thus, an eigenvector corresponding to $\lambda_3 = 2$ is $(0, 0, 1, 0)$.

26. Using computer software Maple V, we find that the eigenvalues of

$$A = \begin{bmatrix} 2 & 3 \\ 3 & -6 \end{bmatrix}$$

are -7 and 3.

28. Using computer software Maple V, we find that the eigenvalues of

$$A = \begin{bmatrix} -6 & 2 \\ 3 & -1 \end{bmatrix}$$

are 0 and -7.

30. Using a TI-86, we find the eigenvalues of

$$A = \begin{bmatrix} \frac{1}{2} & 0 & 5 \\ -2 & \frac{1}{5} & \frac{1}{4} \\ 0 & 0 & 3 \end{bmatrix}$$

are $\frac{1}{5}, \frac{1}{2}$, and 3.

32. Using a TI-86, we find the eigenvalues of

$$A = \begin{bmatrix} 1 & -3 & 3 & 3 \\ -1 & 4 & -3 & -3 \\ -2 & 0 & 1 & 1 \\ 1 & 0 & 0 & 0 \end{bmatrix}$$

are 0, 4, and 1 (repeated).

34. The characteristic equation is

$$|\lambda I - A| = \begin{vmatrix} \lambda - 6 & 1 \\ -1 & \lambda - 5 \end{vmatrix} = \lambda^2 - 11\lambda + 31 = 0.$$

Since,

$$A^2 - 11A + 31I = \begin{bmatrix} 6 & -1 \\ 1 & 5 \end{bmatrix}^2 - 11\begin{bmatrix} 6 & -1 \\ 1 & 5 \end{bmatrix} + 31\begin{bmatrix} 1 & 0 \\ 0 & 1 \end{bmatrix}$$

$$= \begin{bmatrix} 35 & -11 \\ 11 & 24 \end{bmatrix} - \begin{bmatrix} 66 & -11 \\ 11 & 55 \end{bmatrix} + \begin{bmatrix} 31 & 0 \\ 0 & 31 \end{bmatrix} = \begin{bmatrix} 0 & 0 \\ 0 & 0 \end{bmatrix}$$

the theorem holds for this matrix.

36. The characteristic equation is

$$|\lambda I - A| = \begin{vmatrix} \lambda + 3 & -1 & 0 \\ 1 & \lambda - 3 & -2 \\ 0 & -4 & \lambda - 3 \end{vmatrix} = \lambda^3 - 3\lambda^2 - 16\lambda = 0.$$

Since,

$$A^3 - 3A^2 - 16A = \begin{bmatrix} -3 & 1 & 0 \\ -1 & 3 & 2 \\ 0 & 4 & 3 \end{bmatrix}^3 - 3\begin{bmatrix} -3 & 1 & 0 \\ -1 & 3 & 2 \\ 0 & 4 & 3 \end{bmatrix}^2 - 16\begin{bmatrix} -3 & 1 & 0 \\ -1 & 3 & 2 \\ 0 & 4 & 3 \end{bmatrix}$$

$$= \begin{bmatrix} -24 & 16 & 6 \\ -16 & 96 & 68 \\ -12 & 136 & 99 \end{bmatrix} - 3\begin{bmatrix} 8 & 0 & 2 \\ 0 & 16 & 12 \\ -4 & 24 & 17 \end{bmatrix} - 16\begin{bmatrix} -3 & 1 & 0 \\ -1 & 3 & 2 \\ 0 & 4 & 0 \end{bmatrix}$$

$$= \begin{bmatrix} 0 & 0 & 0 \\ 0 & 0 & 0 \\ 0 & 0 & 0 \end{bmatrix}$$

the theorem holds for this matrix.

38. $\lambda = 0$ is an eigenvalue of $A \iff |0I - A| = 0 \iff |A| = 0$.

40. Observe that $|\lambda I - A^T| = |(\lambda I - A)^T| = |\lambda I - A|$. Since the characteristic equations of A and A^T are the same, A and A^T must have the same eigenvalues. However, the eigenspaces are not the same.

42. Let $\mathbf{u} = (u_1, u_2)$ be the fixed vector in R^2, and $\mathbf{v} = (v_1, v_2)$. Then

$$\text{proj}_{\mathbf{u}}\mathbf{v} = \frac{u_1 v_1 + u_2 v_2}{u_1^2 + u_2^2}(u_1, u_2).$$

Since

$$T(1, 0) = \frac{u_1}{u_1^2 + u_2^2}(u_1, u_2) \quad \text{and} \quad T(0, 1) = \frac{u_2}{u_1^2 + u_2^2}(u_1, u_2),$$

the standard matrix A of T is

$$A = \frac{1}{u_1^2 + u_2^2}\begin{bmatrix} u_1^2 & u_1 u_2 \\ u_1 u_2 & u_2^2 \end{bmatrix}.$$

Now,

$$\begin{aligned}
A\mathbf{u} &= \frac{1}{u_1^2 + u_2^2}\begin{bmatrix} u_1^2 & u_1 u_2 \\ u_1 u_2 & u_2^2 \end{bmatrix}\begin{bmatrix} u_1 \\ u_2 \end{bmatrix} \\
&= \frac{1}{u_1^2 + u_2^2}\begin{bmatrix} u_1^3 + u_1 u_2^2 \\ u_1^2 u_2 + u_2^3 \end{bmatrix} = \frac{1}{u_1^2 + u_2^2}\begin{bmatrix} u_1(u_1^2 + u_2^2) \\ u_2(u_1^2 + u_2^2) \end{bmatrix} \\
&= \frac{u_1^2 + u_2^2}{u_1^2 + u_2^2}\begin{bmatrix} u_1 \\ u_2 \end{bmatrix} = 1\mathbf{u}
\end{aligned}$$

and

$$\begin{aligned}
A\begin{bmatrix} u_2 \\ -u_1 \end{bmatrix} &= \frac{1}{u_1^2 + u_2^2}\begin{bmatrix} u_1^2 & u_1 u_2 \\ u_1 u_2 & u_2^2 \end{bmatrix}\begin{bmatrix} u_2 \\ -u_1 \end{bmatrix} \\
&= \frac{1}{u_1^2 + u_2^2}\begin{bmatrix} u_1^2 u_2 - u_1^2 u_2 \\ u_1 u_2^2 - u_1 u_2^2 \end{bmatrix} \\
&= \frac{1}{u_1^2 + u_2^2}\begin{bmatrix} 0 \\ 0 \end{bmatrix} = 0\begin{bmatrix} u_2 \\ -u_1 \end{bmatrix}.
\end{aligned}$$

Thus, $\lambda = 1$ and $\lambda_2 = 0$ are the eigenvalues of A.

44. Let $A^2 = O$ and consider $A\mathbf{x} = \lambda\mathbf{x}$. Then we have

$$O = A^2\mathbf{x} = A(\lambda\mathbf{x}) = \lambda A\mathbf{x} = \lambda^2\mathbf{x}.$$

which implies the $\lambda = 0$.

46. The characteristic equation of A is

$$|\lambda I - A| = \begin{vmatrix} \lambda & -1 \\ 1 & \lambda \end{vmatrix} = \lambda^2 + 1 = 0$$

which has no real solution.

48. (a) *True.* By definition of eigenvalue space $A\mathbf{x} = \lambda\mathbf{x}$ and $\lambda\mathbf{x}$ is parallel to $\mathbf{x}$ for any real number λ.

(b) *False.* Let

$$A = \begin{bmatrix} 1 & 0 \\ 0 & 2 \end{bmatrix}.$$

Then A has two distinct eigenvalues 1 and 2.

(c) *False.* The set of eigenvectors corresponding to λ together with the zero vector (which is never an eigenvector for any eigenvalue) forms a subspace of R^n. (Theorem 7.1 on page 413).

50. Substituting the value $\lambda = 3$ yields the system

$$\begin{bmatrix} \lambda - 3 & -1 & 0 \\ 0 & \lambda - 3 & 0 \\ 0 & 0 & \lambda - 3 \end{bmatrix} \begin{bmatrix} x_1 \\ x_2 \\ x_3 \end{bmatrix} = \begin{bmatrix} 0 \\ 0 \\ 0 \end{bmatrix} \implies \begin{bmatrix} 0 & 1 & 0 \\ 0 & 0 & 0 \\ 0 & 0 & 0 \end{bmatrix} \begin{bmatrix} x_1 \\ x_2 \\ x_3 \end{bmatrix} = \begin{bmatrix} 0 \\ 0 \\ 0 \end{bmatrix}.$$

Thus, 3 has two linearly independent eigenvectors and the dimension of the eigenspace is 2.

52. Substituting the value $\lambda = 3$ yields the system

$$\begin{bmatrix} \lambda - 3 & -1 & -1 \\ 0 & \lambda - 3 & -1 \\ 0 & 0 & \lambda - 3 \end{bmatrix} \begin{bmatrix} x_1 \\ x_2 \\ x_3 \end{bmatrix} = \begin{bmatrix} 0 \\ 0 \\ 0 \end{bmatrix} \implies \begin{bmatrix} 0 & 1 & 0 \\ 0 & 0 & 1 \\ 0 & 0 & 0 \end{bmatrix} \begin{bmatrix} x_1 \\ x_2 \\ x_3 \end{bmatrix} = \begin{bmatrix} 0 \\ 0 \\ 0 \end{bmatrix}.$$

Thus, 3 has one linearly independent eigenvector, and the dimension of the eigenspace is 1.

54. Since

$$T(e^{-2x}) = \frac{d}{dx}(e^{-2x}) = -2e^{-2x},$$

the eigenvalue corresponding to $f(x) = e^{-2x}$ is -2.

56. The standard matrix for T is

$$A = \begin{bmatrix} 2 & 1 & -1 \\ 0 & -1 & 2 \\ 0 & 0 & -1 \end{bmatrix}.$$

The characteristic equation of A is

$$|\lambda I - A| = \begin{vmatrix} \lambda - 2 & -1 & 1 \\ 0 & \lambda + 1 & -2 \\ 0 & 0 & \lambda + 1 \end{vmatrix} = (\lambda - 2)(\lambda + 1)^2.$$

The eigenvalues are $\lambda_1 = 2$ and $\lambda_2 = -1$ (repeated). The corresponding eigenvectors are found by solving

$$\begin{bmatrix} \lambda_i - 2 & -1 & 1 \\ 0 & \lambda_i + 1 & -2 \\ 0 & 0 & \lambda_i + 1 \end{bmatrix} \begin{bmatrix} x_1 \\ x_2 \\ x_3 \end{bmatrix} = \begin{bmatrix} 0 \\ 0 \\ 0 \end{bmatrix}$$

for each λ_i. Thus, $\mathbf{p}_1 = 1$ corresponds to $\lambda_1 = 2$, and $\mathbf{p}_2 = 1 - 3x$ corresponds to $\lambda_2 = -1$.

58. The possible eigenvalues of an idempotent matrix are 0 and 1. For suppose,
$A\mathbf{x} = \lambda\mathbf{x}$, where $A^2 = A$. Then

$$\lambda\mathbf{x} = A\mathbf{x} = A^2\mathbf{x} = A(A\mathbf{x}) = A(\lambda\mathbf{x}) = \lambda^2\mathbf{x} \quad \Rightarrow \quad (\lambda^2 - \lambda)\mathbf{x} = \mathbf{0}.$$

Since $\mathbf{x} \neq \mathbf{0}$, $\quad \lambda^2 - \lambda = 0 \quad \Rightarrow \quad \lambda = 0, 1.$

60. The characteristic equation of A is

$$\begin{vmatrix} \lambda - \cos\theta & \sin\theta \\ -\sin\theta & \lambda - \cos\theta \end{vmatrix} = \lambda^2 - 2\cos\theta\,\lambda + (\cos^2\theta + \sin^2\theta)$$

$$= \lambda^2 - 2\cos\theta\,\lambda + 1.$$

There are real eigenvalues if the discriminant of this quadratic equation in λ is nonnegative:

$$b^2 - 4ac = 4\cos^2\theta - 4 = 4(\cos^2\theta - 1) \geq 0 \quad \Rightarrow \quad \cos^2\theta = 1 \quad \Rightarrow \quad \theta = 0, \pi.$$

The only rotations that send vectors to multiples of themselves are the identity
$(\theta = 0)$ and the 180°–rotation $(\theta = \pi)$.

Section 7.2   Diagonalization

2. $P^{-1} = \begin{bmatrix} \frac{1}{2} & -\frac{1}{2} \\ -\frac{1}{2} & \frac{3}{2} \end{bmatrix}$ and

$$P^{-1}AP = \begin{bmatrix} \frac{1}{2} & -\frac{1}{2} \\ -\frac{1}{2} & \frac{3}{2} \end{bmatrix} \begin{bmatrix} 1 & 3 \\ -1 & 5 \end{bmatrix} \begin{bmatrix} 3 & 1 \\ 1 & 1 \end{bmatrix} = \begin{bmatrix} 2 & 0 \\ 0 & 4 \end{bmatrix}$$

4. $P^{-1} = \begin{bmatrix} 0.25 & 0.25 & 0.25 & 0.25 \\ -0.25 & -0.25 & 0.25 & 0.25 \\ 0 & 0 & 0.5 & -0.5 \\ 0.5 & -0.5 & 0 & 0 \end{bmatrix}$ and

$$P^{-1}AP = \begin{bmatrix} 0.25 & 0.25 & 0.25 & 0.25 \\ -0.25 & -0.25 & 0.25 & 0.25 \\ 0 & 0 & 0.5 & -0.5 \\ 0.5 & -0.5 & 0 & 0 \end{bmatrix} \begin{bmatrix} 0.80 & 0.10 & 0.05 & 0.05 \\ 0.10 & 0.80 & 0.05 & 0.50 \\ 0.05 & 0.05 & 0.80 & 0.10 \\ 0.05 & 0.05 & 0.10 & 0.80 \end{bmatrix} \begin{bmatrix} 1 & -1 & 0 & 1 \\ 1 & -1 & 0 & -1 \\ 1 & 1 & 1 & 0 \\ 1 & 1 & -1 & 0 \end{bmatrix}$$

$$= \begin{bmatrix} 1 & 0 & 0 & 0 \\ 0 & 0.8 & 0 & 0 \\ 0 & 0 & 0.7 & 0 \\ 0 & 0 & 0 & 0.7 \end{bmatrix}$$

6. The matrix A has only one eigenvalue, $\lambda = 0$, and a basis for the eigenspace is $\{(1, -2)\}$. Thus, A does not satisfy Theorem 7.5 and is not diagonalizable.

8. The characteristic equation of

$$\begin{bmatrix} k & 0 \\ 0 & k \end{bmatrix}$$

is $(\lambda - k)^2 = 0$. The eigenvector for the eigenvalue $\lambda = k$ is $(1, 1)$. Because there are not two linearly independent eigenvectors, the matrix is not diagonalizable by Theorem 7.5.

10. The characteristic equation of

$$A = \begin{bmatrix} 2 & 1 & -1 \\ 0 & -1 & 2 \\ 0 & 0 & -1 \end{bmatrix}$$

is $(\lambda - 2)(\lambda + 1)^2 = 0$. For eigenvalue $\lambda_1 = 2$ we find the eigenvector $(1, 0, 0)$. The eigenvector corresponding to $\lambda_2 = -1$ (repeated) is $(1, -3, 0)$. So A has only two linearly independent eigenvectors. Thus A does not satisfy Theorem 7.5 and is not diagonalizable.

12. From Exercise 32, Section 7.1, we know that A has only three linearly independent eigenvectors. Thus, A does not satisfy Theorem 7.5 and is not diagonalizable.

14. The eigenvalue of A is $\lambda = 2$ (repeated). Since A does not have two <u>distinct</u> eigenvalues, Theorem 7.6 does not guarantee that A is diagonalizable.

16. The eigenvalues of A are $\lambda_1 = 4$, $\lambda_2 = 1$, $\lambda_3 = -2$. Since A has three distinct eigenvalues, it is diagonalizable by Theorem 7.6.

18. The eigenvalues of A are $\lambda_1 = \frac{1}{2}$ and $\lambda_2 = \frac{1}{4}$. From Exercise 16, Section 7.1, the corresponding eigenvectors are $(1, 1)$ and $(1, -2)$ which are used to form the column of P. Thus,

$$P = \begin{bmatrix} 1 & 1 \\ 1 & -2 \end{bmatrix} \implies P^{-1} = \begin{bmatrix} \frac{2}{3} & \frac{1}{3} \\ \frac{1}{3} & -\frac{1}{3} \end{bmatrix}, \text{ and}$$

$$P^{-1}AP = \begin{bmatrix} \frac{2}{3} & \frac{1}{3} \\ \frac{1}{3} & -\frac{1}{3} \end{bmatrix}\begin{bmatrix} \frac{1}{4} & \frac{1}{4} \\ \frac{1}{2} & 0 \end{bmatrix}\begin{bmatrix} 1 & 1 \\ 1 & -2 \end{bmatrix} = \begin{bmatrix} \frac{1}{2} & 0 \\ 0 & -\frac{1}{4} \end{bmatrix}.$$

20. The eigenvalues of A are $\lambda_1 = 0$ and $\lambda_2 = 2$ (repeated) (see Exercise 20, section 7.1). The corresponding eigenvectors $(-1, 3, 1)$, $(3, 0, 1)$ and $(-2, 1, 0)$ are used to form the columns of P. Thus,

$$P = \begin{bmatrix} -1 & 3 & -2 \\ 3 & 0 & 1 \\ 1 & 1 & 0 \end{bmatrix} \implies P^{-1} = \begin{bmatrix} \frac{1}{2} & 1 & -\frac{3}{2} \\ -\frac{1}{2} & -1 & \frac{5}{2} \\ -\frac{3}{2} & -2 & \frac{9}{2} \end{bmatrix}, \text{ and}$$

$$P^{-1}AP = \begin{bmatrix} \frac{1}{2} & 1 & -\frac{3}{2} \\ -\frac{1}{2} & -1 & \frac{5}{2} \\ -\frac{3}{2} & -2 & \frac{9}{2} \end{bmatrix}\begin{bmatrix} 3 & 2 & -3 \\ -3 & -4 & 9 \\ -1 & -2 & 5 \end{bmatrix}\begin{bmatrix} -1 & 3 & -2 \\ 3 & 0 & 1 \\ 1 & 1 & 0 \end{bmatrix} = \begin{bmatrix} 0 & 0 & 0 \\ 0 & 2 & 0 \\ 0 & 0 & 2 \end{bmatrix}.$$

22. The eigenvalues of A are $\lambda_1 = \frac{29}{2}$ and $\lambda_2 = \frac{1}{2}$ (repeated) (see Exercise 22, Section 7.1). The corresponding eigenvectors $(1, -4, 3)$, $(-5, 0, 1)$ and $(3, 1, 0)$ are used to form the columns of P. Thus,

$$P = \begin{bmatrix} 1 & -5 & 3 \\ -4 & 0 & 1 \\ 3 & 1 & 0 \end{bmatrix} \implies P^{-1} = \frac{1}{28}\begin{bmatrix} 1 & -3 & 5 \\ -3 & 9 & 13 \\ 4 & 16 & 20 \end{bmatrix}$$

and

$$P^{-1}AP = \frac{1}{28}\begin{bmatrix} 1 & -3 & 5 \\ -3 & 9 & 13 \\ 4 & 16 & 20 \end{bmatrix}\begin{bmatrix} 1 & -\frac{3}{2} & \frac{5}{2} \\ -2 & \frac{13}{2} & -10 \\ \frac{3}{2} & -\frac{9}{2} & 8 \end{bmatrix}\begin{bmatrix} 1 & -5 & 3 \\ -4 & 0 & 1 \\ 3 & 1 & 0 \end{bmatrix} = \begin{bmatrix} \frac{29}{2} & 0 & 0 \\ 0 & \frac{1}{2} & 0 \\ 0 & 0 & \frac{1}{2} \end{bmatrix}$$

24. The eigenvalues of A are $\lambda_1 = 4$ and $\lambda_2 = 2$ (repeated). Furthermore, there are just two linearly independent eigenvectors of A, $\mathbf{x}_1 = (1, 1, 1)$ and $\mathbf{x}_2 = (0, 0, 1)$. Thus, A is not diagonalizable.

26. The eigenvalues of A are $\lambda_1 = 0$ and $\lambda_2 = 1$ (3 times). Furthermore, there are just three linearly independent eigenvectors of $\mathbf{x}_1 = (0, -1, 0, 1)$ (for $\lambda_1 = 0$) $\mathbf{x}_2 = (-1, 0, 1, 0)$, and $\mathbf{x}_3 = (0, 0, 0, 1)$ (for $\lambda_2 = 1$). Thus, A is not diagonalizable.

28. The standard matrix for T is

$$A = \begin{bmatrix} -2 & 2 & -3 \\ 2 & 1 & -6 \\ -1 & -2 & 0 \end{bmatrix}$$

which has eigenvalues $\lambda_1 = 5$, $\lambda_2 = -3$ (repeated), and corresponding eigenvectors $(1, 2, -1)$, $(3, 0, 1)$ and $(-2, 1, 0)$. We let $B = \{(1, 2, -1) \ (3, 0, 1), (-2, 1, 0)\}$ and note that the matrix of T relative to this basis is

$$A' = \begin{bmatrix} 5 & 0 & 0 \\ 0 & -3 & 0 \\ 0 & 0 & -3 \end{bmatrix}.$$

30. The standard matrix for T is

$$A = \begin{bmatrix} 2 & 0 & 1 \\ 0 & 3 & 4 \\ 0 & 0 & 1 \end{bmatrix}$$

which has eigenvalues $\lambda_1 = 2$, $\lambda_2 = 3$ and $\lambda_3 = 1$, and corresponding eigenvectors $(1, 0, 0)$, $(0, 1, 0)$, and $(-1, -2, 1)$. We let $B = \{(1, x, -1 - 2x + x^2)\}$ and note that the matrix of T relative to this basis is

$$A' = \begin{bmatrix} 2 & 0 & 0 \\ 0 & 3 & 0 \\ 0 & 0 & 1 \end{bmatrix}.$$

32. Let P be the matrix of eigenvectors corresponding to the n distinct eigenvalues $\lambda_1, \cdots, \lambda_n$. Then $P^{-1}AP = D$ is a diagonal matrix $\Rightarrow A = PDP^{-1}$. From Exercise 31, $A^k = PD^kP^{-1}$, which show that the eigenvalues of A^k are $\lambda_1^k, \lambda_2^k, \cdots, \lambda_n^k$.

34. The eigenvalues and corresponding eigenvectors of A are $\lambda_1 = 3$, $\lambda_2 = -2$ and $\mathbf{x}_1 = (3, 2)$ and $\mathbf{x}_2 = (-1, 1)$. We construct a nonsingular matrix P from the eigenvectors of A,

$$P = \begin{bmatrix} 3 & -1 \\ 2 & 1 \end{bmatrix}$$

and find a diagonal matrix B similar to A.

$$B = P^{-1}AP = \begin{bmatrix} \frac{1}{5} & \frac{1}{5} \\ -\frac{2}{5} & \frac{3}{5} \end{bmatrix} \begin{bmatrix} 1 & 3 \\ 2 & 0 \end{bmatrix} \begin{bmatrix} 3 & -1 \\ 2 & 1 \end{bmatrix} = \begin{bmatrix} 3 & 0 \\ 0 & -2 \end{bmatrix}$$

Then,

$$A^7 = PB^7P^{-1} = \begin{bmatrix} 3 & -1 \\ 2 & 1 \end{bmatrix} \begin{bmatrix} 3^7 & 0 \\ 0 & (-2)^7 \end{bmatrix} \begin{bmatrix} \frac{1}{5} & \frac{1}{5} \\ -\frac{2}{5} & \frac{3}{5} \end{bmatrix} = \begin{bmatrix} 1261 & 1389 \\ 926 & 798 \end{bmatrix}.$$

36. The eigenvalues and corresponding eigenvectors of A are $\lambda_1 = -1$, $\lambda_2 = 0$, $\lambda_3 = 2$, $\mathbf{x}_1 = (2, 2, 3)$, $\mathbf{x}_2 = (1, 1, 1)$ and $\mathbf{x}_3 = (0, 1, 0)$. We construct a nonsingular matrix P from the eigenvectors of A,

$$P = \begin{bmatrix} 2 & 1 & 0 \\ 2 & 1 & 1 \\ 3 & 1 & 0 \end{bmatrix}$$

and find a diagonal matrix B similar to A.

$$B = P^{-1}AP = \begin{bmatrix} -1 & 0 & 1 \\ 3 & 0 & -2 \\ -1 & 1 & 0 \end{bmatrix} \begin{bmatrix} 2 & 0 & -2 \\ 0 & 2 & -2 \\ 3 & 0 & -3 \end{bmatrix} \begin{bmatrix} 2 & 1 & 0 \\ 2 & 1 & 1 \\ 3 & 1 & 0 \end{bmatrix} = \begin{bmatrix} -1 & 0 & 0 \\ 0 & 0 & 0 \\ 0 & 0 & 2 \end{bmatrix}$$

Then,

$$A^5 = PB^5P^{-1} = P \begin{bmatrix} -1 & 0 & 0 \\ 0 & 0 & 0 \\ 0 & 0 & 32 \end{bmatrix} P^{-1} = \begin{bmatrix} 2 & 0 & -2 \\ -30 & 32 & -2 \\ 3 & 0 & -3 \end{bmatrix}.$$

38. (a) *True.* See Theorem 7.5 on page 425.

(b) *False.* Matrix

$$\begin{bmatrix} 2 & 0 \\ 0 & 2 \end{bmatrix}$$

is diagonalizable (it is already diagonal!) but it has only one eigenvalue $\lambda = 2$ (repeated).

40. Yes, the matrices are similar. Let

$$P = \begin{bmatrix} 0 & 0 & 1 \\ 0 & 1 & 0 \\ 1 & 0 & 0 \end{bmatrix} \quad \Rightarrow \quad P^{-1} = \begin{bmatrix} 0 & 0 & 1 \\ 0 & 1 & 0 \\ 1 & 0 & 0 \end{bmatrix}$$

and observe that

$$P^{-1}AP = \begin{bmatrix} 0 & 0 & 1 \\ 0 & 1 & 0 \\ 1 & 0 & 0 \end{bmatrix} \begin{bmatrix} 1 & 0 & 0 \\ 0 & 2 & 0 \\ 0 & 0 & 3 \end{bmatrix} \begin{bmatrix} 0 & 0 & 1 \\ 0 & 1 & 0 \\ 1 & 0 & 0 \end{bmatrix} = \begin{bmatrix} 3 & 0 & 0 \\ 0 & 2 & 0 \\ 0 & 0 & 1 \end{bmatrix}.$$

42. Consider the characteristic equation

$$|\lambda I - A| = \begin{vmatrix} \lambda - a & -b \\ -c & \lambda - d \end{vmatrix} = \lambda^2 - (a + d)\lambda + (ad - bc) = 0.$$

This equation has real and unequal roots if and only if $(a + d)^2 - 4(ad - bc) > 0$, which is equivalent to $(a - d)^2 > -4bc$. Hence, A is diagonalizable if $-4bc < (a - d)^2$, and not diagonalizable if $-4bc > (a - d)^2$.

44. (a) $X = \begin{bmatrix} 1 & 0 \\ 0 & 1 \end{bmatrix} \quad \Rightarrow \quad e^X = I + I + I/2! + I/3! + \cdots$

$$= \begin{bmatrix} 1 + 1 + \frac{1}{2!} + \frac{1}{3!} + \cdots & 0 \\ 0 & 1 + 1 + \frac{1}{2!} + \frac{1}{3!} + \cdots \end{bmatrix} = \begin{bmatrix} e & 0 \\ 0 & e \end{bmatrix}$$

(b) $X = \begin{bmatrix} 0 & 0 \\ 0 & 0 \end{bmatrix} \quad \Rightarrow \quad e^X = I + \begin{bmatrix} 0 & 0 \\ 0 & 0 \end{bmatrix} + \begin{bmatrix} 0 & 0 \\ 0 & 0 \end{bmatrix}^2 /2! + \cdots = I$

(c) $X = \begin{bmatrix} 1 & 0 \\ 1 & 0 \end{bmatrix} \quad \Rightarrow \quad e^X = I + \begin{bmatrix} 1 & 0 \\ 1 & 0 \end{bmatrix} + \begin{bmatrix} 1 & 0 \\ 1 & 0 \end{bmatrix}/2! + \begin{bmatrix} 1 & 0 \\ 1 & 0 \end{bmatrix}/3! + \cdots$

$$= \begin{bmatrix} e & 0 \\ e - 1 & 1 \end{bmatrix}$$

(d) $X = \begin{bmatrix} 0 & 1 \\ 1 & 0 \end{bmatrix} \quad \Rightarrow \quad e^X = I + \begin{bmatrix} 0 & 1 \\ 1 & 0 \end{bmatrix} + \begin{bmatrix} 1 & 0 \\ 0 & 1 \end{bmatrix}/2! + \begin{bmatrix} 0 & 1 \\ 1 & 0 \end{bmatrix}/3! + \begin{bmatrix} 1 & 0 \\ 0 & 1 \end{bmatrix}/4! + \cdots$

Since $e = 1 + 1 + \frac{1}{2} + \frac{1}{3!} + \frac{1}{4!}$ and $e^{-1} = 1 - 1 + \frac{1}{2} - \frac{1}{3!} + \frac{1}{4!} - \cdots$, we see that

$$e^X = \frac{1}{2}\begin{bmatrix} e + e^{-1} & e - e^{-1} \\ e - e^{-1} & e + e^{-1} \end{bmatrix}.$$

(e) $X = \begin{bmatrix} 2 & 0 \\ 0 & -2 \end{bmatrix} \quad \Rightarrow \quad e^X = I + \begin{bmatrix} 2 & 0 \\ 0 & -2 \end{bmatrix} + \begin{bmatrix} 2^2 & 0 \\ 0 & 2^2 \end{bmatrix}/2! + \begin{bmatrix} 2^3 & 0 \\ 0 & -2^3 \end{bmatrix}/3! + \cdots$

$$= \begin{bmatrix} e^2 & 0 \\ 0 & e^{-2} \end{bmatrix}.$$

46. From Exercise 59, Section 7.1, we know that zero is the only eigenvalue of the nilpotent matrix A. If A were diagonalizable, then there would exist an invertible matrix P, such that $P^{-1}AP = D$, where D is the zero matrix. Thus, $A = PDP^{-1} = O$, which is impossible

Section 7.3   Symmetric Matrices and Orthogonal Diagonalization

2. Since

$$A^T = \begin{bmatrix} 6 & -2 \\ -2 & 1 \end{bmatrix}^T = \begin{bmatrix} 6 & -2 \\ -2 & 1 \end{bmatrix} = A,$$

the matrix is symmetric.

4. Since

$$\begin{bmatrix} 1 & -5 & 4 \\ -5 & 3 & 6 \\ -4 & 6 & 2 \end{bmatrix}^T \neq \begin{bmatrix} 1 & -5 & -4 \\ -5 & 3 & 6 \\ 4 & 6 & 2 \end{bmatrix}$$

the matrix is *not* symmetric.

6. Since

$$\begin{bmatrix} 2 & 0 & 3 & 5 \\ 0 & 11 & 0 & -2 \\ 3 & 0 & 5 & 0 \\ 5 & -2 & 0 & 1 \end{bmatrix}^T = \begin{bmatrix} 2 & 0 & 3 & 5 \\ 0 & 11 & 0 & -2 \\ 3 & 0 & 5 & 0 \\ 5 & -2 & 0 & 1 \end{bmatrix}$$

the matrix *is* symmetric.

8. The characteristic equation of A is

$$|\lambda I - A| = \begin{vmatrix} \lambda - 2 & 0 \\ 0 & \lambda - 2 \end{vmatrix} = (\lambda - 2)^2 = 0.$$

Therefore, the eigenvalue is $\lambda = 2$. The multiplicity of $\lambda = 2$ is 2, so the dimension of the corresponding eigenspace is 2 (by Theorem 7.7).

10. The characteristic equation of A is

$$|\lambda I - A| = \begin{vmatrix} \lambda - 2 & -1 & -1 \\ -1 & \lambda - 2 & -1 \\ -1 & -1 & \lambda - 2 \end{vmatrix} = (\lambda - 1)^2(\lambda - 4) = 0.$$

Therefore, the eigenvalues are $\lambda_1 = 1$ and $\lambda_2 = 4$. The multiplicity of $\lambda_1 = 1$ is 2, so the dimension of the corresponding eigenspace is 2 (by Theorem 7.7). The dimension of the eigenspace corresponding to $\lambda_2 = 4$ is 1.

12. The characteristic equation of A is

$$|\lambda I - A| = \begin{vmatrix} \lambda & -4 & -4 \\ -4 & \lambda - 2 & 0 \\ -4 & 0 & \lambda + 2 \end{vmatrix} = (\lambda - 6)(\lambda + 6)\lambda = 0.$$

Therefore, the eigenvalues are $\lambda_1 = 6$, $\lambda_2 = -6$ and $\lambda_3 = 0$. The dimension of the eigenspace corresponding of each eigenvalue is 1.

14. Because the column vectors of the matrix do not form an orthonormal set, the matrix *is not* orthogonal.

16. Because the column vectors of the matrix form an orthonormal set, the matrix *is* orthogonal.

18. Because the column vectors of the matrix do not form an orthonormal set [the first 2 columns are not orthogonal], the matrix is *not* orthogonal.

20. Because the column vectors of the matrix do not form an orthonormal set [none of the columns is a unit vector], the matrix is *not* orthogonal.

22. The eigenvalues of A are $\lambda_1 = 2$ and $\lambda_2 = 6$, with corresponding eigenvectors $(1, -1)$ and $(1, 1)$, respectively. We normalize each eigenvector to form the columns of P. Then

$$P = \begin{bmatrix} \frac{\sqrt{2}}{2} & \frac{\sqrt{2}}{2} \\ -\frac{\sqrt{2}}{2} & \frac{\sqrt{2}}{2} \end{bmatrix} \text{ and } P^T A P = \begin{bmatrix} \frac{\sqrt{2}}{2} & -\frac{\sqrt{2}}{2} \\ \frac{\sqrt{2}}{2} & \frac{\sqrt{2}}{2} \end{bmatrix} \begin{bmatrix} 4 & 2 \\ 2 & 4 \end{bmatrix} \begin{bmatrix} \frac{\sqrt{2}}{2} & \frac{\sqrt{2}}{2} \\ -\frac{\sqrt{2}}{2} & \frac{\sqrt{2}}{2} \end{bmatrix} = \begin{bmatrix} 2 & 0 \\ 0 & 6 \end{bmatrix}.$$

24. The eigenvalues of A are $\lambda_1 = -1$ (repeated) and $\lambda_2 = 2$, with corresponding eigenvectors $(-1, 0, 1), (-1, 1, 0)$ and $(1, 1, 1)$, respectively. We use Gram–Schmidt Orthonormalization Process to orthonormalize the two eigenvectors corresponding to $\lambda_1 = -1$.

$$(-1, 0, 1) \longrightarrow \left(-\frac{1}{\sqrt{2}}, 0, \frac{1}{\sqrt{2}}\right)$$

$$(-1, 1, 0) - \frac{1}{2}(-1, 0, 1) = \left(-\frac{1}{2}, 1, -\frac{1}{2}\right) \longrightarrow \left(\frac{1}{\sqrt{6}}, -\frac{2}{\sqrt{6}}, \frac{1}{\sqrt{6}}\right)$$

Normalizing the third eigenvector corresponding to $\lambda_2 = 2$, we can form the columns of P. Thus,

$$P = \begin{bmatrix} \frac{1}{\sqrt{3}} & -\frac{1}{\sqrt{2}} & \frac{1}{\sqrt{6}} \\ \frac{1}{\sqrt{3}} & 0 & -\frac{2}{\sqrt{6}} \\ \frac{1}{\sqrt{3}} & \frac{1}{\sqrt{2}} & \frac{1}{\sqrt{6}} \end{bmatrix}$$

and

$$P^T A P = \begin{bmatrix} \frac{1}{\sqrt{3}} & \frac{1}{\sqrt{3}} & \frac{1}{\sqrt{3}} \\ -\frac{1}{\sqrt{2}} & 0 & \frac{1}{\sqrt{2}} \\ \frac{1}{\sqrt{6}} & -\frac{2}{\sqrt{6}} & \frac{1}{\sqrt{6}} \end{bmatrix} \begin{bmatrix} 0 & 1 & 1 \\ 1 & 0 & 1 \\ 1 & 1 & 0 \end{bmatrix} \begin{bmatrix} \frac{1}{\sqrt{3}} & -\frac{1}{\sqrt{2}} & \frac{1}{\sqrt{6}} \\ \frac{1}{\sqrt{3}} & 0 & -\frac{2}{\sqrt{6}} \\ \frac{1}{\sqrt{3}} & \frac{1}{\sqrt{2}} & \frac{1}{\sqrt{6}} \end{bmatrix} = \begin{bmatrix} 2 & 0 & 0 \\ 0 & -1 & 0 \\ 0 & 0 & -1 \end{bmatrix}.$$

26. The eigenvalues of A are $\lambda_1 = 5$, $\lambda_2 = 0$, $\lambda_3 = -5$, with corresponding eigenvectors $(3, 5, 4)$, $(-4, 0, 3)$ and $(3, -5, 4)$ respectively. We normalize each eigenvector to form the columns of P. Then

$$P = \tfrac{1}{10}\begin{bmatrix} 3\sqrt{2} & -8 & 3\sqrt{2} \\ 5\sqrt{2} & 0 & -5\sqrt{2} \\ 4\sqrt{2} & 6 & 4\sqrt{2} \end{bmatrix}$$

and

$$P^T A P = \tfrac{1}{10}\begin{bmatrix} 3\sqrt{2} & 5\sqrt{2} & 4\sqrt{2} \\ -8 & 0 & 6 \\ 3\sqrt{2} & -5\sqrt{2} & 4\sqrt{2} \end{bmatrix}\begin{bmatrix} 0 & 3 & 0 \\ 3 & 0 & 4 \\ 0 & 4 & 0 \end{bmatrix}\tfrac{1}{10}\begin{bmatrix} 3\sqrt{2} & -8 & 3\sqrt{2} \\ 5\sqrt{2} & 0 & -5\sqrt{2} \\ 4\sqrt{2} & 6 & 4\sqrt{2} \end{bmatrix}$$

$$= \begin{bmatrix} 5 & 0 & 0 \\ 0 & 0 & 0 \\ 0 & 0 & -5 \end{bmatrix}.$$

28. The eigenvalues of A are $\lambda_1 = 0$ (repeated) and $\lambda_2 = 2$ (repeated). The eigenvectors corresponding to $\lambda_1 = 0$ are $(1, -1, 0, 0)$ and $(0, 0, 1, -1)$, while those corresponding to $\lambda_2 = 2$ are $(1, 1, 0, 0)$ and $(0, 0, 1, 1)$. Normalizing these eigenvectors to form P, we have

$$P = \begin{bmatrix} \dfrac{\sqrt{2}}{2} & 0 & \dfrac{\sqrt{2}}{2} & 0 \\[2mm] -\dfrac{\sqrt{2}}{2} & 0 & \dfrac{\sqrt{2}}{2} & 0 \\[2mm] 0 & \dfrac{\sqrt{2}}{2} & 0 & \dfrac{\sqrt{2}}{2} \\[2mm] 0 & -\dfrac{\sqrt{2}}{2} & 0 & \dfrac{\sqrt{2}}{2} \end{bmatrix}$$

and

$$P^T A P = \begin{bmatrix} \dfrac{\sqrt{2}}{2} & -\dfrac{\sqrt{2}}{2} & 0 & 0 \\[2mm] 0 & 0 & \dfrac{\sqrt{2}}{2} & -\dfrac{\sqrt{2}}{2} \\[2mm] \dfrac{\sqrt{2}}{2} & \dfrac{\sqrt{2}}{2} & 0 & 0 \\[2mm] 0 & 0 & \dfrac{\sqrt{2}}{2} & \dfrac{\sqrt{2}}{2} \end{bmatrix}\begin{bmatrix} 1 & 1 & 0 & 0 \\ 1 & 1 & 0 & 0 \\ 0 & 0 & 1 & 1 \\ 0 & 0 & 1 & 1 \end{bmatrix}\begin{bmatrix} \dfrac{\sqrt{2}}{2} & 0 & \dfrac{\sqrt{2}}{2} & 0 \\[2mm] -\dfrac{\sqrt{2}}{2} & 0 & \dfrac{\sqrt{2}}{2} & 0 \\[2mm] 0 & \dfrac{\sqrt{2}}{2} & 0 & \dfrac{\sqrt{2}}{2} \\[2mm] 0 & -\dfrac{\sqrt{2}}{2} & 0 & \dfrac{\sqrt{2}}{2} \end{bmatrix}$$

$$= \begin{bmatrix} 0 & 0 & 0 & 0 \\ 0 & 0 & 0 & 0 \\ 0 & 0 & 2 & 0 \\ 0 & 0 & 0 & 2 \end{bmatrix}.$$

30. (a) *False.* The fact that a matrix P is invertible does *not* imply $P^{-1} = P^T$, only that P^{-1} exist. The definition of orthogonal matrix (page 436) requires that a matrix P is invertible *and* $P^{-1} = P^T$. For example,

$$\begin{bmatrix} 1 & 3 \\ 3 & 4 \end{bmatrix}$$

is invertible ($|A| \neq 0$) but $A^{-1} \neq A^T$.

(b) *True.* See Theorem 7.10 on page 440.

32. We have

$$A^T A = \begin{bmatrix} 1 & 4 \\ -3 & -6 \\ 2 & 1 \end{bmatrix} \begin{bmatrix} 1 & -3 & 2 \\ 4 & -6 & 1 \end{bmatrix} = \begin{bmatrix} 17 & -27 & 6 \\ -27 & 45 & -12 \\ 6 & -12 & 5 \end{bmatrix}$$

and

$$AA^T = \begin{bmatrix} 1 & -3 & 2 \\ 4 & -6 & 1 \end{bmatrix} \begin{bmatrix} 1 & 4 \\ -3 & -6 \\ 2 & 1 \end{bmatrix} = \begin{bmatrix} 14 & 24 \\ 24 & 53 \end{bmatrix}.$$

34. $(AB)^{-1} = B^{-1}A^{-1} = B^T A^T = (AB)^T \implies AB$ is orthogonal.

$(BA)^{-1} = A^{-1}B^{-1} = A^T B^T = (BA)^T \implies BA$ is orthogonal.

36. Suppose $P^{-1}AP = D$ is diagonal, with λ the only eigenvalue. Then

$$A = PDP^{-1} = P(\lambda I)P^{-1} = \lambda I.$$

Section 7.4   Applications of Eigenvalues and Eigenvectors

2. $\mathbf{x}_2 = A\mathbf{x}_1 = \begin{bmatrix} 0 & 4 \\ \frac{1}{16} & 0 \end{bmatrix} \begin{bmatrix} 160 \\ 160 \end{bmatrix} = \begin{bmatrix} 640 \\ 10 \end{bmatrix}$

$\mathbf{x}_3 = A\mathbf{x}_2 = \begin{bmatrix} 0 & 4 \\ \frac{1}{16} & 0 \end{bmatrix} \begin{bmatrix} 640 \\ 10 \end{bmatrix} = \begin{bmatrix} 40 \\ 40 \end{bmatrix}$

4. $\mathbf{x}_2 = \begin{bmatrix} 0 & 2 & 2 & 0 \\ \frac{1}{4} & 0 & 0 & 0 \\ 0 & 1 & 0 & 0 \\ 0 & 0 & \frac{1}{2} & 0 \end{bmatrix} \begin{bmatrix} 100 \\ 100 \\ 100 \\ 100 \end{bmatrix} = \begin{bmatrix} 400 \\ 25 \\ 100 \\ 50 \end{bmatrix}$

$\mathbf{x}_3 = \begin{bmatrix} 0 & 2 & 2 & 0 \\ \frac{1}{4} & 0 & 0 & 0 \\ 0 & 1 & 0 & 0 \\ 0 & 0 & \frac{1}{2} & 0 \end{bmatrix} \begin{bmatrix} 400 \\ 25 \\ 100 \\ 50 \end{bmatrix} = \begin{bmatrix} 250 \\ 100 \\ 25 \\ 50 \end{bmatrix}$

6. The eigenvalues are $\frac{1}{2}$ and $-\frac{1}{2}$. Choosing the positive eigenvalue, $\lambda = \frac{1}{2}$, we find the corresponding eigenvector by row-reducing $\lambda I - A = \frac{1}{2}I - A$.

$$\begin{bmatrix} \frac{1}{2} & -4 \\ -\frac{1}{16} & \frac{1}{2} \end{bmatrix} \implies \begin{bmatrix} 1 & -8 \\ 0 & 0 \end{bmatrix}$$

Thus, an eigenvector is $(8, 1)$, and this represents a stable age distribution.

8. The characteristic equation of A is $|\lambda I - A| = \lambda^4 - \frac{1}{2}\lambda^2 - \frac{1}{2}\lambda = \lambda(\lambda - 1)(\lambda^2 + \lambda + \frac{1}{2}) = 0$. Choosing the positive eigenvalue $\lambda = 1$, we find its corresponding eigenvector by row-reducing $\lambda I - A = I - A$. In this case, $(8, 2, 2, 1)$ turns out to be an eigenvector, and this represents a stable age distribution.

10. The eigenvalues of A are $\lambda_1 = 1$ and $\lambda_2 = -1$, with corresponding eigenvector $(2, 1)$ and $(-2, 1)$, respectively. Then A can be diagonalized as follows

$$P^{-1}AP = \begin{bmatrix} \frac{1}{4} & \frac{1}{2} \\ -\frac{1}{4} & \frac{1}{2} \end{bmatrix} \begin{bmatrix} 0 & 2 \\ \frac{1}{2} & 0 \end{bmatrix} \begin{bmatrix} 2 & -2 \\ 1 & 1 \end{bmatrix} = \begin{bmatrix} 1 & 0 \\ 0 & -1 \end{bmatrix} = D.$$

Thus, $A = PDP^{-1}$ and $A^n = PD^nP^{-1}$.

If n is even, $D^n = I$ and $A^n = I$. If n is odd, $D^n = D$ and $A^n = PDP^{-1} = \begin{bmatrix} 0 & 2 \\ \frac{1}{2} & 0 \end{bmatrix} = A$. Thus, $A^n \mathbf{x}_1$ does not approach a limit an n tends to infinity.

12. The solution to the differential equation $y' = ky$ is $y = Ce^{kt}$. Thus, $y_1 = C_1 e^{-3t}$ and $y_2 = C_2 e^{4t}$.

14. The solution to the differential equation $y' = ky$ is $y = Ce^{kt}$. Thus, $y_1 = C_1 e^{5t}$, $y_2 = C_2 e^{-2t}$, and $y_3 = C_3 e^{-3t}$.

16. This system has the matrix form

$$\mathbf{y}' = \begin{bmatrix} y_1' \\ y_2' \end{bmatrix} = \begin{bmatrix} 1 & -4 \\ -2 & 8 \end{bmatrix} \begin{bmatrix} y_1 \\ y_2 \end{bmatrix} = A\mathbf{y}.$$

The eigenvalues of A are $\lambda_1 = 0$ and $\lambda_2 = 9$, with corresponding eigenvectors $(4, 1)$ and $(-1, 2)$, respectively. Thus, we may diagonalize A using a matrix P whose columns are the eigenvectors of A.

$$P = \begin{bmatrix} 4 & -1 \\ 1 & 2 \end{bmatrix} \quad \text{and} \quad P^{-1}AP = \begin{bmatrix} 0 & 0 \\ 0 & 9 \end{bmatrix}$$

The solution of the system $\mathbf{w}' = P^{-1}AP\mathbf{w}$ is $w_1 = C_1$ and $w_2 = C_2 e^{9t}$. We return to the original system by applying the substitution $\mathbf{y} = P\mathbf{w}$.

$$\mathbf{y} = \begin{bmatrix} y_1 \\ y_2 \end{bmatrix} = \begin{bmatrix} 4 & -1 \\ 1 & 2 \end{bmatrix} \begin{bmatrix} w_1 \\ w_2 \end{bmatrix} = \begin{bmatrix} 4w_1 - w_2 \\ w_1 + 2w_2 \end{bmatrix}$$

Thus, the solution is

$$y_1 = 4C_1 - C_2 e^{9t}$$
$$y_2 = C_1 + 2C_2 e^{9t}.$$

18. This system has the matrix form

$$\mathbf{y}' = \begin{bmatrix} y'_1 \\ y'_2 \end{bmatrix} = \begin{bmatrix} 1 & -1 \\ 2 & 4 \end{bmatrix} \begin{bmatrix} y_1 \\ y_2 \end{bmatrix} = A\mathbf{y}.$$

The eigenvalues of A are $\lambda_1 = 2$ and $\lambda_2 = 3$, with corresponding eigenvectors $(1, -1)$ and $(-1, 2)$, respectively. Thus, we may diagonalize A using a matrix P whose columns are the eigenvectors of A.

$$P = \begin{bmatrix} 1 & -1 \\ -1 & 2 \end{bmatrix} \quad \text{and} \quad P^{-1}AP = \begin{bmatrix} 2 & 0 \\ 0 & 3 \end{bmatrix}$$

The solution of the system $\mathbf{w}' = P^{-1}AP\mathbf{w}$ is $w_1 = C_1 e^{2t}$ and $w_2 = C_2 e^{3t}$. We return to the original system by applying the substitution $\mathbf{y} = P\mathbf{w}$.

$$\mathbf{y} = \begin{bmatrix} y_1 \\ y_2 \end{bmatrix} = \begin{bmatrix} 1 & -1 \\ -1 & 2 \end{bmatrix} \begin{bmatrix} w_1 \\ w_2 \end{bmatrix} = \begin{bmatrix} w_1 - w_2 \\ -w_1 + 2w_2 \end{bmatrix}$$

Thus, the solution is

$$y_1 = \quad C_1 e^{2t} - \quad C_2 e^{3t}$$
$$y_2 = -C_1 e^{2t} + 2C_2 e^{3t}.$$

20. This system has the matrix form

$$\mathbf{y}' = \begin{bmatrix} y'_1 \\ y'_2 \\ y'_3 \end{bmatrix} = \begin{bmatrix} -2 & 0 & 1 \\ 0 & 3 & 4 \\ 0 & 0 & 1 \end{bmatrix} \begin{bmatrix} y_1 \\ y_2 \\ y_3 \end{bmatrix} = A\mathbf{y}.$$

The eigenvalues of A are $\lambda_1 = -2, \lambda_2 = 3$ and $\lambda_3 = 1$, with corresponding eigenvectors $(1, 0, 0)$, $(0, 1, 0)$ and $(1, -6, 3)$, respectively. Thus, we may diagonalize A using a matrix P whose columns are the eigenvectors of A.

$$P = \begin{bmatrix} 1 & 0 & 1 \\ 0 & 1 & -6 \\ 0 & 0 & 3 \end{bmatrix} \quad \text{and} \quad P^{-1}AP = \begin{bmatrix} -2 & 0 & 0 \\ 0 & 3 & 0 \\ 0 & 0 & 1 \end{bmatrix}$$

The solution of the system $\mathbf{w}' = P^{-1}AP\mathbf{w}$ is $w_1 = C_1 e^{-2t}$, $w_2 = C_2 e^{3t}$ and $w_3 = C_3 e^t$. We return to the original system by applying the substitution $\mathbf{y} = P\mathbf{w}$.

$$\mathbf{y} = \begin{bmatrix} y_1 \\ y_2 \\ y_3 \end{bmatrix} = \begin{bmatrix} 1 & 0 & 1 \\ 0 & 1 & -6 \\ 0 & 0 & 3 \end{bmatrix} \begin{bmatrix} w_1 \\ w_2 \\ w_3 \end{bmatrix} = \begin{bmatrix} w_1 & & + w_3 \\ & w_2 & -6w_3 \\ & & 3w_3 \end{bmatrix}$$

Thus, the solution is

$$y_1 = C_1 e^{-2t} \qquad + \quad C_3 e^t$$
$$y_2 = \qquad C_2 e^{3t} - 6C_3 e^t$$
$$y_3 = \qquad\qquad\qquad 3C_3 e^t.$$

22. This system has the matrix form

$$\mathbf{y}' = \begin{bmatrix} y'_1 \\ y'_2 \\ y'_3 \end{bmatrix} = \begin{bmatrix} 2 & 1 & 1 \\ 1 & 1 & 0 \\ 1 & 0 & 1 \end{bmatrix} \begin{bmatrix} y_1 \\ y_2 \\ y_3 \end{bmatrix} = A\mathbf{y}.$$

The eigenvalues of A are $\lambda_1 = 0, \lambda_2 = 1$ and $\lambda_3 = 3$, with corresponding eigenvectors $(-1, 1, 1), (0, 1, -1)$ and $(2, 1, 1)$, respectively. Thus, we may diagonalize A using a matrix P whose columns are the eigenvectors.

$$P = \begin{bmatrix} -1 & 0 & 2 \\ 1 & 1 & 1 \\ 1 & -1 & 1 \end{bmatrix} \text{ and } P^{-1}AP = \begin{bmatrix} 0 & 0 & 0 \\ 0 & 1 & 0 \\ 0 & 0 & 3 \end{bmatrix}$$

The solution of the system $\mathbf{w}' = P^{-1}AP\mathbf{w}$ is $w_1 = C_1$, $w_2 = C_2 e^t$ and $w_3 = C_3 e^{3t}$. We return to the original system by applying the substitution $\mathbf{y} = P\mathbf{w}$.

$$\mathbf{y} = \begin{bmatrix} y_1 \\ y_2 \\ y_3 \end{bmatrix} = \begin{bmatrix} -1 & 0 & 2 \\ 1 & 1 & 1 \\ 1 & -1 & 1 \end{bmatrix} \begin{bmatrix} w_1 \\ w_2 \\ w_3 \end{bmatrix} = \begin{bmatrix} -w_1 & & + 2w_3 \\ w_1 + w_2 + & w_3 \\ w_1 - w_2 + & w_3 \end{bmatrix}$$

Thus, the solution is

$$y_1 = -C_1 \qquad\quad + 2C_3 e^{3t}$$
$$y_2 = \;\; C_1 + C_2 e^t + \;\; C_3 e^{3t}$$
$$y_3 = \;\; C_1 - C_2 e^t + \;\; C_3 e^{3t}.$$

24. Since

$$\mathbf{y}' = \begin{bmatrix} y'_1 \\ y'_2 \end{bmatrix} = \begin{bmatrix} 1 & -1 \\ 1 & 1 \end{bmatrix} \begin{bmatrix} y_1 \\ y_2 \end{bmatrix} = A\mathbf{y}$$

the system represented by $\mathbf{y}' = A\mathbf{y}$ is

$$y'_1 = y_1 - y_2$$
$$y'_2 = y_1 + y_2.$$

Note that

$$y'_1 = C_1 e^t \cos t - C_1 e^t \sin t + C_2 e^t \sin t + C_2 e^t \cos t = y_1 - y_2$$

and

$$y'_2 = -C_2 e^t \cos t + C_2 e^t \sin t + C_1 e^t \sin t + C_1 e^t \cos t = y_1 + y_2.$$

26. Since

$$\mathbf{y}' = \begin{bmatrix} y'_1 \\ y'_2 \\ y'_3 \end{bmatrix} = \begin{bmatrix} 0 & 1 & 0 \\ 0 & 0 & 1 \\ 1 & -3 & 3 \end{bmatrix} \begin{bmatrix} y_1 \\ y_2 \\ y_3 \end{bmatrix} = A\mathbf{y}$$

the system represented by $\mathbf{y}' = A\mathbf{y}$ is

$$
\begin{aligned}
y'_1 &= \quad\quad y_2 \\
y'_2 &= \quad\quad\quad\quad y_3 \\
y'_3 &= y_1 - 3y_2 + 3y_3.
\end{aligned}
$$

Note that

$$
\begin{aligned}
y'_1 &= C_1 e^t + C_2 t e^t + C_2 e^t + C_3 t^2 e^t + 2C_3 t e^t = y_2 \\
y'_2 &= (C_1 + C_2)e^t + (C_2 + 2C_3)t e^t + (C_2 + 2C_3)e^t + C_3 t^2 e^t + 2C_3 t e^t = y_3 \\
y'_3 &= (C_1 + 2C_2 + 2C_3)e^t + (C_2 + 4C_3)t e^t + (C_2 + 4C_3)e^t + C_3 t^2 e^t + 2C_3 t e^t \\
&= (C_1 e^t + C_2 t e^t + C_3 t^2 e^t) - 3((C_1 + C_2)e^t + (C_2 + 2C_3)t e^t + C_3 t^2 e^t) \\
&\quad + 3((C_1 + 2C_2 + 2C_3)e^t + (C_2 + 4C_3)t e^t + C_3 t^2 e^t) \\
&= y_1 - 3y_2 + 3y_3.
\end{aligned}
$$

28. The matrix of the quadratic form is

$$A = \begin{bmatrix} a & b/2 \\ b/2 & c \end{bmatrix} = \begin{bmatrix} 1 & -2 \\ -2 & 1 \end{bmatrix}.$$

30. The matrix of the quadratic form is

$$A = \begin{bmatrix} a & b/2 \\ b/2 & c \end{bmatrix} = \begin{bmatrix} 12 & -5/2 \\ -5/2 & 0 \end{bmatrix}.$$

32. The matrix of the quadratic form is

$$A = \begin{bmatrix} a & b/2 \\ b/2 & c \end{bmatrix} = \begin{bmatrix} 16 & -2 \\ -2 & 20 \end{bmatrix}.$$

34. The matrix of the quadratic form is

$$A = \begin{bmatrix} a & b/2 \\ b/2 & c \end{bmatrix} = \begin{bmatrix} 5 & -1 \\ -1 & 5 \end{bmatrix}.$$

The eigenvalues of A are $\lambda_1 = 4$ and $\lambda_2 = 6$, with corresponding eigenvectors $\mathbf{x}_1 = (1, 1)$ and $\mathbf{x}_2 = (-1, 1)$ respectively. Using unit vectors in the direction of $\mathbf{x}_1$ and $\mathbf{x}_2$ to form the columns of P, we have

$$P = \begin{bmatrix} \dfrac{\sqrt{2}}{2} & -\dfrac{\sqrt{2}}{2} \\ \dfrac{\sqrt{2}}{2} & \dfrac{\sqrt{2}}{2} \end{bmatrix} \text{ and } P^T A P = \begin{bmatrix} 4 & 0 \\ 0 & 6 \end{bmatrix}.$$

36. The matrix of the quadratic form is

$$A = \begin{bmatrix} a & b/2 \\ b/2 & c \end{bmatrix} = \begin{bmatrix} 3 & -\sqrt{3} \\ -\sqrt{3} & 1 \end{bmatrix}.$$

The eigenvalues of A are $\lambda_1 = 0$ and $\lambda_2 = 4$, with corresponding eigenvectors $\mathbf{x}_1 = (1, \sqrt{3})$ and $\mathbf{x}_2 = (-\sqrt{3}, 1)$, respectively. Using unit vectors in the direction of $\mathbf{x}_1$ and $\mathbf{x}_2$ to form the columns of P, we have

$$P = \begin{bmatrix} \dfrac{1}{2} & -\dfrac{\sqrt{3}}{2} \\ \dfrac{\sqrt{3}}{2} & \dfrac{1}{2} \end{bmatrix} \text{ and } P^T A P = \begin{bmatrix} 0 & 0 \\ 0 & 4 \end{bmatrix}.$$

38. The matrix of the quadratic form is

$$A = \begin{bmatrix} a & b/2 \\ b/2 & c \end{bmatrix} = \begin{bmatrix} 17 & 16 \\ 16 & -7 \end{bmatrix}.$$

The eigenvalues of A are $\lambda_1 = -15$ and $\lambda_2 = 25$, with corresponding eigenvectors $\mathbf{x}_1 = (1, -2)$ and $\mathbf{x}_2 = (2, 1)$, respectively. Using unit vectors in the direction of $\mathbf{x}_1$ and $\mathbf{x}_2$ to form the columns of P, we have

$$P = \begin{bmatrix} \dfrac{1}{\sqrt{5}} & \dfrac{2}{\sqrt{5}} \\ -\dfrac{2}{\sqrt{5}} & \dfrac{1}{\sqrt{5}} \end{bmatrix} \text{ and } P^T A P = \begin{bmatrix} -15 & 0 \\ 0 & 25 \end{bmatrix}.$$

40. The matrix of the quadratic form is

$$A = \begin{bmatrix} a & b/2 \\ b/2 & c \end{bmatrix} = \begin{bmatrix} 1 & 2 \\ 2 & 1 \end{bmatrix}.$$

This matrix has eigenvalues of -1 and 3, and corresponding unit eigenvectors $(1/\sqrt{2}, -1/\sqrt{2})$ and $(1/\sqrt{2}, 1/\sqrt{2})$, respectively. Thus, we let

$$P = \begin{bmatrix} \dfrac{1}{\sqrt{2}} & \dfrac{1}{\sqrt{2}} \\ -\dfrac{1}{\sqrt{2}} & \dfrac{1}{\sqrt{2}} \end{bmatrix} \text{ and } P^T A P = \begin{bmatrix} -1 & 0 \\ 0 & 3 \end{bmatrix}.$$

This implies that the rotated conic is a hyperbola with equation $-(x')^2 + 3(y')^2 = 9$.

42. The matrix of the quadratic form is

$$A = \begin{bmatrix} a & b/2 \\ b/2 & c \end{bmatrix} = \begin{bmatrix} 2 & -2 \\ -2 & 5 \end{bmatrix}.$$

This matrix has eigenvalues of 1 and 6, and corresponding unit eigenvectors and $(2/\sqrt{5}, 1/\sqrt{5})$ and $(-1/\sqrt{5}, 2/\sqrt{5})$, respectively. Thus, we let

$$P = \begin{bmatrix} \dfrac{2}{\sqrt{5}} & -\dfrac{1}{\sqrt{5}} \\ \dfrac{1}{\sqrt{5}} & \dfrac{2}{\sqrt{5}} \end{bmatrix} \text{ and } P^T A P = \begin{bmatrix} 1 & 0 \\ 0 & 6 \end{bmatrix}.$$

This implies that the rotated conic is an ellipse with equation $(x')^2 + 6(y')^2 - 36 = 0$.

44. The matrix of the quadratic form is

$$A = \begin{bmatrix} a & b/2 \\ b/2 & c \end{bmatrix} = \begin{bmatrix} 8 & 4 \\ 4 & 8 \end{bmatrix}.$$

This matrix has eigenvalues of 4 and 12, and corresponding unit eigenvectors $(1/\sqrt{2}, -1/\sqrt{2})$ and $(1/\sqrt{2}, 1/\sqrt{2})$, respectively. Thus, we let

$$P = \begin{bmatrix} \dfrac{1}{\sqrt{2}} & \dfrac{1}{\sqrt{2}} \\ -\dfrac{1}{\sqrt{2}} & \dfrac{1}{\sqrt{2}} \end{bmatrix} \text{ and } P^T A P = \begin{bmatrix} 4 & 0 \\ 0 & 12 \end{bmatrix}.$$

This implies that the rotated conic is an ellipse. Furthermore,

$$[d \quad e]P = [10\sqrt{2} \quad 26\sqrt{2}] \begin{bmatrix} \dfrac{1}{\sqrt{2}} & \dfrac{1}{\sqrt{2}} \\ -\dfrac{1}{\sqrt{2}} & \dfrac{1}{\sqrt{2}} \end{bmatrix} = [-16 \quad 36] = [d' \quad e'],$$

so the equation in the $x'y'$ – coordinate system is

$$4(x')^2 + 12(y')^2 - 16x' + 36y' + 31 = 0.$$

46. The matrix of the quadratic form is

$$A = \begin{bmatrix} a & b/2 \\ b/2 & c \end{bmatrix} = \begin{bmatrix} 5 & -1 \\ -1 & 5 \end{bmatrix}.$$

This matrix eigenvalues of A are 4 and 6, corresponding unit eigenvectors $(1/\sqrt{2}, 1/\sqrt{2})$ and $(-1/\sqrt{2}, 1/\sqrt{2})$, respectively. Thus, we let

$$P = \begin{bmatrix} \dfrac{1}{\sqrt{2}} & -\dfrac{1}{\sqrt{2}} \\ \dfrac{1}{\sqrt{2}} & \dfrac{1}{\sqrt{2}} \end{bmatrix} \text{ and } P^T A P = \begin{bmatrix} 4 & 0 \\ 0 & 6 \end{bmatrix}.$$

This implies that the rotated conic is an ellipse. Furthermore,

$$[d \quad e]P = [10\sqrt{2} \quad 0]\begin{bmatrix} \dfrac{1}{\sqrt{2}} & -\dfrac{1}{\sqrt{2}} \\ \dfrac{1}{\sqrt{2}} & \dfrac{1}{\sqrt{2}} \end{bmatrix} = [10 \quad -10] = [d' \quad e'],$$

so the equation in the $x'y'$ – coordinate system is

$$4(x')^2 + 6(y')^2 + 10x' + 10y' = 0.$$

48. The matrix of the quadratic form is

$$A = \begin{bmatrix} 2 & 1 & 1 \\ 1 & 2 & 1 \\ 1 & 1 & 2 \end{bmatrix}.$$

The eigenvalues of A are 1, 1 and 4, corresponding unit eigenvectors $(1/\sqrt{6}, 1/\sqrt{6}, -2/\sqrt{6})$, $(-1/\sqrt{2}, 1/\sqrt{2}, 0)$ and $(1/\sqrt{3}, 1/\sqrt{3}, 1/\sqrt{3})$, respectively. Then we let

$$P = \begin{bmatrix} \dfrac{1}{\sqrt{6}} & -\dfrac{1}{\sqrt{2}} & \dfrac{1}{\sqrt{3}} \\ \dfrac{1}{\sqrt{6}} & \dfrac{1}{\sqrt{2}} & \dfrac{1}{\sqrt{3}} \\ -\dfrac{2}{\sqrt{6}} & 0 & \dfrac{1}{\sqrt{3}} \end{bmatrix} \text{ and } P^T A P = \begin{bmatrix} 1 & 0 & 0 \\ 0 & 1 & 0 \\ 0 & 0 & 4 \end{bmatrix}.$$

Thus, the equation of the rotated quadratic surface is

$$(x')^2 + (y')^2 + 4(z')^2 - 1 = 0 \quad \text{(ellipsoid)}.$$

Chapter 7 ☐ Review Exercises

2. (a) The characteristic equation of A is given by

$$|\lambda I - A| = \begin{vmatrix} \lambda - 2 & -1 \\ 4 & \lambda + 2 \end{vmatrix} = \lambda^2 = 0.$$

(b) The eigenvalue of A is $\lambda = 0$ (repeated).

(c) To find the eigenvectors corresponding to $\lambda = 0$, we solve the matrix equation $(\lambda I - A)\mathbf{x} = \mathbf{0}$. Row reducing the augmented matrix,

$$\begin{bmatrix} -2 & -1 & \vdots & 0 \\ 4 & 2 & \vdots & 0 \end{bmatrix} \Rightarrow \begin{bmatrix} 2 & 1 & \vdots & 0 \\ 0 & 0 & \vdots & 0 \end{bmatrix}$$

we see that a basis for the eigenspace is $\{(-1, 2)\}$.

4. (a) The characteristic equation of A is given by

$$|\lambda I - A| = \begin{vmatrix} \lambda + 4 & -1 & -2 \\ 0 & \lambda - 1 & -1 \\ 0 & 0 & \lambda - 3 \end{vmatrix} = (\lambda + 4)(\lambda - 1)(\lambda - 3) = 0.$$

(b) The eigenvalues of A are $\lambda_1 = -4$, $\lambda_2 = 1$, and $\lambda_3 = 3$..

(c) To find the eigenvectors corresponding to $\lambda_1 = -4$, we solve the matrix equation $(\lambda_1 I - A)\mathbf{x} = \mathbf{0}$. Row reducing the augmented matrix,

$$\begin{bmatrix} 0 & -1 & -2 & \vdots & 0 \\ 0 & -5 & -1 & \vdots & 0 \\ 0 & 0 & -7 & \vdots & 0 \end{bmatrix} \Rightarrow \begin{bmatrix} 0 & 1 & 0 & \vdots & 0 \\ 0 & 0 & 1 & \vdots & 0 \\ 0 & 0 & 0 & \vdots & 0 \end{bmatrix}$$

we see that a basis for the eigenspace $\lambda_1 = -4$ is $\{(1, 0, 0)\}$. Similarly, we solve $(\lambda_2 I - A)\mathbf{x} = \mathbf{0}$ for $\lambda_2 = 1$, and see that $\{(1, 5, 0)\}$ is a basis for the eigenspace of $\lambda_2 = 1$. Finally, we solve $(\lambda_3 I - A)\mathbf{x} = \mathbf{0}$ for $\lambda_3 = 3$, and determine that $\{(5, 7, 14)\}$ is a basis for its eigenspace.

6. (a) The characteristic equation of A is given by

$$|\lambda I - A| = \begin{vmatrix} \lambda - 2 & -1 & 0 & 0 \\ -1 & \lambda - 2 & 0 & 0 \\ 0 & 0 & \lambda - 2 & -1 \\ 0 & 0 & -1 & \lambda - 2 \end{vmatrix} = (\lambda - 1)^2(\lambda - 3)^2 = 0.$$

(b) The eigenvalues of A are $\lambda_1 = 1$ (repeated) and $\lambda_2 = 3$ (repeated).

(c) To find the eigenvectors corresponding to $\lambda_1 = 1$, we solve the matrix equation $(\lambda_1 I - A)\mathbf{x} = \mathbf{0}$ for $\lambda_1 = 1$. Row reducing the augmented matrix,

$$\begin{bmatrix} -1 & -1 & 0 & 0 & \vdots & 0 \\ -1 & -1 & 0 & 0 & \vdots & 0 \\ 0 & 0 & -1 & -1 & \vdots & 0 \\ 0 & 0 & -1 & -1 & \vdots & 0 \end{bmatrix} \Rightarrow \begin{bmatrix} 1 & 1 & 0 & 0 & \vdots & 0 \\ 0 & 0 & 1 & 1 & \vdots & 0 \\ 0 & 0 & 0 & 0 & \vdots & 0 \\ 0 & 0 & 0 & 0 & \vdots & 0 \end{bmatrix}$$

we see that a basis for the eigenspace $\lambda_1 = 1$ is $\{(1, -1, 0, 0), (0, 0, 1, -1)\}$. Similarly, we solve $(\lambda_2 I - A)\mathbf{x} = \mathbf{0}$ for $\lambda_2 = 3$, and discover that a basis for the eigenspace of $\lambda_2 = 3$ is $\{(1, 1, 0, 0), (0, 0, 1, 1)\}$.

8. The eigenvalues of A are the solutions of

$$|\lambda I - A| = \begin{vmatrix} \lambda - 3 & 2 & -2 \\ 2 & \lambda & 1 \\ -2 & 1 & \lambda \end{vmatrix} = (\lambda + 1)^2(\lambda - 5) = 0.$$

Therefore, the eigenvalues are -1 (repeated) and 5. The corresponding eigenvectors are solutions of $(\lambda I - A)\mathbf{x} = \mathbf{0}$.

Thus, $(1, 1, -1)$ and $(2, 5, 1)$ are eigenvectors corresponding to $\lambda_1 = -1$, while $(2, -1, 1)$ corresponds to $\lambda_2 = 5$. We now form P from these eigenvectors and note that

$$P = \begin{bmatrix} 1 & 2 & 2 \\ 1 & 5 & -1 \\ -1 & 1 & 1 \end{bmatrix} \text{ and } P^{-1}AP = \begin{bmatrix} -1 & 0 & 0 \\ 0 & -1 & 0 \\ 0 & 0 & 5 \end{bmatrix}.$$

10. The eigenvalues of A are the solutions of

$$|\lambda I - A| = \begin{vmatrix} \lambda - 2 & 1 & -1 \\ 2 & \lambda - 3 & 2 \\ 1 & -1 & \lambda \end{vmatrix} = (\lambda - 1)^2(\lambda - 3) = 0.$$

Therefore, the eigenvalues are $\lambda_1 = 1$ (repeated) and $\lambda_2 = 3$. The corresponding eigenvectors are solutions of $(\lambda I - A)\mathbf{x} = \mathbf{0}$. Thus, $(-1, 0, 1)$ and $(1, 1, 0)$ are eigenvectors corresponding to $\lambda_1 = 1$, while $(-1, 2, 1)$ corresponds to $\lambda_2 = 3$. We now form P from these eigenvectors and note that

$$P = \begin{bmatrix} -1 & 1 & -1 \\ 0 & 1 & 2 \\ 1 & 0 & 1 \end{bmatrix} \text{ and } P^{-1}AP = \begin{bmatrix} 1 & 0 & 0 \\ 0 & 1 & 0 \\ 0 & 0 & 3 \end{bmatrix}.$$

12. The characteristic equation of A is given by

$$|\lambda I - A| = \begin{vmatrix} \lambda & -1 \\ -a & \lambda-1 \end{vmatrix} = \lambda^2 - \lambda - a = 0.$$

The discriminant of d of this quadratic equation in λ is $1 + 4a$.

(a) A has an eigenvalue of multiplicity 2 if and only if $d = 1 + 4a = 0$; that is, $a = -\frac{1}{4}$.

(b) A has -1 and 2 as eigenvalues if and only if $\lambda^2 - \lambda - a = (\lambda + 1)(\lambda - 2)$; that is, $a = 2$.

(c) A has real eigenvalues if and only if $d = 1 + 4a \geq 0$; that is $a \geq -\frac{1}{4}$.

14. The eigenvalue is $\lambda = -1$ (repeated). To find its corresponding eigenspace, we solve $(\lambda I - A)\mathbf{x} = 0$ with $\lambda = -1$.

$$\begin{bmatrix} \lambda + 1 & -2 & \vdots & 0 \\ 0 & \lambda + 1 & \vdots & 0 \end{bmatrix} = \begin{bmatrix} 0 & -2 & \vdots & 0 \\ 0 & 0 & \vdots & 0 \end{bmatrix} \Rightarrow \begin{bmatrix} 0 & 1 & \vdots & 0 \\ 0 & 0 & \vdots & 0 \end{bmatrix}$$

Since the eigenspace is only one-dimensional, the matrix A is not diagonalizable.

16. The eigenvalues are $\lambda = -2$ (repeated) and $\lambda = 4$. Since the eigenspace corresponding to $\lambda = -2$ is only one-dimensional, the matrix is not diagonalizable.

18. Since the eigenspace corresponding to $\lambda = 1$ of matrix A has dimension 1, while that of matrix B has dimension 2, the matrices are not similar.

20. Since

$$A^T = \begin{bmatrix} -\frac{2}{3} & \frac{2}{3} & \frac{1}{3} \\ \frac{1}{3} & \frac{2}{3} & -\frac{2}{3} \\ -\frac{2}{3} & -\frac{1}{3} & \frac{2}{3} \end{bmatrix} \neq A,$$

A is *not* symmetric. Since the column vectors of A do not form an orthonormal set (columns 2 and 3 are not orthogonal), A is *not* orthogonal.

22. Since

$$A^T = \begin{bmatrix} \frac{4}{5} & 0 & -\frac{3}{5} \\ 0 & 1 & 0 \\ \frac{3}{5} & 0 & \frac{4}{5} \end{bmatrix} \neq A,$$

A is *not* symmetric. However, the column vectors form an orthonormal set, so A *is* orthogonal.

24. The eigenvalues of A are 17 and -17, with corresponding unit eigenvectors $\left(\dfrac{5}{\sqrt{34}}, \dfrac{3}{\sqrt{34}}\right)$ and $\left(-\dfrac{3}{\sqrt{34}}, \dfrac{5}{\sqrt{34}}\right)$, respectively. We form the columns of P with the eigenvectors of A

$$P = \begin{bmatrix} \dfrac{5}{\sqrt{34}} & -\dfrac{3}{\sqrt{34}} \\ \dfrac{3}{\sqrt{34}} & \dfrac{5}{\sqrt{34}} \end{bmatrix}.$$

26. The eigenvalues of A are 3, -1 and 5, with corresponding eigenvectors

$$\left(\dfrac{1}{\sqrt{2}}, \dfrac{1}{\sqrt{2}}, 0\right), \left(\dfrac{1}{\sqrt{2}}, -\dfrac{1}{\sqrt{2}}, 0\right), (0, 0, 1).$$

We form the columns of P from the eigenvectors of A

$$P = \begin{bmatrix} \dfrac{1}{\sqrt{2}} & \dfrac{1}{\sqrt{2}} & 0 \\ \dfrac{1}{\sqrt{2}} & -\dfrac{1}{\sqrt{2}} & 0 \\ 0 & 0 & 1 \end{bmatrix}.$$

28. The eigenvalues of A are $-\frac{1}{2}$ and 1. The eigenvectors corresponding to $\lambda = 1$ are $\mathbf{x} = t(2, 1)$. By choosing $t = \frac{1}{3}$, we find the steady state probability vector for A to be $\mathbf{v} = \left(\frac{2}{3}, \frac{1}{3}\right)$. Note that

$$A\mathbf{v} = \begin{bmatrix} \frac{1}{2} & 1 \\ \frac{1}{2} & 0 \end{bmatrix} \begin{bmatrix} \frac{2}{3} \\ \frac{1}{3} \end{bmatrix} = \begin{bmatrix} \frac{2}{3} \\ \frac{1}{3} \end{bmatrix} = \mathbf{v}.$$

30. The eigenvalues of A are $-0.2060, 0.5393$ and 1. The eigenvectors corresponding to $\lambda = 1$ are $\mathbf{x} = t(2, 1, 2)$. By choosing $t = \frac{1}{5}$, we find the steady state probability vector for A to be $\mathbf{v} = \left(\frac{2}{5}, \frac{1}{5}, \frac{2}{5}\right)$. Note that

$$A\mathbf{v} = \begin{bmatrix} \frac{1}{3} & \frac{2}{3} & \frac{1}{3} \\ \frac{1}{3} & \frac{1}{3} & 0 \\ \frac{1}{3} & 0 & \frac{2}{3} \end{bmatrix} \begin{bmatrix} \frac{2}{5} \\ \frac{1}{5} \\ \frac{2}{5} \end{bmatrix} = \begin{bmatrix} \frac{2}{5} \\ \frac{1}{5} \\ \frac{2}{5} \end{bmatrix} = \mathbf{v}.$$

32. The eigenvalues of A are $\frac{1}{2}$ and 1. The eigenvectors corresponding to $\lambda = 1$ are $\mathbf{x} = t(3, 2)$. By choosing $t = \frac{1}{5}$, we find the steady state probability vector for A to be $\mathbf{v} = \left(\frac{3}{5}, \frac{2}{5}\right)$. Note that

$$A\mathbf{v} = \begin{bmatrix} 0.8 & 0.3 \\ 0.2 & 0.7 \end{bmatrix} \begin{bmatrix} \frac{3}{5} \\ \frac{2}{5} \end{bmatrix} = \begin{bmatrix} \frac{3}{5} \\ \frac{2}{5} \end{bmatrix} = \mathbf{v}.$$

34. For the sake of simplicity, we assume $a_n = 1$, and observe that the following proof holds for any nonzero a_n. First we show by induction that for the $n \times n$ matrix C_n,

$$|C_n| = \begin{vmatrix} \lambda & -1 & 0 & \cdots & 0 \\ 0 & \lambda & -1 & \cdots & 0 \\ \vdots & \vdots & \vdots & & -1 \\ b_0 & b_1 & b_2 & \cdots & b_{n-1} \end{vmatrix} = b_{n-1}\lambda^{n-1} + \cdots + b_1\lambda + b_0.$$

For $n = 1$, $|C_1| = b_0$, and for $n = 2$,

$$|C_2| = \begin{vmatrix} \lambda & -1 \\ b_0 & b_1 \end{vmatrix} = b_1\lambda + b_0.$$

Assuming the property for n, we see that

$$|C_{n+1}| = \begin{vmatrix} \lambda & -1 & 0 & \cdots & 0 \\ 0 & \lambda & -1 & \cdots & 0 \\ \vdots & \vdots & \vdots & \vdots & -1 \\ b_0 & b_1 & b_2 & \cdots & b_n \end{vmatrix} = b_n\lambda^n + |C_n| = b_n\lambda^n + b_{n-1}\lambda^{n-1} + b_1\lambda + b_0.$$

Thus, showing the property is valid for $n + 1$. We can now evaluate the characteristic equation of A as follows.

$$|\lambda I - A| = \begin{vmatrix} \lambda & -1 & 0 & \cdots & 0 \\ 0 & \lambda & -1 & \cdots & 0 \\ \vdots & \vdots & \vdots & & \vdots \\ 0 & 0 & 0 & \vdots & -1 \\ a_0 & a_1 & a_2 & \vdots & \lambda + a_{n-1} \end{vmatrix}$$

$$= (\lambda + a_{n-1})\lambda^{n-1} + |C_{n-2}|$$

$$= \lambda^n + a_{n-1}\lambda^{n-1} + a_{n-2}\lambda^{n-2} + \ldots + a_1\lambda + a_0.$$

36. From the form $p(\lambda) = a_0 + a_1\lambda + a_2\lambda^2 + a_3\lambda^3$, we have $a_0 = 189$, $a_1 = -120$, $a_2 = -7$ and $a_3 = 2$. This implies that the companion matrix of p is

$$A = \begin{bmatrix} 0 & 1 & 0 \\ 0 & 0 & 1 \\ -\frac{189}{2} & 60 & \frac{7}{2} \end{bmatrix}.$$

The eigenvalues of A are $\frac{3}{2}$, 9, and -7 the zeros of p.

38. The characteristic equation of A is

$$|\lambda I - A| = \lambda^3 - 20\lambda^2 + 128\lambda - 256 = 0.$$

Since $A^3 - 20A^2 + 128A - 256I = O$, we have

$$A^2 = \begin{bmatrix} 9 & 4 & -3 \\ -2 & 0 & 6 \\ -1 & -4 & 11 \end{bmatrix} \begin{bmatrix} 9 & 4 & -3 \\ -2 & 0 & 6 \\ -1 & -4 & 11 \end{bmatrix} = \begin{bmatrix} 76 & 48 & -36 \\ -24 & -32 & 72 \\ -12 & -48 & 100 \end{bmatrix}$$

and

$$A^3 = 20A^2 - 128A + 256I$$

$$= 20 \begin{bmatrix} 76 & 48 & -32 \\ -24 & -32 & 72 \\ -12 & -48 & 100 \end{bmatrix} - 128 \begin{bmatrix} 9 & 4 & -3 \\ -2 & 0 & 6 \\ -1 & -4 & 11 \end{bmatrix} + 256 \begin{bmatrix} 1 & 0 & 0 \\ 0 & 1 & 0 \\ 0 & 0 & 1 \end{bmatrix}$$

$$= \begin{bmatrix} 624 & 448 & -336 \\ -224 & -384 & 672 \\ -112 & -448 & 848 \end{bmatrix}$$

40. $(A + cI)\mathbf{x} = A\mathbf{x} + cI\mathbf{x} = \lambda\mathbf{x} + c\mathbf{x} = (\lambda + c)\mathbf{x}$. Hence, $\mathbf{x}$ is an eigenvector of $(A + cI)$ with eigenvalue $(\lambda + c)$.

42. (a) The eigenvalues of A are 3 and 1, with corresponding eigenvectors $(1, 1)$ and $(1, -1)$. Letting these eigenvectors form the columns of P, we can diagonalize A

$$P = \begin{bmatrix} 1 & 1 \\ 1 & -1 \end{bmatrix} \qquad P^{-1}AP = \begin{bmatrix} 3 & 0 \\ 0 & 1 \end{bmatrix} = D.$$

Hence,

$$A = PDP^{-1} = P \begin{bmatrix} 3 & 0 \\ 0 & 1 \end{bmatrix} P^{-1}.$$

Letting

$$B = P \begin{bmatrix} \sqrt{3} & 0 \\ 0 & 1 \end{bmatrix} P^{-1} = \frac{1}{2} \begin{bmatrix} \sqrt{3} + 1 & \sqrt{3} - 1 \\ \sqrt{3} - 1 & \sqrt{3} + 1 \end{bmatrix}$$

we have

$$B = \left(P \begin{bmatrix} \sqrt{3} & 0 \\ 0 & 1 \end{bmatrix} P^{-1} \right)^2 = P \begin{bmatrix} \sqrt{3} & 0 \\ 0 & 1 \end{bmatrix}^2 P^{-1} = P \begin{bmatrix} 3 & 0 \\ 0 & 1 \end{bmatrix} P^{-1} = A.$$

(b) In general, let $A = PDP^{-1}$, D diagonal with positive eigenvalues on the diagonal. Let D' be the diagonal matrix consisting of the square roots of the diagonal entries of D. Then if $B = PD'P^{-1}$,

$$B^2 = (PD'P^{-1})(PD'P^{-1}) = P(D')^2P^{-1} = PDP^{-1} = A.$$

44. Since $A\mathbf{x} = A^2\mathbf{x}$ and $A^2\mathbf{x} = A(A\mathbf{x}) = A(\lambda\mathbf{x}) = \lambda^2\mathbf{x}$, we see that $\lambda\mathbf{x} = \lambda^2\mathbf{x}$, or $\lambda = \lambda^2 \implies \lambda = 0$ or 1.

46. If A is symmetric and has 0 as its only eigenvalue, then $P^T A P = \mathbf{0}$, the zero matrix, which implies that $A = \mathbf{0}$.

48. (a) *True.* See Theorem 7.2 on page 414.

   (b) *False.* See remark after the definition of eigenvalue and eigenvector on page 411. If $\mathbf{x} = \mathbf{0}$ is allowed to be an eigenvector, then the definition of eigenvalue would be meaningless, because $A\mathbf{0} = \lambda\mathbf{0}$ for *all* real numbers λ.

   (c) *True.* See page 440.

50. The population after one transition is

$$\mathbf{x}_2 = \begin{bmatrix} 0 & 1 \\ \frac{3}{4} & 0 \end{bmatrix} \begin{bmatrix} 32 \\ 32 \end{bmatrix} = \begin{bmatrix} 32 \\ 24 \end{bmatrix}$$

and after two transitions is

$$\mathbf{x}_3 = \begin{bmatrix} 0 & 1 \\ \frac{3}{4} & 0 \end{bmatrix} \begin{bmatrix} 32 \\ 24 \end{bmatrix} = \begin{bmatrix} 24 \\ 24 \end{bmatrix}.$$

The eigenvalues of A are $\pm\sqrt{3}/2$. We choose the positive eigenvalue and find the corresponding eigenvector to be $(2, \sqrt{3})$, which is a stable age distribution.

52. The population after one transition is

$$\mathbf{x}_2 = \begin{bmatrix} 0 & 2 & 2 \\ \frac{1}{2} & 0 & 0 \\ 0 & 0 & 0 \end{bmatrix} \begin{bmatrix} 240 \\ 240 \\ 240 \end{bmatrix} = \begin{bmatrix} 960 \\ 120 \\ 0 \end{bmatrix}$$

and after two transitions is

$$\mathbf{x}_3 = \begin{bmatrix} 0 & 2 & 2 \\ \frac{1}{2} & 0 & 0 \\ 0 & 0 & 0 \end{bmatrix} \begin{bmatrix} 960 \\ 120 \\ 0 \end{bmatrix} = \begin{bmatrix} 240 \\ 480 \\ 0 \end{bmatrix}.$$

The positive eigenvalue 1 has corresponding eigenvector $(2, 1, 0)$ which is a stable distribution.

54. The matrix corresponds to the system $\mathbf{y}' = A\mathbf{y}$ is

$$A = \begin{bmatrix} 3 & 0 \\ 1 & -1 \end{bmatrix}.$$

This matrix has eigenvalues 3 and -1, with corresponding eigenvectors $(4, 1)$ and $(0, 1)$. Thus, a matrix P that diagonalizes A is

$$P = \begin{bmatrix} 4 & 0 \\ 1 & 1 \end{bmatrix} \quad \text{and} \quad P^{-1}AP = \begin{bmatrix} 3 & 0 \\ 0 & -1 \end{bmatrix}.$$

The system represented by $\mathbf{w}' = P^{-1}AP\mathbf{w}$ has solutions $w_1 = C_1 e^{3t}$ and $w_2 = C_2 e^{-t}$. We substitute $\mathbf{y} = P\mathbf{w}$ and obtain

$$\begin{bmatrix} y_1 \\ y_2 \end{bmatrix} = \begin{bmatrix} 4 & 0 \\ 1 & 1 \end{bmatrix} \begin{bmatrix} w_1 \\ w_2 \end{bmatrix} = \begin{bmatrix} 4w_1 \\ w_1 + w_2 \end{bmatrix}$$

which yields the solution

$$y_1 = 4C_1 e^{3t}$$
$$y_2 = C_1 e^{3t} + C_2 e^{-t}.$$

56. The matrix corresponding to the system $\mathbf{y}' = A\mathbf{y}$ is

$$A = \begin{bmatrix} 6 & -1 & 2 \\ 0 & 3 & -1 \\ 0 & 0 & 1 \end{bmatrix}.$$

The eigenvalues of A are 6, 3, and 1, with corresponding eigenvectors $(1, 0, 0)$, $(1, 3, 0)$ and $(-3, 5, 10)$. Thus, we can diagonalize A by forming P.

$$P = \begin{bmatrix} 1 & 1 & -3 \\ 0 & 3 & 5 \\ 0 & 0 & 10 \end{bmatrix} \quad \text{and} \quad P^{-1}AP = \begin{bmatrix} 6 & 0 & 0 \\ 0 & 3 & 0 \\ 0 & 0 & 1 \end{bmatrix}.$$

The system represented by $\mathbf{w}' = P^{-1}AP\mathbf{w}$ has solutions $w_1 = C_1 e^{6t}$, $w_2 = C_2 e^{3t}$ and $w_3 = C_3 e^{t}$. We substitute $\mathbf{y} = P\mathbf{w}$ and obtain

$$\begin{bmatrix} y_1 \\ y_2 \\ y_3 \end{bmatrix} = \begin{bmatrix} 1 & 1 & -3 \\ 0 & 3 & 5 \\ 0 & 0 & 10 \end{bmatrix} \begin{bmatrix} w_1 \\ w_2 \\ w_3 \end{bmatrix} = \begin{bmatrix} w_1 + w_2 - 3w_3 \\ 3w_2 + 5w_3 \\ 10w_3 \end{bmatrix}$$

which yields the solution

$$y_1 = C_1 e^{6t} + C_2 e^{3t} - 3C_3 e^{t}$$
$$y_2 = 3C_2 e^{3t} + 5C_3 e^{t}$$
$$y_3 = 10C_3 e^{t}.$$

58. The matrix of the quadratic form is

$$A = \begin{bmatrix} a & \frac{b}{2} \\ \frac{b}{2} & c \end{bmatrix} = \begin{bmatrix} 1 & -\frac{\sqrt{3}}{2} \\ -\frac{\sqrt{3}}{2} & 2 \end{bmatrix}.$$

The eigenvalues are $\frac{1}{2}$ and $\frac{5}{2}$, with corresponding unit eigenvectors $\left(\frac{\sqrt{3}}{2}, \frac{1}{2}\right)$ and $\left(-\frac{1}{2}, \frac{\sqrt{3}}{2}\right)$.

We use these eigenvectors to form the columns of P.

$$P = \begin{bmatrix} \frac{\sqrt{3}}{2} & -\frac{1}{2} \\ \frac{1}{2} & \frac{\sqrt{3}}{2} \end{bmatrix} \text{ and } P^T A P = \begin{bmatrix} \frac{1}{2} & 0 \\ 0 & \frac{5}{2} \end{bmatrix}.$$

This implies that the equation of the rotated conic is

$\frac{1}{2}(x')^2 + \frac{5}{2}(y')^2 = 10$, an ellipse.

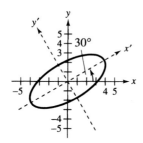

60. The matrix of the quadratic form is

$$A = \begin{bmatrix} 1 & \frac{b}{2} \\ \frac{b}{2} & c \end{bmatrix} = \begin{bmatrix} 9 & -12 \\ -12 & 16 \end{bmatrix}.$$

The eigenvalues are 0 and 25, with corresponding unit eigenvectors $\left(\frac{4}{5}, \frac{3}{5}\right)$ and $\left(-\frac{3}{5}, \frac{4}{5}\right)$. We use these eigenvectors to form the columns of P.

$$P = \begin{bmatrix} \frac{4}{5} & -\frac{3}{5} \\ \frac{3}{5} & \frac{4}{5} \end{bmatrix} \text{ and } P^T A P = \begin{bmatrix} 0 & 0 \\ 0 & 25 \end{bmatrix}.$$

This implies that the equation of the rotated conic is a parabola. Furthermore,

$$[d \quad e]P = [-400 \quad -300] \begin{bmatrix} \frac{4}{5} & -\frac{3}{5} \\ \frac{3}{5} & \frac{4}{5} \end{bmatrix} = [-500 \quad 0] = [d' \quad e']$$

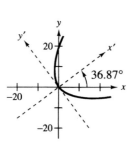

so the equation in the $x'y'$ – coordinate system is $25(y')^2 - 500x' = 0$.

Chapter 7 ❏ Project Solutions

1 Population Growth and Dynamical Systems

1. $A = \begin{bmatrix} 0.5 & 0.6 \\ -0.4 & 3.0 \end{bmatrix}$ $\lambda_1 = 0.6, \mathbf{w}_1 = \begin{bmatrix} 6 \\ 1 \end{bmatrix}$

$$\lambda_2 = 2.9, \mathbf{w}_2 = \begin{bmatrix} 1 \\ 4 \end{bmatrix}$$

$$P = \begin{bmatrix} 6 & 1 \\ 1 & 4 \end{bmatrix}, \quad P^{-1} = \tfrac{1}{23}\begin{bmatrix} 4 & -1 \\ -1 & 6 \end{bmatrix}, \quad P^{-1}AP = \begin{bmatrix} 0.6 & 0 \\ 0 & 2.9 \end{bmatrix}$$

$$\mathbf{w}_1 = C_1 e^{0.6t}, \quad \mathbf{w}_2 = C_2 e^{2.9t}, \quad \mathbf{y} = P\mathbf{w}$$

$$\begin{bmatrix} y_1 \\ y_2 \end{bmatrix} = \begin{bmatrix} 6 & 1 \\ 1 & 4 \end{bmatrix}\begin{bmatrix} C_1 e^{0.6t} \\ C_2 e^{2.9t} \end{bmatrix} = \begin{bmatrix} 6C_1 e^{0.6t} + C_2 e^{2.9t} \\ C_1 e^{0.6t} + 4C_2 e^{2.9t} \end{bmatrix}$$

$$\begin{cases} y_1(0) = 36 \Rightarrow 6C_1 + C_2 = 36 \\ y_2(0) = 121 \Rightarrow C_1 + 4C_2 = 121 \end{cases} \Rightarrow C_1 = 1, C_2 = 30.$$

$$y_1 = 6e^{0.6t} + 30e^{2.9t}$$

$$y_2 = e^{0.6t} + 120e^{2.9t}$$

2. No, neither species disappears. As $t \to \infty$, $y_1 \to 30e^{2.9t}$ and $y_2 \to 120e^{2.9t}$.

3.

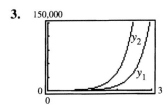

4. As $t \to \infty$, $y_1 \to 30e^{2.9t}$, $y_2 \to 120e^{2.9t}$, and $\dfrac{y_2}{y_1} = 4$.

5. The population y_2 ultimately disappears around $t = 1.6$.

2 The Fibonacci Sequence

1. $x_1 = 1$ $x_4 = 3$ $x_7 = 13$ $x_{10} = 55$

    $x_2 = 1$ $x_5 = 5$ $x_8 = 21$ $x_{11} = 89$

    $x_3 = 2$ $x_6 = 8$ $x_9 = 34$ $x_{12} = 144$

2. $\begin{bmatrix} 1 & 1 \\ 1 & 0 \end{bmatrix}\begin{bmatrix} x_{n-1} \\ x_{n-2} \end{bmatrix} = \begin{bmatrix} x_{n-1} + x_{n-2} \\ x_{n-1} \end{bmatrix} = \begin{bmatrix} x_n \\ x_{n-1} \end{bmatrix}.$ x_n generated from $\begin{bmatrix} x_{n-1} \\ x_{n-2} \end{bmatrix}$

3. $A \begin{bmatrix} 1 \\ 1 \end{bmatrix} = A \begin{bmatrix} x_2 \\ x_1 \end{bmatrix} = \begin{bmatrix} x_3 \\ x_2 \end{bmatrix} = \begin{bmatrix} 2 \\ 1 \end{bmatrix}$

$A^2 \begin{bmatrix} 1 \\ 1 \end{bmatrix} = \begin{bmatrix} 3 \\ 2 \end{bmatrix} = \begin{bmatrix} x_4 \\ x_3 \end{bmatrix}$

In general, $A^n \begin{bmatrix} 1 \\ 1 \end{bmatrix} = \begin{bmatrix} x_{n+2} \\ x_{n+1} \end{bmatrix}$ or $A^{n-2} \begin{bmatrix} 1 \\ 1 \end{bmatrix} = \begin{bmatrix} x_n \\ x_{n-1} \end{bmatrix}$.

4. $\begin{vmatrix} \lambda - 1 & -1 \\ -1 & \lambda \end{vmatrix} = \lambda^2 - \lambda - 1 = 0 \implies \lambda = \dfrac{1 \pm \sqrt{5}}{2}$

$\lambda_1 = \dfrac{1 + \sqrt{5}}{2}$ eigenvector: $\begin{bmatrix} 2 \\ -1 + \sqrt{5} \end{bmatrix}$

$\lambda_2 = \dfrac{1 - \sqrt{5}}{2}$ eigenvector: $\begin{bmatrix} 2 \\ -1 - \sqrt{5} \end{bmatrix}$

$P = \begin{bmatrix} 2 & 2 \\ -1 + \sqrt{5} & -1 - \sqrt{5} \end{bmatrix}$

$P^{-1} = \dfrac{1}{4\sqrt{5}} \begin{bmatrix} 1 + \sqrt{5} & 2 \\ -1 + \sqrt{5} & -2 \end{bmatrix}$

$P^{-1}AP = \begin{bmatrix} \lambda_1 & 0 \\ 0 & \lambda_2 \end{bmatrix}$

5. $P^{-1}AP = D$

$P^{-1}A^{n-2}P = D^{n-2}$

$A^{n-2} = PD^{n-2}P^{-1}$

$= \dfrac{1}{4\sqrt{5}} \begin{bmatrix} 2 & 2 \\ -1 + \sqrt{5} & -1 - \sqrt{5} \end{bmatrix} \begin{bmatrix} \left(\dfrac{1 + \sqrt{5}}{2}\right)^{n-2} & 0 \\ 0 & \left(\dfrac{1 - \sqrt{5}}{2}\right)^{n-2} \end{bmatrix} \begin{bmatrix} 1 + \sqrt{5} & 2 \\ -1 + \sqrt{5} & -2 \end{bmatrix}$

$= \dfrac{1}{4\sqrt{5}} \begin{bmatrix} 2(\lambda_1)^{n-2} & 2(\lambda_2)^{n-2} \\ (-1 + \sqrt{5})(\lambda_1)^{n-2} & (-1 - \sqrt{5})(\lambda_2)^{n-2} \end{bmatrix} \begin{bmatrix} 1 + \sqrt{5} & 2 \\ -1 + \sqrt{5} & -2 \end{bmatrix}$

$= \dfrac{1}{4\sqrt{5}} \begin{bmatrix} 2(1 + \sqrt{5})(\lambda_1)^{n-2} + 2(-1 + \sqrt{5})(\lambda_2)^{n-2} & 4(\lambda_1)^{n-2} - 4\lambda_2^{n-2} \\ +4\lambda_1^{n-2} - 4\lambda_2^{n-2} & 2(-1 + \sqrt{5})\lambda_1^{n-2} + 2(1 + \sqrt{5})\lambda_2^{n-2} \end{bmatrix}$

—CONTINUED—

5. —CONTINUED—

$$A^{n-2}\begin{bmatrix}1\\1\end{bmatrix} = \begin{bmatrix}x_n\\x_{n-1}\end{bmatrix} \implies$$

$$x_n = \frac{1}{4\sqrt{5}}[2(1 + \sqrt{5})\lambda_1^{n-2} + 2(-1 + \sqrt{5})\lambda_2^{n-2} + 4\lambda_1^{n-2} - 4\lambda_2^{n-2}]$$

$$= \frac{1}{\sqrt{5}}[\lambda_1^n - \lambda_2^n]$$

$$x_n = \frac{1}{\sqrt{5}}\left[\left(\frac{1 + \sqrt{5}}{2}\right)^n - \left(\frac{1 - \sqrt{5}}{2}\right)^n\right]$$

$$x_1 = \frac{1}{\sqrt{5}}(\sqrt{5}) = 1$$

$$x_2 = \frac{1}{\sqrt{5}}\left[\frac{6 + 2\sqrt{5}}{4} - \frac{6 - 2\sqrt{5}}{4}\right] = 1$$

$$x_3 = \frac{1}{\sqrt{5}}\left[\frac{6 + 2\sqrt{5}}{4} \cdot \frac{1 + \sqrt{5}}{2} - \frac{6 - 2\sqrt{5}}{4} \cdot \frac{1 - \sqrt{5}}{2}\right] = \frac{1}{\sqrt{5}}\left[\frac{16 + 8\sqrt{5}}{8} - \frac{16 - 8\sqrt{5}}{8}\right] = 2.$$

6. $x_{10} = 55, x_{20} = 6765$

7. For example, $\dfrac{x_{20}}{x_{19}} = \dfrac{6765}{4181} = 1.618\ldots$

The quotients seem to be approaching a fixed value near 1.618.

8. Let the limit be $\dfrac{x_n}{x_{n-1}} = b$. Then for large n, $n \to \infty$.

$$b \approx \frac{x_n}{x_{n-1}} = \frac{x_{n-1} + x_{n-2}}{x_{n-1}} \approx 1 + \frac{1}{b} \implies b^2 - b - 1 = 0 \implies b = \frac{1 \pm \sqrt{5}}{2}.$$

Taking the positive value, $b = \dfrac{1 + \sqrt{5}}{2} \approx 1.618$.

CHAPTER 1
Systems of Linear Equations

Section 1.1   Introduction to Systems of Linear Equations

1. Which of the following equations is *not* linear?

    (a) $-3 - 2a = -a - 5$ (b) $-3 = -2a + (-2)$ (c) $-3a - 2 = -5$ (d) $\left|-3\right| + a = -5$

2. Which of the following is a linear equation?

    (a) $y = 4\sqrt{y} - \dfrac{4}{7}$ (b) $\dfrac{x - y}{4} = -7$ (c) $x = 1\sqrt{y} - 4$ (d) $x = -\dfrac{7}{y}$

3. Is the following equation linear or nonlinear?
    $-1 = -4n + (-4)$

4. Is the equation $y = 9x - 1$ linear or nonlinear?

5. Which shows the graph and solution to the system of equations?
    $$\begin{cases} x + y = 5 \\ y = 3x - 7 \end{cases}$$

    (a)
    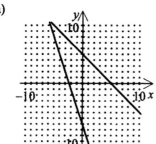
    $(-6, 11)$

    (b)
    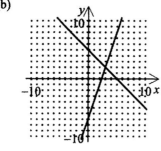
    $(3, 2)$

(c)

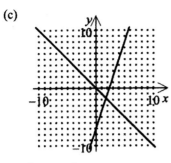

$$\left(\frac{7}{4}, -\frac{7}{4}\right)$$

(d)

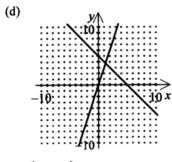

$$\left(\frac{5}{4}, \frac{15}{4}\right)$$

(5.)

6. Find the graph of the system of linear equations.

$$\begin{cases} x + y = 7 \\ y = -x - 5 \end{cases}$$

(a)
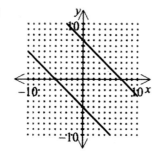

(b)
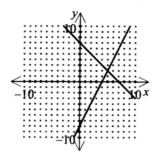

(c)
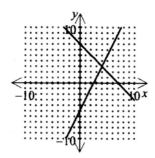

(d)
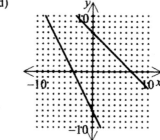

7. Graph the system of equations as a pair of lines in the xy-plane and find the solution.

$$\begin{cases} 2x = 3y - 11 \\ 2y = 3x + 9 \end{cases}$$

8. Graph the system of equations as a pair of lines in the xy-plane.

$$\begin{cases} x + 2y = -6 \\ 2x - y = -2 \end{cases}$$

9. Use back-substitution to solve the system of linear equations.

$$\begin{cases} 8x + 3y + 5z = 7 \\ 4y + 8z = 8 \\ z = 4 \end{cases}$$

(a) $\left(-\dfrac{5}{8},\ -6,\ 4\right)$ (b) $\left(-\dfrac{19}{8},\ 2,\ 4\right)$ (c) $\left(\dfrac{5}{8},\ -6,\ 4\right)$ (d) $\left(2,\ -\dfrac{29}{3},\ 4\right)$

10. Use elimination to solve the system of linear equations.

$$\begin{cases} 2x + 7y = -24 \\ 4x + 3y = -4 \end{cases}$$

(a) $(2, -4)$ (b) $(a, -a-3)$ (c) $(1, 7)$ (d) no solution

11. Use back-substitution to solve the system of linear equations.

$$\begin{cases} 2x + 6y + 6z = 7 \\ 4y + 3z = 1 \\ z = 2 \end{cases}$$

12. Classify the system of equations as independent, inconsistent, or dependent. If the system is independent, find its solution.

$$\begin{cases} 2x + y = 6 \\ 8x + 4y = 24 \end{cases}$$

Section 1.2   Gaussian Elimination and Gauss-Jordan Elimination

13. Which shows the resulting matrix after the following row operations are performed on the matrix $\begin{bmatrix} 3 & 8 & -2 \\ 1 & 0 & 4 \\ 4 & -9 & 10 \end{bmatrix}$?

a. Interchange R_1 and R_2.

b. Add -3 times R_1 to R_2 to produce a new R_2.

c. Add -4 times R_1 to R_3 to produce a new R_3.

(a) $\begin{bmatrix} 8 & -9 & 9 \\ -6 & -9 & -2 \\ 4 & 8 & -18 \end{bmatrix}$ (b) $\begin{bmatrix} 1 & 0 & 4 \\ 0 & 8 & -14 \\ 0 & -9 & -6 \end{bmatrix}$ (c) $\begin{bmatrix} 8 & -9 & 9 \\ -6 & -9 & -6 \\ 4 & 8 & -14 \end{bmatrix}$ (d) $\begin{bmatrix} 1 & -9 & -8 \\ 0 & 8 & -18 \\ 0 & -9 & -2 \end{bmatrix}$

14. Which shows the augmented matrix for the system in row-echelon form?

$$\begin{cases} x - 2y + z = 6 \\ 3x - 5y - 18z = -4 \\ 2x - 6y + 45z = 5 \end{cases}$$

(a) $\begin{bmatrix} 1 & -2 & 1 & \vdots & 6 \\ 0 & 1 & -21 & \vdots & -22 \\ 0 & 0 & 1 & \vdots & -51 \end{bmatrix}$

(b) $\begin{bmatrix} 1 & -2 & 1 & \vdots & 6 \\ 0 & 1 & 25 & \vdots & -22 \\ 0 & 0 & 1 & \vdots & -7 \end{bmatrix}$

(c) $\begin{bmatrix} 1 & -2 & 1 & \vdots & 6 \\ 0 & 1 & 25 & \vdots & 2 \\ 0 & 0 & 1 & \vdots & 1 \end{bmatrix}$

(d) $\begin{bmatrix} 1 & -2 & 1 & \vdots & 6 \\ 0 & 1 & -22 & \vdots & -51 \\ 0 & 0 & 1 & \vdots & -21 \end{bmatrix}$

15. Perform the following sequence of row operations on the matrix $\begin{bmatrix} -5 & -3 & -6 \\ 3 & 8 & 7 \\ 1 & -1 & -4 \end{bmatrix}$.

    a. Interchange R_1 and R_3.

    b. Add -3 times R_1 to R_2 to produce a new R_2.

    c. Add 5 times R_1 to R_3 to produce a new R_3.

16. Find the reduced row-echelon form of the augmented matrix and solve the system of linear equations.

$$\begin{cases} x - 2y + z = 2 \\ 3x - 5y - 6z = 5 \\ 2x - 6y + 21z = 3 \end{cases}$$

17. If possible, solve the system of equations using Gauss-Jordan elimination.

$$\begin{cases} -3x - 4y + 2z = 7 \\ x - 3y + 4z = 5 \\ 26x + 13y + 6z = -24 \end{cases}$$

    (a) $(13, -4, 3)$ (b) $(3, 8, 13)$ (c) $\left(-\frac{10}{13}a - \frac{1}{13}, \frac{14}{13}a - \frac{22}{13}, a\right)$ (d) inconsistent

18. If possible, solve the system of equations using Gauss-Jordan elimination.

$$\begin{cases} 2x - 7y = 3 \\ 6x + y = 0 \end{cases}$$

    (a) $\left(-\frac{9}{22}, \frac{3}{44}\right)$ (b) $\left(\frac{1}{36}, \frac{1}{756}\right)$ (c) $\left(\frac{1}{756}, \frac{1}{36}\right)$ (d) $\left(\frac{3}{44}, -\frac{9}{22}\right)$

19. If possible, solve the system of equations using Gauss-Jordan elimination.
$$\begin{cases} x - 2y + z = -6 \\ 3x - 5y + 8z = 3 \\ 2x - 6y - 7z = 11 \end{cases}$$

20. If possible, solve the system of equations using Gauss-Jordan elimination.
$$\begin{cases} 5x + 3y - 9z - 3w = 21 \\ 8x + 5y + 8z + 7w = -19 \\ -2x + 2y - 6z - 3w = 25 \\ 2x - 8y + z - 4w = -47 \end{cases}$$

21. Which is the solution to the homogeneous system of linear equations?
$$\begin{cases} -2x + 2y - 3z = 0 \\ x + y + 2z = 0 \end{cases}$$

    (a) $x = -7t,\ y = -t,\ z = -4t$ (b) $x = 7t,\ y = t,\ z = -4t$

    (c) $x = -7t,\ y = t,\ z = -4t$ (d) $x = 7t,\ y = -t,\ z = -4t$

22. Which is the solution to the homogeneous system of linear equations?
$$\begin{cases} -4x + 6y - 6z = 0 \\ 5x + 4y + 5z = 0 \end{cases}$$

    (a) $x = -\dfrac{27}{5}t,\ y = t,\ z = \dfrac{23}{5}t$ (b) $x = \dfrac{27}{5}t,\ y = t,\ z = \dfrac{23}{5}t$

    (c) $x = -\dfrac{27}{5}t,\ y = -t,\ z = \dfrac{23}{5}t$ (d) $x = \dfrac{27}{5}t,\ y = -t,\ z = \dfrac{23}{5}t$

23. Solve the homogeneous system of linear equations.
$$\begin{cases} 3x - 3y + 2z = 0 \\ 2x + 2y + z = 0 \end{cases}$$

24. Solve the homogeneous system of linear equations.
$$\begin{cases} 5x - 4y + 5z = 0 \\ 6x + 5y + 4z = 0 \end{cases}$$

Section 1.3   Applications of Systems of Linear Equations

25. A quadratic equation $y = ax^2 + bx + c$ passes through the points $(-2, 7)$, $(1, -8)$, and $(2, -1)$.

   a. Which shows the system of equations that will allow you to find the values a, b, and c?

   b. Find the quadratic equation.

(a) a. $\begin{cases} 4a - 2b + c = 7 \\ a + b + c = -8 \\ 4a + 2b + c = -1 \end{cases}$

    b. $y = -3x^2 + 2x + 9$

(b) a. $\begin{cases} 4a - 2b + c = 7 \\ a + b + c = -8 \\ 4a + 2b + c = -1 \end{cases}$

    b. $y = 3x^2 - 2x - 9$

(c) a. $\begin{cases} -4a + 2b - c = 7 \\ -a - b - c = -8 \\ -4a - 2b - c = -1 \end{cases}$

    b. $y = 3x^2 - 2x - 9$

(d) a. $\begin{cases} -4a + 2b - c = 7 \\ -a - b - c = -8 \\ -4a - 2b - c = -1 \end{cases}$

    b. $y = -3x^2 + 2x + 9$

26. Find a polynomial that fits the points $(0, 4)$, $(1, 6)$, $(3, 28)$, and $\left(\dfrac{3}{2}, \dfrac{5}{2}\right)$.

(a) $y = x^4 - 5x^3 - 3x^2 - 8x + 4$

(b) $y = x^4 - 5x^3 - 3x^2 + 8x + 4$

(c) $y = 2x^4 - 5x^3 - 3x^2 + 8x + 4$

(d) $y = 2x^4 - 5x^3 - 3x^2 - 8x - 4$

27. A quadratic equation $y = ax^2 + bx + c$ passes through the points $(-1, 7)$, $(-3, -9)$, and $(-2, 1)$.

   a. Write the system of equations that will allow you to find the values a, b, and c.

   b. Find the quadratic equation.

28. Determine the polynomial whose graph passes through the points $(0, 12)$, $(1, 18)$, $(-1, -12)$, and $\left(\dfrac{3}{2}, \dfrac{21}{2}\right)$.

29. Find the solution to the network system for the water flow represented by x_1, x_2, x_3, x_4, and x_5.

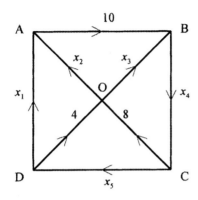

(a) $x_1 = t - 4$, $x_2 = 14 - t$, $x_3 = t - 2$, $x_4 = t + 8$, $x_5 = t$

(b) $x_1 = t - 4$, $x_2 = t + 14$, $x_3 = t - 2$, $x_4 = t + 8$, $x_5 = t$

(c) $x_1 = t - 4$, $x_2 = 14 - t$, $x_3 = t - 4$, $x_4 = t + 8$, $x_5 = t$

(d) $x_1 = t - 4$, $x_2 = 14 - t$, $x_3 = t - 2$, $x_4 = t - 8$, $x_5 = t$

30. Find the currents I_1, I_2, and I_3 for the electric network.

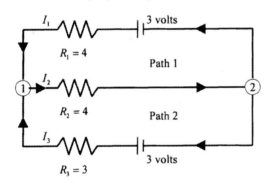

(a) $I_1 = 0.225$, $I_2 = 0$, $I_3 = 0.3$

(b) $I_1 = 0.325$, $I_2 = 0.525$, $I_3 = 0.3$

(c) $I_1 = 0.325$, $I_2 = 0.525$, $I_3 = 0.4$

(d) $I_1 = 0.225$, $I_2 = 0.525$, $I_3 = 0.3$

31. Solve the network system for the water flow represented by x_1, x_2, x_3, x_4, and x_5.

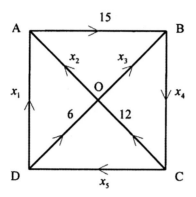

32. Find the currents I_1, I_2, and I_3 for the electric network.

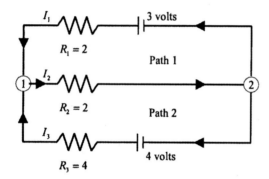

CHAPTER 1
Systems of Linear Equations (Answer Key)

Section 1.1   Introduction to Systems of Linear Equations

[1] (d)

[2] (b)

[3] linear

[4] linear

[5] (b)

[6] (a)

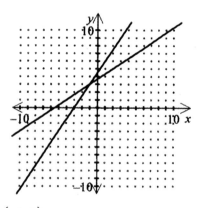

[7] $(-1, 3)$

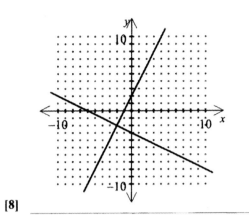

[8] _____

[9] (c) _____

[10] (a) _____

[11] $\left(\dfrac{5}{4}, \ -\dfrac{5}{4}, \ 2 \right)$ _____

[12] dependent; infinitely many solutions _____

Section 1.2   Gaussian Elimination and Gauss-Jordan Elimination

[13] (b) _____

[14] (a) _____

[15] $\begin{bmatrix} 1 & -1 & -4 \\ 0 & 11 & 19 \\ 0 & -8 & -26 \end{bmatrix}$ _____

$\begin{bmatrix} 1 & 0 & 0 & \vdots & -51 \\ 0 & 1 & 0 & \vdots & -28 \\ 0 & 0 & 1 & \vdots & -3 \end{bmatrix}$

[16] $x = -51, \ y = -28, \ z = -3$ _____

[17] (c) _____

[18] (d)

[19] $(-679, -304, 65)$

[20] $(-3, 2, -5, 5)$

[21] (b)

[22] (a)

[23] $x = -7t, y = t, z = 12t$

[24] $x = -\dfrac{41}{10}t, y = t, z = \dfrac{49}{10}t$

Section 1.3   Applications of Systems of Linear Equations

[25] (b)

[26] (c)

a. $\begin{cases} a - b + c = 7 \\ 9a - 3b + c = -9 \\ 4a - 2b + c = 1 \end{cases}$

[27] b. $y = -2x^2 + 9$

[28] $y = 2x^4 - 5x^3 - 11x^2 + 20x + 12$

[29] (a)

[30] (d)

[31] $x_1 = t - 6, x_2 = 21 - t, x_3 = t - 3, x_4 = t + 12, x_5 = t$

[32] $I_1 = 0.5, I_2 = 1, I_3 = 0.5$

CHAPTER 2
Matrices

Section 2.1   Operations with Matrices

1. Evaluate the expression $A - B$.

$$A = \begin{bmatrix} -\frac{22}{3} & -3 \\ 25 & -\frac{43}{10} \end{bmatrix}, \quad B = \begin{bmatrix} \frac{57}{5} & -5 \\ 31 & -7 \end{bmatrix}$$

(a) $\begin{bmatrix} -\frac{281}{15} & -34 \\ 30 & \frac{27}{10} \end{bmatrix}$
(b) $\begin{bmatrix} -\frac{281}{15} & 30 \\ -34 & \frac{27}{10} \end{bmatrix}$
(c) $\begin{bmatrix} -\frac{281}{15} & 2 \\ -6 & \frac{27}{10} \end{bmatrix}$
(d) $\begin{bmatrix} \frac{61}{15} & -8 \\ 56 & -\frac{113}{10} \end{bmatrix}$

2. Evaluate the expression $-6A + 6B$.

$$A = \begin{bmatrix} 2 & -3 & 4 \\ -6 & -4 & 6 \\ -5 & -10 & -7 \end{bmatrix}, \quad B = \begin{bmatrix} 4 & -4 & 3 \\ -9 & 6 & 0 \\ -10 & 5 & -7 \end{bmatrix}$$

(a) $\begin{bmatrix} -36 & 42 & -42 \\ 90 & -12 & -36 \\ 90 & 30 & 84 \end{bmatrix}$
(b) $\begin{bmatrix} -12 & 6 & 6 \\ 18 & -60 & 36 \\ 30 & -90 & 0 \end{bmatrix}$
(c) $\begin{bmatrix} 36 & -42 & 42 \\ -90 & 12 & 36 \\ -90 & -30 & -84 \end{bmatrix}$
(d) $\begin{bmatrix} 12 & -6 & -6 \\ -18 & 60 & -36 \\ -30 & 90 & 0 \end{bmatrix}$

3. If $A = \begin{bmatrix} 4 & -4 & 6 \\ -1 & 9 & -6 \\ 1 & -7 & 7 \end{bmatrix}$ and $B = \begin{bmatrix} 3 & -2 & 5 \\ -6 & 6 & -1 \\ 7 & -7 & -5 \end{bmatrix}$, find $A + B$.

4. Evaluate:

$$-8\begin{bmatrix} 3 & -8 & -7 \\ -1 & -9 & -5 \\ 4 & 8 & -10 \end{bmatrix} - 3\begin{bmatrix} -2 & -4 & -10 \\ 4 & -5 & 2 \\ -8 & -9 & 5 \end{bmatrix}$$

5. Evaluate $4A$.

$$A = \begin{bmatrix} -8 & 0 & -7 \\ 6 & 1 & 7 \\ -5 & 4 & -3 \end{bmatrix}$$

(a) $\begin{bmatrix} -4 & 4 & -3 \\ 10 & 5 & 11 \\ -9 & 8 & 1 \end{bmatrix}$ (b) $\begin{bmatrix} -32 & 0 & -28 \\ 24 & 4 & -12 \\ -20 & 16 & 28 \end{bmatrix}$ (c) $\begin{bmatrix} -4 & 4 & -3 \\ 10 & 5 & 1 \\ -9 & 8 & 11 \end{bmatrix}$ (d) $\begin{bmatrix} -32 & 0 & -28 \\ 24 & 4 & 28 \\ -20 & 16 & -12 \end{bmatrix}$

6. If $A = \begin{bmatrix} 0 & 4 & 9 \\ 8 & 2 & -9 \\ -7 & -3 & 6 \end{bmatrix}$ and $B = \begin{bmatrix} 7 & -8 & 3 \\ 5 & -2 & -5 \\ -6 & -4 & 1 \end{bmatrix}$, find $5A + 4B$.

(a) $\begin{bmatrix} 28 & -12 & 57 \\ 60 & 2 & -65 \\ -59 & -31 & 34 \end{bmatrix}$ (b) $\begin{bmatrix} 28 & -12 & 33 \\ 60 & 18 & -14 \\ -59 & -7 & 34 \end{bmatrix}$ (c) $\begin{bmatrix} 7 & -4 & 12 \\ 13 & 18 & -25 \\ -13 & 1 & 26 \end{bmatrix}$ (d) $\begin{bmatrix} 7 & -4 & 12 \\ 13 & 0 & -14 \\ -13 & -7 & 7 \end{bmatrix}$

7. Evaluate $-5A$.

$$A = \begin{bmatrix} 6 & 9 & -7 \\ -5 & 1 & 4 \\ -2 & -3 & -6 \end{bmatrix}$$

8. Solve:

$$4\begin{bmatrix} 8 & 9 & 5 \\ 2 & -8 & 0 \\ 6 & -2 & -3 \end{bmatrix}$$

9. Find the product AB, if possible.

$$A = \begin{bmatrix} 0 & 4 & 1 \\ -5 & -1 & 0 \end{bmatrix}, \quad B = \begin{bmatrix} 1 & -3 \\ 0 & 1 \\ 2 & -1 \end{bmatrix}$$

(a) $\begin{bmatrix} 2 & 3 \\ -5 & 14 \end{bmatrix}$ (b) $\begin{bmatrix} 2 & -5 \\ 3 & 14 \end{bmatrix}$ (c) $\begin{bmatrix} 15 & 7 & 1 \\ -5 & -1 & 0 \\ 5 & 9 & 0 \end{bmatrix}$ (d) $\begin{bmatrix} 0 & 15 \\ 0 & -1 \\ 0 & 0 \end{bmatrix}$

10. If $A = \begin{bmatrix} 6 & -3 & -1 \\ 0 & 10 & -2 \end{bmatrix}$ and $B = \begin{bmatrix} 1 \\ -10 \\ -5 \end{bmatrix}$, find AB.

   (a) $\begin{bmatrix} 41 & -90 \end{bmatrix}$ (b) $\begin{bmatrix} -90 \\ 41 \end{bmatrix}$ (c) $\begin{bmatrix} 41 \\ -90 \end{bmatrix}$ (d) undefined

11. If $A = \begin{bmatrix} -5 & -1 & -4 \\ 4 & 2 & 3 \\ -3 & 5 & -1 \end{bmatrix}$ and $B = \begin{bmatrix} 4 & 5 & 3 \\ 1 & -2 & -4 \\ -3 & 5 & 2 \end{bmatrix}$, find AB.

12. Find the product B^2, if possible.

   $A = \begin{bmatrix} 4 & 4 \\ -2 & -8 \end{bmatrix}$, $B = \begin{bmatrix} 10 & 8 \\ 4 & -4 \end{bmatrix}$

13. Which is the matrix equation of the form $A\mathbf{x} = \mathbf{b}$ and solution for the given system of equations?
   $\begin{cases} 3x + 4y = -1 \\ 5x - 4y = -55 \end{cases}$

   (a) $\begin{bmatrix} 3 & -4 \\ 5 & 4 \end{bmatrix}\begin{bmatrix} x \\ y \end{bmatrix} = \begin{bmatrix} -1 \\ -55 \end{bmatrix}$; no solution   (b) $\begin{bmatrix} -1 \\ -55 \end{bmatrix}\begin{bmatrix} x & y \end{bmatrix} = \begin{bmatrix} 3 & 5 \\ 4 & -4 \end{bmatrix}$; infinitely many solutions

   (c) $\begin{bmatrix} 3 & 4 \\ 5 & -4 \end{bmatrix}\begin{bmatrix} x \\ y \end{bmatrix} = \begin{bmatrix} -1 \\ -55 \end{bmatrix}$; $(-7, 5)$ (d) $\begin{bmatrix} x & y \end{bmatrix}\begin{bmatrix} 3 & 5 \\ 4 & -4 \end{bmatrix} = \begin{bmatrix} -1 & -55 \end{bmatrix}$; $(-13, -3)$

14. Find the solution set to the matrix equation $A\mathbf{x} = \mathbf{b}$.
   $\begin{bmatrix} 9 & -1 \\ 7 & 4 \end{bmatrix}\begin{bmatrix} x_1 \\ x_2 \end{bmatrix} = \begin{bmatrix} 6 \\ -2 \end{bmatrix}$

   (a) $\mathbf{x} = \begin{bmatrix} x_1 \\ x_2 \end{bmatrix} = \begin{bmatrix} \frac{22}{43} \\ -\frac{60}{43} \end{bmatrix}$ (b) $\mathbf{x} = \begin{bmatrix} x_1 \\ x_2 \end{bmatrix} = \begin{bmatrix} -\frac{60}{43} \\ \frac{22}{43} \end{bmatrix}$

   (c) $\mathbf{x} = \begin{bmatrix} x_1 \\ x_2 \end{bmatrix} = \begin{bmatrix} \frac{43}{22} \\ -\frac{43}{60} \end{bmatrix}$ (d) either no solution or infinite number of solutions

15. Write the system of linear equations in the form $A\mathbf{x} = \mathbf{b}$ and solve this matrix equation for **x**.

$$\begin{cases} 2x_1 - 6x_2 + 9x_3 - 2x_2 = -46 \\ 8x_1 + 8x_2 - 7x_3 - 8x_2 = 84 \\ -2x_1 + 4x_2 - 4x_3 - 5x_2 = 20 \\ 9x_1 + 7x_2 - 8x_3 - 5x_2 = 89 \end{cases}$$

16. Solve the matrix equation $A\mathbf{x} = \mathbf{b}$ for **x**.

$$\begin{bmatrix} 7 & 9 \\ 3 & -5 \end{bmatrix} \begin{bmatrix} x_1 \\ x_2 \end{bmatrix} = \begin{bmatrix} -2 \\ 1 \end{bmatrix}$$

17. Solve the system of equations using partitioned matrices.

$$\begin{bmatrix} 3 & -7 \\ 6 & -2 \end{bmatrix} \begin{bmatrix} x \\ y \end{bmatrix} = \begin{bmatrix} -1 \\ -10 \end{bmatrix}$$

(a) $\left(-\dfrac{17}{9}, -\dfrac{2}{3}\right)$ (b) $\left(-\dfrac{9}{17}, -\dfrac{3}{2}\right)$ (c) $\left(-\dfrac{2}{3}, -\dfrac{17}{9}\right)$ (d) either dependent or inconsistent

18. Solve the system of equations using partitioned matrices.

$-9x + 2y = -8$

$-7x + 6y = -2$

(a) $\left(-\dfrac{11}{10}, -\dfrac{19}{20}\right)$ (b) $\left(\dfrac{19}{20}, \dfrac{11}{10}\right)$ (c) $\left(\dfrac{11}{10}, \dfrac{19}{20}\right)$ (d) either dependent or inconsistent

19. Solve the system of equations using partitioned matrices.

$$\begin{bmatrix} -10 & 2 \\ -4 & 4 \end{bmatrix} \begin{bmatrix} x \\ y \end{bmatrix} = \begin{bmatrix} 10 \\ 8 \end{bmatrix}$$

20. Solve the system of equations using partitioned matrices.

$3x - 10y = -8$

$x - 3y = 2$

Section 2.2   Properties of Matix Operations

21. Determine whether the equation $A(BC) = (AB)C$ is true for the given matrices.

$$A = \begin{bmatrix} 1 & -2 \\ -1 & 4 \end{bmatrix}, \ B = \begin{bmatrix} 1 & 2 \\ 5 & 3 \end{bmatrix}, \ C = \begin{bmatrix} -5 & -3 \\ -4 & 0 \end{bmatrix}$$

(a) True   (b) False

22. Which is true for matrices A and B?

$$A = \begin{bmatrix} -3 & -4 \\ -5 & -2 \end{bmatrix}, \quad B = \begin{bmatrix} 6 & -1 \\ 9 & 7 \end{bmatrix}$$

(a) $AB = BA$

$$AB = \begin{bmatrix} 1 & 0 \\ 0 & 1 \end{bmatrix} \text{ and } BA = \begin{bmatrix} 1 & 0 \\ 0 & 1 \end{bmatrix}$$

(b) $AB \neq BA$

$$AB = \begin{bmatrix} -54 & -25 \\ -48 & -9 \end{bmatrix} \text{ and } BA = \begin{bmatrix} -13 & -22 \\ -62 & -50 \end{bmatrix}$$

(c) AB is not defined because the dimensions of A and B do not allow multiplication.

(d) BA is not defined because the dimensions of A and B do not allow multiplication.

23. Determine whether the equation $BCA = CBA$ is true for the given matrices.

$$A = \begin{bmatrix} -4 & -4 \\ -1 & -3 \end{bmatrix}, B = \begin{bmatrix} 5 & 1 \\ 2 & 0 \end{bmatrix}, C = \begin{bmatrix} 3 & 4 \\ -2 & -5 \end{bmatrix}$$

24. Write the identity matrix I_n for matrix C and verify that $CI_n = I_nC = C$.

$$C = \begin{bmatrix} -4 & 9 & 8 \\ 1 & 3 & -7 \\ -1 & 0 & -6 \end{bmatrix}$$

25. Find F^T.

$$F = \begin{bmatrix} -4 & -7 & 5 & 9 \\ 2 & -5 & 6 & 4 \\ 3 & -3 & 3 & 1 \end{bmatrix}$$

(a) $\begin{bmatrix} -4 & 6 & 3 \\ 9 & -5 & 3 \\ 5 & 2 & 1 \\ -7 & 4 & 3 \end{bmatrix}$
(b) $\begin{bmatrix} 9 & -7 & -5 & -4 \\ 4 & 6 & 5 & 2 \\ 1 & -3 & 3 & 6 \end{bmatrix}$
(c) $\begin{bmatrix} -4 & 4 & -7 \\ 4 & 2 & 5 \\ 9 & 3 & 5 \end{bmatrix}$
(d) $\begin{bmatrix} -4 & 2 & 3 \\ -7 & -5 & -3 \\ 5 & 6 & 3 \\ 9 & 4 & 1 \end{bmatrix}$

26. Find the transpose of matrix A.

$$A = \begin{bmatrix} 7 & -4 & 3 \\ 8 & -2 & 3 \\ -4 & -2 & 1 \end{bmatrix}$$

(a) $\begin{bmatrix} 7 & 8 & -4 \\ 9 & -2 & -2 \\ 3 & 3 & -1 \end{bmatrix}$
(b) $\begin{bmatrix} 7 & 8 & -4 \\ -4 & -2 & -2 \\ 3 & 3 & 1 \end{bmatrix}$
(c) $\begin{bmatrix} 7 & -4 & -3 \\ 3 & -2 & 3 \\ -4 & -2 & -1 \end{bmatrix}$
(d) $\begin{bmatrix} 7 & 9 & 3 \\ 8 & -2 & 3 \\ -4 & -2 & 1 \end{bmatrix}$

27. Find the sum of S and R^T.

$$S = \begin{bmatrix} 3 & 1 \\ 2 & 6 \end{bmatrix}, \quad R = \begin{bmatrix} -2 & 0 \\ 3 & -6 \end{bmatrix}$$

28. Does $A = A^T$?

$$A = \begin{bmatrix} 6 & -1 & 5 \\ 8 & 1 & 4 \\ 0 & 2 & 6 \end{bmatrix}$$

Section 2.3   The Inverse of a Matrix

29. Determine whether the matrix B is the inverse of matrix A.

$$A = \begin{bmatrix} 1 & 0 & -5 \\ -1 & 1 & 9 \\ 0 & 0 & 1 \end{bmatrix}, \quad B = \begin{bmatrix} 1 & 0 & 5 \\ 1 & 1 & -4 \\ 0 & 0 & 1 \end{bmatrix}$$

(a) B is not the inverse of A.

$$AB = \begin{bmatrix} 6 & 0 & 4 \\ 6 & 5 & 6 \\ 5 & 3 & 0 \end{bmatrix} \text{ and } BA = \begin{bmatrix} 3 & 1 & 5 \\ 2 & 2 & 2 \\ 1 & 4 & 4 \end{bmatrix}$$

(b) B is the inverse of A.

$$AB = \begin{bmatrix} 1 & 0 & 0 \\ 0 & 1 & 0 \\ 0 & 0 & 1 \end{bmatrix} \text{ and } BA = \begin{bmatrix} 1 & 0 & 0 \\ 0 & 1 & 0 \\ 0 & 0 & 1 \end{bmatrix}$$

(c) AB is not defined because the dimensions of A and B do not allow multiplication. B is not the inverse of A.

(d) BA is not defined because the dimensions of A and B do not allow multiplication. B is not the inverse of A.

30. Use Gauss-Jordan elimination to find the inverse of the matrix (if it exists).

$$\begin{bmatrix} -2 & -1 & 4 \\ 0 & 0 & 3 \\ 0 & 0 & -4 \end{bmatrix}$$

(a) $\begin{bmatrix} 1 & 0 & 0 \\ 1 & 1 & 0 \\ -3 & -3 & 1 \end{bmatrix}$ (b) $\begin{bmatrix} 0 & 1 & 1 \\ 0 & 0 & -3 \\ 1 & 0 & 0 \end{bmatrix}$ (c) $\begin{bmatrix} 1 & 1 & -3 \\ 0 & 1 & -3 \\ 0 & 0 & 1 \end{bmatrix}$ (d) does not exist

31. Find the inverse of the 2×2 matrix.

$$\begin{bmatrix} 4 & -4 \\ -1 & 2 \end{bmatrix}$$

32. Show that matrix B is the inverse of matrix A.

$$A = \begin{bmatrix} -8 & -5 \\ -4 & -3 \end{bmatrix}, \quad B = \begin{bmatrix} -\frac{3}{4} & \frac{5}{4} \\ 1 & -2 \end{bmatrix}$$

33. If possible, solve the system of equations using an inverse matrix.

$$\begin{cases} 3x - 2y + z = 0 \\ x - 2y - z = 0 \\ 3x - 2y - z = 0 \end{cases}$$

(a) $(-2, -4, -5)$ (b) $\left(-2, -\frac{1}{2}, -1\right)$ (c) $(-3, 4, 14)$ (d) $(0, 0, 0)$

34. If possible, solve the system of equations using an inverse matrix.

$$\begin{cases} -4x - 6y = -1 \\ -5x + 8y = 0 \end{cases}$$

(a) $\left(\frac{5}{62}, \frac{4}{31}\right)$ (b) $\left(-\frac{4}{31}, -\frac{5}{62}\right)$ (c) $\left(\frac{4}{31}, \frac{5}{62}\right)$ (d) no solution

35. If possible, use an inverse matrix to solve the system of linear equations.

$$\begin{cases} 8x - 5y + z + 7w = 0 \\ -7x + y - 5z - 8w = 0 \\ -5x - 8y - 7z + w = 0 \\ -7x + y + 5z + 8w = 0 \end{cases}$$

36. Use an inverse matrix to find the solution to the matrix equation.

$$\begin{bmatrix} 8 & -5 \\ 2 & 10 \end{bmatrix}\begin{bmatrix} x \\ y \end{bmatrix} = \begin{bmatrix} -6 \\ 9 \end{bmatrix}$$

Section 2.4   Elementary Matrices

37. Find an LU-factorization of the matrix $A = \begin{bmatrix} -4 & -8 \\ -8 & -9 \end{bmatrix}$.

(a) $A = \begin{bmatrix} 5 & 0 \\ 8 & -1 \end{bmatrix} \cdot \begin{bmatrix} -2 & -2 \\ 0 & -7 \end{bmatrix}$

(b) $A = \begin{bmatrix} 4 & 0 \\ 8 & -1 \end{bmatrix} \cdot \begin{bmatrix} -1 & 0 \\ 0 & -7 \end{bmatrix}$

(c) $A = \begin{bmatrix} 4 & 0 \\ 8 & -1 \end{bmatrix} \cdot \begin{bmatrix} -1 & -2 \\ 0 & -7 \end{bmatrix}$

(d) $A = \begin{bmatrix} 4 & 0 \\ 9 & -1 \end{bmatrix} \cdot \begin{bmatrix} -1 & -2 \\ 0 & -7 \end{bmatrix}$

38. Which of the following matrices is not elementary?

(a) $\begin{bmatrix} -8 & 0 & 0 \\ 0 & 1 & 0 \\ 0 & 0 & 1 \end{bmatrix}$

(b) $\begin{bmatrix} 1 & 0 & 0 \\ 0 & 1 & 0 \\ 7 & 0 & 1 \end{bmatrix}$

(c) $\begin{bmatrix} 1 & 0 & 0 \\ 0 & 8 & 0 \\ 0 & 0 & -7 \end{bmatrix}$

(d) $\begin{bmatrix} 8 & 0 & 0 \\ 0 & 1 & 0 \\ 0 & 0 & 1 \end{bmatrix}$

39. Find an LU-factorization of the matrix $A = \begin{bmatrix} -4 & -8 \\ -8 & -9 \end{bmatrix}$.

40. Is the matrix $A = \begin{bmatrix} 1 & 0 & 0 \\ 0 & -2 & 0 \\ 0 & 0 & 3 \end{bmatrix}$ an elementary matrix?

Section 2.5   Applications of Matrix Operations

41. Which of the following matrices is not stochastic?

(a) $\begin{bmatrix} 0.4 & 0.5 & 0.8 \\ 0.3 & 0.1 & 0 \\ 0.3 & 0.4 & 0.2 \end{bmatrix}$

(b) $\begin{bmatrix} 1.4 & 0.5 & 0.2 \\ 0.8 & -0.4 & 0.4 \\ -1.2 & 0.9 & 0.4 \end{bmatrix}$

(c) $\begin{bmatrix} -1.2 & 0.5 & 0.2 \\ 0.6 & -0.4 & 0.4 \\ 1.6 & 0.9 & -0.4 \end{bmatrix}$

(d) $\begin{bmatrix} 1 & 0 & 1 \\ -1 & 0 & 0 \\ 1 & 1 & 0 \end{bmatrix}$

42. A matrix of transition probabilities is given by $P = \begin{bmatrix} 0.4 & 0.3 \\ -0.8 & -0.9 \end{bmatrix}$. Find $P^2 X$ for the state matrix $X = \begin{bmatrix} 100 \\ 400 \end{bmatrix}$.

(a) $\begin{bmatrix} -0.15 \\ 0.57 \end{bmatrix}$ (b) $\begin{bmatrix} -68 \\ 268 \end{bmatrix}$ (c) $\begin{bmatrix} -0.08 \\ 0.4 \end{bmatrix}$ (d) $\begin{bmatrix} -0.08 \\ 0.57 \end{bmatrix}$

43. Is the matrix $A = \begin{bmatrix} -1 & 0 & 1 \\ 1 & 0 & 0 \\ 1 & 1 & 0 \end{bmatrix}$ a stochastic matrix? Write Yes or No.

44. A matrix of transition probabilities is given by $P = \begin{bmatrix} -0.9 & -0.5 \\ -0.4 & -0.3 \end{bmatrix}$. Find $P^2 X$ for the state matrix $X = \begin{bmatrix} 200 \\ 500 \end{bmatrix}$.

45. Which is a cryptogram for the words "AGE BEFORE BEAUTY" made using the matrix $A = \begin{bmatrix} 2 & 1 & -1 \\ -1 & 1 & 0 \\ 0 & 2 & -1 \end{bmatrix}$?

(a) −5 18 −6 −2 12 −5 −3 57 −24 10 9 −7 9 48 −26 15 45 −20

(b) 4 6 9 −3 2 −1 9 9 12 8 −5 −2 −10 −4 −19 65 5 50

(c) 4 7 9 −3 3 −1 9 8 12 8 −4 −2 −10 −5 −19 65 6 50

(d) −5 19 −6 −2 13 −5 −3 58 −24 10 10 −7 9 47 −26 15 44 −20

46. Matrix $A = \begin{bmatrix} 0 & 1 & 2 \\ 1 & -1 & 0 \\ 0 & 0 & -1 \end{bmatrix}$ was used to create the cryptogram below.

18 −11 5 4 10 28 15 5 40 0 1 −6 12 −11 −18

Use A^{-1} to decode the cryptogram.

(a) TOWER OF STRENGTH   (b) LEAPS AND BOUNDS
(c) IN BROAD DAYLIGHT   (d) GRIND TO A HALT

47. Write a cryptogram for the words "FEW AND FAR BETWEEN" using the matrix $A = \begin{bmatrix} -1 & 0 & 1 \\ 1 & 0 & 0 \\ -1 & 2 & -1 \end{bmatrix}$.

48. Matrix $A = \begin{bmatrix} 0 & -1 & 1 \\ 1 & 1 & 0 \\ 1 & 0 & -1 \end{bmatrix}$ was used to create the cryptogram below.

8 −14 16 18 −1 11 35 20 −15 29 14 −15 5 −9 14

Use A^{-1} to decode the cryptogram.

49. Let A be the technology matrix for a simple economy.

$$A = \begin{bmatrix} & P_1 & P_2 & P_3 & P_4 \\ 0.42 & 0.27 & 0.04 & 0.28 & P_1 \\ 0.44 & 0.08 & 0.49 & 0.23 & P_2 \\ 0.10 & 0.25 & 0.40 & 0.29 & P_3 \\ 0.17 & 0.46 & 0.21 & 0.31 & P_4 \end{bmatrix}$$

P_1 = Fuels, P_2 = Agriculture, P_3 = Manufacturing, P_4 = Food Industries

How many units from the manufacturing goods are required to produce 200 units of food product?

(a) 50 units   (b) 80 units   (c) 58 units   (d) 0.68 units

50. Find the gross production of steel and agriculture if surpluses of 216 units of steel and 72 units of agricultural are desired.

$$A = \begin{bmatrix} & P_1 & P_2 \\ 0.2 & 0.6 & P_1 \\ 0.4 & 0.4 & P_2 \end{bmatrix}$$

P_1 = Steel, P_2 = Agriculture

(a) P_1: 720   (b) P_1: 60   (c) P_1: 72   (d) P_1: 72
    P_2: 600 P_2: 72 P_2: 730 P_2: 600

51. Does the following technology matrix show a closed model of a simple economy?

$$A = \begin{bmatrix} & P_1 & P_2 & P_3 \\ 0.3 & 0.4 & 0.3 & P_1 \\ 0.3 & 0.8 & 0.4 & P_2 \\ 0.1 & 0.6 & 0.3 & P_3 \end{bmatrix}$$

P_1 = Utilities, P_2 = Agriculture, P_3 = Manufacturing

52. Suppose the technology matrix for a closed model of a simple economy is given by A.

$$A = \begin{array}{c} \\ \\ \end{array} \begin{array}{ccc} P_1 & P_2 & P_3 \\ \left[\begin{array}{ccc} 0.4 & 0.1 & 0.9 \\ 0.4 & 0.1 & 0 \\ 0.2 & 0.8 & 0.1 \end{array}\right] & & \begin{array}{c} P_1 \\ P_2 \\ P_3 \end{array} \end{array}$$

Let column matrix X be the gross production matrix for the industries. The technological equation is given by $(I - A) X = 0$. Find the gross production.

53. Find the least squares regression line for the points $(3, 4)$, $(4, 4)$, $(2, 2)$, and $(1, 2)$.

   (a) $y = 1.8x + 1$ (b) $y = 0.8x + 1$ (c) $y = -0.8x + 1$ (d) $y = -1.8x + 1$

54. Find the least squares regression line through the points $(5, -8)$ and $(-9, 8)$.

   (a) $y = 1.14x - 2.29$ (b) $y = -1.14x + 2.29$ (c) $y = -1.14x - 2.29$ (d) $y = -1.14x + 1.29$

55. Find the least squares regression line for the points $(-1, 5)$, $(2, 5)$, $(4, 4)$, and $(5, 1)$.

56. Find the least squares regression line through the points $(3, -2)$ and $(-3, -4)$.

CHAPTER 2
Matrices (Answer Key)

Section 2.1   Operations with Matrices

[1] (c)

[2] (d)

[3] $\begin{bmatrix} 7 & -6 & 11 \\ -7 & 15 & -7 \\ 8 & -14 & 2 \end{bmatrix}$

[4] $\begin{bmatrix} -18 & 76 & 86 \\ -4 & 87 & 34 \\ -8 & -37 & 65 \end{bmatrix}$

[5] (d)

[6] (a)

[7] $\begin{bmatrix} -30 & -45 & 35 \\ 25 & -5 & -20 \\ 10 & 15 & 30 \end{bmatrix}$

[8] $\begin{bmatrix} 32 & 36 & 20 \\ 8 & -32 & 0 \\ 24 & -8 & -12 \end{bmatrix}$

[9] (a)

[10] (c)

[11] $\begin{bmatrix} -9 & -43 & -19 \\ 9 & 31 & 10 \\ -4 & -30 & -31 \end{bmatrix}$

[12] $\begin{bmatrix} 132 & 48 \\ 24 & 48 \end{bmatrix}$

[13] (c)

[14] (a)

$$\begin{bmatrix} 2 & -6 & 9 & -2 \\ 8 & 8 & -7 & -8 \\ -2 & 4 & -4 & -5 \\ 9 & 7 & -8 & -5 \end{bmatrix} \begin{bmatrix} x_1 \\ x_2 \\ x_3 \\ x_4 \end{bmatrix} = \begin{bmatrix} -46 \\ 84 \\ 20 \\ 89 \end{bmatrix}$$

[15] $\mathbf{x} = \begin{bmatrix} x_1 \\ x_2 \\ x_3 \\ x_4 \end{bmatrix} = \begin{bmatrix} 4 \\ 3 \\ -4 \\ 0 \end{bmatrix}$

[16] $\mathbf{x} = \begin{bmatrix} x_1 \\ x_2 \end{bmatrix} = \begin{bmatrix} -\frac{1}{62} \\ -\frac{13}{62} \end{bmatrix}$

[17] (a)

[18] (c)

[19] $\left(-\frac{3}{4}, \frac{5}{4} \right)$

[20] $(44, 14)$

Section 2.2   Properties of Matix Operations

[21] (a)

[22] (b)

[23] False

$$I_3 = \begin{bmatrix} 1 & 0 & 0 \\ 0 & 1 & 0 \\ 0 & 0 & 1 \end{bmatrix}, \; CI_3 = \begin{bmatrix} -4 & 9 & 8 \\ 1 & 3 & -7 \\ -1 & 0 & -6 \end{bmatrix}, \; I_3C = \begin{bmatrix} -4 & 9 & 8 \\ 1 & 3 & -7 \\ -1 & 0 & -6 \end{bmatrix}$$
[24]

[25] (d)

[26] (b)

[27] $\begin{bmatrix} 1 & 4 \\ 2 & 0 \end{bmatrix}$

[28] No

Section 2.3 The Inverse of a Matrix

[29] (b)

[30] (d)

[31] $\begin{bmatrix} \frac{1}{2} & 1 \\ \frac{1}{4} & 1 \end{bmatrix}$

Student must show that $AB = I$ and $BA = I$.

$$\begin{bmatrix} -8 & -5 \\ -4 & -3 \end{bmatrix}\begin{bmatrix} -\frac{3}{4} & \frac{5}{4} \\ 1 & -2 \end{bmatrix} = \begin{bmatrix} 1 & 0 \\ 0 & 1 \end{bmatrix} \text{ and } \begin{bmatrix} -\frac{3}{4} & \frac{5}{4} \\ 1 & -2 \end{bmatrix}\begin{bmatrix} -8 & -5 \\ -4 & -3 \end{bmatrix} = \begin{bmatrix} 1 & 0 \\ 0 & 1 \end{bmatrix}$$
[32]

[33] (d)

[34] (c)

[35] no solution

[36] $\left(-\dfrac{1}{6}, \dfrac{14}{15}\right)$

Section 2.4   Elementary Matrices

[37] (c)

[38] (c)

[39] $A = \begin{bmatrix} 4 & 0 \\ 8 & -1 \end{bmatrix} \cdot \begin{bmatrix} -1 & -2 \\ 0 & -7 \end{bmatrix}$

[40] No

Section 2.5   Applications of Matrix Operations

[41] (c)

[42] (b)

[43] Yes

[44] $\begin{bmatrix} 502 \\ 241 \end{bmatrix}$

[45] (a)

[46] (d)

[47] −24 46 −17 −13 28 −14 −10 12 −2 17 0 1 −17 40 −18 −23 10 18 −14 0 14

[48] SECOND TO NONE

[49] (c)

[50] (a)

[51] No

[52] infinite number of solutions
$$P_1 = \frac{81}{50}k \, , \, P_2 = \frac{18}{25}k \, , \, P_3 = k$$

[53] (b)

[54] (c)

[55] $y = -0.55x + 5.12$

[56] $y = 0.33x - 3$

CHAPTER 3
Determinants

Section 3.1   The Determinant of a Matrix

1. Find the cofactor C_{21} of the matrix $A = \begin{bmatrix} 3 & -6 & 8 \\ 5 & 2 & -4 \\ -9 & -1 & 7 \end{bmatrix}$.

    (a) 93   (b) –93   (c) 34   (d) –34

2. Find the determinant of the triangular matrix $A = \begin{bmatrix} -6 & 3 & -6.5 & 6 \\ 0 & 9.5 & 9 & 2 \\ 0 & 0 & 3 & -3 \\ 0 & 0 & 0 & 2.58 \end{bmatrix}$.

    (a) –441.18   (b) 9.08   (c) –90.48   (d) –168.42

3. Find the minor M_{12} of the matrix $A = \begin{bmatrix} 9 & -7 & -8 \\ 1 & 6 & -3 \\ -5 & -4 & 2 \end{bmatrix}$.

4. Find the determinant of the triangular matrix $A = \begin{bmatrix} 2 & -4 & 4 \\ 0 & -3 & 5 \\ 0 & 0 & 1 \end{bmatrix}$.

Section 3.2   Evaluation of a Determinant Using Elementary Opterations

5. Use elementary row or column operations to evaluate the determinant $\begin{vmatrix} 4 & 3 & -4 \\ -1 & 5 & 3 \\ -2 & 2 & -1 \end{vmatrix}$.

    (a) 97   (b) 107   (c) –107   (d) –97

6. Use elementary row or column operations to evaluate the determinant $\begin{vmatrix} 5 & 2 & 1 \\ 4 & 1 & 3 \\ 3 & 5 & 4 \end{vmatrix}$.

    (a) 52   (b) 28   (c) –52   (d) –28

7. Use elementary row or column operations to evaluate the determinant $\begin{vmatrix} 4 & -3 & -7 \\ -10 & 1 & -5 \\ -3 & -6 & 0 \end{vmatrix}$.

8. Find the determinant by expanding by minors along the third column.

$$\begin{vmatrix} -2 & -2 & -2 \\ 2 & -2 & -2 \\ 0 & 2 & -2 \end{vmatrix}$$

Section 3.3   Properties of Determinants

9. Determine whether the equation $ABC = ACB$ is true for the given matrices.

$A = \begin{bmatrix} 4 & 2 \\ -2 & 1 \end{bmatrix}$, $B = \begin{bmatrix} -3 & 0 \\ 5 & 3 \end{bmatrix}$, $C = \begin{bmatrix} -5 & -1 \\ 4 & -4 \end{bmatrix}$

(a) True   (b) False

10. Solve the matrix equation. If the coefficient matrix has no inverse, choose no unique solution.

$$\begin{bmatrix} 3 & 1 & -2 \\ 3 & -1 & 2 \\ 3 & 1 & 2 \end{bmatrix}\begin{bmatrix} x \\ y \\ z \end{bmatrix} = \begin{bmatrix} -21 \\ -3 \\ -5 \end{bmatrix}$$

(a) $(-4, -1, 4)$ (b) $(-4, 1, -2)$ (c) $(-3, 1, 4)$ (d) no unique solution

11. Determine whether the equation $\det(ACB) = \det(BAC)$ is true for the given matrices.

$A = \begin{bmatrix} -2 & 0 \\ -1 & -2 \end{bmatrix}$, $B = \begin{bmatrix} -5 & 5 \\ 3 & 4 \end{bmatrix}$, $C = \begin{bmatrix} -4 & -3 \\ 2 & 1 \end{bmatrix}$

12. Use the determinant of the coefficient matrix to determine whether the following system has a unique solution.

$$\begin{cases} 2x + y + z = 4 \\ -x + 2y + z = 3 \\ 9x + 2y + 3z = 13 \end{cases}$$

13. Find $\left| FF^T \right|$ if $F = \begin{bmatrix} -3 & 2 & 5 & 0 \\ -2 & -2 & 3 & 0 \\ 2 & -4 & 1 & -2 \end{bmatrix}$.

(a) 10,148   (b) 22,575   (c) 5992   (d) 3544

14. Let A be a 4×4 matrix such that $\det(A) = -5$. Find $\det\left((3A)^{-1}\right)$.

(a) $-\dfrac{1}{3^4 \times 5}$ (b) $-3^4 \times 5$ (c) $-\dfrac{1}{5}$ (d) $-\dfrac{1}{15}$

15. True or False: If A is a square matrix, then $\det\left(A^T A\right) \geq 0$.

16. Calculate and determine if $|A| = |A^T|$ for the matrix $A = \begin{bmatrix} 6 & 1 & 3 \\ -7 & -2 & 0 \\ -1 & -4 & 1 \end{bmatrix}$.

Section 3.4   Introduction to Eigenvalues

Section 3.5   Applications of Determinants

17. Find the adjoint of the matrix $A = \begin{bmatrix} -4 & -6 & 2 \\ 8 & -6 & 4 \\ 8 & 2 & 6 \end{bmatrix}$.

(a) $\begin{bmatrix} -44 & -16 & 64 \\ 40 & -40 & -40 \\ -12 & 32 & 72 \end{bmatrix}$ (b) $\begin{bmatrix} -44 & -16 & 64 \\ -40 & -40 & -40 \\ -12 & 33 & 72 \end{bmatrix}$

(c) $\begin{bmatrix} -44 & 16 & 64 \\ 40 & -40 & -39 \\ -12 & 32 & 72 \end{bmatrix}$ (d) $\begin{bmatrix} 44 & -16 & 64 \\ 40 & -41 & -40 \\ -12 & 32 & 73 \end{bmatrix}$

18. Find the adjoint of the matrix $A = \begin{bmatrix} 7 & 1 & 9 \\ -3 & -5 & -1 \\ 5 & -9 & -3 \end{bmatrix}$.

(a) $\begin{bmatrix} -6 & -14 & 52 \\ -78 & 66 & 68 \\ 44 & -20 & 32 \end{bmatrix}$ (b) $\begin{bmatrix} 6 & 14 & 52 \\ -78 & -66 & -68 \\ 44 & -20 & -32 \end{bmatrix}$ (c) $\begin{bmatrix} 6 & -14 & 52 \\ 78 & -66 & 68 \\ 44 & 20 & -32 \end{bmatrix}$ (d) $\begin{bmatrix} 6 & -14 & 52 \\ -78 & -66 & 68 \\ 44 & -20 & -32 \end{bmatrix}$

19. Find the adjoint of the matrix $A = \begin{bmatrix} -6 & -2 & 8 \\ 4 & -2 & 4 \\ -6 & -8 & -6 \end{bmatrix}$.

20. Find the adjoint of the matrix $A = \begin{bmatrix} -5 & -9 & -3 \\ 7 & 1 & 1 \\ 3 & 5 & -7 \end{bmatrix}$.

21. Use Cramer's Rule to solve (if possible) the system of equations.
$$\begin{cases} x - 3y + 2z = -18 \\ x + 3y - 2z = 14 \\ x - 3y - 2z = 2 \end{cases}$$

    (a) $(1, 0, 2)$ (b) $(2, -2, 5)$ (c) $(-1, 0, -2)$ (d) $(-2, 2, -5)$

22. Use Cramer's Rule to solve (if possible) the system of equations.
$$\begin{cases} 4x - 5y = -11 \\ 2x + 7y = 23 \end{cases}$$

    (a) $(0, 2)$ (b) $(3, 5)$ (c) $(-1, 3)$ (d) $(1, 3)$

23. Use Cramer's Rule to solve (if possible) the system of equations.
$$\begin{cases} 4x - 5y = -11 \\ x - 9y = 36 \end{cases}$$

24. Use Cramer's Rule to solve (if possible) the system of equations.
$$\begin{cases} 2x + 3y + z = 10 \\ 2x + 3y - z = 12 \\ 2x - 3y + z = -20 \end{cases}$$

25. The matrix below represents the vertices of a triangle. Use those vertices and a determinant to find the area of the triangle.
$$\begin{bmatrix} -3 & 8 \\ -4 & -5 \\ 7 & -3 \end{bmatrix}$$

    (a) 71 (b) 69 (c) $\frac{139}{2}$ (d) $\frac{141}{2}$

26. Use a determinant to find an equation of the line passing through the points $(0, \ 4)$ and $(-6, \ 8)$.

    (a) $2x - 3y + 12 = 0$ (b) $-3x + 2y - 8 = 0$ (c) $2x + 3y - 12 = 0$ (d) $3x + 2y - 8 = 0$

27. The vertices of a triangle are $(2.5, \ 4)$, $(-10, \ -9.5)$, and $(-9.5, \ 1)$. Use a determinant and the vertices of the triangle to find the area of the triangle.

28. Use a determinant to find an equation of the line passing through the points $\left(-\frac{7}{2}, \ -2\right)$ and $\left(-\frac{1}{2}, \ \frac{3}{2}\right)$.

CHAPTER 3
Determinants (Answer Key)

Section 3.1   The Determinant of a Matrix

[1]   (c)

[2]   (a)

[3]   –13

[4]   –6

Section 3.2   Evaluation of a Determinant Using Elementary Opterations

[5]   (d)

[6]   (c)

[7]   –606

[8]   –32

Section 3.3   Properties of Determinants

[9]   (b)

[10]   (a)

[11]   True

[12]   no unique solution

[13]   (d)

[14]   (a)

[15] True

[16] 73; Yes

Section 3.4   Introduction to Eigenvalues

Section 3.5   Applications of Determinants

[17] (a)

[18] (d)

[19] $\begin{bmatrix} 44 & 0 & -44 \\ -76 & 84 & -36 \\ 8 & 56 & 20 \end{bmatrix}$

[20] $\begin{bmatrix} -12 & 52 & 32 \\ -78 & 44 & -2 \\ -6 & -16 & 58 \end{bmatrix}$

[21] (d)

[22] (d)

[23] $(-9, -5)$

[24] $(-2, 5, -1)$

[25] (d)

[26] (c)

[27] 62.25

[28] $14x - 12y = -25$

CHAPTER 4
Vector Spaces

Section 4.1   Vectors in R^n

1. If $u = (-9, 8)$ and $v = (2, -3)$, find $3u + 4v$.

    (a) $(0, 12)$ (b) $(-19, 12)$ (c) $(-1, -4)$ (d) $(-25, 21)$

2. If $u = (-4, -2)$ and $v = (3, 3)$, which expression is represented by the dashed segment in the graph?

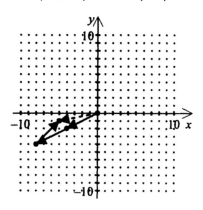

    (a) $2v + u$ (b) $2u - v$ (c) $2u + v$ (d) $2v - u$

3. If $u = (-6, 8)$ and $v = (2, 4)$, find $u + 2v$.

4. If $u = (3, -1)$ and $v = (3, -3)$, find the expression that is represented by the dashed segment in the graph.

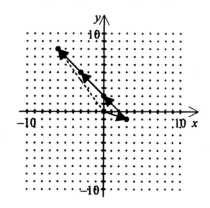

5. If $v = (-4, 6, 0)$ and $w = (0, -1, 0)$, find $3v - 2w$.

    (a) $(-12, 20, 0)$ (b) $(-12, 18, -2)$ (c) $(-12, 16, 0)$ (d) $(-12, 18, 2)$

6. Which shows $v = (16, 1, -32)$ as a linear combination of $u_1 = (4, 2, -3)$, $u_2 = (-3, -2, -4)$, and $u_3 = (-5, -1, 0)$?

    (a) $v = 4u_1 + 5u_2 + 3u_3$ (b) $v = 4u_1 + 5u_2 + (-3u_3)$ (c) $v = 8u_1 - 10u_2 + 3u_3$ (d) none of these

7. If $u = (-8, -9, -7)$ and $v = (-3, 1, 2)$, solve for w in the equation $2w = 2u - 4v$.

8. If possible, write $v = (-10, 7, 12)$ as a linear combination of $u_1 = (3, 1, 4)$, $u_2 = (-4, -2, 0)$, and $u_3 = (-1, 4, 0)$.

Section 4.2   Vector Spaces

Section 4.3   Subspaces of Vector Spaces

9. Which subset of R^3 is a subspace of R^3?

    (a) $\{(x, y, z) \mid y = 1\}$ (b) $\{(x, y, z) \mid xy = 0\}$ (c) $\{(x, y, z) \mid z \geq 0\}$ (d) $\{(x, y, z) \mid 2x + y + z = 0\}$

10. Which of the following statements is true?

    (a) The plane $3x - 2y + 4z = 1$ in R^3 is a subspace of R^3.

    (b) The set of all polynomials satisfying $p(1) = 0$ is not a subspace of P_4.

    (c) The set of all polynomials satisfying $p(0) = 1$ is a subspace of P_4.

    (d) The set of all polynomials satisfying $p(0) = 0$ is a subspace of P_4.

11. True or False: The subset $\{(x, y, z) \mid x + y = z\}$ of R^3 is a subspace of R^3.

12. Let V be the vector space of all 2×2 matrices and W consists of all matrices which commute with a given matrix B. Is the subset W a subspace of V? Write Yes or No.

Section 4.4   Spanning Sets and Linear Independence

13. Identify the subspace of R^3 spanned by the vectors in $S = \{(-1, 1, 4),(1, -1, -4),(1, 1, 4)\}$.

    (a) a point in R^3 (b) a line in R^3 (c) a plane in R^3 (d) all of R^3

14. Which set spans R^3 ?

    (a) $S = \{(4, -4, 1),(-3, 2, 0),(-2, 1, -1)\}$ (b) $S = \{(1, 2, 3), (1, 1, 2), (1, -1, 0)\}$

    (c) $S = \{(6, -4, 1), (-2, 2, 0), (-3, 1, -1)\}$ (d) $S = \{(2, -3, 1), (-1, 0, 1), (-2, -2, 4)\}$

15. True or False: The vector $(1, 2, 2)$ can be written as a linear combination of the vectors in
    $S = \{(1, 2, 3),(0, 1, 2),(-1, 0, 1)\}$.

16. Does the set $S = \{(1, 2, 3),(1, 2, 2),(2, -1, 0)\}$ span R^3 ?

17. Which of the following sets of vectors is linearly dependent?

    (a) $\{(1, 1, -1, 2), (1, 3, 0, 1), (2, 4, -2, 1)\}$ (b) $\{(1, 1, 1), (1, 0, 1), (1, 1, 3)\}$

    (c) $\{(1, 2), (-2, -4)\}$ (d) $\{(1, 0, 0), (0, 1, 0), (0, 0, 1)\}$

18. Is the set $S = \{(1, 1, 1), (1, 0, 1), (1, 1, 3)\}$ of vectors in R^3 linearly independent or linearly dependent?

    (a) linearly dependent   (b) linearly independent

19. Do the polynomials $x^2 - 2x$, $x^2 - 4$, and $1 - x^2$ form a linearly dependent or linearly independent set in P_2 ?

20. Is the set $S = \{(1, 1, -1, 2), (1, 3, 0, 1), (2, 4, -2, 1)\}$ of vectors in R^4 linearly independent or linearly dependent?

Section 4.5   Basis and Dimension

21. Which of the following sets is not a basis for R^4?

    (a) $\{(1,\ 0,\ 0,\ 0),\ (0,\ 1,\ 0,\ 0),\ (0,\ 0,\ 1,\ 0),\ (0,\ 0,\ 0,\ 1)\}$

    (b) $\{(2,\ 1,\ 1,\ 1),\ (0,\ 1,\ -1,\ 1),\ (0,\ 0,\ 1,\ 1),\ (2,\ 2,\ 1,\ 2)\}$

    (c) $\{(1,\ -1,\ 1,\ 1),\ (1,\ 1,\ 1,\ -1),\ (0,\ 1,\ 0,\ 1),\ (2,\ 1,\ 2,\ 1)\}$

    (d) $\{(1,\ 1,\ 0,\ 0),\ (0,\ 1,\ 1,\ 0),\ (0,\ 0,\ 1,\ 1),\ (1,\ 0,\ 0,\ 1)\}$

22. Find the dimension of the subspace W of R^4 where $W = \{(a,\ b,\ c,\ d) \mid a+b+c+d=0\}$.

    (a) 1   (b) 4   (c) 3   (d) 2

23. True or False: The set $S = \{(-1,\ 1),\ (1,\ -1)\}$ is a basis for R^2.

24. Find the dimension of the subspace W of R^4 where $W = \{(a,\ b,\ c,\ d) \mid d = 2a+b,\ c=a-3b\}$.

Section 4.6   Rank of a Matrix and Systems of Linear Equations

25. Find the rank and nullity of the matrix $\begin{bmatrix} -9 & -3 & 9 \\ -6 & 2 & -2 \\ -3 & 5 & -6 \end{bmatrix}$.

    (a) 2; 0   (b) 2; 1   (c) 3; 1   (d) 3; 0

26. Find the nullspace of the matrix $\begin{bmatrix} -5 & 4 & -5 \\ 6 & 5 & 4 \end{bmatrix}$.

    (a) $t\begin{bmatrix} -\frac{41}{10} \\ 1 \\ \frac{49}{10} \end{bmatrix}$ (b) $t\begin{bmatrix} \frac{41}{10} \\ 1 \\ \frac{49}{10} \end{bmatrix}$ (c) $t\begin{bmatrix} \frac{41}{10} \\ -1 \\ \frac{49}{10} \end{bmatrix}$ (d) $t\begin{bmatrix} -\frac{41}{10} \\ -1 \\ \frac{49}{10} \end{bmatrix}$

27. Find the rank and nullity of the matrix $\begin{bmatrix} 8 & -4 & -4 \\ 7 & 7 & 7 \\ -6 & -9 & 4 \end{bmatrix}$.

28. True or False: If A is an $m \times n$ matrix of rank r, then the dimension of the solution space of $Ax = 0$ is $n - r$.

29. Find the set of all solution vectors of the system of linear equations.

$$\begin{cases} 2x + y - 3z = 4 \\ y - z = -6 \\ 4x + 3y - 7z = 2 \end{cases}$$

(a) $\begin{bmatrix} 1 \\ 0 \\ 1 \end{bmatrix} + t \begin{bmatrix} 5 \\ 6 \\ 0 \end{bmatrix}$ (b) $\begin{bmatrix} 5 \\ -6 \\ 0 \end{bmatrix} + t \begin{bmatrix} 1 \\ 1 \\ 1 \end{bmatrix}$ (c) $\begin{bmatrix} 1 \\ 1 \\ 1 \end{bmatrix} + t \begin{bmatrix} 5 \\ -6 \\ 0 \end{bmatrix}$ (d) $\begin{bmatrix} 5 \\ 6 \\ 0 \end{bmatrix} + t \begin{bmatrix} 1 \\ 0 \\ 1 \end{bmatrix}$

30. Determine which **b** is contained in the given column space of A.

(a) $A = \begin{bmatrix} 2 & 2 \\ 1 & -2 \end{bmatrix}$, $\mathbf{b} = \begin{bmatrix} 0 \\ -9 \end{bmatrix}$ (b) $A = \begin{bmatrix} 1 & -1 \\ 2 & -2 \end{bmatrix}$, $\mathbf{b} = \begin{bmatrix} 1 \\ -4 \end{bmatrix}$

(c) $A = \begin{bmatrix} 1 & -3 \\ 2 & -6 \end{bmatrix}$, $\mathbf{b} = \begin{bmatrix} 3 \\ -12 \end{bmatrix}$ (d) $A = \begin{bmatrix} 1 & 3 \\ 2 & 6 \end{bmatrix}$, $\mathbf{b} = \begin{bmatrix} -3 \\ 12 \end{bmatrix}$

31. Find the set of all solution vectors of the system of linear equations.

$$\begin{cases} 2x + y + z = 2 \\ y + 3z = 4 \\ 4x + 3y + 5z = 8 \end{cases}$$

32. Is **b** in the column space of A?

$$A = \begin{bmatrix} 2 & -2 \\ 3 & 2 \end{bmatrix}, \mathbf{b} = \begin{bmatrix} 2 \\ 22 \end{bmatrix}$$

33. Which is a true statement?

(a) The system of linear equations $A\mathbf{x} = \mathbf{b}$ is inconsistent if and only if **b** is in the column space of A.

(b) Column vectors of a 3×4 matrix form a linearly independent set.

(c) Non zero row vectors of a matrix in row-echelon form are linearly dependent.

(d) Row vectors of a 4×3 matrix form a linearly dependent set.

34. Which is a true statement?

(a) If B is row-equivalent to A, then the column space of A is the same as the column space of B.

(b) The dimension of the row space of any matrix A is equal to the dimension of the column space of A.

(c) If A is an $n \times n$ invertible matrix, then the n row vectors of A are linearly dependent.

(d) If A is an $n \times n$ invertible matrix, then $\text{rank}(A) = n + 1$.

35. True or False: Column vectors of a 3×4 matrix form a linearly independent set.

36. True or False: The dimension of the row space of any matrix A is equal to the dimension of the column space of A.

Section 4.7   Coordinates and Change of Basis

37. Find the coordinate matrix of $\mathbf{x} = (12,\ 6)$ relative to the basis $B = \{(4,\ 0),\ (0,\ 3)\}$.

(a) $[x]_B = \begin{bmatrix} 3 \\ 2 \end{bmatrix}$ (b) $[x]_B = \begin{bmatrix} -2 \\ 3 \end{bmatrix}$ (c) $[x]_B = \begin{bmatrix} 2 \\ 3 \end{bmatrix}$ (d) $[x]_B = \begin{bmatrix} 3 \\ -2 \end{bmatrix}$

38. If $[x]_B = [1,\ -1,\ 1]^T$ is the coordinate vector of $\mathbf{x}$ relative to the basis $B = \{(1,\ 1,\ 1),\ (1,\ 1,\ 0),\ (1,\ 0,\ 0)\}$, find the coordinate vector of $\mathbf{x}$ relative to the standard basis in R^3.

(a) $\mathbf{x} = (1,\ 0,\ 1)$ (b) $\mathbf{x} = (0,\ -1,\ 1)$ (c) $\mathbf{x} = (0,\ 1,\ 2)$ (d) $\mathbf{x} = (2,\ 1,\ 1)$

39. Find the coordinate matrix of $\mathbf{x} = (5,\ 4)$ relative to the basis $B = \{(1,\ 0),\ (1,\ 2)\}$.

40. If $[x]_B = [4,\ 1]^T$ is the coordinate vector of $\mathbf{x}$ relative to the basis $B = \{(-2,\ -1),\ (0,\ 1)\}$, find the coordinate vector of $\mathbf{x}$ relative to the standard basis in R^2.

41. Find the transition matrix from $B = \{(1,\ 0),\ (0,\ 1)\}$ to $B' = \{(2,\ 4),\ (1,\ 3)\}$.

(a) $\begin{bmatrix} -2 & 1 \\ 1.5 & -0.5 \end{bmatrix}$ (b) $\begin{bmatrix} 1.5 & -0.5 \\ -2 & 1 \end{bmatrix}$ (c) $\begin{bmatrix} 1.5 & -0.5 \\ 1 & -2 \end{bmatrix}$ (d) $\begin{bmatrix} 1 & -0.5 \\ 1.5 & -2 \end{bmatrix}$

42. Find the transition matrix from $B = \{(1,\ 1,\ 1),\ (1,\ -1,\ 1),\ (0,\ 0,\ 1)\}$ to $B' = \{(2,\ 2,\ 0),\ (0,\ 1,\ 1),\ (1,\ 0,\ 1)\}$.

(a) $\begin{bmatrix} 0.5 & -0.5 & 0.5 \\ 0.25 & -0.25 & -0.25 \\ 0.5 & 1.5 & 0.5 \end{bmatrix}$ (b) $\begin{bmatrix} 0.25 & -0.25 & -0.25 \\ 0.5 & 1.5 & 0.5 \\ 0.5 & -0.5 & 0.5 \end{bmatrix}$

(c) $\begin{bmatrix} -0.25 & 0.25 & -0.25 \\ -0.5 & 0.5 & 0.5 \\ 1.5 & 0.5 & 0.5 \end{bmatrix}$ (d) $\begin{bmatrix} 0.25 & -0.25 & -0.25 \\ 0.5 & -0.5 & 0.5 \\ 0.5 & 1.5 & 0.5 \end{bmatrix}$

43. Find the transition matrix from $B = \{(2, 0), (1, 1)\}$ to $B' = \{(1, 0), (1, -1)\}$.

44. Find the transition matrix from $B = \{(1, 0, 0), (0, 0, 1), (0, -1, 0)\}$ to $B' = \{(0, 1, 1), (1, 0, 1), (1, 1, 0)\}$.

45. Find the coordinate matrix of $p = x - 17$ relative to the standard basis $S = \{1, x, x^2\}$ in P_2.

(a) $[p]_S = \begin{bmatrix} 0 \\ -1 \\ 17 \end{bmatrix}$ 　(b) $[p]_S = \begin{bmatrix} 17 \\ -1 \\ 0 \end{bmatrix}$ 　(c) $[p]_S = \begin{bmatrix} -17 \\ 1 \\ 0 \end{bmatrix}$ 　(d) $[p]_S = \begin{bmatrix} 0 \\ 1 \\ -17 \end{bmatrix}$

46. Find the coordinate matrix of $X = \begin{bmatrix} -8 \\ -7 \\ 8 \end{bmatrix}$ relative to the standard basis in $M_{3,1}$.

(a) $[X]_S = \begin{bmatrix} 7 \\ -6 \\ -8 \end{bmatrix}$ 　(b) $[X]_S = \begin{bmatrix} -8 \\ -7 \\ 8 \end{bmatrix}$ 　(c) $[X]_S = \begin{bmatrix} 8 \\ -6 \\ 8 \end{bmatrix}$ 　(d) $[X]_S = \begin{bmatrix} -6 \\ 7 \\ 11 \end{bmatrix}$

47. Find the coordinate matrix of $p = x - 17$ relative to the standard basis $S = \{1, x, x^2\}$ in P_2.

48. Find the coordinate matrix of $X = \begin{bmatrix} 3 \\ 0 \\ 6 \end{bmatrix}$ relative to the standard basis in $M_{3,1}$.

Section 4.8   Applications of Vector Spaces

49. Find the general solution of the differential equation $y'' + 11y = 0$.

(a) $y = e^{\sqrt{11}x}(c_1 + c_2 x)$

(b) $y = c_1 e^{\sqrt{11}x} + c_2 e^{-\sqrt{11}x}$

(c) $y = c_1 \cos\left(\sqrt{11}x\right) + c_2 \sin\left(\sqrt{11}x\right)$

(d) $y = c_1 e^{\sqrt{11}x}\cos\left(\sqrt{11}x\right) + c_2 e^{-\sqrt{11}x}\sin\left(\sqrt{11}x\right)$

50. Find all linearly independent solutions of the differential equation $y'' - 10y' + 21y = 0$.

(a) $y_1 = e^{3x}$ 　　(b) $y_1 = e^{-3x}$ 　　(c) $y_1 = e^{-3x}$ 　　(d) $y_1 = e^{3x}$

　　$y_2 = e^{-4x}$ 　　　　$y_2 = e^{7x}$ 　　　　$y_2 = e^{-4x}$ 　　　　$y_2 = e^{7x}$

51. Find the general solution of the differential equation $y'' - 9y = 0$.

52. Find all linearly independent solutions of the differential equation $y'' - 2y' - 8y = 0$.

53. Which equation describes a circle?

(a) $-2y^2 - 8y + 2x^2 + 4x + 5 = 0$

(b) $5x^2 - 8x + 10y^2 - 2y = -6$

(c) $4x^2 - 8x + 4y^2 + 5y - 2 = 0$

(d) $5y^2 - 8x - 2y = -1$

54. Which shows the performed rotation of axes to eliminate the xy-term for $5x^2 - 2xy + 5y^2 - 24 = 0$?

(a) $\dfrac{(x')^2}{6} + \dfrac{(y')^2}{4} = 1$

(b) $\dfrac{(x')^2}{9} - \dfrac{(y')^2}{1/6} = 1$

(c) $\dfrac{(x')^2}{4} + \dfrac{(y')^2}{9} = 1$

(d) $\dfrac{(x')^2}{6} - \dfrac{(y')^2}{24} = 1$

55. Identify the graph of the equation $-7x^2 - 7y^2 - 3x + 9y - 9 = 0$.

56. Perform a rotation of axes to eliminate the xy-term for $4x^2 + 2xy + 4y^2 - 15 = 0$.

CHAPTER 4
Vector Spaces (Answer Key)

Section 4.1   **Vectors in R^n**

[1]   (b)

[2]   (c)

[3] $(-2, 16)$

[4] $u - 3v$

[5]   (a)

[6]   (b)

[7] $(-2, -11, -11)$

[8] $v = 3u_1 + 4u_2 + 3u_3$

Section 4.2   **Vector Spaces**

Section 4.3   **Subspaces of Vector Spaces**

[9]   (d)

[10]   (d)

[11]   True

[12]   Yes

Section 4.4   **Spanning Sets and Linear Independence**

[13]   (c)

[14] (a)

[15] False

[16] Yes

[17] (c)

[18] (b)

[19] linearly independent

[20] linearly independent

Section 4.5   Basis and Dimension

[21] (c)

[22] (c)

[23] False

[24] 2

Section 4.6   Rank of a Matrix and Systems of Linear Equations

[25] (d)

[26] (a)

[27] 3; 0

[28] True

[29] (b)

[30] (a)

[31] $\begin{bmatrix} -1 \\ 4 \\ 0 \end{bmatrix} + t \begin{bmatrix} 1 \\ -3 \\ 1 \end{bmatrix}$

[32] Yes

[33] (d)

[34] (b)

[35] False

[36] True

Section 4.7   Coordinates and Change of Basis

[37] (a)

[38] (a)

[39] $[x]_B = \begin{bmatrix} 3 \\ 2 \end{bmatrix}$

[40] $x = (8, \ -3)$

[41] (b)

[42] (d)

[43] $\begin{bmatrix} 2 & 2 \\ 0 & -1 \end{bmatrix}$

[44] $\begin{bmatrix} -0.5 & 0.5 & -0.5 \\ 0.5 & 0.5 & 0.5 \\ 0.5 & -0.5 & -0.5 \end{bmatrix}$

[45] (c)

[46] (b)

[47] $[p]_s = \begin{bmatrix} -17 \\ 1 \\ 0 \end{bmatrix}$

[48] $[p]_s = \begin{bmatrix} 3 \\ 0 \\ 6 \end{bmatrix}$

Section 4.8   Applications of Vector Spaces

[49] (c)

[50] (d)

[51] $c_1 e^{3x} + c_2 e^{-3x}$

[52] $y_1 = e^{4x}$
$y_2 = e^{-2x}$

[53] (c)

[54] (a)

[55] circle

[56] $\dfrac{(x')^2}{3} + \dfrac{(y')^2}{5} = 1$

CHAPTER 5
Inner Product Spaces

Section 5.1   Length and Dot Product in R^n

1. Find the distance between $\mathbf{u} = (-7, 2, 3)$ and $\mathbf{v} = (-9, -8, 8)$.

   (a) $\sqrt{129}$ (b) $2\sqrt{132}$ (c) 130   (d) 129

2. Find the distance between $\mathbf{u} = (3, 7, -8)$ and $\mathbf{v} = (-4, 2, 6)$.

   (a) 84   (b) $3\sqrt{30}$ (c) $\sqrt{82}$ (d) 60

3. Find the distance between $\mathbf{u} = (-3, -5, 6)$ and $\mathbf{v} = (9, 1, -3)$.

4. Find the distance between $\mathbf{u} = (-5, 6, 7)$ and $\mathbf{v} = (-9, 3, 8)$.

5. If $\mathbf{u} = (-4, -2)$, $\mathbf{v} = (2, -1)$, and $\mathbf{w} = (2, -5)$, find each of the following.
   a. $(\mathbf{u} \cdot \mathbf{v})\mathbf{w}$

   b. $-4\mathbf{u} \cdot \mathbf{v}$

   (a) a. $(-12, 30)$ (b) a. $(0, 0)$ (c) a. $(12, -30)$ (d) a. $(-20, 50)$
        b. 24   b. 0   b. -24 b. 40

6. Find the angle between the vectors $\mathbf{u} = (-4, 4)$ and $\mathbf{v} = (4, 3)$.

   (a) $\theta = 98°$ (b) $\theta = 172°$ (c) $\theta = 8°$ (d) $\theta = 82°$

7. Find $\mathbf{u} \cdot \mathbf{v}$ given $\|\mathbf{u}\| = 28$, $\|\mathbf{v}\| = 52$, and $\theta = \dfrac{2\pi}{3}$ is the angle between $\mathbf{u}$ and $\mathbf{v}$.

8. If $\mathbf{u} = (-4, 0)$, $\mathbf{v} = (-1, 3)$, and $\mathbf{w} = (2, -3)$, find $\mathbf{u} \cdot (\mathbf{v} - \mathbf{w})$.

9. Find two vectors in opposite directions that are orthogonal to the vector $u = \left(\dfrac{7}{25}, \dfrac{24}{25} \right)$.

    (a) $\left(\dfrac{24}{25}, -\dfrac{7}{25} \right), \left(\dfrac{14}{25}, \dfrac{48}{25} \right)$

    (b) $\left(\dfrac{24}{25}, -\dfrac{7}{25} \right), \left(\dfrac{48}{25}, -\dfrac{14}{25} \right)$

    (c) $\left(\dfrac{24}{25}, -\dfrac{7}{25} \right), \left(-\dfrac{48}{25}, \dfrac{14}{25} \right)$

    (d) $\left(\dfrac{14}{25}, \dfrac{48}{25} \right), \left(-\dfrac{24}{25}, \dfrac{7}{25} \right)$

10. Identify the vector that is a unit vector in the same direction as $u = (-8,\ 6)$.

    (a) $\left(-\dfrac{4}{5}, \dfrac{3}{5} \right)$
    (b) $\left(\dfrac{4}{5}, -\dfrac{3}{5} \right)$
    (c) $\left(-\dfrac{4}{7}, \dfrac{3}{7} \right)$
    (d) $\left(1, -\dfrac{3}{4} \right)$

11. Use the dot product to determine a vector perpendicular to the vector $u = (12,\ -10)$.

12. Determine whether $(4,\ 5,\ -3)$ and $(-2,\ -5,\ -11)$ are orthogonal, parallel, or neither.

Section 5.2   Inner Product Spaces

13. Find the orthogonal projection of $u = (-2,\ -4,\ -3)$ onto $v = (-1,\ -3,\ -4)$.

    (a) $\left(-\dfrac{52}{29}, -\dfrac{104}{29}, -\dfrac{78}{29} \right)$
    (b) $\left(-\dfrac{26}{29}, -\dfrac{78}{29}, -\dfrac{104}{29} \right)$
    (c) $(-2,\ -4,\ -3)$
    (d) $(-1,\ -3,\ -4)$

14. Find $\langle u,\ v \rangle$ for the inner product space defined by $\langle u,\ v \rangle = 3u_1 v_1 + u_2 v_2$. if $u = (-4,\ 3)$ and $v = (0,\ 5)$.

    (a) -12
    (b) 3
    (c) 8
    (d) 15

15. Find the orthogonal projection of $u = (1,\ 5,\ 4)$ onto $v = (-2,\ -3,\ -4)$.

16. Find $\langle u,\ v \rangle$ for the inner product space defined by $\langle u,\ v \rangle = 3u_1 v_1 + u_2 v_2$. if $u = (-4,\ 3)$ and $v = (0,\ 5)$.

Section 5.3   Orthonormal Bases: Gram-Schmidt Process

17. Which statement is true?

    (a) For the vectors $\mathbf{u}$ and $\mathbf{v}$ in an inner product space V, if $\|\mathbf{u}-\mathbf{v}\|^2 = \|\mathbf{u}\|^2 + \|\mathbf{v}\|^2$, then $\mathbf{u}$ and $\mathbf{v}$ are orthogonal.

    (b) Given any set S of vectors in an inner product space V, the Gram-Schmidt orthonormalization process necessarily transforms S into an orthonormal basis of V.

    (c) If $S = \{\mathbf{v}_1, \mathbf{v}_2, \mathbf{v}_3, \ldots, \mathbf{v}_n\}$ is an orthogonal set of nonzero vectors in an inner product space V, then S is linearly dependent.

    (d) Let W be a subspace of R^n and $X = \{\mathbf{v}: \mathbf{w} \cdot \mathbf{v} = 0 \text{ for every } \mathbf{w} \in W\}$, then $W \cap X = \varnothing$.

18. Use the Gram-Schmidt orthonormalization process to transform the basis $\{(1, -1, 0), (-1, 0, 1)\}$ into an orthonormal basis.

    (a) $\left\{\left(\dfrac{\sqrt{2}}{2}, -\dfrac{\sqrt{2}}{2}, 0\right), \left(-\dfrac{1}{\sqrt{6}}, -\dfrac{1}{\sqrt{6}}, \dfrac{2}{\sqrt{6}}\right)\right\}$
    (b) $\left(\dfrac{\sqrt{2}}{2}, \dfrac{\sqrt{2}}{2}, 0\right), \left(-\dfrac{\sqrt{2}}{2}, \dfrac{\sqrt{2}}{2}, 0\right), (0, 0, 1)$

    (c) $\left(\dfrac{\sqrt{2}}{2}, \dfrac{\sqrt{2}}{2}\right), \left(-\dfrac{\sqrt{2}}{2}, \dfrac{\sqrt{2}}{2}\right)$
    (d) $\left(\dfrac{1}{\sqrt{2}}, 0, \dfrac{1}{\sqrt{2}}\right), \left(-\dfrac{1}{\sqrt{6}}, \dfrac{2}{\sqrt{6}}, \dfrac{1}{\sqrt{6}}\right), \left(-\dfrac{1}{\sqrt{3}}, -\dfrac{1}{\sqrt{3}}, \dfrac{1}{\sqrt{3}}\right)$

19. Is the set $W = \left\{\left(\dfrac{1}{\sqrt{2}}, \dfrac{1}{\sqrt{2}}, 0\right), \left(-\dfrac{\sqrt{2}}{6}, \dfrac{\sqrt{2}}{6}, \dfrac{2\sqrt{2}}{3}\right), \left(\dfrac{2}{3}, -\dfrac{2}{3}, \dfrac{1}{3}\right)\right\}$ of vectors in R^3 an orthonormal set?

20. Use the Gram-Schmidt orthonormalization process to transform the basis $\{(1, 1), (0, 1)\}$ into an orthonormal basis.

Section 5.4   Mathematical Models and Least Squares Analysis

21. Which statement is true?

    (a) Let S be a subspace of R^n and $\mathbf{v} \in R^n$. Then for every $\mathbf{u} \in S$, $\mathbf{u} \neq \text{proj}_s \mathbf{v}$, $\|\mathbf{v} - \text{proj}_s \mathbf{v}\| = \|\mathbf{v} - \mathbf{u}\|$.

    (b) Let S be a subspace of R^n. Then $\dim(S) + \dim(S^\perp) = n + 1$.

    (c) Let W be a subspace of R^n and $W^\perp = \{\mathbf{v} \in R^n: \mathbf{w} \cdot \mathbf{v} = 0 \text{ for every } \mathbf{w} \in W\}$, then $W \cap W^\perp = \{\mathbf{0}\}$.

    (d) Two subspaces S_1 and S_2 of R^n are orthogonal if $\mathbf{v}_1 \cdot \mathbf{v}_2 = 1$ for every $\mathbf{v}_1 \in S_1$, $\mathbf{v}_2 \in S_2$.

22. Which pair of sets S_1 and S_2 are orthogonal?

(a) $S_1 = \text{Span}\left\{\begin{bmatrix} 2 \\ 1 \\ -1 \end{bmatrix}, \begin{bmatrix} 0 \\ 1 \\ 1 \end{bmatrix}\right\}$, $S_2 = \text{Span}\left\{\begin{bmatrix} -1 \\ 2 \\ 0 \end{bmatrix}\right\}$

(b) $S_1 = \text{Span}\left\{\begin{bmatrix} 2 \\ 1 \\ 6 \end{bmatrix}, \begin{bmatrix} 0 \\ 1 \\ 0 \end{bmatrix}\right\}$, $S_2 = \text{Span}\left\{\begin{bmatrix} -3 \\ 0 \\ 1 \end{bmatrix}\right\}$

(c) $S_1 = \text{Span}\left\{\begin{bmatrix} -1 \\ 0 \\ 1 \end{bmatrix}, \begin{bmatrix} 1 \\ 1 \\ 0 \end{bmatrix}\right\}$, $S_2 = \text{Span}\left\{\begin{bmatrix} -1 \\ -1 \\ 1 \end{bmatrix}\right\}$

(d) $S_1 = \text{Span}\left\{\begin{bmatrix} 1 \\ -2 \\ 1 \end{bmatrix}, \begin{bmatrix} 0 \\ -1 \\ 1 \end{bmatrix}\right\}$, $S_2 = \text{Span}\left\{\begin{bmatrix} 0 \\ 1 \\ 2 \end{bmatrix}\right\}$

23. True or False:
Let W be a subspace of R^n and $W^\perp = \{v \in R^n : w \cdot v = 0 \text{ for every } w \in W\}$, then $W \cap W^\perp = \{0\}$.

24. Determine whether or not the sets S_1 and S_2 are orthogonal.

$S_1 = \text{Span}\left\{\begin{bmatrix} 1 \\ -2 \\ 1 \end{bmatrix}, \begin{bmatrix} 0 \\ -1 \\ 1 \end{bmatrix}\right\}$, $S_2 = \text{Span}\left\{\begin{bmatrix} 0 \\ 1 \\ 2 \end{bmatrix}\right\}$

25. Which statement is true?

(a) The four fundamental subspaces of an $m \times n$ matrix A are the nullspace of A, column space of A, row space of A^T, and column space of A^T.

(b) If A is an $m \times n$ matrix, then the direct sum of the column space of A and nullspace of $A^T = R^n$.

(c) If A is an $m \times n$ matrix, then the column space of A^T and the nullspace of A are orthogonal subspaces of R^n.

(d) If A is an $m \times n$ matrix, then the direct sum of the column space of A^T and $A = R^m$.

26. Which statement is true?
Let A be an $m \times n$ matrix.

(a) If A and B have the same shape, then $N(A) \neq N(B) \Leftrightarrow R(A^T) = R(B^T)$.

(b) Let P be a nonsingular matrix such that $PA = U$ where U is in row-echelon form and suppose Rank $(A) = r$. Then the spanning set for $N(A^T) =$ the last $m - r + 1$ rows of P.

(c) Let P be a nonsingular matrix such that $PA = U$ where U is in row-echelon form and suppose Rank $(A) = r$. Then the spanning set for $R(A^T) =$ the nonzero rows in U.

(d) If A and B have the same shape, then $R(A) = R(B) \Leftrightarrow N(A^T) \neq N(B^T)$.

27. True or False:
The four fundamental subspaces of an $m \times n$ matrix A are the nullspace of A, column space of A, row space of A^T, and column space of A^T.

28. True or False: Let A be an $m \times n$ matrix. Let P be a nonsingular matrix such that $PA = U$ where U is in row-echelon form and suppose Rank $(A) = r$. Then the spanning set for $N(A^T) =$ the last $m - r + 1$ rows of P.

29. Find the least squares regression line for the given points.
$(-3, 3)$, $(-2, 1)$, $(0, 3)$, $(3, -4)$

  (a) $f(x) = -\dfrac{43}{20}x - \dfrac{1}{2}$ (b) $f(x) = -\dfrac{43}{42}x + \dfrac{5}{21}$ (c) $f(x) = \dfrac{43}{42}x - \dfrac{1}{2}$ (d) $f(x) = -\dfrac{43}{20}x + \dfrac{5}{21}$

30. Find the least squares regression quadratic for the given points.
$(-1, 2)$, $(0, -2)$, $(1, -5)$, $(2, -8)$

  (a) $f(x) = \dfrac{1}{4}x^2 - \dfrac{71}{20}x + \dfrac{19}{100}$

  (b) $f(x) = \dfrac{1}{4}x^2 + \dfrac{38}{21}x + \dfrac{37}{20}$

  (c) $f(x) = \dfrac{1}{4}x^2 + \dfrac{38}{21}x + \dfrac{19}{100}$

  (d) $f(x) = \dfrac{1}{4}x^2 - \dfrac{71}{20}x - \dfrac{37}{20}$

31. Find the least squares regression line for the given points.
$(-2, 3)$, $(-1, 0)$, $(1, -3)$, $(4, -8)$

32. Find the solution of the least squares problem $A\mathbf{x} = \mathbf{b}$.
$$\begin{bmatrix} 1 & -1 \\ 1 & 1 \\ 1 & 2 \end{bmatrix} \begin{bmatrix} c_0 \\ c_1 \end{bmatrix} = \begin{bmatrix} 2 \\ 4 \\ 3 \end{bmatrix}$$

33. In a study of the relationship between the number of anteaters A and the number of anthills C in an area, the following data was collected. Find the graph that expresses C as a function of A and has a least squares regression line that fits the data.

Anteaters (A)	34	49	63	77	91	106	120
Anthills (C)	810	990	1180	1060	1250	1430	1320

(a)

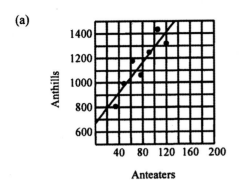

$$C = 6.21A + 669.22$$

(b)

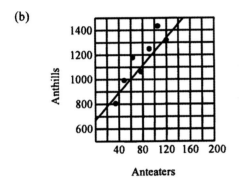

$$C = 5.59A + 669.22$$

(c)

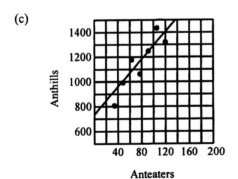

$$C = 5.59A + 736.14$$

(d)

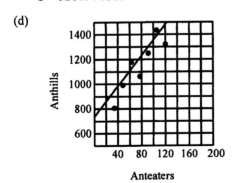

$$C = 6.21A + 736.14$$

34. Early in the 1900s, an airplane manufacturer was able to increase the time its planes could stay aloft by constantly refining its techniques. Which exponential equation best models the data? Assume x is the number of years after 1910 and y is the time aloft in hours.

Years after 1910	1	2	3	4	5	6
Time aloft (h)	0.72	1.2	2.5	3.4	4.1	5.3

   (a) $y = 0.576x^{1.491}$ (b) $y = 1.491(0.576)^x$ (c) $y = 0.72(5.3)^x$ (d) $y = 0.576(1.491)^x$

35. A study collected data on the population of a city and the average commuting distance to work. The table shows this data for various sized cities.

Population (1000s)	5.9	20	88	148	421
Commute (mi)	11.1	11.7	12.1	12.5	12.6

   Find the logarithmic model for the data if P is the population and C is the commute distance.

36. The table shows Christine's best javelin throws each year. Determine an equation for the line of best fit for the data. Use $x = 0$ for 1989.

Year	1989	1990	1991	1992	1993	1994	1995	1996
Distance (m)	31.4	30.8	34.7	32.85	35.75	37.15	36.05	35.7

Section 5.5   Applications of Inner Product Spaces

37. Find the unit vector that is orthogonal to both $\mathbf{a} = -2\mathbf{i} - 2\mathbf{j} - 2\mathbf{k}$ and $\mathbf{b} = 4\mathbf{i} + 2\mathbf{j} - 2\mathbf{k}$.

   (a) $\dfrac{4}{\sqrt{14}}\mathbf{i} - \dfrac{3}{\sqrt{14}}\mathbf{j} + \dfrac{2}{\sqrt{14}}\mathbf{k}$

   (b) $-\dfrac{2}{\sqrt{14}}\mathbf{i} + \dfrac{3}{\sqrt{14}}\mathbf{j} + \dfrac{1}{\sqrt{14}}\mathbf{k}$

   (c) $\dfrac{2}{\sqrt{14}}\mathbf{i} - \dfrac{3}{\sqrt{14}}\mathbf{j} + \dfrac{1}{\sqrt{14}}\mathbf{k}$

   (d) $\dfrac{2}{\sqrt{14}}\mathbf{i} + \dfrac{3}{\sqrt{14}}\mathbf{j} + \dfrac{1}{\sqrt{14}}\mathbf{k}$

38. Find $\mathbf{r} \times (\mathbf{s} + \mathbf{t})$ if $\mathbf{r} = 6\mathbf{i} - 2\mathbf{j} + 2\mathbf{k}$, $\mathbf{s} = -4\mathbf{i} + 7\mathbf{j} + 2\mathbf{k}$, and $\mathbf{t} = 6\mathbf{i} - 7\mathbf{j} - \mathbf{k}$.

   (a) $-\mathbf{i} - 3\mathbf{j} + 3\mathbf{k}$ (b) $-2\mathbf{i} - 3\mathbf{j} + 4\mathbf{k}$ (c) $-3\mathbf{i} - 2\mathbf{j} - 2\mathbf{k}$ (d) $-2\mathbf{i} - 2\mathbf{j} + 4\mathbf{k}$

39. Find $\mathbf{v} \times \mathbf{w}$ if $\mathbf{v} = 7\mathbf{i} - 4\mathbf{j} - 5\mathbf{k}$ and $\mathbf{w} = 5\mathbf{i} - 8\mathbf{j} - 3\mathbf{k}$.

40. Find the area of a parallelogram with adjacent sides of $\mathbf{v} = -5\mathbf{i} + 8\mathbf{j}$ and $\mathbf{w} = -8\mathbf{i} + 2\mathbf{j}$.

41. Find the quadratic least square approximating function g for the function $f(x) = x^3$ on the interval $[0, 1]$.

    (a) $\dfrac{1}{20} - \dfrac{3}{5}x + \dfrac{3}{2}x^2$ (b) $\dfrac{3}{5} - \dfrac{3}{2}x + \dfrac{5}{4}x^2$ (c) $\dfrac{3}{5}x + \dfrac{3}{2}x^2$ (d) $\dfrac{1}{2} + \dfrac{3}{5}x + \dfrac{3}{2}x^2$

42. Find the linear least square approximating function g for the function $f(x) = x^3$ on the interval $[0, 2]$.

    (a) $7.8 - 0.2x$ (b) $-1.6 + 3.6x$ (c) $1.6x - 0.6$ (d) $3.75 + 2.5x$

43. Find the linear least square approximating function g for the function $f(x) = x^4$ on the interval $[-1, 1]$.

44. Find the linear least square approximating function g for the function $f(x) = x^2$ on the interval $[0, 1]$.

45. Suppose that the eighth-order Fourier approximation for a function f is
    $q_8(x) = -4\cos(3x) + 3\sin(4x) - 7\cos(4x) - \sin(6x) + \cos(8x)$. Which is the sixth-order Fourier approximation for f?

    (a) $q_6(x) = 4 + 2\cos(4x) + 3\sin(4x)$ (b) $q_6(x) = 4 + 2\sin(3x) + 3\cos(3x)$

    (c) $q_6(x) = -4\cos(3x) + 3\sin(4x) - 7\cos(4x) - \sin(6x)$ (d) $q_6(x) = 4$

46. Which is the coefficient a_1 in the first-order Fourier approximation of the function $f(x) = x^2$?

    (a) $a_1 = \dfrac{1}{2}$ (b) $a_1 = -4$ (c) $a_1 = 5$ (d) $a_1 = 4$

47. Suppose that the eighth-order Fourier approximation for a function f is
    $q_8(x) = -4\cos(3x) + 3\sin(4x) - 7\cos(4x) - \sin(6x) + \cos(8x)$. What is the fifth-order Fourier approximation for f?

48. What is the coefficient a_3 in the sixth-order Fourier approximation of the function $f(x) = x^2$?

CHAPTER 5
Inner Product Spaces (Answer Key)

Section 5.1   Length and Dot Product in R^n

[1] (a)

[2] (b)

[3] $3\sqrt{29}$

[4] $\sqrt{26}$

[5] (a)

[6] (a)

[7] −728

[8] 12

[9] (c)

[10] (a)

[11] Answers may vary. Sample answer: $(5, 6)$

[12] orthogonal

Section 5.2   Inner Product Spaces

[13] (d)

[14] (d)

[15] $\left(\dfrac{66}{29}, \dfrac{99}{29}, \dfrac{132}{29}\right)$

[16] 15

Section 5.3   Orthonormal Bases: Gram-Schmidt Process

[17] (a)

[18] (a)

[19] True

[20] $\left\{\left(\dfrac{\sqrt{2}}{2}, \dfrac{\sqrt{2}}{2}\right), \left(-\dfrac{\sqrt{2}}{2}, \dfrac{\sqrt{2}}{2}\right)\right\}$

Section 5.4   Mathematical Models and Least Squares Analysis

[21] (c)

[22] (b)

[23] True

[24] not orthogonal

[25] (c)

[26] (c)

[27] False

[28] False

[29] (b)

[30] (d)

[31] $f(x) = -\dfrac{37}{21}x - \dfrac{47}{42}$

[32] $f(x) = \dfrac{3}{7}x + \dfrac{19}{7}$

[33] (a)

[34] (d)

[35] $C = 10.541 + 0.359 \ln P$

[36] $y = 0.793x + 31.525$

Section 5.5   Applications of Inner Product Spaces

[37] (c)

[38] (d)

[39] $-28\mathbf{i} - 4\mathbf{j} - 36\mathbf{k}$

[40] 54 square units

[41] (a)

[42] (b)

[43] $\dfrac{1}{5}$

[44] $-0.17 + x$

[45] (c)

[46] (d)

[47] $q_5(x) = -4\cos(3x) + 3\sin(4x) - 7\cos(4x)$

[48] $a_3 = \dfrac{4}{9}$

CHAPTER 6
Linear Transformations

Section 6.1   Introduction to Linear Transformations

Section 6.2   The Kernel and Range of a Linear Transformation

1. Which of the following statements is true?

   (a) If $T:V \to W$ is a linear transformation, then the kernel of T is the set of all vectors $\mathbf{v}$ in V that satisfy $T(\mathbf{v}) = \mathbf{v}$.

   (b) If $T:R^n \to R^m$ is a linear transformation given by $T(\mathbf{x}) = A\mathbf{x}$, then the kernel of T is equal to the solution space of $A\mathbf{x} = \mathbf{x}$.

   (c) The kernel of a linear transformation $T:V \to W$ is a subspace of V.

   (d) The kernel of a linear transformation $T:V \to W$ is a subspace of W.

2. Which of the following statements is true?

   (a) The range of a linear transformation $T:V \to W$ is a subspace of W.

   (b) If $T:V \to W$ is a linear transformation, then the dimension of the range of T is the nullity of T.

   (c) If $T:V \to W$ is a linear transformation, then the dimension of the kernel of T is greater than the dimension of V.

   (d) If $T:V \to W$ is a linear transformation from an n-dimensional vector space V into a vector space W, then $\text{rank}(T) - \text{nullity}(T) = n$.

3. True or False: If $T:V \to W$ is a linear transformation, the kernel of T is the set of all vectors $\mathbf{v}$ in V that satisfy $T(\mathbf{v}) = \mathbf{0}$.

4. True or False: If $T:V \to W$ is a linear transformation, then the dimension of the range of T is the nullity of T.

5. Which of the following statements is true?

   (a) Let $T:V \to W$ be a linear transformation. Then T is one-to-one if $\ker(T) \neq \{\mathbf{0}\}$.

   (b) Let $T:V \to W$ be a linear transformation. Then T is one-to-one if and only if $\ker(T) = \{\mathbf{0}\}$.

   (c) Let $T:V \to W$ be a linear transformation. If the zero vector is the only vector $\mathbf{v}$ such that $T(\mathbf{v}) = \mathbf{v}$, then T is one-to-one.

   (d) The linear transformation $T: M_{m,n} \to M_{n,m}$ given by $T(A) = A^T$ is not one-to-one.

6. Which of the following statements is true?

    (a) If $T:V \to W$ is a linear transformation with vector spaces V and W both of dimension n, then T is one-to-one if and only if it is onto.

    (b) A function $T:V \to W$ is said to be onto if at most one element in W has a preimage in V.

    (c) If $T:V \to W$ is a linear transformation with vector spaces V and W both of dimension n, then T is one-to-one if and only if it is not onto.

    (d) The zero transformation $T:R^3 \to R^3$ is one-to-one.

7. True or False: A function $T:V \to W$ is one-to-one if the preimage of every **w** in the range consists of a single vector.

8. True or False: If $T:V \to W$ is a linear transformation, then T is one-to-one if and only if the rank of T equals the dimension of V.

9. Which vector space is isomorphic to R^8 ?

    (a) P_7 (b) $M_{1,7}$ (c) $M_{4,4}$ (d) P_8

10. Which of the following statements is true?

    (a) If a linear transformation $T:V \to W$ is onto, it will be an isomorphism.

    (b) If V and W are finite dimensional vector spaces, such that $\dim(W) < \dim(V)$, then there is a linear transformation $T:V \to W$ which is one-to-one.

    (c) If B is an invertible $n \times n$ matrix, the linear transformation $T: M_{n,n} \to M_{n,n}$ given by $T(A) = AB$ is an isomorphism.

    (d) If $T:V \to W$ is a linear transformation such that $\text{rank}(T) < \dim(V)$, then T is one-to-one.

11. Is the vector space $M_{8,1}$ isomorphic to R^8 ?

12. True or False:
    A linear transformation $T:V \to W$ that is one-to-one and onto is called an isomorphism.

Section 6.3   Matrices for Linear Transformations

13. Find the standard matrix for the linear transformation $T(x, y) = (x, 0)$.

    (a) $\begin{bmatrix} 0 & 1 \\ 0 & 1 \end{bmatrix}$ (b) $\begin{bmatrix} 1 & 0 \\ 1 & 0 \end{bmatrix}$ (c) $\begin{bmatrix} 1 & 0 \\ 0 & 0 \end{bmatrix}$ (d) $\begin{bmatrix} 0 & 1 \\ 0 & 0 \end{bmatrix}$

14. Find the standard matrix for $T = T_1 \circ T_2$ if $T_1 : R^3 \to R^3$, $T_1(x, y, z) = (x, x+y, x+y+z)$ and $T_2 : R^3 \to R^3$, $T_2(x, y, z) = (-x+2y, x+y, x-z)$.

(a) $\begin{bmatrix} -1 & 2 & 0 \\ 0 & 3 & 0 \\ 1 & 3 & -1 \end{bmatrix}$ (b) $\begin{bmatrix} 0 & 2 & -1 \\ 0 & 3 & 0 \\ -1 & 3 & 1 \end{bmatrix}$ (c) $\begin{bmatrix} 1 & 2 & 0 \\ 2 & 1 & 0 \\ 0 & -1 & -1 \end{bmatrix}$ (d) $\begin{bmatrix} 0 & 2 & 1 \\ 0 & 1 & 2 \\ -1 & -1 & 0 \end{bmatrix}$

15. Find the standard matrix for the linear transformation $T(x, y, z) = (x - 2y + 5z, \ 2x + 3z, \ 4x + y - 2z)$.

16. Find the standard matrix for $T = T_1 \circ T_2$ if $T_1 : R^3 \to R^3$, $T_1(x, y, z) = (x, x+y, x+y+z)$ and $T_2 : R^3 \to R^3$, $T_2(x, y, z) = (-x+2y, x+y, x-z)$.

17. Which of the following statements is true?

(a) If $T: R^3 \to R^2$ is a linear transformation given by $T(x, y, z) = (x+z, x+y)$,
$B = \{(1, 1, 1), (1, -1, 0), (1, 0, 0)\}$, $B' = \{(1, 1), (1, -1)\}$, and $\mathbf{v} = (2, 1, 1)$, then $T(\mathbf{v}) = (3, -3)$.

(b) If $\mathbf{v}_1, \mathbf{v}_2, ..., \mathbf{v}_m$ are fixed vectors in R^n and $T: R^n \to R^n$ is the function defined by
$T(\mathbf{x}) = (x \cdot \mathbf{v}_1, x \cdot \mathbf{v}_2, ..., x \cdot \mathbf{v}_m)$ where $x \cdot \mathbf{v}_i$ is the Euclidean product on R^n, then T is a linear transformation.

(c) If $\mathbf{v}_1, \mathbf{v}_2, ..., \mathbf{v}_m$ are fixed vectors in R^n and $T: R^n \to R^n$ is the function defined by
$T(\mathbf{x}) = (x \cdot \mathbf{v}_1, x \cdot \mathbf{v}_2, ..., x \cdot \mathbf{v}_m)$ where $x \cdot \mathbf{v}_i$ is the Euclidean product on R^n, then
the standard matrix for T is the matrix with column vectors $\mathbf{v}_1, \mathbf{v}_2, ..., \mathbf{v}_m$.

(d) If $T: R^3 \to R^2$ is a linear transformation given by $T(x, y, z) = (x+z, x+y)$,
$B = \{(1, 1, 1), (1, -1, 0), (1, 0, 0)\}$, $B' = \{(1, 1), (1, -1)\}$, and $\mathbf{v} = (2, 2, 2)$, then $T(\mathbf{v}) = (3, -2)$.

18. Which of the following statements is true?

(a) If the columns of a square matrix are orthonormal, then the rows cannot be orthonormal.

(b) Let S and T be linear transformations from $\mathbf{v}$ into W. Then $S + T$ and kT are both
linear transformations where $(S + T)(\mathbf{v}) = S(\mathbf{v}) + T(\mathbf{v})$ and $(kT)(\mathbf{v}) = kT(\mathbf{v})$.

(c) Let $T: R^2 \to R^2$ be a linear transformation given by $T(x, y) = (x - 3y, y - x)$ and
$B' = \{(1, -1), (1, 1)\}$, then the matrix A' for T relative to the basis B' is not
similar to A, the standard matrix for T.

(d) If a collection of vectors is dependent, then any one of the vectors in the collection may be deleted without
shrinking the span of the collection.

19. True or False:

If $T: R^3 \to R^2$ is given by $T(x, y, z) = (x+z, x+y)$, $B = \{(1, 1, 1), (1, -1, 0), (1, 0, 0)\}$,

$B' = \{(1, 1), (1, -1)\}$, and $\mathbf{v} = (1, 2, 1)$, then $T(\mathbf{v}) = (1, -2)$.

20. True or False:

If $T: P_3 \to R$ is given by $T(a_0 + a_1 x + a_2 x^2 + a_3 x^3) = a_0 + a_1 + a_2 + a_3$, then T is linear.

Section 6.4   Transition Matrices and Similarity

21. Find the matrix for $T: R^3 \to R^3$, $T(x, y, z) = (2x+y, y, z-x)$ relative to the basis

$\{(1, 1, -1), (1, -1, 0), (1, 0, 0)\}$.

(a) $\begin{bmatrix} 2 & 1 & 0 \\ -1 & 2 & -1 \\ 0 & -2 & 1 \end{bmatrix}$
(b) $\begin{bmatrix} -3 & -1 & 1 \\ -1 & -2 & -1 \\ 5 & -2 & -2 \end{bmatrix}$
(c) $\begin{bmatrix} -2 & 1 & -1 \\ 1 & -2 & 1 \\ 0 & 2 & 0 \end{bmatrix}$
(d) $\begin{bmatrix} 2 & 1 & 1 \\ 1 & 2 & 1 \\ 0 & -2 & 0 \end{bmatrix}$

22. Which of the following statements is true?

(a) The trace of a square matrix A is the product of the diagonal entries of A.

(b) If A and B are nonsingular matrices, A^{-1} and B^{-1} are similar.

(c) If A and B are similar matrices, then A^4 may not be similar to B^4.

(d) Let A and B be square matrices of order n. Then $\text{tr}(AB) > \text{tr}(BA)$.

23. Find the matrix for $T: R^3 \to R^3$, $T(x, y, z) = (x-y+2z, 2x+y-z, x+2y+z)$ relative to the basis

$\{(1, 0, 1), (0, 2, 2), (1, 2, 0)\}$.

24. True or False: If A and B are similar $n \times n$ matrices, then $\text{tr}(A) = \text{tr}(B)$.

Section 6.5   Applications of Linear Transformations

25. Find the image of the rectangle with vertices $(0, 0)$, $(1, 0)$, $(1, 1)$, $(0, 1)$ under the shear given by
$T(x, y) = (x, y + 3x)$.

(a)
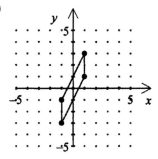

(b)
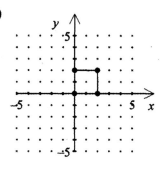

(c)
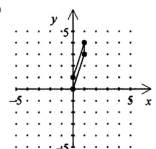

(d)
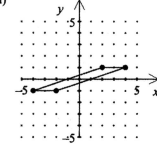

26. If $T: R^2 \rightarrow R^2$ is a reflection in the y-axis, find the image of $(f, -g)$.

(a) $(-f, g)$ (b) $(f, -g)$ (c) (f, g) (d) $(-f, -g)$

27. Sketch the image of the rectangle with vertices $(0, 0)$, $(0, 2)$, $(1, 2)$, $(1, 0)$ under the shear given by
$$T(x, y) = \left(x, \frac{y}{2} \right).$$

28. If $T: R^2 \rightarrow R^2$ is a reflection in the y-axis, find the image of $(f, -g)$.

29. Find the matrix that will produce a $60°$ rotation about the z-axis.

(a) $\begin{bmatrix} 0 & -\frac{\sqrt{3}}{2} & \frac{1}{2} \\ 0 & \frac{1}{2} & \frac{\sqrt{3}}{2} \\ 1 & 0 & 0 \end{bmatrix}$ (b) $\begin{bmatrix} \frac{1}{2} & -\frac{\sqrt{3}}{2} & 0 \\ \frac{\sqrt{3}}{2} & \frac{1}{2} & 0 \\ 0 & 0 & 1 \end{bmatrix}$ (c) $\begin{bmatrix} \frac{1}{6} & \frac{\sqrt{3}}{2} & 0 \\ -\frac{\sqrt{3}}{2} & \frac{1}{2} & 0 \\ 2 & 0 & 1 \end{bmatrix}$ (d) $\begin{bmatrix} 0 & \frac{\sqrt{3}}{2} & \frac{1}{6} \\ 0 & \frac{1}{2} & -\frac{\sqrt{3}}{2} \\ 1 & 0 & 2 \end{bmatrix}$

30. Find the image of the vector $(1,\ 1,\ -1)$ under a 90° rotation about the z -axis.

    (a) $(-1,\ 1,\ 1)$ (b) $(-1,\ -1,\ 1)$ (c) $(1,\ -1,\ 1)$ (d) $(-1,\ 1,\ -1)$

31. Find the matrix that will produce a 90° rotation about the y -axis.

32. Find the image of the vector $(1,\ 1,\ 1)$ under a 60° rotation about the x -axis.

CHAPTER 6
Linear Transformations (Answer Key)

Section 6.1   Introduction to Linear Transformations

Section 6.2   The Kernel and Range of a Linear Transformation

[1] (c)

[2] (a)

[3] True

[4] False

[5] (b)

[6] (a)

[7] True

[8] True

[9] (a)

[10] (c)

[11] Yes

[12] True

Section 6.3   Matrices for Linear Transformations

[13] (c)

[14] (a)

[15] $\begin{bmatrix} 1 & -2 & 5 \\ 2 & 0 & 3 \\ 4 & 1 & -2 \end{bmatrix}$

[16] $\begin{bmatrix} -1 & 2 & 0 \\ 0 & 3 & 0 \\ 1 & 3 & -1 \end{bmatrix}$

[17] (b)

[18] (b)

[19] False

[20] True

Section 6.4   Transition Matrices and Similarity

[21] (d)

[22] (b)

[23] $\begin{bmatrix} \frac{7}{3} & \frac{10}{3} & -\frac{1}{3} \\ -\frac{1}{6} & \frac{4}{3} & \frac{8}{3} \\ \frac{2}{3} & -\frac{4}{3} & -\frac{2}{3} \end{bmatrix}$

[24] True

Section 6.5   Applications of Linear Transformations

[25] (c)

[26] (d)

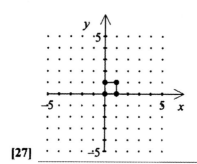

[27]

---

[28] $(-f, -g)$

---

[29] (b)

---

[30] (d)

---

[31] $\begin{bmatrix} 0 & 0 & 1 \\ 0 & 1 & 0 \\ -1 & 0 & 0 \end{bmatrix}$

---

[32] $(1, -0.366, 1.366)$

CHAPTER 7
Eigenvalues and Eigenvectors

Section 7.1   Eigenvalues and Eigenvectors

1. Which of the following vectors is not an eigenvector of $\begin{bmatrix} 1 & 3 \\ 1 & -1 \end{bmatrix}$?

    (a) $(1, -1)$ (b) $(2, -6)$ (c) $(-4, 4)$ (d) $(9, 3)$

2. Which of the following vectors is an eigenvector of $\begin{bmatrix} 3 & 1 & 2 \\ 0 & 0 & 0 \\ -1 & 2 & 0 \end{bmatrix}$?

    (a) $(0, 0, 0)$ (b) $(2, 0, -1)$ (c) $(7, 2, 1)$ (d) $(1, -1, 0)$

3. Is the vector $(6, 2)$ an eigenvector of $\begin{bmatrix} 1 & 3 \\ 1 & -1 \end{bmatrix}$?

4. Is the vector $(1, 2, -3)$ an eigenvector of $\begin{bmatrix} 3 & 1 & 2 \\ 0 & 0 & 0 \\ -1 & 2 & 0 \end{bmatrix}$?

5. Find the eigenvalues and corresponding eigenvectors of the matrix $\begin{bmatrix} 1 & 10 & 5 \\ 0 & -4 & 0 \\ 5 & 10 & 1 \end{bmatrix}$.

    (a) $-4, \begin{bmatrix} -2 \\ -1 \\ 0 \end{bmatrix}; -4, \begin{bmatrix} -1 \\ 0 \\ 1 \end{bmatrix}; 6, \begin{bmatrix} -1 \\ 0 \\ 1 \end{bmatrix}$ (b) $-4, \begin{bmatrix} -2 \\ 1 \\ 0 \end{bmatrix}; -4, \begin{bmatrix} -1 \\ 0 \\ 1 \end{bmatrix}; 6, \begin{bmatrix} 1 \\ 0 \\ 1 \end{bmatrix}$

    (c) $-4, \begin{bmatrix} -2 \\ 1 \\ 0 \end{bmatrix}; -4, \begin{bmatrix} -1 \\ 0 \\ -1 \end{bmatrix}; 6, \begin{bmatrix} 1 \\ 0 \\ -1 \end{bmatrix}$ (d) $-4, \begin{bmatrix} 2 \\ 1 \\ 0 \end{bmatrix}; -4, \begin{bmatrix} -1 \\ 0 \\ 1 \end{bmatrix}; 6, \begin{bmatrix} -1 \\ 0 \\ 1 \end{bmatrix}$

6. Find the eigenvalues and corresponding eigenvectors of the matrix $\begin{bmatrix} 3 & 1 \\ 2 & 4 \end{bmatrix}$.

   (a) $-1, \begin{bmatrix} 0 \\ -1 \end{bmatrix}; 5, \begin{bmatrix} 1 \\ 2 \end{bmatrix}$ (b) $-1, \begin{bmatrix} 0 \\ -1 \end{bmatrix}; 4, \begin{bmatrix} -1 \\ 2 \end{bmatrix}$ (c) $2, \begin{bmatrix} 1 \\ -1 \end{bmatrix}; 5, \begin{bmatrix} 1 \\ 2 \end{bmatrix}$ (d) $2, \begin{bmatrix} 1 \\ -1 \end{bmatrix}; 4, \begin{bmatrix} -1 \\ 2 \end{bmatrix}$

7. Find the eigenvalues and corresponding eigenvectors of the matrix $\begin{bmatrix} 1 & 0 & 0 \\ 0 & 2 & 0 \\ 0 & 0 & 3 \end{bmatrix}$.

8. Find the eigenvalues and corresponding eigenvectors of the matrix $\begin{bmatrix} 1 & 0 \\ 0 & 2 \end{bmatrix}$.

9. Which of the following statements is true?

   (a) If $A^2 = 0$, then 0 and 1 are the only eigenvalues of A.

   (b) Let A be an $n \times n$ invertible matrix and let λ be an eigenvalue of A. Then $-\lambda$ will be an eigenvalue of A^{-1}.

   (c) If a triangular matrix A has real and nonzero eigenvalues, then A is singular.

   (d) The constant term of the characteristic polynomial is given by $\pm|A|$.

10. Which of the following statements is true?

    (a) If A is an $n \times n$ nonsingular matrix, then 0 is an eigenvalue of A.

    (b) A triangular matrix A is nonsingular if and only if its eigenvalues are real and nonzero.

    (c) For any invertible matrix A, A and A^{-1} have the same eigenvalues.

    (d) Let $T: R^2 \to R^2$ be given by $T(\mathbf{v}) = \text{proj}_u \mathbf{v}$, where u is a fixed vector in R^2.
        Then the eigenvalues of the standard matrix of T are -1 and 1.

11. True or False:
    A and A^T have the same eigenvalues.

12. True or False: A number λ is called the eigenvalue of a linear transformation $T: V \to V$ if there is a nonzero vector $\mathbf{x}$ such that $T(\mathbf{x}) = \lambda\mathbf{x}$.

Section 7.2   Diagonalization

13. Which of the following statements is true?

(a) If A is a diagonalizable matrix, then A has n distinct eigenvalues.

(b) Let A be a diagonalizable $n \times n$ matrix and P be an invertible $n \times n$ matrix such that $B = P^{-1}AP$ is the diagonal form of A. Then $A^k = PB^kP^{-1}$, where k is a positive integer.

(c) If T is a linear operator on a finite dimensional vector space V, then there always exists a basis B of V such that the matrix for T with respect to B is diagonal.

(d) Nonzero nilpotent matrices are diagonalizable.

14. Which of the following matrices is not diagonalizable?

(a) $\begin{bmatrix} 1 & 3 & 0 \\ 3 & 1 & 0 \\ 0 & 0 & -2 \end{bmatrix}$
(b) $\begin{bmatrix} 1 & -2 & 1 \\ 0 & 0 & 1 \\ 0 & 0 & -3 \end{bmatrix}$
(c) $\begin{bmatrix} 0 & 0 & 0 \\ 0 & 1 & 0 \\ 0 & 1 & 1 \end{bmatrix}$
(d) $\begin{bmatrix} 1 & -1 & -1 \\ 1 & 3 & 1 \\ -3 & 1 & -1 \end{bmatrix}$

15. True or False:
If A and B are similar matrices, then their eigenvalues may not be the same.

16. Is the matrix $\begin{bmatrix} -1 & 0 \\ 1 & -1 \end{bmatrix}$ diagonalizable?

Section 7.3   Symmetric Matrices and Orthogonal Diagonalization

17. Which of the following matrices is symmetric?

(a) $\begin{bmatrix} 1 & 2 & 3 \\ 2 & 2 & -4 \\ 3 & 4 & 3 \end{bmatrix}$
(b) $\begin{bmatrix} 1 & 0 & 1 \\ 0 & 1 & 0 \\ 0 & 0 & 5 \end{bmatrix}$
(c) $\begin{bmatrix} 0 & 0 & -1 \\ 1 & 1 & 0 \\ 0 & 0 & 1 \end{bmatrix}$
(d) $\begin{bmatrix} 0 & 0 & 2 \\ 0 & 1 & -1 \\ 2 & -1 & -1 \end{bmatrix}$

18. Which of the following matrices is not orthogonal?

(a) $\begin{bmatrix} -\frac{\sqrt{2}}{2} & -\frac{\sqrt{2}}{2} \\ \frac{\sqrt{2}}{2} & -\frac{\sqrt{2}}{2} \end{bmatrix}$
(b) $\begin{bmatrix} -\frac{\sqrt{6}}{6} & \frac{\sqrt{2}}{2} & \frac{\sqrt{3}}{3} \\ \frac{\sqrt{6}}{3} & 0 & \frac{\sqrt{3}}{3} \\ \frac{\sqrt{6}}{6} & \frac{\sqrt{2}}{2} & -\frac{\sqrt{3}}{3} \end{bmatrix}$
(c) $\begin{bmatrix} \frac{1}{3} & \frac{2}{3} & \frac{2}{3} \\ -\frac{2}{\sqrt{5}} & \frac{1}{\sqrt{5}} & 0 \\ -\frac{2}{3\sqrt{5}} & -\frac{4}{3\sqrt{5}} & \frac{5}{3\sqrt{5}} \end{bmatrix}$
(d) $\begin{bmatrix} 2 & 2 & -2 \\ 2 & -1 & 4 \\ -2 & 4 & -1 \end{bmatrix}$

19. Is the matrix $\begin{bmatrix} 1 & 1 & 1 \\ 1 & 1 & 1 \\ 1 & 1 & 1 \end{bmatrix}$ symmetric?

20. Is the matrix $\begin{bmatrix} 0 & 1 & 1 \\ 1 & 0 & 1 \\ 1 & 1 & 0 \end{bmatrix}$ orthogonal?

21. Which of the following matrices is orthogonally diagonalizable?

(a) $\begin{bmatrix} \frac{1}{3} & -\frac{2}{3} & \frac{2}{3} \\ \frac{2}{3} & \frac{1}{3} & -\frac{2}{3} \\ -\frac{2}{3} & -\frac{2}{3} & \frac{1}{3} \end{bmatrix}$ (b) $\begin{bmatrix} 1 & 0 & 1 \\ 0 & 1 & 0 \\ 0 & 0 & 5 \end{bmatrix}$ (c) $\begin{bmatrix} 0 & 0 & -1 \\ 1 & 1 & 0 \\ 0 & 0 & 1 \end{bmatrix}$ (d) $\begin{bmatrix} 0 & 0 & 2 \\ 0 & 1 & -1 \\ 2 & -1 & -1 \end{bmatrix}$

22. Which is the true statement?

(a) An $n \times n$ matrix A is orthogonally diagonalizable and has real eigenvalues if and only if A is not symmetric.

(b) If A is a symmetric $n \times n$ matrix, then A is not orthogonally diagonalizable.

(c) If A is a symmetric $n \times n$ matrix, then A is orthogonal.

(d) If A is an $m \times n$ matrix, $A^T A$ and AA^T are symmetric.

23. Is the matrix $\begin{bmatrix} 1 & 0 & 1 \\ 0 & 1 & 0 \\ 0 & 0 & 5 \end{bmatrix}$ orthogonally diagonalizable?

24. True or False: If A be any $n \times m$ matrix, AA^T has an orthogonal set of n eigenvectors.

Section 7.4   Applications of Eigenvalues and Eigenvectors

25. Use the age transition matrix $A = \begin{bmatrix} 0 & 3 \\ 5 & 0 \end{bmatrix}$ and age distribution vector $\mathbf{x}_1 = \begin{bmatrix} 15 \\ 15 \end{bmatrix}$ to find the age distribution vector $\mathbf{x}_2$.

(a) $\begin{bmatrix} 35 \\ 60 \end{bmatrix}$ (b) $\begin{bmatrix} 45 \\ 70 \end{bmatrix}$ (c) $\begin{bmatrix} 45 \\ 75 \end{bmatrix}$ (d) $\begin{bmatrix} 55 \\ 75 \end{bmatrix}$

26. Use the age transition matrix $A = \begin{bmatrix} 0 & 6 & 8 \\ 0.5 & 0 & 0 \\ 0 & 0.5 & 0 \end{bmatrix}$ and age distribution vector $x_1 = \begin{bmatrix} 24 \\ 24 \\ 20 \end{bmatrix}$ to find the age distribution

vector x_2.

(a) $\begin{bmatrix} 304 \\ 24 \\ 12 \end{bmatrix}$ (b) $\begin{bmatrix} 196 \\ 12 \\ 24 \end{bmatrix}$ (c) $\begin{bmatrix} 304 \\ 12 \\ 12 \end{bmatrix}$ (d) $\begin{bmatrix} 30 \\ 12 \\ 6 \end{bmatrix}$

27. Use the age transition matrix $A = \begin{bmatrix} 0 & 3 \\ 5 & 0 \end{bmatrix}$ and age distribution vector $x_1 = \begin{bmatrix} 15 \\ 15 \end{bmatrix}$ to find the age distribution vector

x_2.

28. Use the age transition matrix $A = \begin{bmatrix} 0 & 3 & 12 \\ 1 & 0 & 0 \\ 0 & \frac{1}{6} & 0 \end{bmatrix}$ and age distribution vector $x_1 = \begin{bmatrix} 300 \\ 300 \\ 300 \end{bmatrix}$ to find the age distribution

vector x_2.

29. Solve the system of linear differential equations.

$y_1' = 3y_1 + 2y_2$

$y_2' = 6y_1 - y_2$

(a) $y_1 = c_1 e^{-3t} + c_2 e^{5t}$
$\quad y_2 = 3c_1 e^{-3t} + 4c_2 e^{-5t}$

(b) $y_1 = c_1 e^{-3t} + c_2 e^{5t}$
$\quad y_2 = -3c_1 e^{-3t} + c_2 e^{5t}$

(c) $y_1 = c_1 e^{-2t} + c_2 e^{5t}$
$\quad y_2 = -3c_1 e^{-3t} + c_2 e^{5t}$

(d) $y_1 = c_1 e^{-2t} + c_2 e^{5t}$
$\quad y_2 = 3c_1 e^{-3t} + 4c_2 e^{-5t}$

30. Solve the system of linear differential equations.

$y_1' = y_2$

$y_2' = 2y_1 - y_2$

(a) $y_1 = c_1 e^{-2t} + c_2 e^t$
$\quad y_2 = 2c_1 e^{2t} + c_2 e^{-2t}$

(b) $y_1 = c_1 e^{-2t} + c_2 e^t$
$\quad y_2 = -2c_1 e^{-2t} + c_2 e^t$

(c) $y_1 = 2c_1 e^{-2t} + c_2 e^{3t}$
$\quad y_2 = 2c_1 e^{2t} + c_2 e^{-2t}$

(d) $y_1 = 2c_1 e^{-2t} + c_2 e^{3t}$
$\quad y_2 = -2c_1 e^{-2t} + c_2 e^t$

31. Solve the system of linear differential equations.

$y_1' = 4y_1$

$y_2' = -y_2$

32. Solve the system of linear differential equations.

$$y_1' = -y_1$$

$$y_2' = 2y_2$$

33. Find the matrix of the quadratic form associated with the equation $10xy - 10y^2 + 4x - 48 = 0$.

(a) $\begin{bmatrix} 5 & 0 \\ -10 & 5 \end{bmatrix}$
(b) $\begin{bmatrix} 0 & 5 \\ 5 & -10 \end{bmatrix}$
(c) $\begin{bmatrix} 0 & 5 & 0 \\ 5 & 0 & -10 \\ 0 & -10 & 0 \end{bmatrix}$
(d) $\begin{bmatrix} 5 & 0 & 0 \\ 0 & 5 & -10 \\ 0 & -10 & 5 \end{bmatrix}$

34. Use the Principal Axes Theorem to perform a rotation of axes to eliminate the xy -term in the quadratic equation $5x^2 + 6xy + 5y^2 = 8$. Identify the equation in the new coordinate system.

(a) $(x')^4 + (y')^2 = 1$
(b) $(x')^2 + \dfrac{(y')^2}{8} = 1$
(c) $(x')^2 + \dfrac{(y')^2}{4} = 1$
(d) $(x')^2 + \dfrac{(y')}{4} = 1$

35. Write the matrix of the quadratic form associated with the equation $4x^2 + 9y^2 - 36 = 0$.

36. Use the Principal Axes Theorem to perform a rotation of axes to eliminate the xy -term in the quadratic equation $5x^2 + 6xy + 5y^2 = 8$. Write the equation in the new coordinate system.

CHAPTER 7
Eigenvalues and Eigenvectors (Answer Key)

Section 7.1   Eigenvalues and Eigenvectors

[1] (b)

[2] (b)

[3] Yes

[4] No

[5] (b)

[6] (c)

[7] $1, \begin{bmatrix} 1 \\ 0 \\ 0 \end{bmatrix}; \; 2, \begin{bmatrix} 0 \\ 1 \\ 0 \end{bmatrix}; \; 3, \begin{bmatrix} 0 \\ 0 \\ 1 \end{bmatrix}$

[8] $1, \begin{bmatrix} 1 \\ 0 \end{bmatrix}; \; 2, \begin{bmatrix} 0 \\ 1 \end{bmatrix}$

[9] (d)

[10] (b)

[11] True

[12] True

Section 7.2   Diagonalization

[13] (b)

[14] (c)

[15] False

[16] No

Section 7.3   Symmetric Matrices and Orthogonal Diagonalization

[17] (d)

[18] (d)

[19] Yes

[20] No

[21] (d)

[22] (d)

[23] No

[24] True

Section 7.4   Applications of Eigenvalues and Eigenvectors

[25] (c)

[26] (c)

[27] $\begin{bmatrix} 45 \\ 75 \end{bmatrix}$

[28] $\begin{bmatrix} 4500 \\ 300 \\ 50 \end{bmatrix}$

[29] (b)

[30] (b)

[31] $y_1 = c_1 e^{4t}$
$y_2 = c_2 e^{-t}$

[32] $y_1 = c_1 e^{-t}$
$y_2 = c_2 e^{2t}$

[33] (b)

[34] (c)

[35] $\begin{bmatrix} 4 & 0 \\ 0 & 9 \end{bmatrix}$

[36] $(x')^2 + \dfrac{(y')^2}{4} = 1$